MICROWAVE ENGINEERS' HANDBOOK

VOLUME I

compiled and edited by
THEODORE S. SAAD

co-editors
ROBERT C. HANSEN
GERSHON J. WHEELER

Publishers

ARTECH HOUSE, INC.
Dedham, Massachusetts

affilated with
Horizon House-Microwave, Inc.

Library of Congress catalog card number: 76-168891

MICROWAVE ENGINEERS' HANDBOOK

VOLUME I

CONTENTS

PREFACE

Each year since 1962, the **microwave journal** has published and mailed free to its qualified readers the Microwave Engineers' Handbook (Microwave Engineers' Technical & Buyers Guide Edition). In the process, we have collected and published many valuable graphs, charts and tables. The cost of supplying this information has been paid for by our advertisers, the companies in the microwave industry.

Few publications in our field have seen more useful service than the Handbook. With each succeeding edition we solicited and added new material and deleted some of the old. Much of the material can be found only in the Handbook. Over the years our readers have protested the deletion of useful material. To still the protests and at the same time provide what we feel will prove to be an important addition to the microwave engineer's library, we decided to combine all of our material from 1962 on, eliminate the redundancies and organize them into a new edition of the Microwave Engineers' Handbook.

Because of the large amount of material, we decided to publish two volumes. We felt that some of our readers will want only one volume, but others will find both volumes useful.

In addition to the material that appeared in our past issues, we have added new material specifically for this new edition. An example of the new material is the set of Waveguide Tables, in Volume 1, prepared by Mike Brady specifically for this publication.

The project of publishing this book started 10 years ago and many people have participated and contributed. The basic concepts and the contents of the publication were reviewed and edited with the help of our co-editors, Dr. Robert C. Hansen and Gersh Wheeler. Bill Peyser and Phil Rossignol of the **microwave journal** have been responsible for most of the editing and production aspects in preparing the material for publication. Our contributing editors of past Handbooks, whose names appear below, have been instrumental in soliciting, generating and reviewing the material we have used. And finally there are our readers, who have supplied charts, tables and graphs to make this publication possible. Their names appear throughout the two volumes.

CONTRIBUTING EDITORS

Dr. Frank Brand
C. Louis Cuccia
Dr. William A. Edson
Jurgan Elkan
Eugene J. Feldman
George N. Krassner
Charles P. Marsden, Jr.
Dr. Alex Mayer
Matthew S. Miller
W. W. Mumford
Dr. John M. Osepchuk
Robert F. Patterson, Jr.
Dr. John E. Pippin
Harold E. Stinehelfer
Robert Tenenholtz
Dr. Robert J. Wenzel

TRANSMISSION LINE THEORY

Summary of Transmission Line Equations

Quantity	General Line Expression	Ideal Line Expression
Propagation constant	$\gamma = \alpha + j\beta = \sqrt{(R + j\omega L)(G + j\omega C)}$	$\gamma = j\omega\sqrt{LC}$
Phase constant β	Imaginary part of γ	$\beta = \omega\sqrt{LC} = \frac{2\pi}{\lambda}$
Attenuation constant α	Real part of γ	0
Characteristic impedance	$Z_o = \sqrt{\frac{R + j\omega L}{G + j\omega C}}$	$Z_o = \sqrt{\frac{L}{C}}$
Input impedance	$Z_{-\ell} = Z_o \frac{Z_r + Z_o \tanh \gamma\ell}{Z_o + Z_r \tanh \gamma\ell}$	$Z_{-\ell} = Z_o \frac{Z_r + jZ_o \tan \beta\ell}{Z_o + jZ_r \tan \beta\ell}$
Impedance of short-circuited line. $Z_r = 0$	$Z_{s.c.} = Z_o \tanh \gamma\ell$	$Z_{s.c.} = jZ_o \tan \beta\ell$
Impedance of open-circuited line. $Z_r = \infty$	$Z_{o.c.} = Z_o \coth \gamma\ell$	$Z_{o.c.} = -jZ_o \cot \beta\ell$
Impedance of line an odd number of quarter wavelengths long	$Z = Z_o \frac{Z_r + Z_o \coth \alpha\ell}{Z_o + Z_r \coth \alpha\ell}$	$Z = \frac{Z_o^2}{Z_r}$
Impedance of line an integral number of half wavelengths long	$Z = Z_o \frac{Z_r + Z_o \tanh \alpha\ell}{Z_o + Z_r \tanh \alpha\ell}$	$Z = Z_r$
Voltage along line	$V_{-\ell} = V_i(1 + \Gamma_o e^{-2\gamma\ell})$	$V_{-\ell} = V_i(1 + \Gamma_o e^{-2j\beta\ell})$
Current along line	$I_{-\ell} = I_i(1 - \Gamma_o e^{-2\gamma\ell})$	$I_{-\ell} = I_i(1 - \Gamma_o e^{-2j\beta\ell})$
Voltage reflection coefficient	$\Gamma = \frac{Z_r - Z_o}{Z_r + Z_o}$	$\Gamma = \frac{Z_r - Z_o}{Z_r + Z_o}$

Useful approximations for small VSWR's

If u and v are both small with respect to unity,

(a) $(1 + u)(1 + v) = 1 + u + v$

(b) $(1 - u)(1 - v) = 1 - u - v$

(c) $(1 \pm u)^2 = 1 \pm 2u$

(d) $\frac{1 + v}{1 + u} = 1 + v - u$

Examples:

(a) If $r_1 = 1.03$ and $r_2 = 1.08$, then $r_1 r_2 = 1.11$

(b) If $\Gamma_1 = .96$ and $\Gamma_2 = .95$, then $\Gamma_1\Gamma_2 = .91$

(c) If $r = 1.04$, $r^2 = 1.08$

If $\Gamma = .96$, $\Gamma^2 = .92$

(d) If $r_1 = 1.03$ and $r_2 = 1.08$, then $\frac{r_2}{r_1} = 1.05$

(Top) Reprinted from Microwave Transmission Circuits, MIT Rad. Lab. Series vol. 9, edited by George L. Ragan, copyright 1948 by McGraw-Hill Book Co., Inc., (Bottom) Courtesy of Gershon J. Wheeler.

Some Miscellaneous Relations in Low-Loss Transmission Lines

Equation	Explanation
$r = \dfrac{1 + \lvert\Gamma\rvert}{1 - \lvert\Gamma\rvert}$ $\lvert\Gamma\rvert = \dfrac{r - 1}{r + 1}$	r = VSWR $\lvert\Gamma\rvert$ = magnitude of reflection coefficient
$\Gamma = \dfrac{R - Z_o}{R + Z_o}$ $r = \dfrac{R}{Z_o}$ $r = \dfrac{Z_o}{R}$	Γ = reflection coefficient (real) at a point in a line where impedance is real (R) $R > Z_o$ (at voltage maximum) $R < Z_o$ (at voltage minimum)
$\dfrac{P_r}{P_i} = \lvert\Gamma\rvert^2 = \left(\dfrac{r - 1}{r + 1}\right)^2$ $\dfrac{P_t}{P_i} = 1 - \lvert\Gamma\rvert^2 = \dfrac{4r}{(r + 1)^2}$	P_r = reflected power P_i = incident power P_t = transmitted power
$\dfrac{P_b}{P_m} = \dfrac{1}{r}$	P_b = net power transmitted to load at onset of breakdown in a line where VSWR = r exists P_m = same when line is matched, r = 1
$\dfrac{\alpha_r}{\alpha_m} = \dfrac{1 + \Gamma^2}{1 - \Gamma^2} = \dfrac{r^2 + 1}{2r}$	α_m = attenuation constant when r = 1, matched line. α_r = attenuation constant allowing for increased ohmic loss caused by standing waves.
$r_{max} = r_1 r_2$ $r_{min} = \dfrac{r_2}{r_1} \quad r_2 > r_1$	r_{max} = maximum VSWR when r_1 and r_2 combine in worst phase. r_{min} = minimum VSWR when r_1 and r_2 are in best phase.
$\lvert\Gamma\rvert = \dfrac{\lvert X\rvert}{\sqrt{X^2 + 4}}$ $\lvert X\rvert = \dfrac{r - 1}{\sqrt{r}}$	Relations for a normalized reactance X in series with resistance Z_o
$\lvert\Gamma\rvert = \dfrac{\lvert B\rvert}{\sqrt{B^2 + 4}}$ $\lvert B\rvert = \dfrac{r - 1}{\sqrt{r}}$	Relations for a normalized susceptance B in shunt with admittance Y_o

Reprinted from Microwave Transmission Circuits, MIT Rad. Lab. Series vol. 9, edited by George L. Ragan, copyright 1948 by McGraw-Hill Book Co., Inc.

MATRIX ANALYSIS

The analysis of a cascade of two-terminal pair networks may be carried out by use of the ABCD matrix. The voltages and currents of two-port junctions are related by matrix equations. The matrices of some useful circuit elements are shown below.

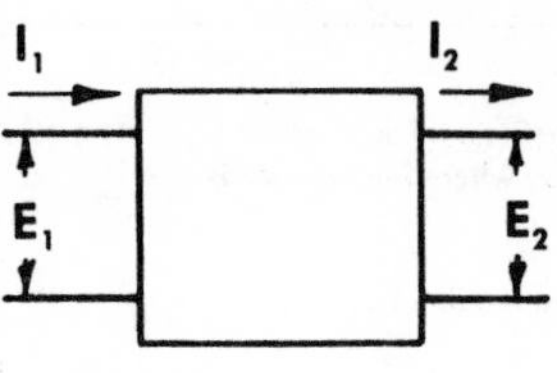

$$\begin{bmatrix} E_1 \\ I_1 \end{bmatrix} = \begin{bmatrix} A & B \\ C & D \end{bmatrix} \times \begin{bmatrix} E_2 \\ I_2 \end{bmatrix}$$

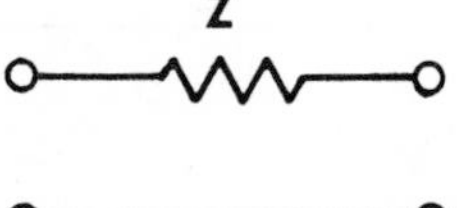

Series Impedance $\begin{bmatrix} 1 & Z \\ 0 & 1 \end{bmatrix}$

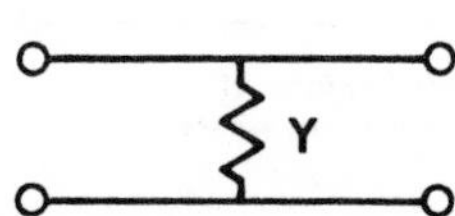

Shunt Admittance $\begin{bmatrix} 1 & 0 \\ Y & 1 \end{bmatrix}$

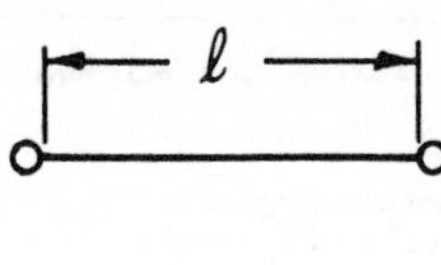

Length of Lossless Line of Normalized Impedance Z $\begin{bmatrix} \cos\frac{2\pi\ell}{\lambda} & jZ\sin\frac{2\pi\ell}{\lambda} \\ \frac{j}{Z}\sin\frac{2\pi\ell}{\lambda} & \cos\frac{2\pi\ell}{\lambda} \end{bmatrix}$

The impedance and admittances are all normalized with respect to that of a matched generator and load.

For reciprocity AD − BC = 1; for forward-to-back symmetry, A = D.

$$T = \frac{2}{A + B + C + D}$$ = **insertion voltage transmission coefficient between matched generator and load.**

$$Z_1 = \frac{E_1}{I_1} = \frac{A + B}{C + D}$$ = **input impedance with matched load.**

$$\Gamma = \frac{A + B - C - D}{A + B + C + D}$$ = **voltage reflection coefficient with matched load.**

Prepared by John Reed, Gershon J. Wheeler and members of the staff, Surface Radar and Navigation Operation, Raytheon Co.

VSWR AND RELATED PARAMETERS

VSWR	Rho V	Rho P	R dB	Tau V	Tau P	T dB
1.001	0.0005	0.00000	66.025	1.00000	1.00000	0.0000
1.002	0.0010	0.00000	60.009	1.00000	1.00000	0.0000
1.003	0.0015	0.00000	56.491	1.00000	1.00000	0.0000
1.004	0.0020	0.00000	53.997	1.00000	1.00000	0.0000
1.005	0.0025	0.00001	52.063	1.00000	0.99999	0.0000
1.006	0.0030	0.00001	50.484	1.00000	0.99999	0.0000
1.007	0.0035	0.00001	49.149	0.99999	0.99999	0.0001
1.008	0.0040	0.00002	47.993	0.99999	0.99998	0.0001
1.009	0.0045	0.00002	46.975	0.99999	0.99998	0.0001
1.010	0.0050	0.00002	46.064	0.99999	0.99998	0.0001
1.011	0.0055	0.00003	45.240	0.99999	0.99997	0.0001
1.012	0.0060	0.00004	44.489	0.99998	0.99996	0.0002
1.013	0.0065	0.00004	43.798	0.99998	0.99996	0.0002
1.014	0.0070	0.00005	43.159	0.99998	0.99995	0.0002
1.015	0.0074	0.00006	42.564	0.99997	0.99994	0.0002
1.016	0.0079	0.00006	42.007	0.99997	0.99994	0.0003
1.017	0.0084	0.00007	41.485	0.99996	0.99993	0.0003
1.018	0.0089	0.00008	40.993	0.99996	0.99992	0.0003
1.019	0.0094	0.00009	40.528	0.99996	0.99991	0.0004
1.020	0.0099	0.00010	40.086	0.99995	0.99990	0.0004
1.021	0.0104	0.00011	39.667	0.99995	0.99989	0.0005
1.022	0.0109	0.00012	39.267	0.99994	0.99988	0.0005
1.023	0.0114	0.00013	38.885	0.99994	0.99987	0.0006
1.024	0.0119	0.00014	38.520	0.99993	0.99986	0.0006
1.025	0.0123	0.00015	38.170	0.99992	0.99985	0.0007
1.026	0.0128	0.00016	37.833	0.99992	0.99984	0.0007
1.027	0.0133	0.00018	37.510	0.99991	0.99982	0.0008
1.028	0.0138	0.00019	37.198	0.99990	0.99981	0.0008
1.029	0.0143	0.00020	36.898	0.99990	0.99980	0.0009
1.030	0.0148	0.00022	36.607	0.99989	0.99978	0.0009
1.031	0.0153	0.00023	36.327	0.99988	0.99977	0.0010
1.032	0.0157	0.00025	36.055	0.99988	0.99975	0.0011
1.033	0.0162	0.00026	35.792	0.99987	0.99974	0.0011
1.034	0.0167	0.00028	35.537	0.99986	0.99972	0.0012
1.035	0.0172	0.00030	35.290	0.99985	0.99970	0.0013
1.036	0.0177	0.00031	35.049	0.99984	0.99969	0.0014
1.037	0.0182	0.00033	34.816	0.99984	0.99967	0.0014
1.038	0.0186	0.00035	34.588	0.99983	0.99965	0.0015
1.039	0.0191	0.00037	34.367	0.99982	0.99963	0.0016
1.040	0.0196	0.00038	34.151	0.99981	0.99962	0.0017
1.041	0.0201	0.00040	33.941	0.99980	0.99960	0.0018
1.042	0.0206	0.00042	33.736	0.99979	0.99958	0.0018
1.043	0.0210	0.00044	33.536	0.99978	0.99956	0.0019
1.044	0.0215	0.00046	33.341	0.99977	0.99954	0.0020
1.045	0.0220	0.00048	33.150	0.99976	0.99952	0.0021
1.046	0.0225	0.00051	32.963	0.99975	0.99949	0.0022
1.047	0.0230	0.00053	32.780	0.99974	0.99947	0.0023
1.048	0.0234	0.00055	32.602	0.99973	0.99945	0.0024
1.049	0.0239	0.00057	32.427	0.99971	0.99943	0.0025
1.050	0.0244	0.00059	32.256	0.99970	0.99941	0.0026

VSWR	Rho V	Rho P	R dB	Tau V	Tau P	T dB
1.051	0.0249	0.00062	32.088	0.99969	0.99938	0.0027
1.052	0.0253	0.00064	31.923	0.99968	0.99936	0.0028
1.053	0.0258	0.00067	31.762	0.99967	0.99933	0.0029
1.054	0.0263	0.00069	31.604	0.99965	0.99931	0.0030
1.055	0.0268	0.00072	31.449	0.99964	0.99928	0.0031
1.056	0.0272	0.00074	31.297	0.99963	0.99926	0.0032
1.057	0.0277	0.00077	31.147	0.99962	0.99923	0.0033
1.058	0.0282	0.00079	31.000	0.99960	0.99921	0.0035
1.059	0.0287	0.00082	30.856	0.99959	0.99918	0.0036
1.060	0.0291	0.00085	30.714	0.99958	0.99915	0.0037
1.061	0.0296	0.00088	30.575	0.99956	0.99912	0.0038
1.062	0.0301	0.00090	30.438	0.99955	0.99910	0.0039
1.063	0.0305	0.00093	30.303	0.99953	0.99907	0.0041
1.064	0.0310	0.00096	30.171	0.99952	0.99904	0.0042
1.065	0.0315	0.00099	30.040	0.99950	0.99901	0.0043
1.066	0.0319	0.00102	29.912	0.99949	0.99898	0.0044
1.067	0.0324	0.00105	29.785	0.99947	0.99895	0.0046
1.068	0.0329	0.00108	29.661	0.99946	0.99892	0.0047
1.069	0.0333	0.00111	29.538	0.99944	0.99889	0.0048
1.070	0.0338	0.00114	29.417	0.99943	0.99886	0.0050
1.071	0.0343	0.00118	29.298	0.99941	0.99882	0.0051
1.072	0.0347	0.00121	29.181	0.99940	0.99879	0.0052
1.073	0.0352	0.00124	29.066	0.99938	0.99876	0.0054
1.074	0.0357	0.00127	28.952	0.99936	0.99873	0.0055
1.075	0.0361	0.00131	28.839	0.99935	0.99869	0.0057
1.076	0.0366	0.00134	28.728	0.99933	0.99866	0.0058
1.077	0.0371	0.00137	28.619	0.99931	0.99863	0.0060
1.078	0.0375	0.00141	28.511	0.99930	0.99859	0.0061
1.079	0.0380	0.00144	28.405	0.99928	0.99856	0.0063
1.080	0.0385	0.00148	28.299	0.99926	0.99852	0.0064
1.081	0.0389	0.00152	28.196	0.99924	0.99848	0.0066
1.082	0.0394	0.00155	28.093	0.99922	0.99845	0.0067
1.083	0.0398	0.00159	27.992	0.99921	0.99841	0.0069
1.084	0.0403	0.00162	27.892	0.99919	0.99838	0.0071
1.085	0.0408	0.00166	27.794	0.99917	0.99834	0.0072
1.086	0.0412	0.00170	27.696	0.99915	0.99830	0.0074
1.087	0.0417	0.00174	27.600	0.99913	0.99826	0.0076
1.088	0.0421	0.00178	27.505	0.99911	0.99822	0.0077
1.089	0.0426	0.00182	27.411	0.99909	0.99818	0.0079
1.090	0.0431	0.00185	27.318	0.99907	0.99815	0.0081
1.091	0.0435	0.00189	27.226	0.99905	0.99811	0.0082
1.092	0.0440	0.00193	27.135	0.99903	0.99807	0.0084
1.093	0.0444	0.00197	27.046	0.99901	0.99803	0.0086
1.094	0.0449	0.00202	26.957	0.99899	0.99798	0.0088
1.095	0.0453	0.00206	26.869	0.99897	0.99794	0.0089
1.096	0.0458	0.00210	26.782	0.99895	0.99790	0.0091
1.097	0.0463	0.00214	26.697	0.99893	0.99786	0.0093
1.098	0.0467	0.00218	26.612	0.99891	0.99782	0.0095
1.099	0.0472	0.00222	26.528	0.99889	0.99778	0.0097
1.100	0.0476	0.00227	26.444	0.99887	0.99773	0.0099

LEGEND

VSWR Voltage Standing Wave Ratio
Rho V (ρ_v) Voltage Reflection Coefficient
Rho P (ρ_p) Power Reflection Coefficient
R dB Return Loss in dB
Tau V (τ_v) Voltage Transmission Coefficient $(\tau_p)^{1/2}$
Tau P (τ_p) Power Transmission Coefficient $(1-\rho_p)$
T dB Transmission Loss in dB

Courtesy of Professor F. E. Gardiol, EPF, Lausanne, Switzerland

5

VSWR AND RELATED PARAMETERS

VSWR	Rho V	Rho P	R dB	Tau V	Tau P	T dB
1.102	0.0485	0.00235	26.281	0.99882	0.99765	0.0102
1.104	0.0494	0.00244	26.120	0.99878	0.99756	0.0106
1.106	0.0503	0.00253	25.963	0.99873	0.99747	0.0110
1.108	0.0512	0.00262	25.809	0.99869	0.99738	0.0114
1.110	0.0521	0.00272	25.658	0.99864	0.99728	0.0118
1.112	0.0530	0.00281	25.510	0.99859	0.99719	0.0122
1.114	0.0539	0.00291	25.364	0.99854	0.99709	0.0126
1.116	0.0548	0.00301	25.221	0.99850	0.99699	0.0131
1.118	0.0557	0.00310	25.081	0.99845	0.99690	0.0135
1.120	0.0566	0.00320	24.943	0.99840	0.99680	0.0139
1.122	0.0575	0.00331	24.808	0.99835	0.99669	0.0144
1.124	0.0584	0.00341	24.675	0.99829	0.99659	0.0148
1.126	0.0593	0.00351	24.544	0.99824	0.99649	0.0153
1.128	0.0602	0.00362	24.415	0.99819	0.99638	0.0157
1.130	0.0610	0.00373	24.289	0.99814	0.99628	0.0162
1.132	0.0619	0.00383	24.164	0.99808	0.99617	0.0167
1.134	0.0628	0.00394	24.042	0.99803	0.99606	0.0172
1.136	0.0637	0.00405	23.921	0.99797	0.99595	0.0176
1.138	0.0645	0.00417	23.803	0.99791	0.99583	0.0181
1.140	0.0654	0.00428	23.686	0.99786	0.99572	0.0186
1.142	0.0663	0.00439	23.571	0.99780	0.99561	0.0191
1.144	0.0672	0.00451	23.457	0.99774	0.99549	0.0196
1.146	0.0680	0.00463	23.346	0.99768	0.99537	0.0201
1.148	0.0689	0.00475	23.235	0.99762	0.99525	0.0207
1.150	0.0698	0.00487	23.127	0.99756	0.99513	0.0212
1.152	0.0706	0.00499	23.020	0.99750	0.99501	0.0217
1.154	0.0715	0.00511	22.914	0.99744	0.99489	0.0223
1.156	0.0724	0.00524	22.810	0.99738	0.99476	0.0228
1.158	0.0732	0.00536	22.708	0.99732	0.99464	0.0233
1.160	0.0741	0.00549	22.607	0.99725	0.99451	0.0239
1.162	0.0749	0.00561	22.507	0.99719	0.99439	0.0245
1.164	0.0758	0.00574	22.408	0.99712	0.99426	0.0250
1.166	0.0766	0.00587	22.311	0.99706	0.99413	0.0256
1.168	0.0775	0.00600	22.215	0.99699	0.99400	0.0262
1.170	0.0783	0.00614	22.120	0.99693	0.99386	0.0267
1.172	0.0792	0.00627	22.027	0.99686	0.99373	0.0273
1.174	0.0800	0.00641	21.934	0.99679	0.99359	0.0279
1.176	0.0809	0.00654	21.843	0.99672	0.99346	0.0285
1.178	0.0817	0.00668	21.753	0.99665	0.99332	0.0291
1.180	0.0826	0.00682	21.664	0.99659	0.99318	0.0297
1.182	0.0834	0.00696	21.576	0.99652	0.99304	0.0303
1.184	0.0842	0.00710	21.489	0.99644	0.99290	0.0309
1.186	0.0851	0.00724	21.403	0.99637	0.99276	0.0316
1.188	0.0859	0.00738	21.318	0.99630	0.99262	0.0322
1.190	0.0868	0.00753	21.234	0.99623	0.99247	0.0328
1.192	0.0876	0.00767	21.151	0.99616	0.99233	0.0334
1.194	0.0884	0.00782	21.069	0.99608	0.99218	0.0341
1.196	0.0893	0.00797	20.988	0.99601	0.99203	0.0347
1.198	0.0901	0.00811	20.907	0.99593	0.99189	0.0354
1.200	0.0909	0.00826	20.828	0.99586	0.99174	0.0360

VSWR	Rho V	Rho P	R dB	Tau V	Tau P	T dB
1.210	0.0959	0.00903	20.443	0.99548	0.99097	0.0394
1.220	0.0991	0.00982	20.079	0.99508	0.99018	0.0429
1.230	0.1031	0.01064	19.732	0.99467	0.98936	0.0464
1.240	0.1071	0.01148	19.401	0.99424	0.98852	0.0501
1.250	0.1111	0.01235	19.085	0.99381	0.98765	0.0540
1.260	0.1150	0.01324	18.783	0.99336	0.98676	0.0579
1.270	0.1189	0.01415	18.493	0.99290	0.98585	0.0619
1.280	0.1228	0.01508	18.216	0.99243	0.98492	0.0660
1.290	0.1266	0.01604	17.949	0.99195	0.98396	0.0702
1.300	0.1304	0.01701	17.692	0.99146	0.98299	0.0745
1.310	0.1342	0.01801	17.445	0.99095	0.98199	0.0789
1.320	0.1379	0.01902	17.207	0.99044	0.98098	0.0834
1.330	0.1416	0.02006	16.977	0.98992	0.97994	0.0880
1.340	0.1453	0.02111	16.755	0.98939	0.97889	0.0927
1.350	0.1489	0.02218	16.540	0.98885	0.97782	0.0974
1.360	0.1525	0.02327	16.332	0.98830	0.97673	0.1023
1.370	0.1561	0.02437	16.131	0.98774	0.97563	0.1072
1.380	0.1597	0.02549	15.936	0.98717	0.97451	0.1121
1.390	0.1632	0.02663	15.747	0.98660	0.97337	0.1172
1.400	0.1667	0.02778	15.563	0.98601	0.97222	0.1223
1.410	0.1701	0.02894	15.385	0.98542	0.97106	0.1275
1.420	0.1736	0.03012	15.211	0.98482	0.96988	0.1328
1.430	0.1770	0.03131	15.043	0.98422	0.96869	0.1382
1.440	0.1803	0.03252	14.879	0.98361	0.96748	0.1436
1.450	0.1837	0.03374	14.719	0.98299	0.96626	0.1490
1.460	0.1870	0.03497	14.564	0.98236	0.96503	0.1546
1.470	0.1903	0.03621	14.412	0.98173	0.96379	0.1602
1.480	0.1935	0.03746	14.264	0.98109	0.96254	0.1658
1.490	0.1968	0.03873	14.120	0.98045	0.96127	0.1715
1.500	0.2000	0.04000	13.979	0.97980	0.96000	0.1773
1.520	0.2063	0.04258	13.708	0.97848	0.95742	0.1890
1.540	0.2126	0.04520	13.449	0.97714	0.95480	0.2009
1.560	0.2188	0.04785	13.201	0.97578	0.95215	0.2130
1.580	0.2248	0.05054	12.964	0.97440	0.94946	0.2252
1.600	0.2308	0.05325	12.736	0.97301	0.94675	0.2377
1.620	0.2366	0.05600	12.518	0.97160	0.94400	0.2503
1.640	0.2424	0.05877	12.308	0.97017	0.94123	0.2630
1.660	0.2481	0.06156	12.107	0.96873	0.93844	0.2760
1.680	0.2537	0.06438	11.913	0.96727	0.93562	0.2890
1.700	0.2593	0.06722	11.725	0.96581	0.93278	0.3022
1.720	0.2647	0.07007	11.545	0.96433	0.92993	0.3155
1.740	0.2701	0.07294	11.370	0.96284	0.92706	0.3289
1.760	0.2754	0.07582	11.202	0.96134	0.92418	0.3425
1.780	0.2806	0.07872	11.039	0.95983	0.92128	0.3561
1.800	0.2857	0.08163	10.881	0.95831	0.91837	0.3698
1.820	0.2908	0.08455	10.729	0.95679	0.91545	0.3837
1.840	0.2958	0.08748	10.581	0.95526	0.91252	0.3976
1.860	0.3007	0.09042	10.437	0.95372	0.90958	0.4116
1.880	0.3056	0.09336	10.298	0.95217	0.90664	0.4257
1.900	0.3103	0.09631	10.163	0.95062	0.90369	[illegible]

VSWR AND RELATED PARAMETERS

VSWR	Rho V	Rho P	R dB	Tau V	Tau P	T dB
1.920	0.3151	0.09927	10.032	0.94907	0.90073	0.4540
1.940	0.3197	0.10223	9.904	0.94751	0.89777	0.4683
1.960	0.3243	0.10519	9.780	0.94595	0.89481	0.4827
1.980	0.3289	0.10815	9.660	0.94438	0.89185	0.4971
2.000	0.3333	0.11111	9.542	0.94281	0.88889	0.5115
2.100	0.3548	0.12591	8.999	0.93493	0.87409	0.5844
2.200	0.3750	0.14062	8.519	0.92702	0.85938	0.6582
2.300	0.3939	0.15519	8.091	0.91914	0.84481	0.7324
2.400	0.4118	0.16955	7.707	0.91129	0.83045	0.8069
2.500	0.4286	0.18367	7.360	0.90351	0.81633	0.8814
2.600	0.4444	0.19753	7.044	0.89581	0.80247	0.9557
2.700	0.4595	0.21110	6.755	0.88820	0.78890	1.0298
2.800	0.4737	0.22438	6.490	0.88069	0.77562	1.1035
2.900	0.4872	0.23734	6.246	0.87330	0.76266	1.1767
3.000	0.5000	0.25000	6.021	0.86603	0.75000	1.2494
3.100	0.5122	0.26234	5.811	0.85887	0.73766	1.3215
3.200	0.5238	0.27438	5.617	0.85184	0.72562	1.3929
3.300	0.5349	0.28610	5.435	0.84493	0.71390	1.4636
3.400	0.5455	0.29752	5.265	0.83814	0.70248	1.5337
3.500	0.5556	0.30864	5.105	0.83148	0.69136	1.6030
3.600	0.5652	0.31947	4.956	0.82494	0.68053	1.6715
3.700	0.5745	0.33001	4.815	0.81853	0.66999	1.7393
3.800	0.5833	0.34028	4.682	0.81223	0.65972	1.8064
3.900	0.5918	0.35027	4.556	0.80606	0.64973	1.8727
4.000	0.6000	0.36000	4.437	0.80000	0.64000	1.9382
4.100	0.6078	0.36947	4.324	0.79406	0.63053	2.0030
4.200	0.6154	0.37870	4.217	0.78823	0.62130	2.0670
4.300	0.6226	0.38768	4.115	0.78251	0.61232	2.1302
4.400	0.6296	0.39643	4.018	0.77690	0.60357	2.1927
4.500	0.6364	0.40496	3.926	0.77139	0.59504	2.2545
4.600	0.6429	0.41327	3.838	0.76599	0.58673	2.3156
4.700	0.6491	0.42136	3.753	0.76068	0.57864	2.3759
4.800	0.6552	0.42925	3.673	0.75548	0.57075	2.4355
4.900	0.6610	0.43694	3.596	0.75037	0.56306	2.4945
5.000	0.6667	0.44444	3.522	0.74536	0.55556	2.5527
5.200	0.6774	0.45890	3.383	0.73560	0.54110	2.6672
5.400	0.6875	0.47266	3.255	0.72618	0.52734	2.7791
5.600	0.6970	0.48577	3.136	0.71710	0.51423	2.8884
5.800	0.7059	0.49827	3.025	0.70833	0.50173	2.9953
6.000	0.7143	0.51020	2.923	0.69985	0.48980	3.0998
6.200	0.7222	0.52160	2.827	0.69166	0.47840	3.2021
6.400	0.7297	0.53251	2.737	0.68374	0.46749	3.3022
6.600	0.7368	0.54294	2.653	0.67606	0.45706	3.4002
6.800	0.7436	0.55293	2.573	0.66864	0.44707	3.4962
7.000	0.7500	0.56250	2.499	0.66144	0.43750	3.5902
7.200	0.7561	0.57168	2.428	0.65446	0.42832	3.6824
7.400	0.7619	0.58050	2.362	0.64769	0.41950	3.7727
7.600	0.7674	0.58897	2.299	0.64112	0.41103	3.8612
7.800	0.7727	0.59711	2.239	0.63474	0.40289	3.9481
8.000	0.7778	0.60494	2.183	0.62854	0.39506	4.0333

VSWR	Rho V	Rho P	R dB	Tau V	Tau P	T dB
8.200	0.7826	0.61248	2.129	0.62251	0.38752	4.1170
8.400	0.7872	0.61974	2.078	0.61665	0.38026	4.1992
8.600	0.7917	0.62674	2.029	0.61095	0.37326	4.2798
8.800	0.7959	0.63349	1.983	0.60540	0.36651	4.3591
9.000	0.8000	0.64000	1.938	0.60000	0.36000	4.4370
9.200	0.8039	0.64629	1.896	0.59474	0.35371	4.5135
9.400	0.8077	0.65237	1.855	0.58960	0.34763	4.5888
9.600	0.8113	0.65824	1.816	0.58460	0.34176	4.6628
9.800	0.8148	0.66392	1.779	0.57972	0.33608	4.7356
10.000	0.8182	0.66942	1.743	0.57496	0.33058	4.8073
11.000	0.8333	0.69444	1.584	0.55277	0.30556	5.1491
12.000	0.8462	0.71598	1.451	0.53294	0.28402	5.4665
13.000	0.8571	0.73469	1.339	0.51508	0.26531	5.7625
14.000	0.8667	0.75111	1.243	0.49889	0.24889	6.0399
15.000	0.8750	0.76562	1.160	0.48412	0.23438	6.3009
16.000	0.8824	0.77855	1.087	0.47059	0.22145	6.5472
17.000	0.8889	0.79012	1.023	0.45812	0.20988	6.7804
18.000	0.8947	0.80055	0.966	0.44659	0.19945	7.0017
19.000	0.9000	0.81000	0.915	0.43589	0.19000	7.2125
20.000	0.9048	0.81859	0.869	0.42592	0.18141	7.4135
22.000	0.9130	0.83365	0.790	0.40786	0.16635	7.7897
24.000	0.9200	0.84640	0.724	0.39192	0.15360	8.1361
26.000	0.9259	0.85734	0.668	0.37771	0.14266	8.4569
28.000	0.9310	0.86683	0.621	0.36493	0.13317	8.7558
30.000	0.9355	0.87513	0.579	0.35337	0.12487	9.0354
32.000	0.9394	0.88246	0.543	0.34284	0.11754	9.2982
34.000	0.9429	0.88898	0.511	0.33320	0.11102	9.5460
36.000	0.9459	0.89481	0.483	0.32432	0.10519	9.7804
38.000	0.9487	0.90007	0.457	0.31612	0.09993	10.0028
40.000	0.9512	0.90482	0.434	0.30852	0.09518	10.2145
42.000	0.9535	0.90914	0.414	0.30143	0.09086	10.4163
44.000	0.9556	0.91309	0.395	0.29481	0.08691	10.6091
46.000	0.9574	0.91670	0.378	0.28861	0.08330	10.7938
48.000	0.9592	0.92003	0.362	0.28278	0.07997	10.9709
50.000	0.9608	0.92311	0.347	0.27730	0.07689	11.1411
55.000	0.9643	0.92985	0.316	0.26486	0.07015	11.5395
60.000	0.9672	0.93550	0.290	0.25397	0.06450	11.9045
65.000	0.9697	0.94031	0.267	0.24431	0.05969	12.2411
70.000	0.9718	0.94446	0.248	0.23568	0.05554	12.5536
75.000	0.9737	0.94806	0.232	0.22790	0.05194	12.8450
80.000	0.9753	0.95123	0.217	0.22085	0.04877	13.1182
85.000	0.9767	0.95403	0.204	0.21441	0.04597	13.3752
90.000	0.9780	0.95653	0.193	0.20850	0.04347	13.6178
95.000	0.9792	0.95877	0.183	0.20306	0.04123	13.8476
100.000	0.9802	0.96079	0.174	0.19802	0.03921	14.0658

7

8

NORMALIZED SUSCEPTANCE VS V S W R

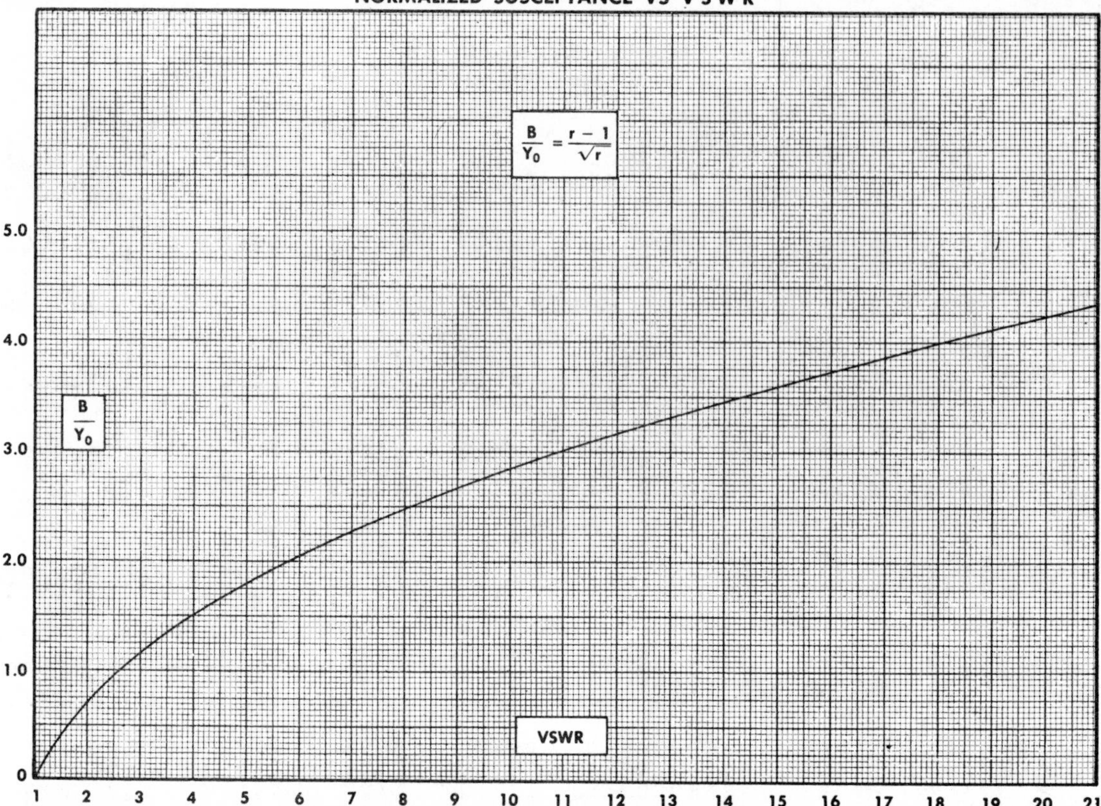

NORMALIZED SUSCEPTANCE VS VSWR EXPANDED

$\frac{B}{Y_0} = \frac{r-1}{\sqrt{r}}$

$\frac{B}{Y_0}$

VSWR

0.7
0.6
0.5
0.4
0.3
0.2
0.1
0

1.0 1.1 1.2 1.3 1.4 1.5 1.6 1.7 1.8 1.9 2.0

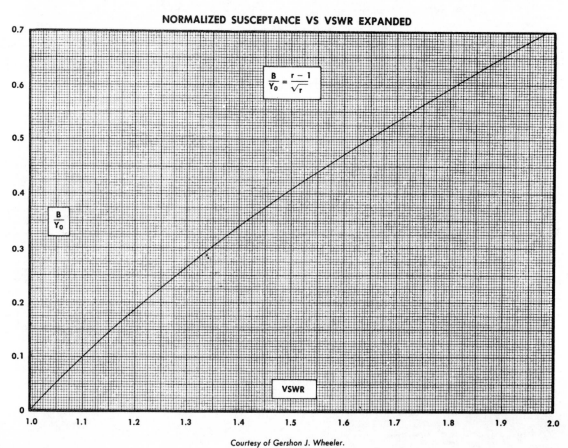

Courtesy of Gershon J. Wheeler.

MAXIMUM AND MINIMUM RESULTANT VSWR FROM TWO MISMATCHES

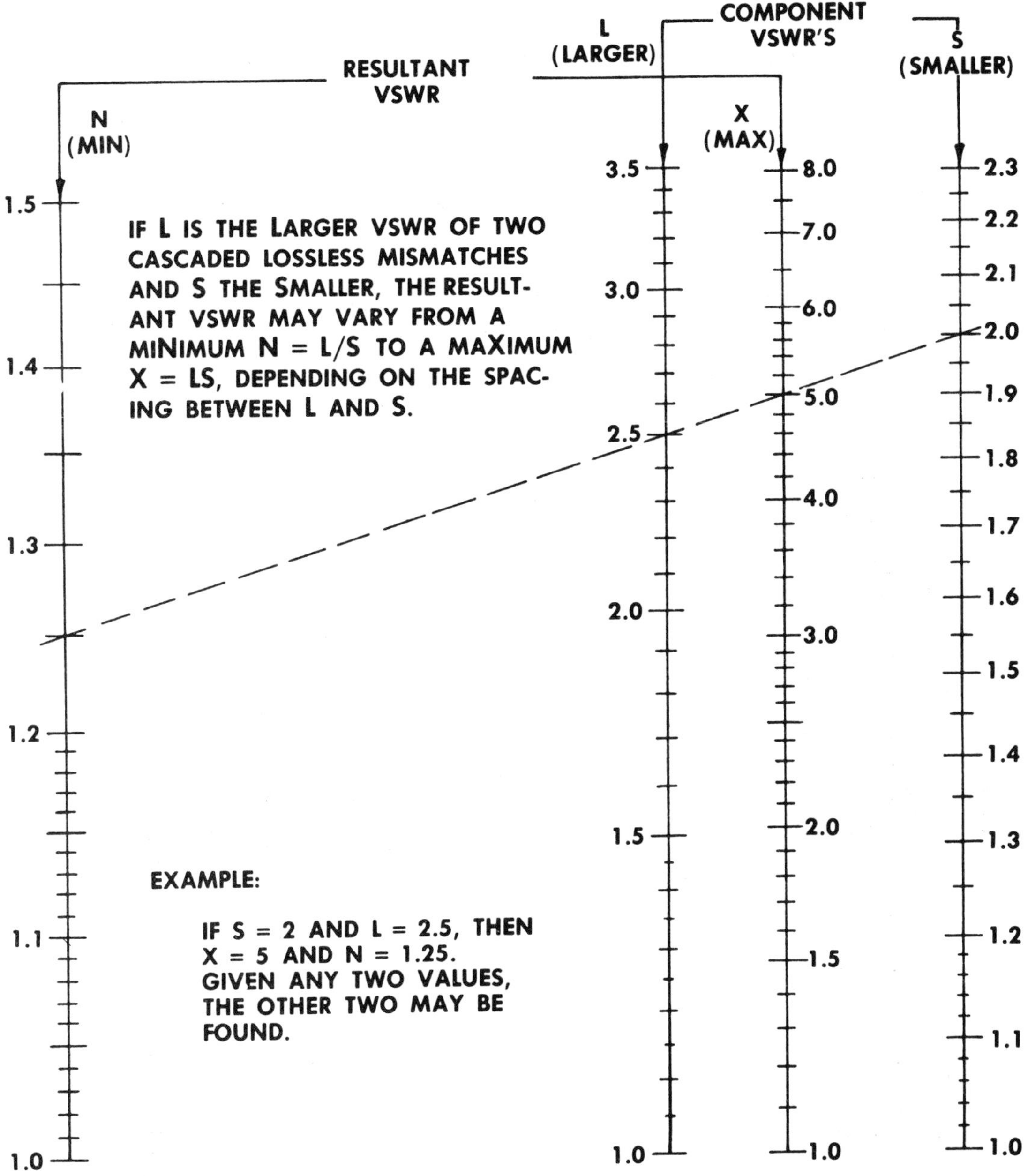

Courtesy of Joseph Gindsberg, Laboratory For Electronics, Boston 15, Mass., and Thomas J. Manning Jr., Raytheon Co., Bedford Research and Development Center, Bedford, Mass.

VSWR AND $|\Gamma|$ CALCULATION NOMOGRAPH

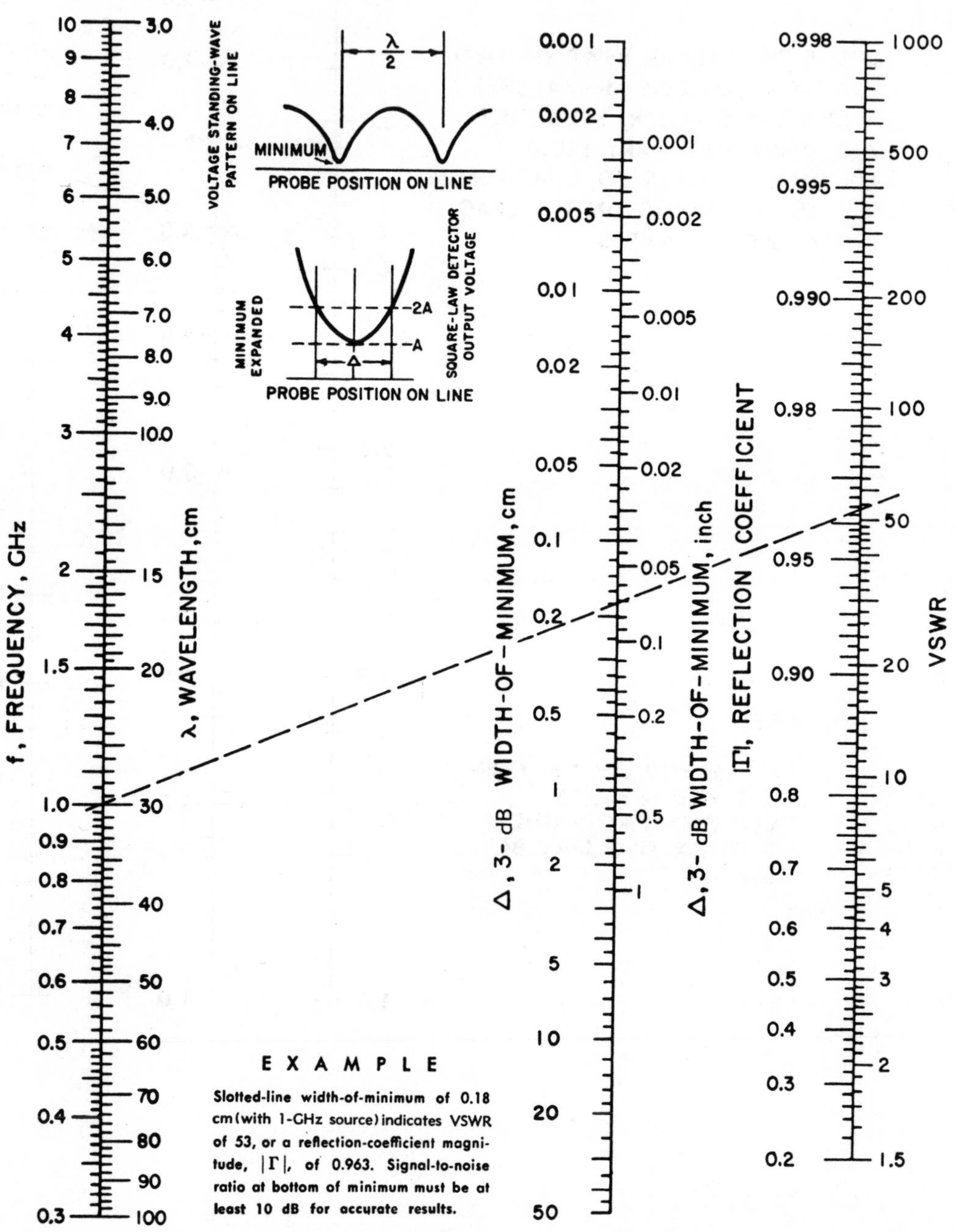

Courtesy of General Radio Co., West Concord, Mass.

NOMOGRAM OF MISMATCH ERROR LIMITS

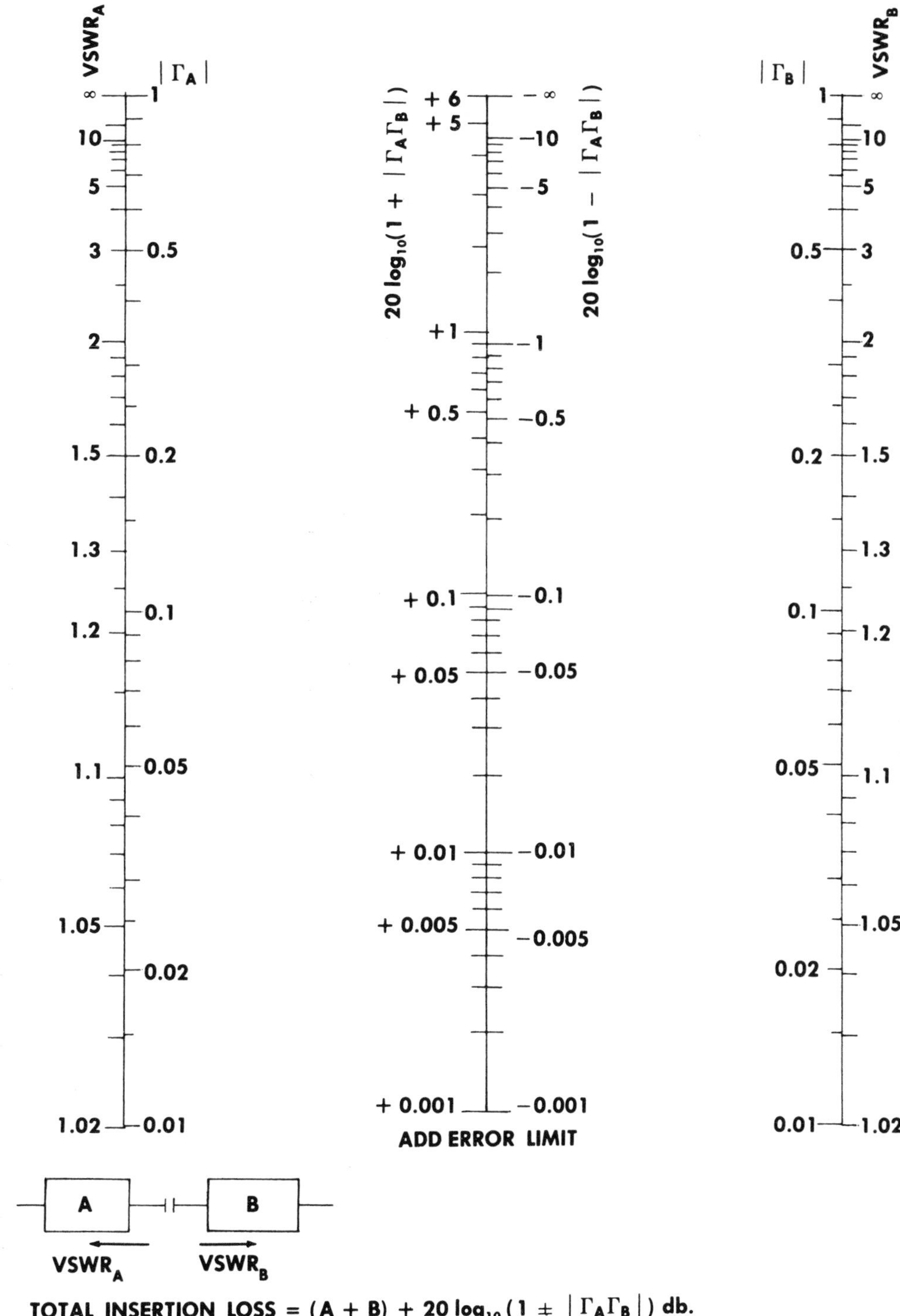

TOTAL INSERTION LOSS = (A + B) + 20 $\log_{10}(1 \pm |\Gamma_A \Gamma_B|)$ db.

Courtesy of Herman J. Feist, The Boeing Co., Seattle, Wash. Reprinted from the microwave journal, October 1961.

REDUCTION OF VSWR BY MATCHED ATTENUATOR

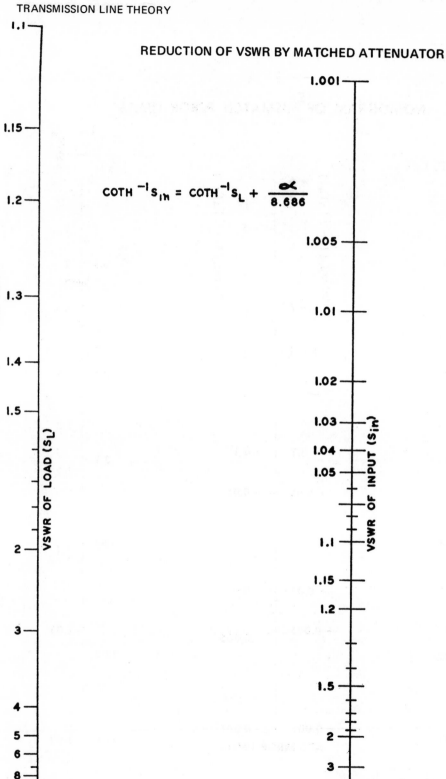

$$\coth^{-1} S_{in} = \coth^{-1} S_L + \frac{\alpha}{8.686}$$

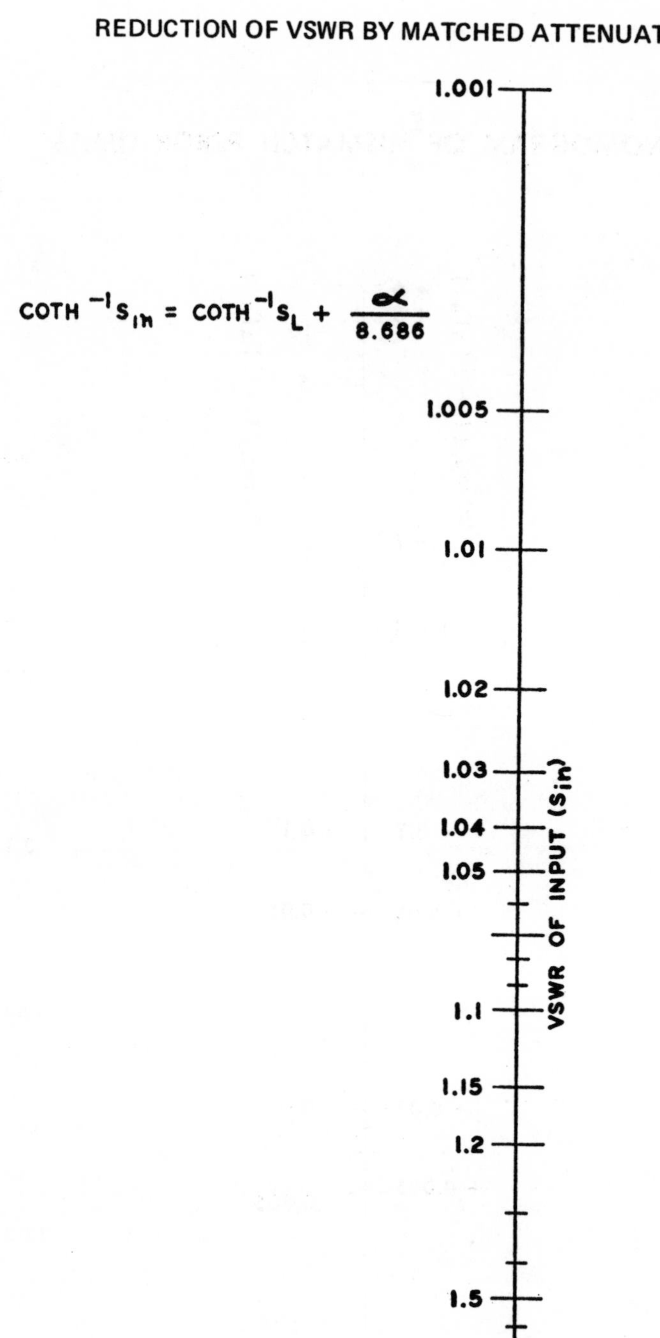

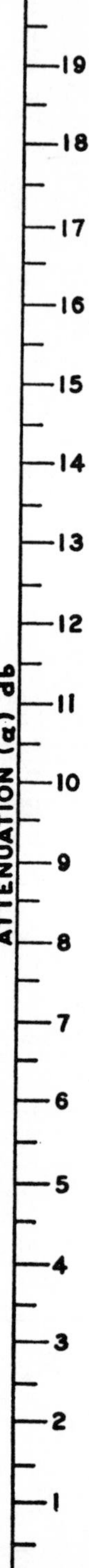

Courtesy of Dr. Roland Reisley, Burlingame Associates.

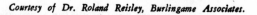

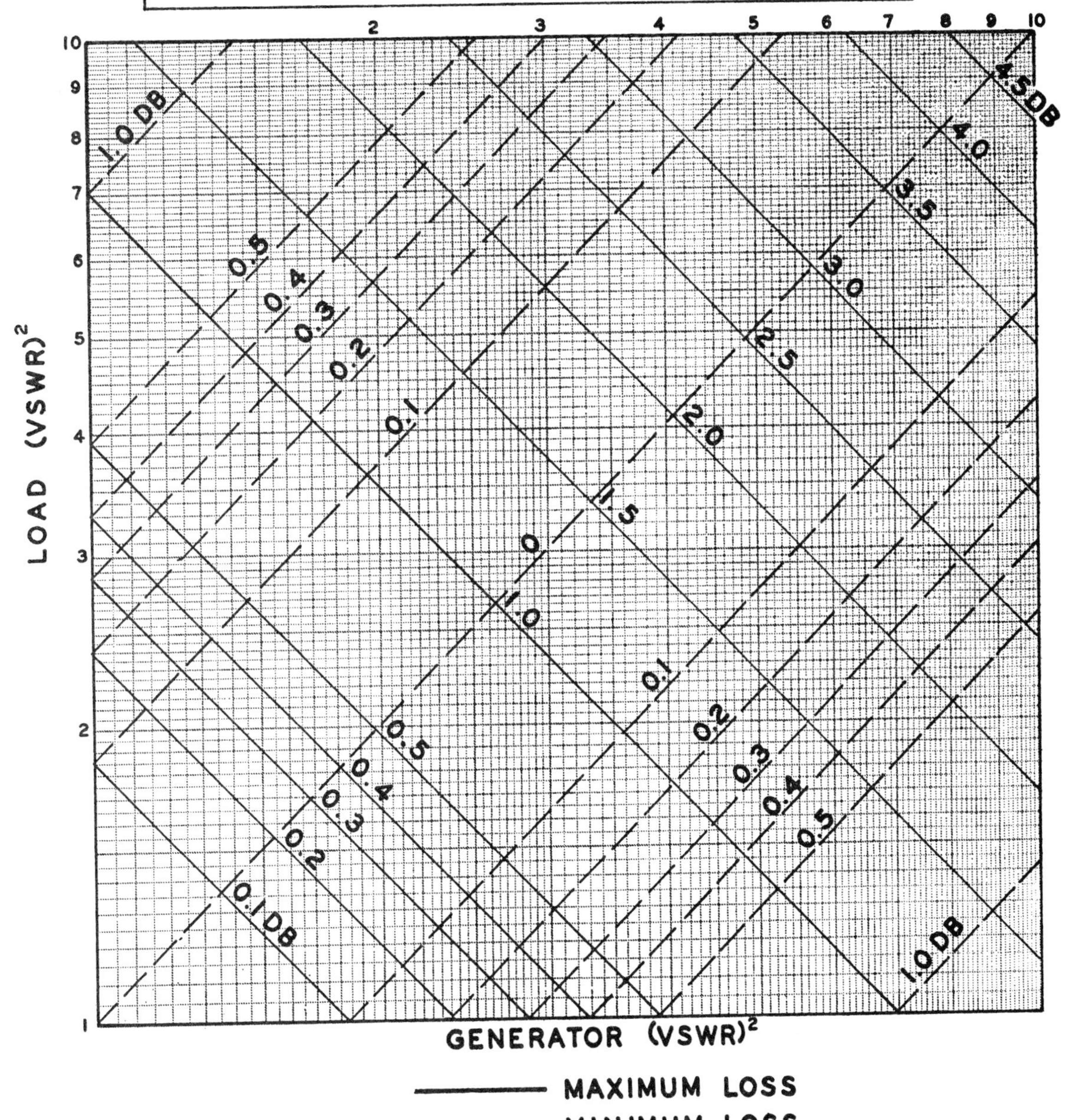

Courtesy of Sperry Microwave Electronics Co., Division of Sperry Rand Corp.

CAPACITANCE – VSWR CHART

Notes on the use of CAPACITANCE vs. VSWR CHART

The determining of the resultant VSWR caused by junction capacitances on a 50 ohm line at various frequencies can easily be obtained from this graph.

The chart has become very useful in calibrating the TDR (Time Domain Reflectometer) graphical display with a precision capacitive susceptance. In this way, the amplitude of the unknown discontinuity is compared with the precision standards and the resultant VSWR produced by the discontinuity interpreted by the graph.

Courtesy of Harold E. Stinehelfer, Microwave Associates, Inc.

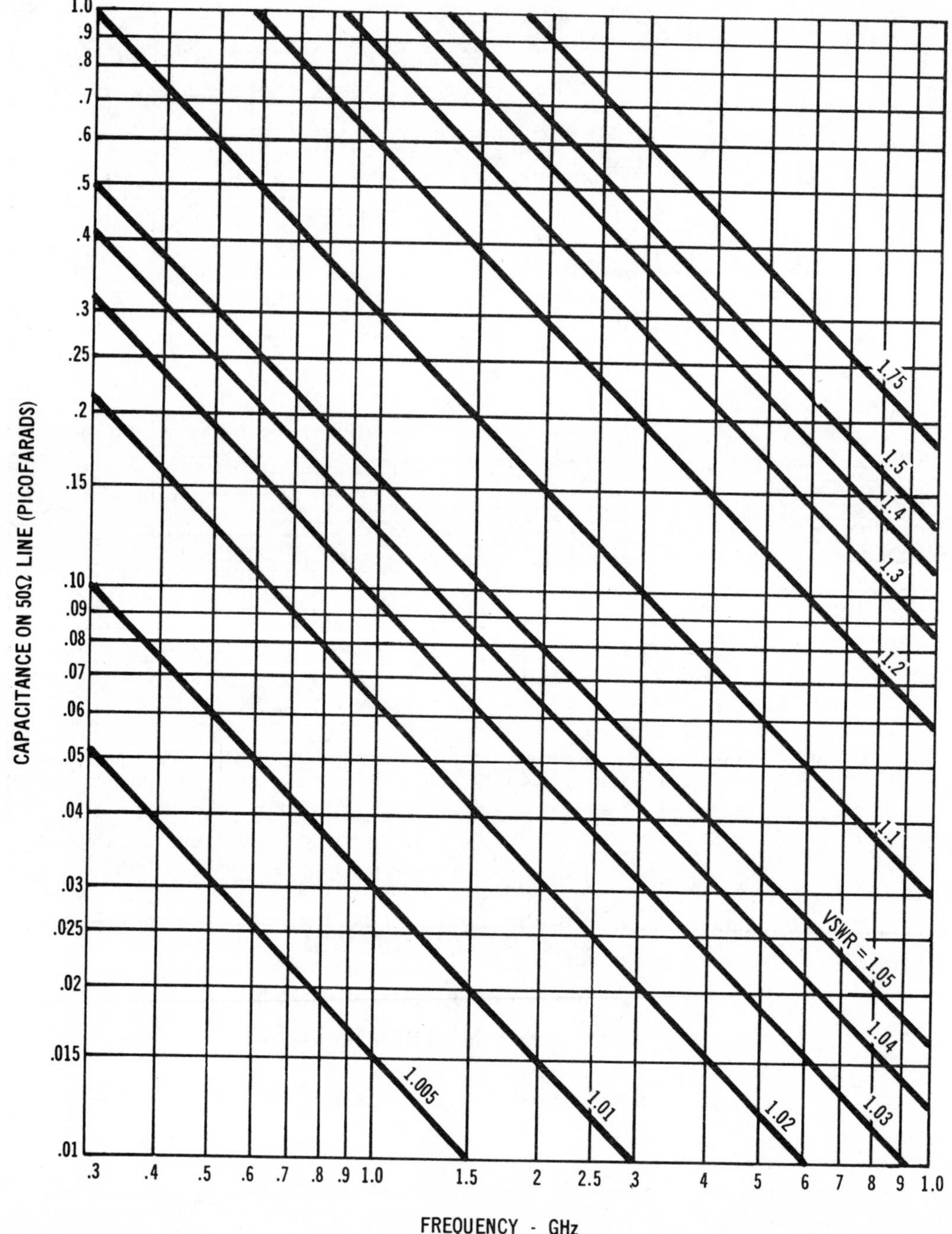

NOMOGRAPH FOR ATTENUATION IN DIELECTRIC #1

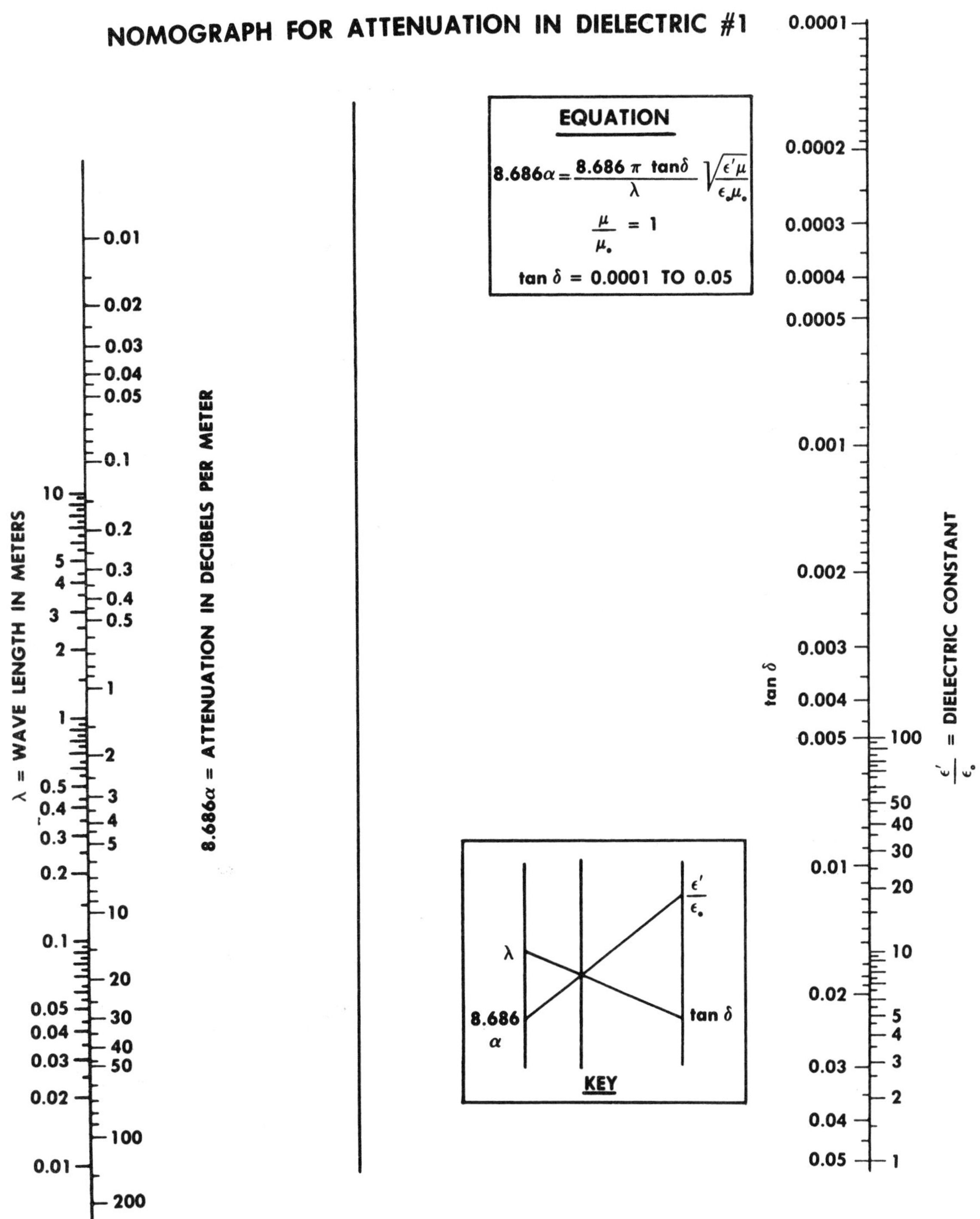

Reprinted with permission of A. R. von Hippel, Dielectrics and Waves, 1954, John Wiley and Sons, Inc. and the MIT Press of t Massachusetts Institute of Technology.

16

NOMOGRAPH FOR ATTENUATION IN DIELECTRIC #2

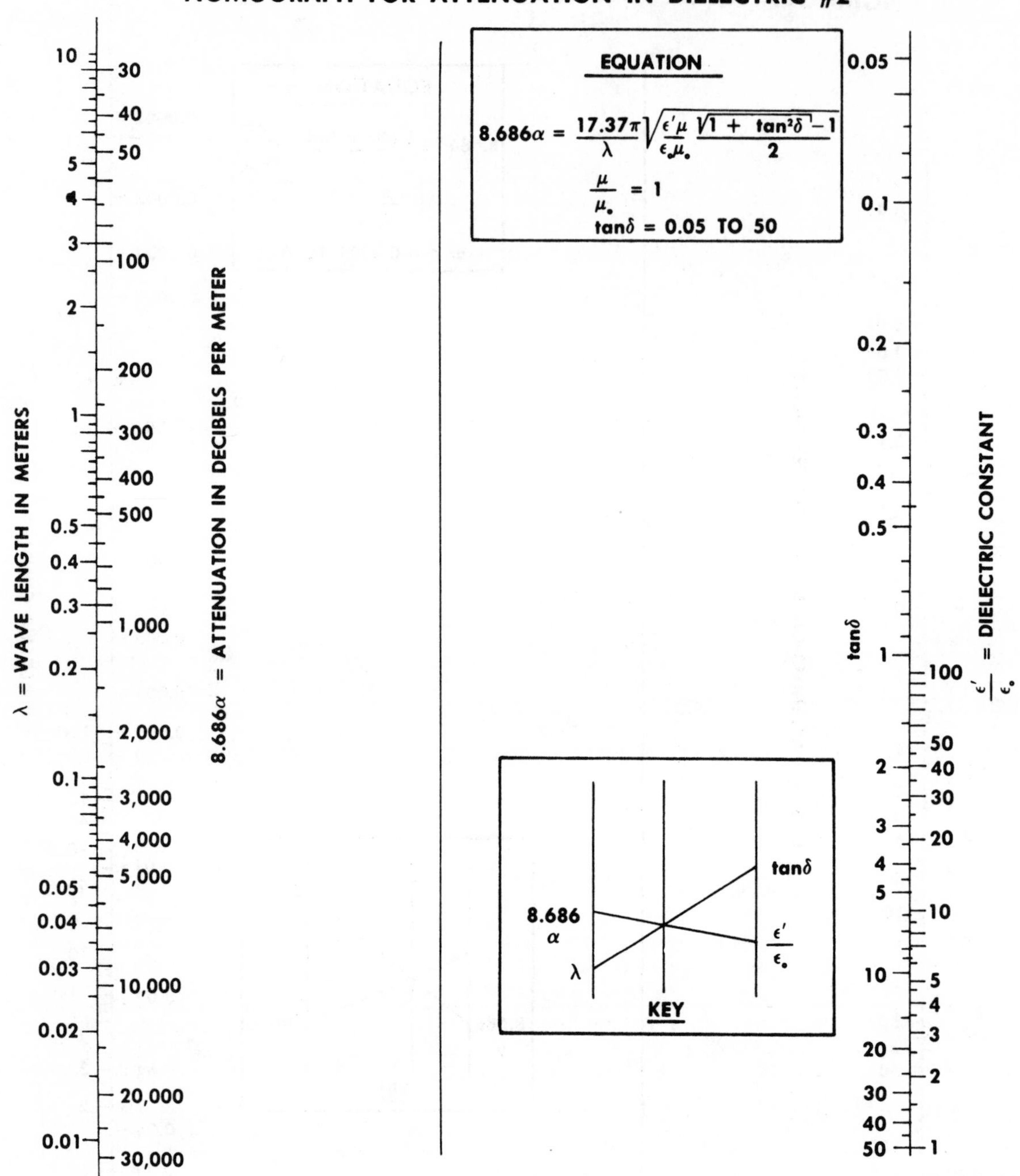

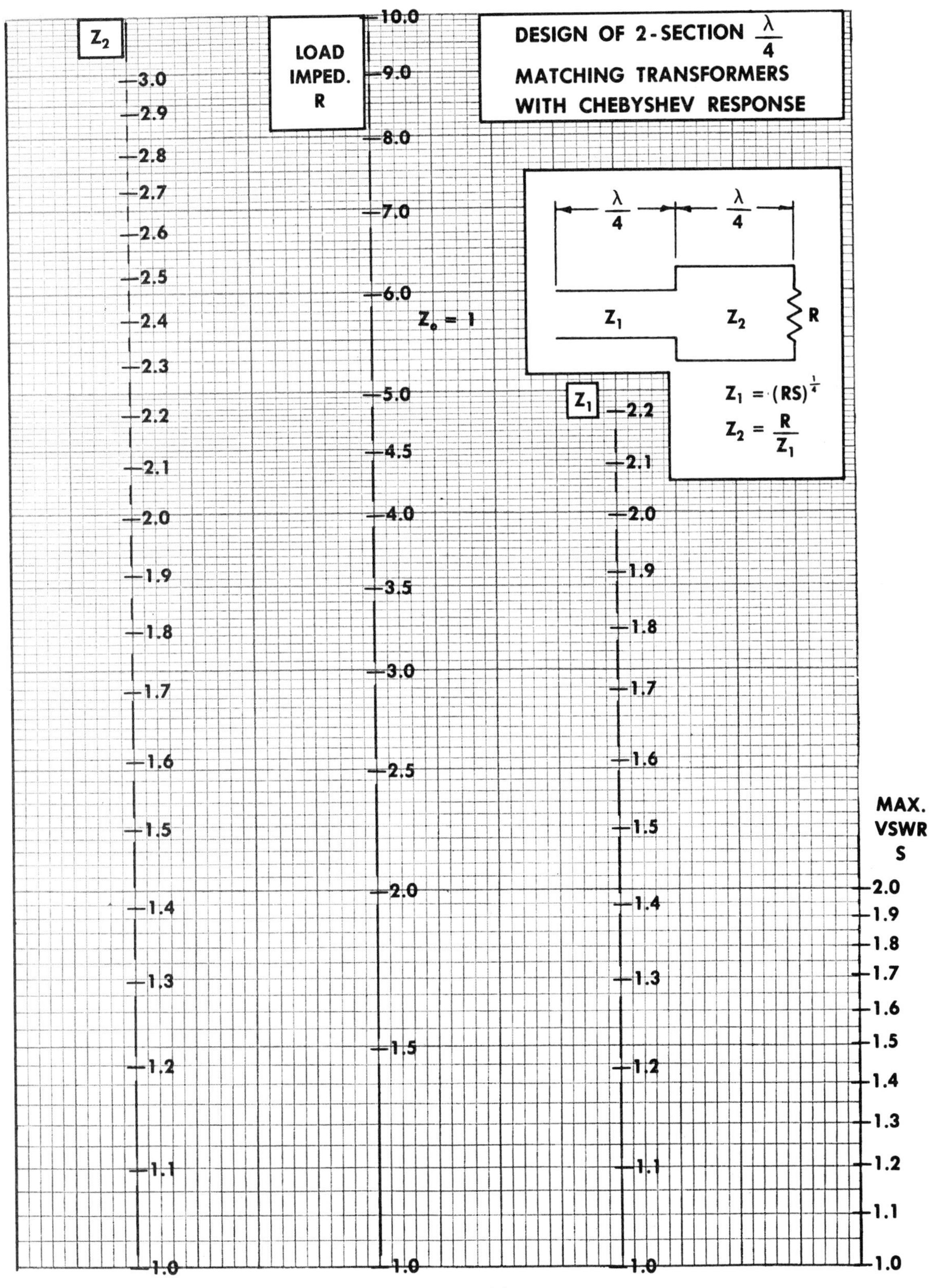

Value of S obtained from next page.

Courtesy of Gershon J. Wheeler.

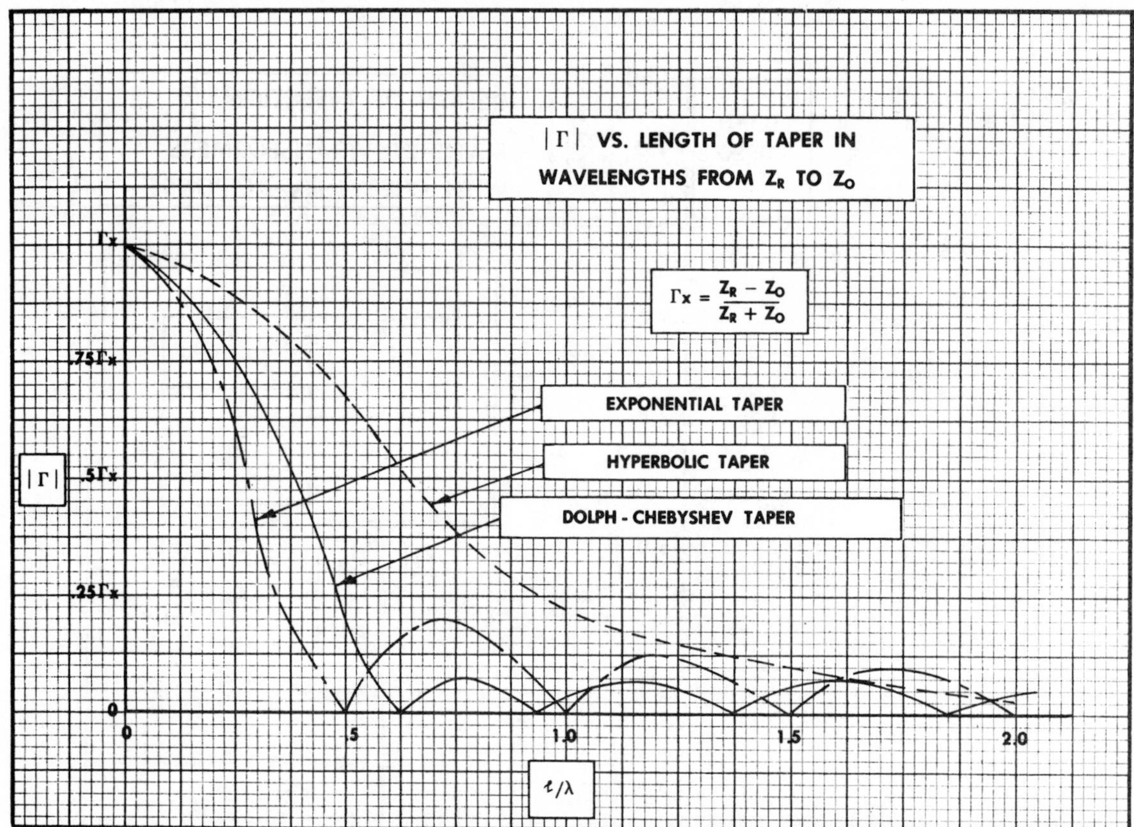
|Γ| VS. LENGTH OF TAPER IN
WAVELENGTHS FROM Z_R TO Z_O
$\Gamma x = \frac{Z_R - Z_O}{Z_R + Z_O}$
EXPONENTIAL TAPER
HYPERBOLIC TAPER
DOLPH - CHEBYSHEV TAPER
Γx
.75Γx
.5Γx
.25Γx
|Γ|
0
.5
1.0
1.5
2.0
ℓ/λ

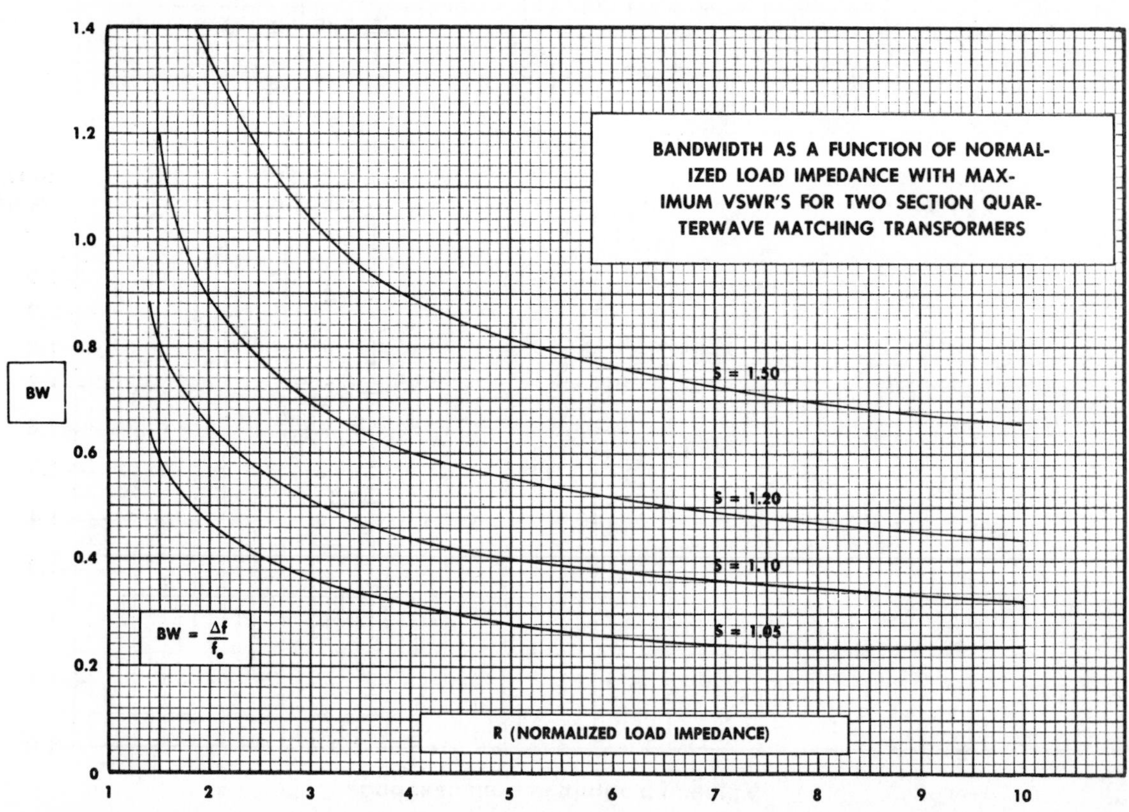
BANDWIDTH AS A FUNCTION OF NORMALIZED LOAD IMPEDANCE WITH MAXIMUM VSWR'S FOR TWO SECTION QUARTERWAVE MATCHING TRANSFORMERS
S = 1.50
S = 1.20
S = 1.10
S = 1.05
BW
$BW = \frac{\Delta f}{f_o}$
R (NORMALIZED LOAD IMPEDANCE)
1.4
1.2
1.0
0.8
0.6
0.4
0.2
0
1
2
3
4
5
6
7
8
9
10

Courtesy of Gershon J. Wheeler.

WAVEGUIDES

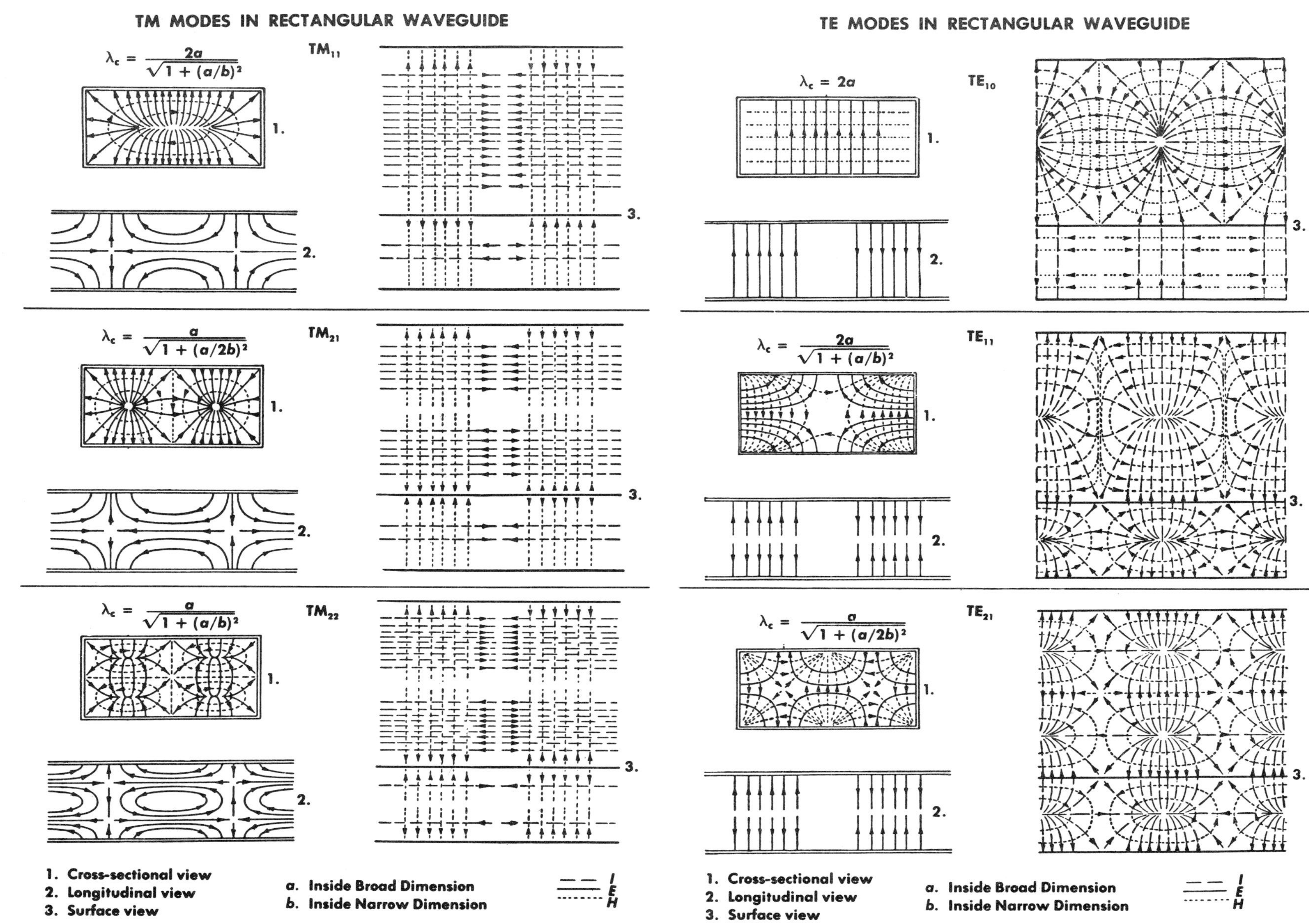
TM MODES IN RECTANGULAR WAVEGUIDE
TM$_{11}$
$\lambda_c = \frac{2a}{\sqrt{1 + (a/b)^2}}$
TM$_{21}$
$\lambda_c = \frac{a}{\sqrt{1 + (a/2b)^2}}$
TM$_{22}$
$\lambda_c = \frac{a}{\sqrt{1 + (a/b)^2}}$
1.
2.
3.
1. Cross-sectional view
2. Longitudinal view
3. Surface view
a. Inside Broad Dimension
b. Inside Narrow Dimension
I
E
H
TE MODES IN RECTANGULAR WAVEGUIDE
TE$_{10}$
$\lambda_c = 2a$
TE$_{11}$
$\lambda_c = \frac{2a}{\sqrt{1 + (a/b)^2}}$
TE$_{21}$
$\lambda_c = \frac{a}{\sqrt{1 + (a/2b)^2}}$
1.
2.
3.
1. Cross-sectional view
2. Longitudinal view
3. Surface view
a. Inside Broad Dimension
b. Inside Narrow Dimension
I
E
H
21

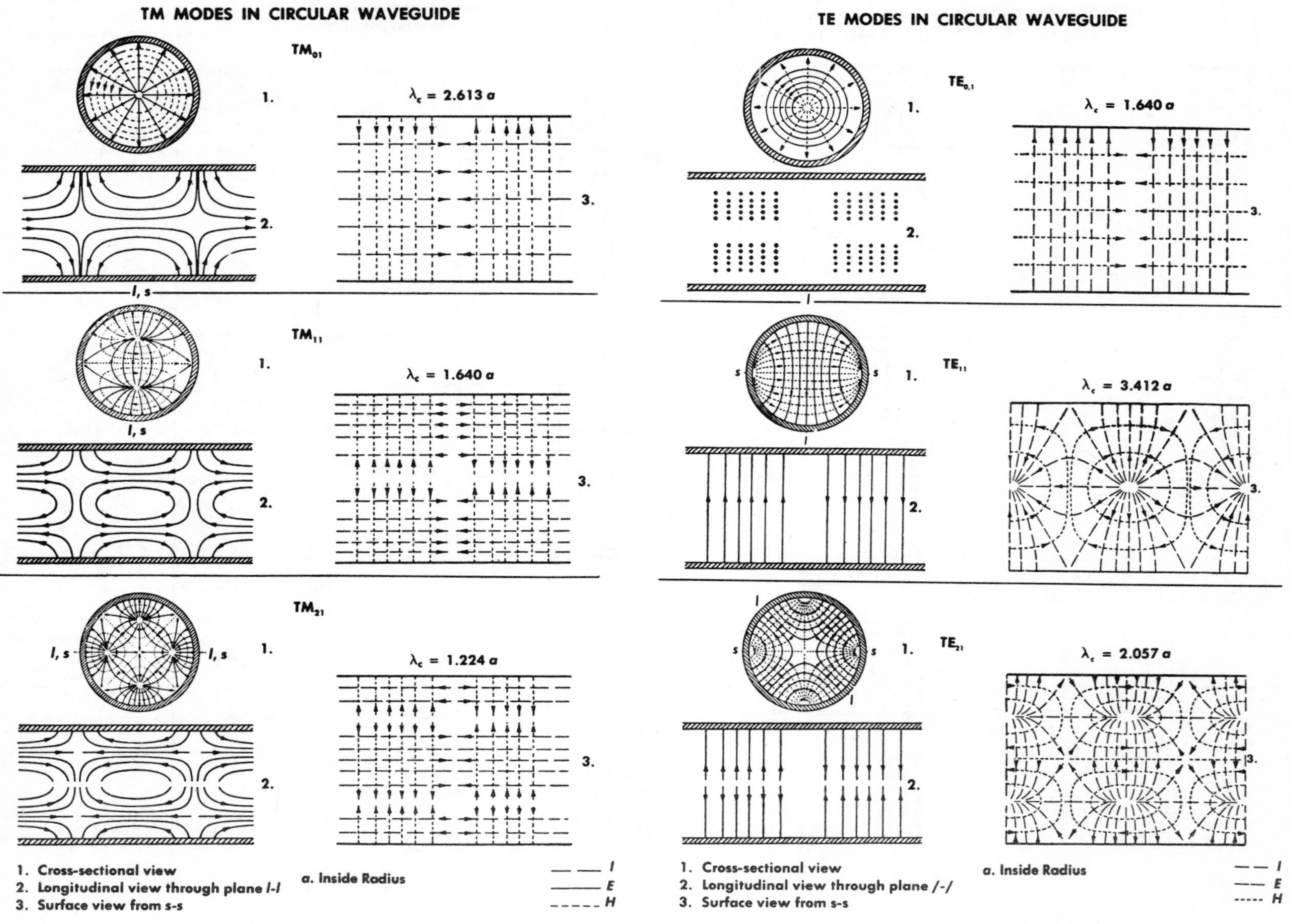

Reprinted from Waveguide Handbook, MIT Rad. Lab. Series, vol. 10, edited by N. Marcuvitz, copyright 1951 by McGraw-Hill Book Co., Inc.

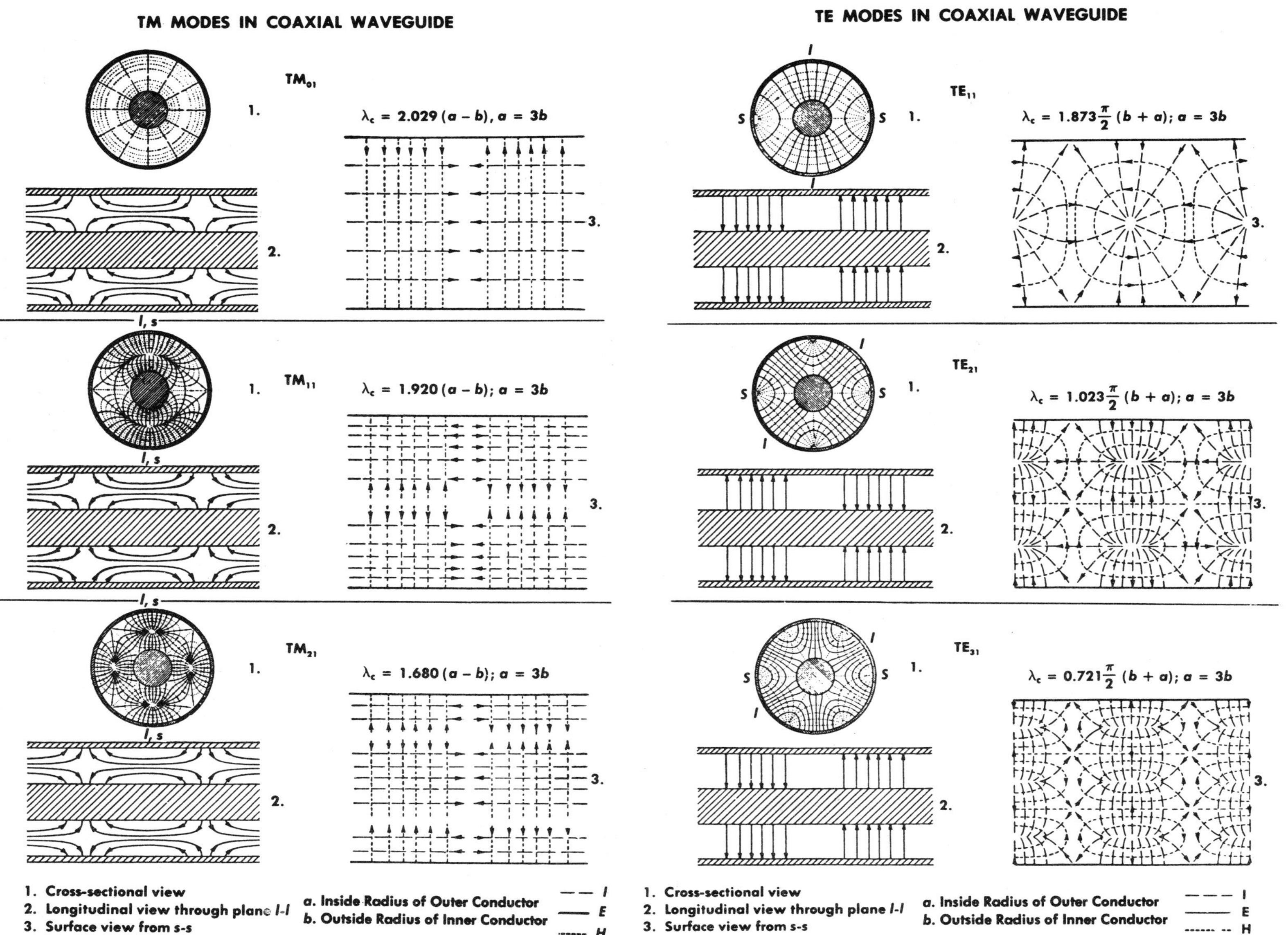

TM MODES IN COAXIAL WAVEGUIDE
TM$_{01}$
1.
$\lambda_c = 2.029\,(a - b),\ a = 3b$
2.
3.
l, s
TM$_{11}$
1.
$\lambda_c = 1.920\,(a - b);\ a = 3b$
2.
3.
l, s
TM$_{21}$
1.
$\lambda_c = 1.680\,(a - b);\ a = 3b$
2.
3.
1. Cross-sectional view
2. Longitudinal view through plane l-l
3. Surface view from s-s
a. Inside Radius of Outer Conductor
b. Outside Radius of Inner Conductor
l
E
H
TE MODES IN COAXIAL WAVEGUIDE
TE$_{11}$
1.
$\lambda_c = 1.873\,\frac{\pi}{2}\,(b + a);\ a = 3b$
2.
3.
TE$_{21}$
1.
$\lambda_c = 1.023\,\frac{\pi}{2}\,(b + a);\ a = 3b$
2.
3.
TE$_{31}$
1.
$\lambda_c = 0.721\,\frac{\pi}{2}\,(b + a);\ a = 3b$
2.
3.
1. Cross-sectional view
2. Longitudinal view through plane l-l
3. Surface view from s-s
a. Inside Radius of Outer Conductor
b. Outside Radius of Inner Conductor
l
E
H

WAVEGUIDES OF MORE GENERAL CROSS SECTION (RIDGE WAVEGUIDE)

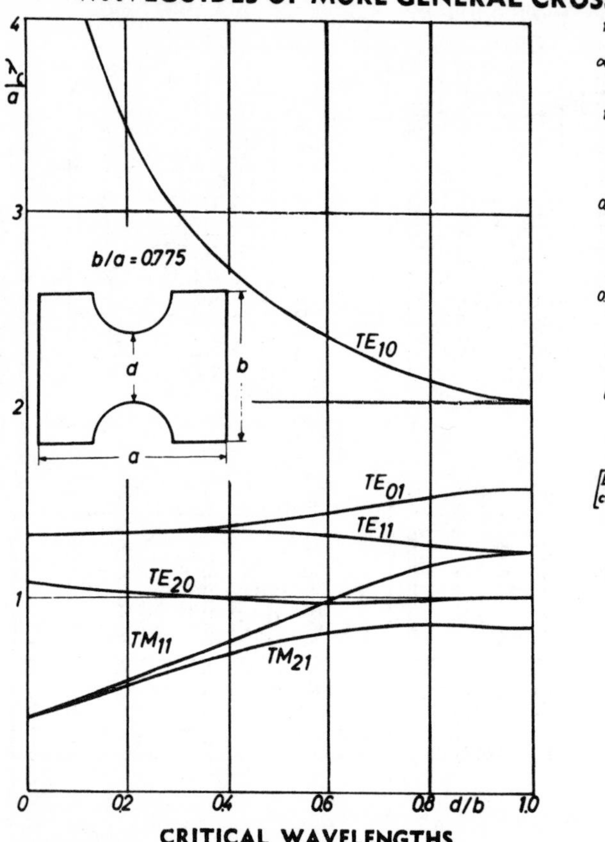

CRITICAL WAVELENGTHS

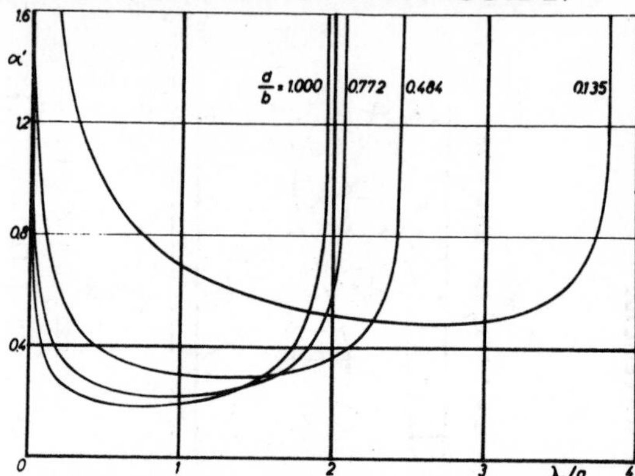

ATTENUATION CONSTANT TE_{10}-MODE

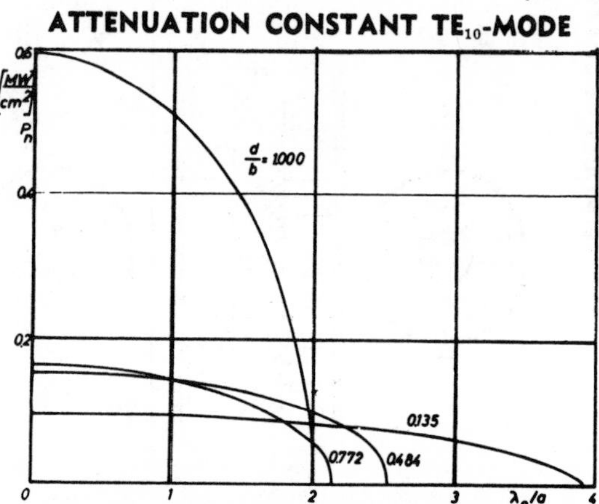

POWER CAPACITY TE_{10}-MODE

Attenuation constant of the basic TE-mode in the ridge waveguide:

$$\alpha = 8.69 \cdot \alpha' / \sqrt{\sigma \cdot a^3} \qquad \text{dB}$$

a = inner broad side dimension of the ridge waveguide in cm

σ = specific dc-conductivity of the waveguide material in Mho/cm

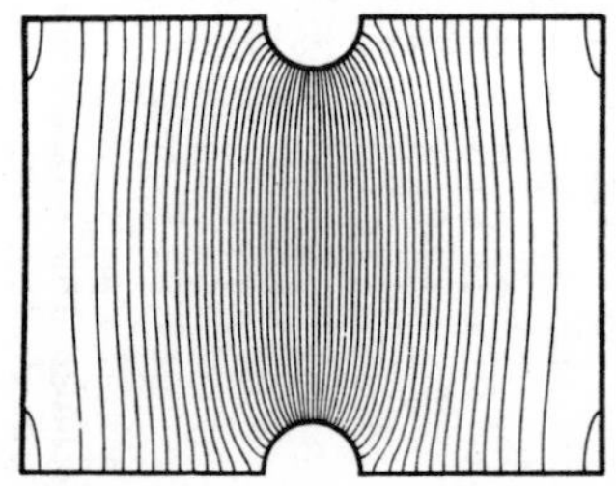

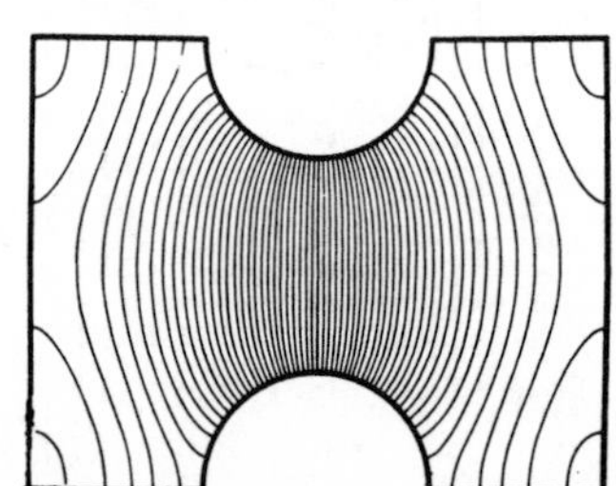

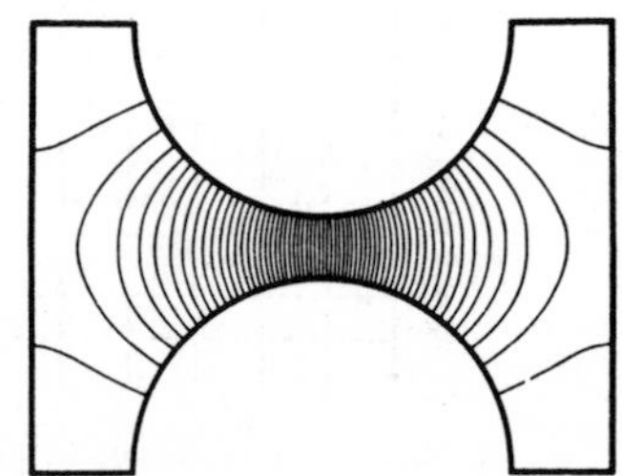

TRANSVERSE ELECTRICAL FIELD LINES TE_{10}-MODE

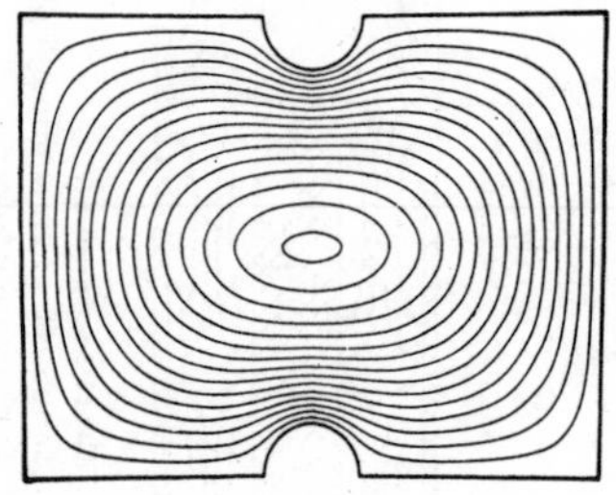

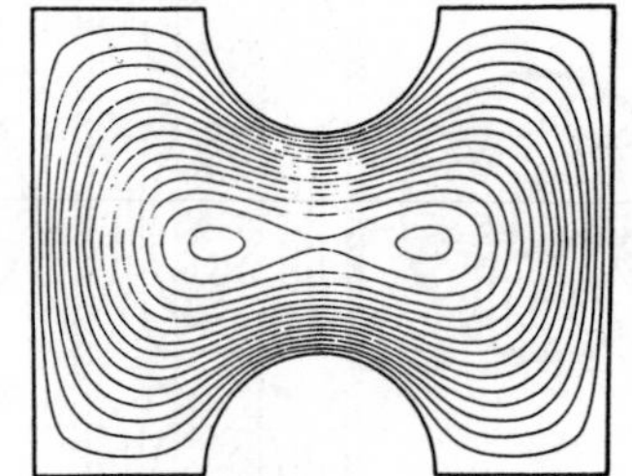

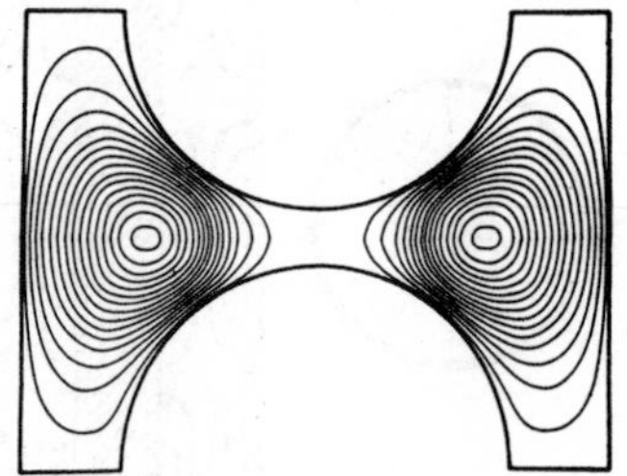

TRANSVERSE MAGNETICAL FIELD LINES TM_{11}-MODE

H. H. Meinke and W. Baier, courtesy of Institut fur Hochfrequenztechnik der Technischen Hochschule Munchen.

WAVEGUIDES OF MORE GENERAL CROSS SECTION (LUNAR GUIDE)

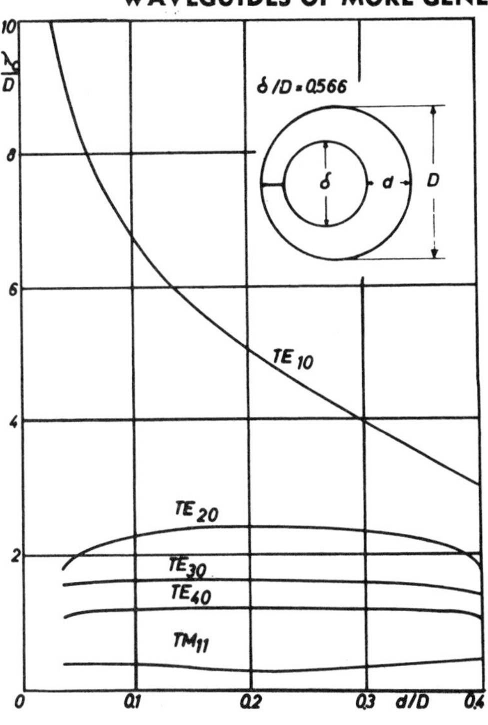

CRITICAL WAVELENGTHS

Attenuation constant of the basic TE-mode in the lunar guide:

$$\alpha = 8.69 \cdot \alpha' / \sqrt{\sigma \cdot D^3} \qquad \text{dB}$$

D = inner diameter of the lunar guide in cm

σ = specific dc-conductivity of the waveguide material in Mho/cm

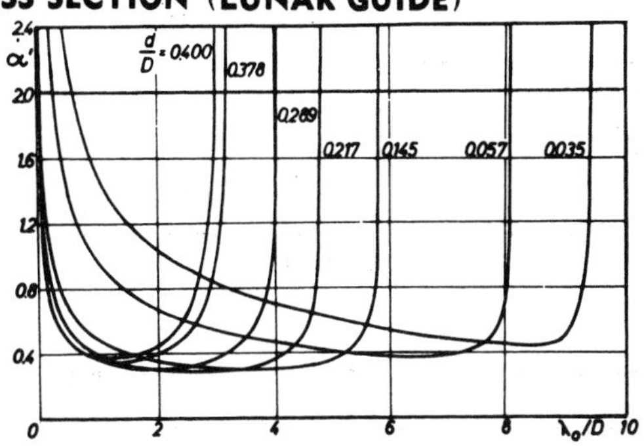

ATTENUATION CONSTANT TE_{10}-MODE

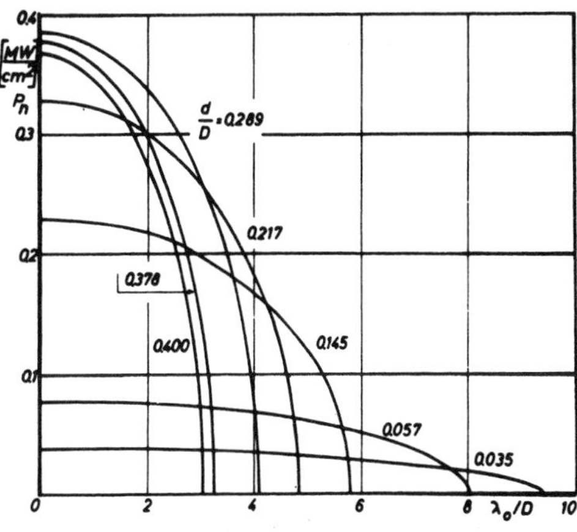

POWER CAPACITY TE_{10}-MODE

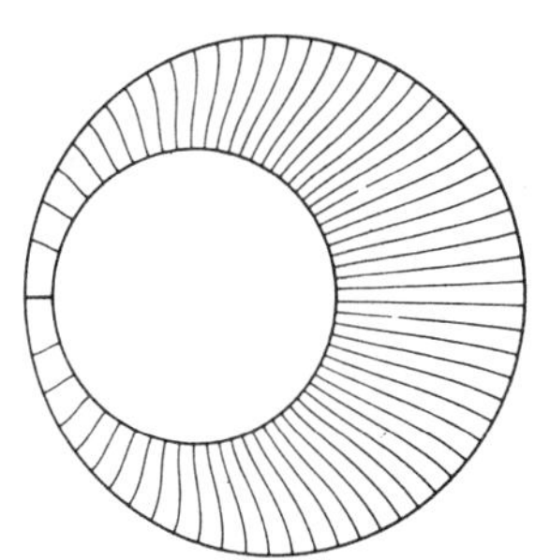

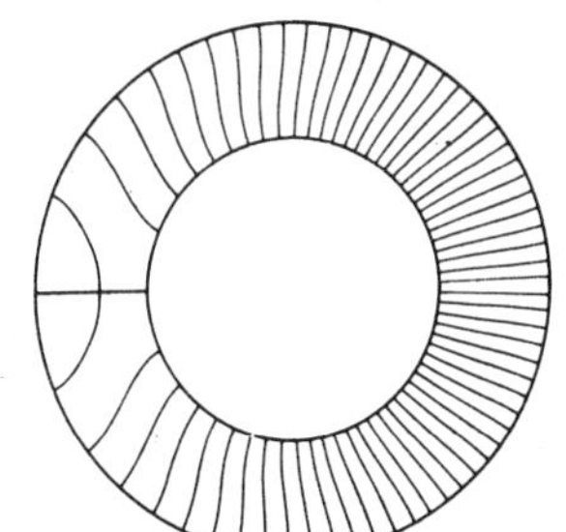

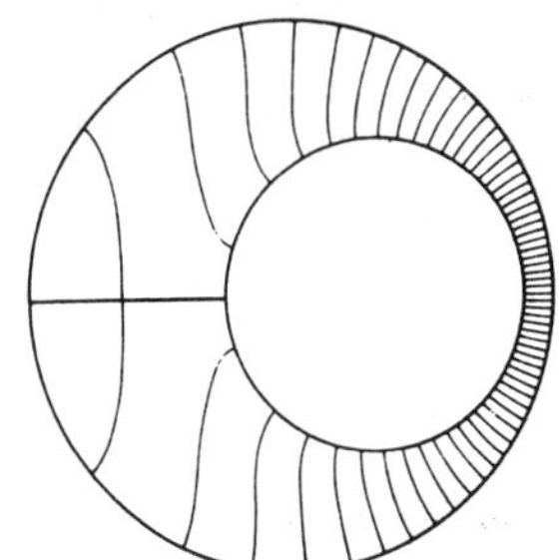

TRANSVERSE ELECTRICAL FIELD LINES TE_{10}-MODE

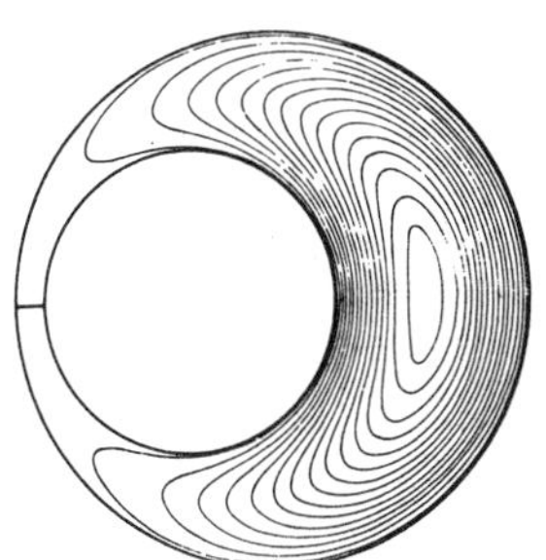

TRANSVERSE MAGNETICAL FIELD LINES TM_{11}-MODE

H. H. Meinke and W. Baier, courtesy of Institut fur Hochfrequenztechnik der Technischen Hochschule Munchen.

FOUR WAVEGUIDE CROSS SECTIONS WITH THEIR APPROXIMATE CUTOFF—WAVELENGTH FORMULAS.

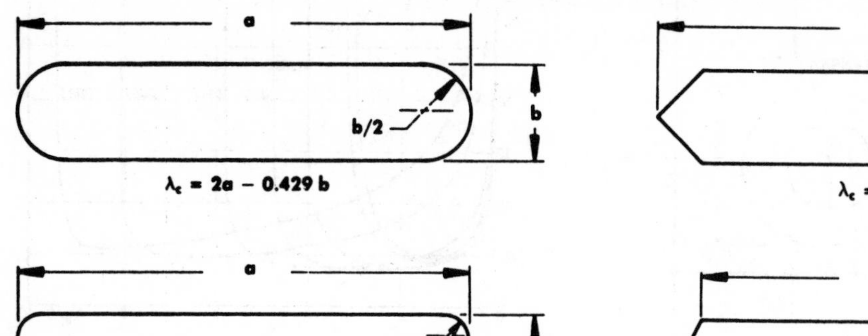

$\lambda_c = 2a - 0.429\,b$

$\lambda_c = 2(a-c)$

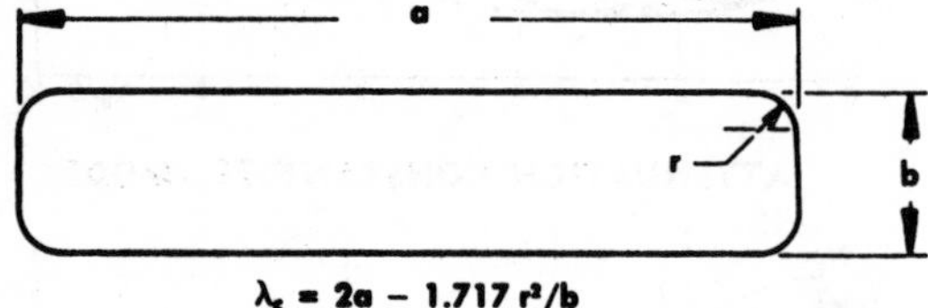

$\lambda_c = 2a - 1.717\,r^2/b$

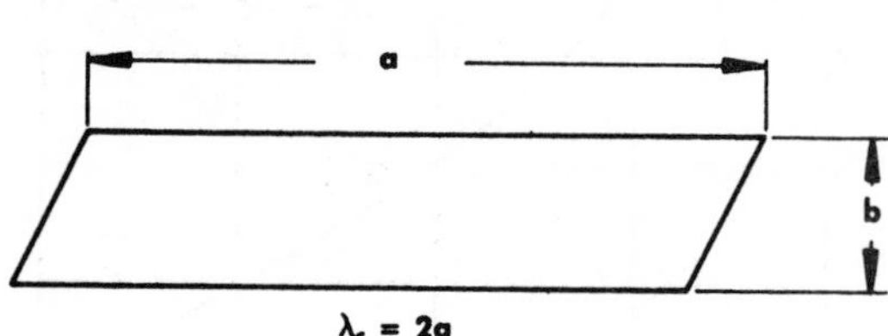

$\lambda_c = 2a$

WAVEGUIDES OF MORE GENERAL CROSS SECTION (HEXAGONAL GUIDE)

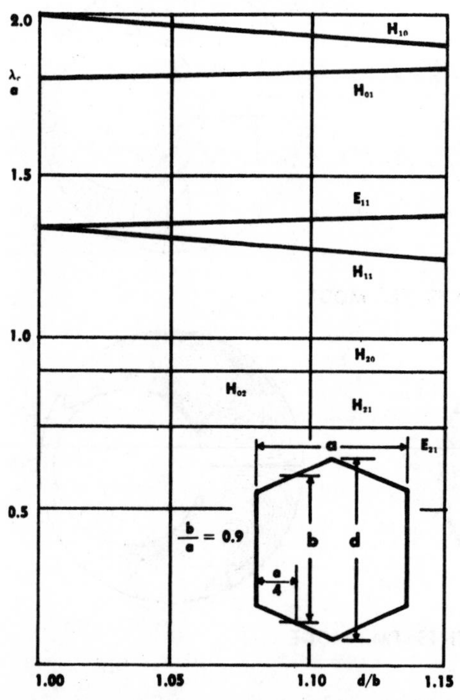

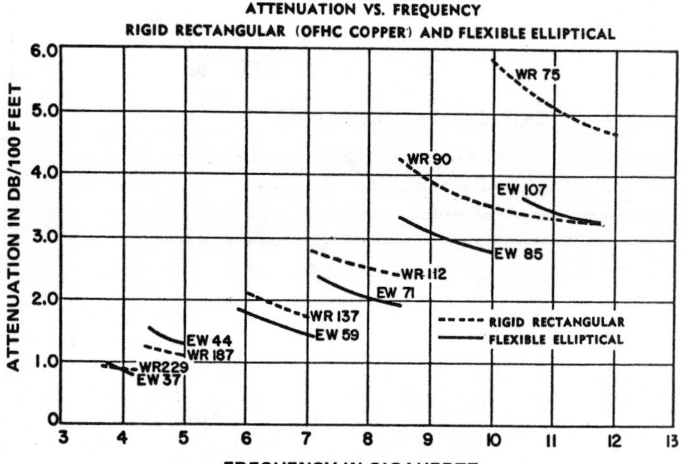

Top: Courtesy of Seymour B. Cohn, Rantec Corp., Calabasas, Cal. Center: From Heliax Elliptical Waveguides, courtesy of the Andrew Corp. Bottom: H. H. Meinke and W. Baier, courtesy of Institut fur Hochfrequenztechnik der Technischen Hochschule Munchen.

DISPERSION CHARACTERISTICS

Dispersion characteristics of the eight lowest modes in rectangular waveguides containing a longitudinal dielectric rod (λ_g = wavelength in the waveguide; λ_o = wavelength in free space).

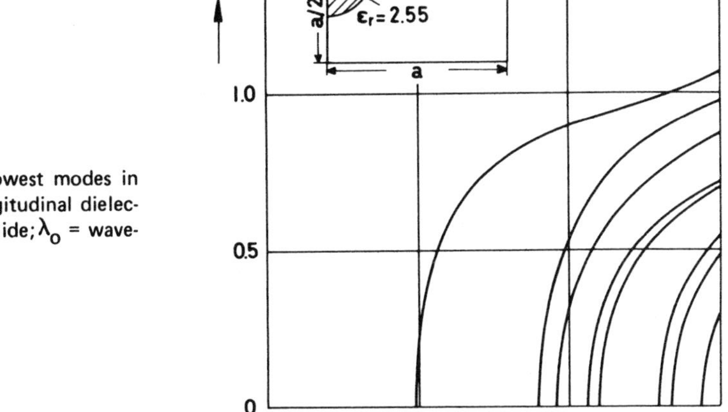

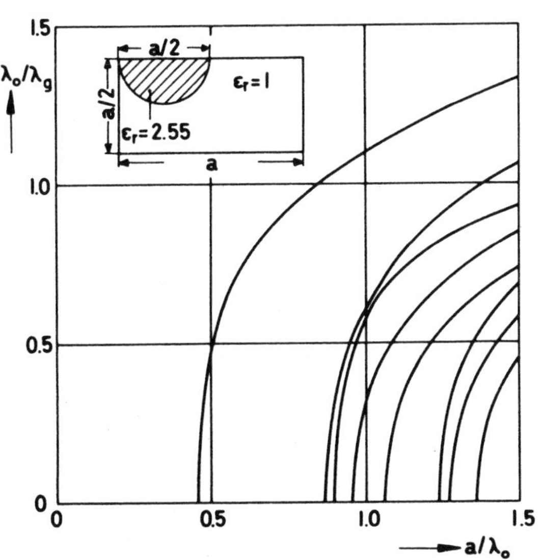

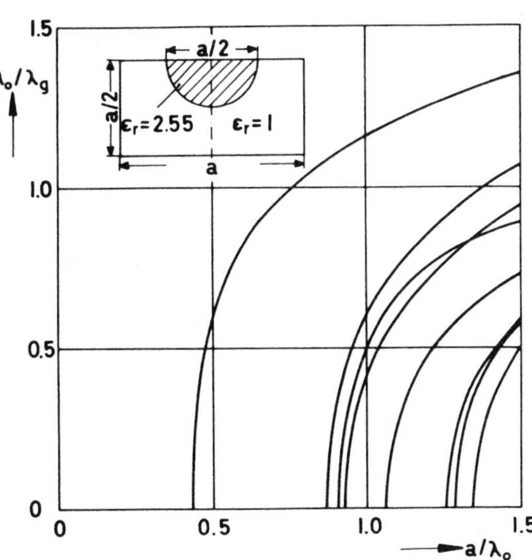

H. H. Meinke and W. Baier, courtesy of Institut fur Hochfrequenztechnik der Technischen Hochschule Munchen.

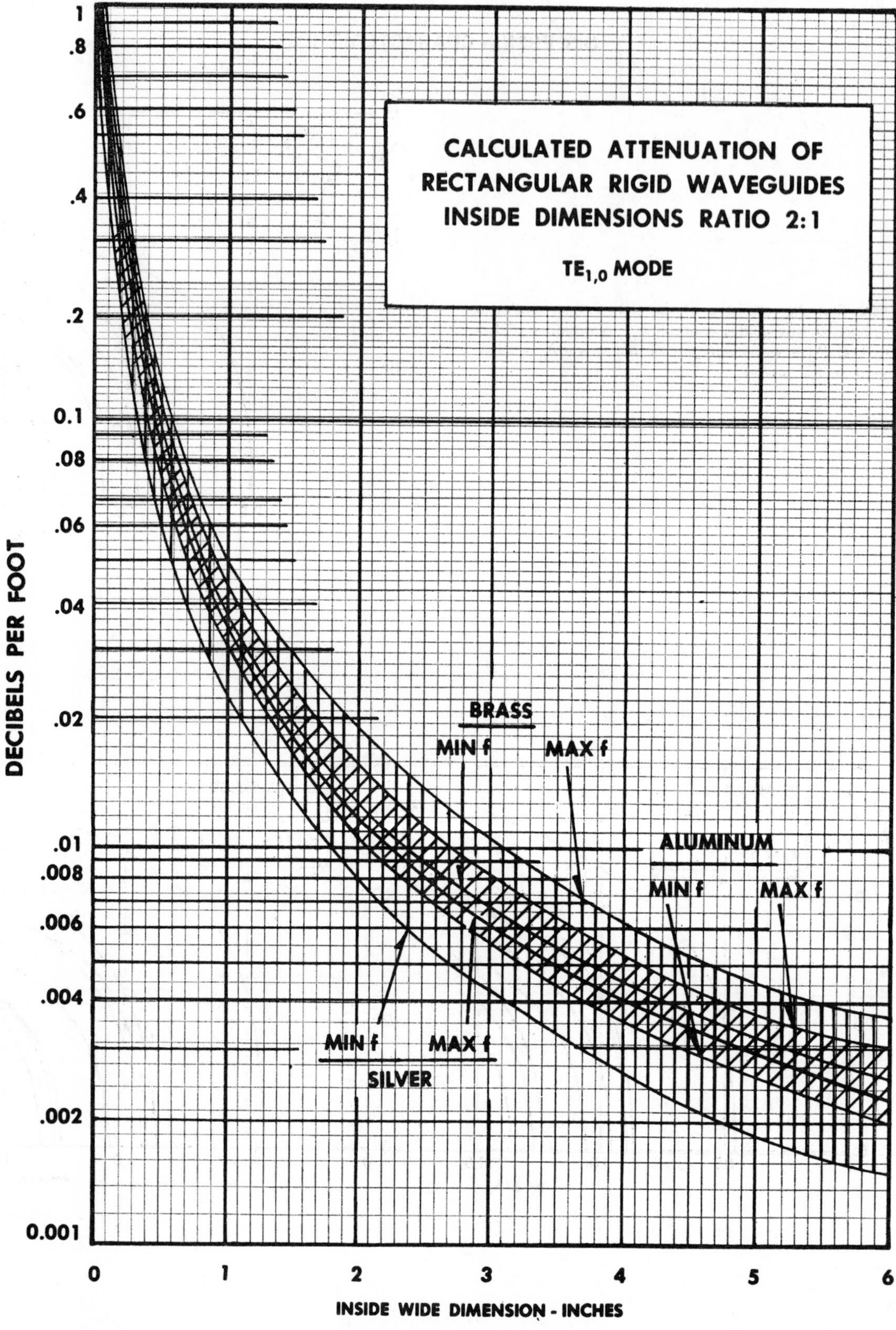

Courtesy of Airtron, a Division of Litton Industries.

AVERAGE POWER VS. TEMPERATURE RISE
FOR RIGID WAVEGUIDE

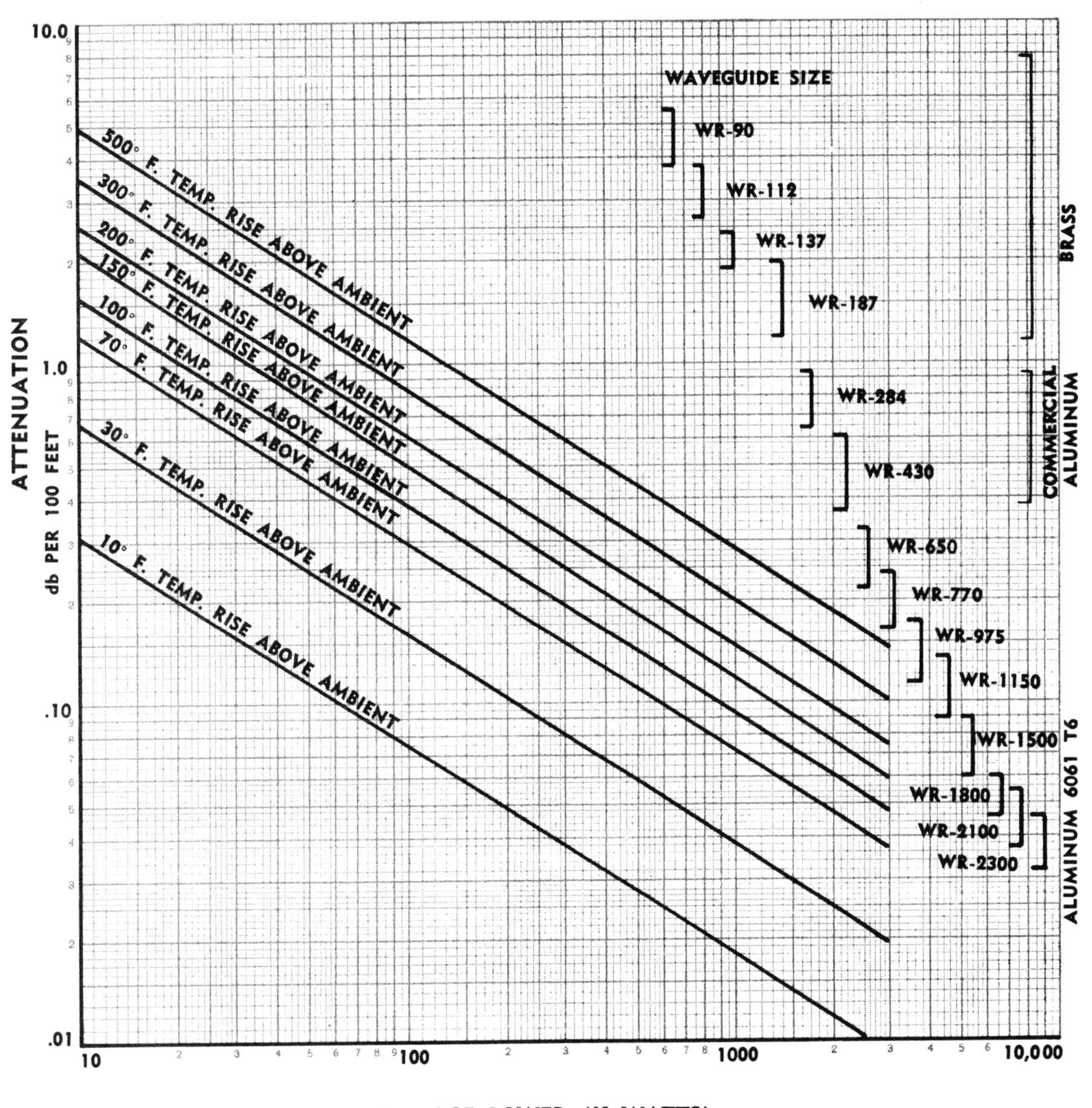

Courtesy of Thomas J. Vaughan.

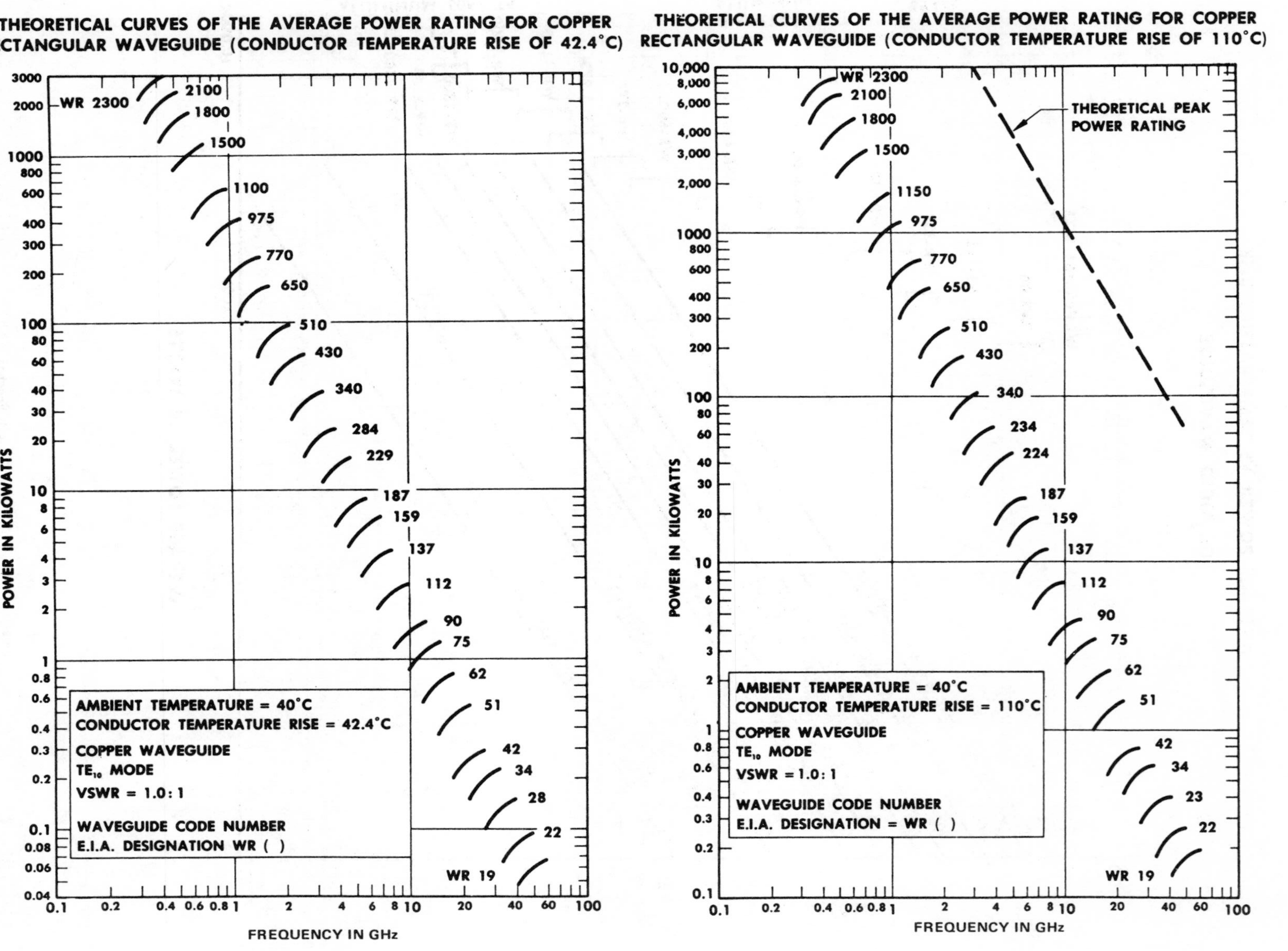

H. E. King, "Rectangular Waveguide Theoretical CW Average Power Rating," PGMTT Transactions, July 1961.

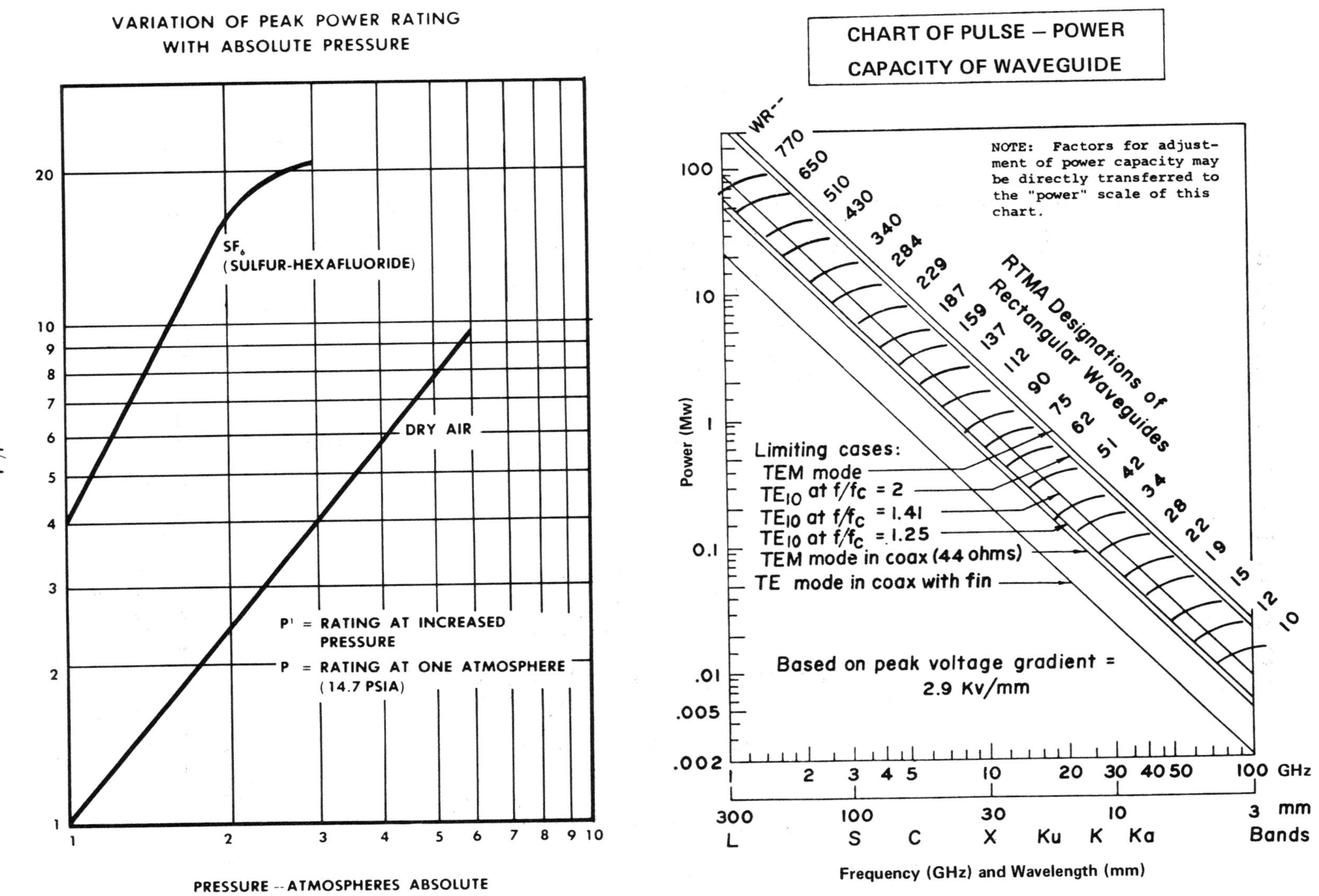
VARIATION OF PEAK POWER RATING
WITH ABSOLUTE PRESSURE
SF6 (SULFUR-HEXAFLUORIDE)
DRY AIR
P' = RATING AT INCREASED PRESSURE
P = RATING AT ONE ATMOSPHERE (14.7 PSIA)
P'/P
1 2 3 4 5 6 7 8 9 10 20
1 2 3 4 5 6 7 8 9 10
PRESSURE --ATMOSPHERES ABSOLUTE
CHART OF PULSE – POWER
CAPACITY OF WAVEGUIDE
NOTE: Factors for adjustment of power capacity may be directly transferred to the "power" scale of this chart.
RTMA Designations of Rectangular Waveguides
WR-- 770 650 510 430 340 284 229 187 159 137 112 90 75 62 51 42 34 28 22 19 15 12 10
Limiting cases:
TEM mode
TE10 at f/fc = 2
TE10 at f/fc = 1.41
TE10 at f/fc = 1.25
TEM mode in coax (44 ohms)
TE mode in coax with fin
Based on peak voltage gradient = 2.9 Kv/mm
Power (Mw)
100 10 1 0.1 .01 .005 .002
2 3 4 5 10 20 30 40 50 100 GHz
300 100 30 10 3 mm
L S C X Ku K Ka Bands
Frequency (GHz) and Wavelength (mm)

WAVEGUIDE DEFLECTION VS. PRESSURE

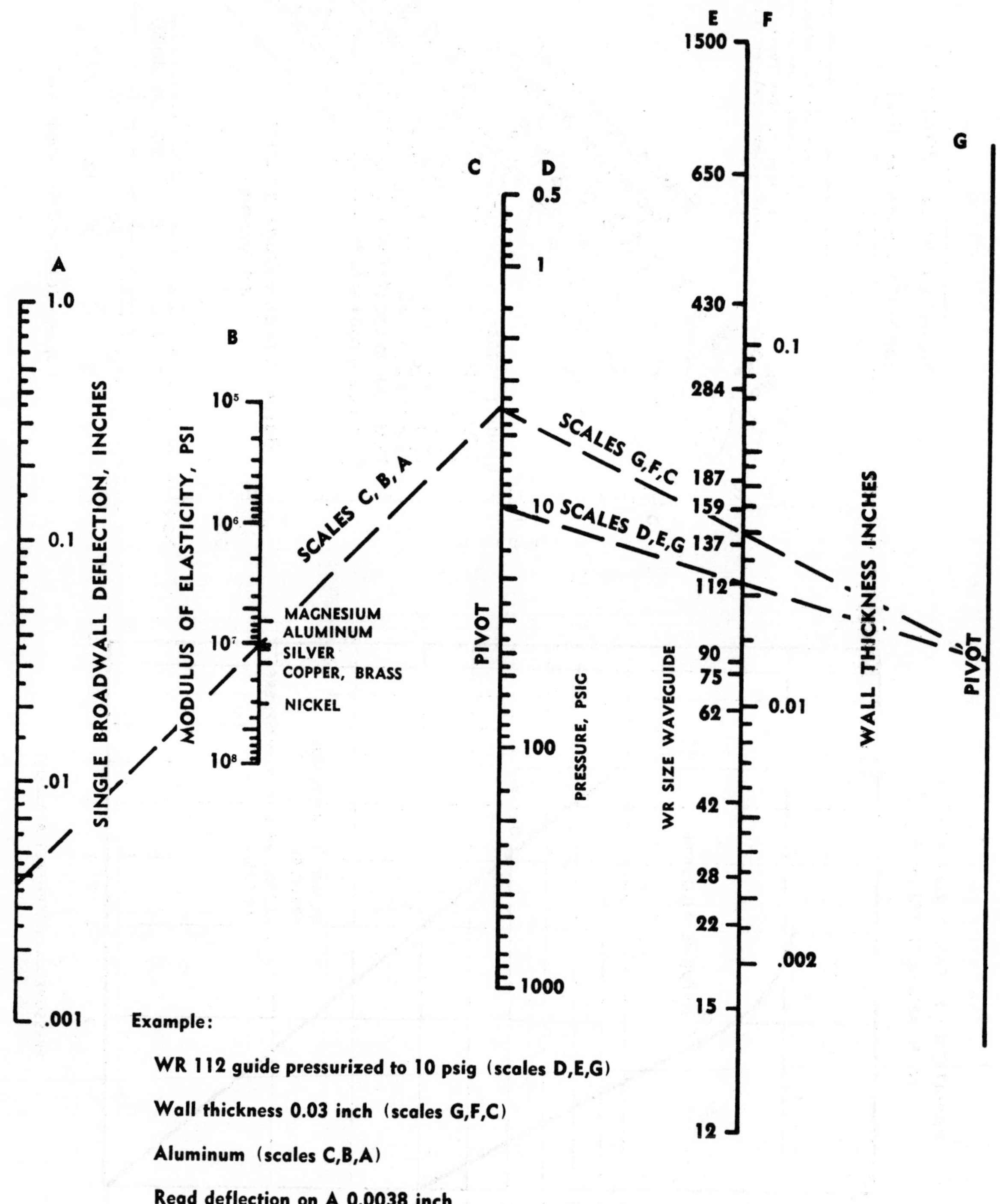

Example:

WR 112 guide pressurized to 10 psig (scales D,E,G)

Wall thickness 0.03 inch (scales G,F,C)

Aluminum (scales C,B,A)

Read deflection on A 0.0038 inch

Courtesy of William C. Morchin.

STRESS IN PRESSURIZED WAVEGUIDE

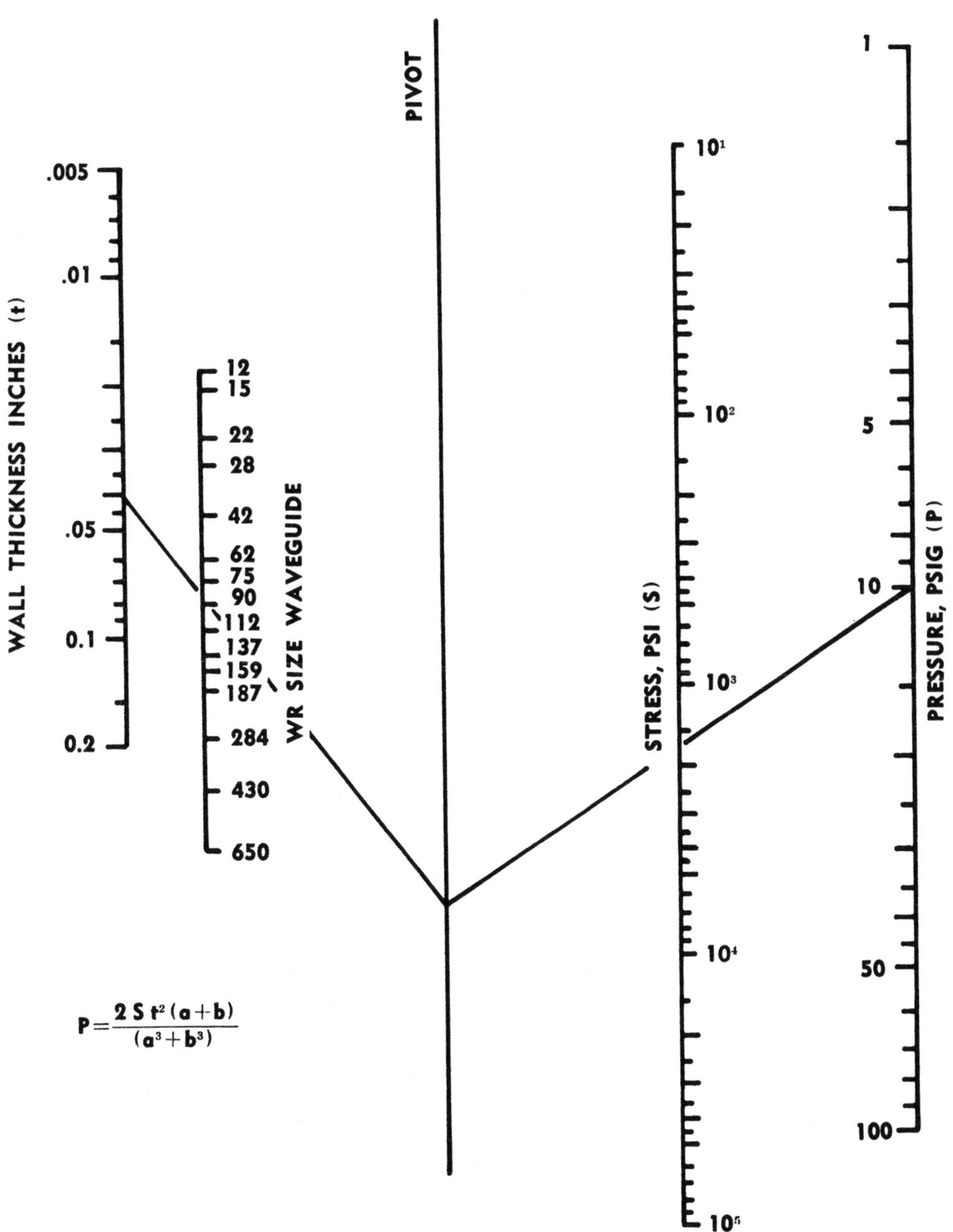

$$P = \frac{2\,S\,t^2\,(a+b)}{(a^3+b^3)}$$

Courtesy of William C. Morchin.

CUTOFF WAVELENGTH IN CIRCULAR WAVEGUIDE

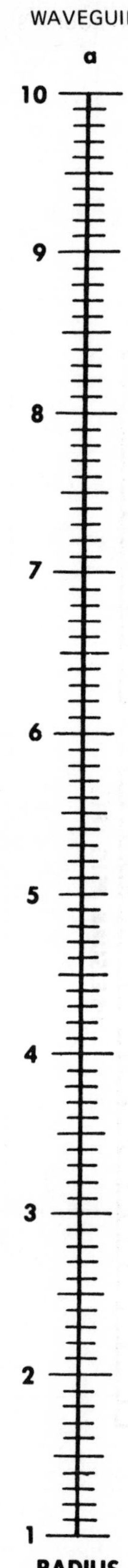

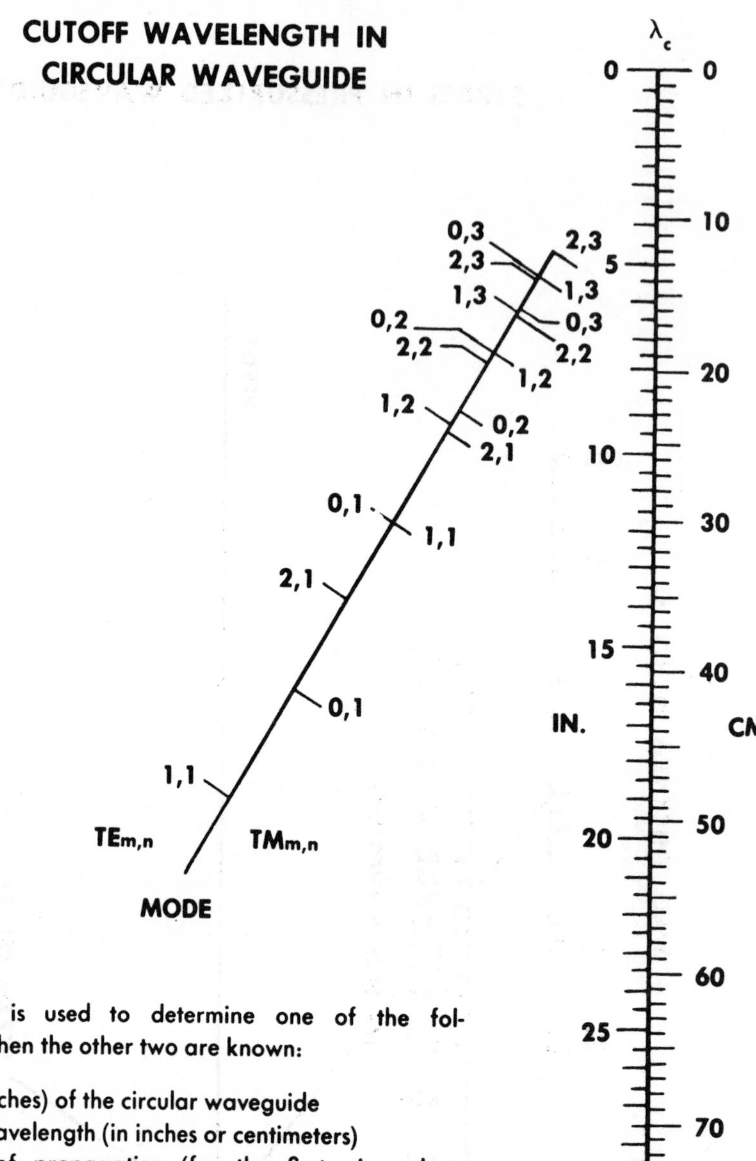

This nomogram is used to determine one of the following quantities when the other two are known:

1. radius (in inches) of the circular waveguide
2. the cutoff wavelength (in inches or centimeters)
3. the mode of propagation (for the first nine electric or magnetic modes)

The scale on the left, *a*, is the inner radius of the waveguide in inches. The scale on the right is the cutoff wavelength, and is calibrated in inches and centimeters. The diagonal scale gives the mode of propagation.

If the nomogram does not cover the desired range of *a* and λ_c, multiply those two scales by a constant 10^n.

For example, in a waveguide having an inner radius .75 inches, propagating in the TM_{01} mode, the cutoff wavelength is 4.98 cm. (1.96 inches).

Courtesy of Burrell R. Hatcher, Chu Associates, Littleton, Mass.

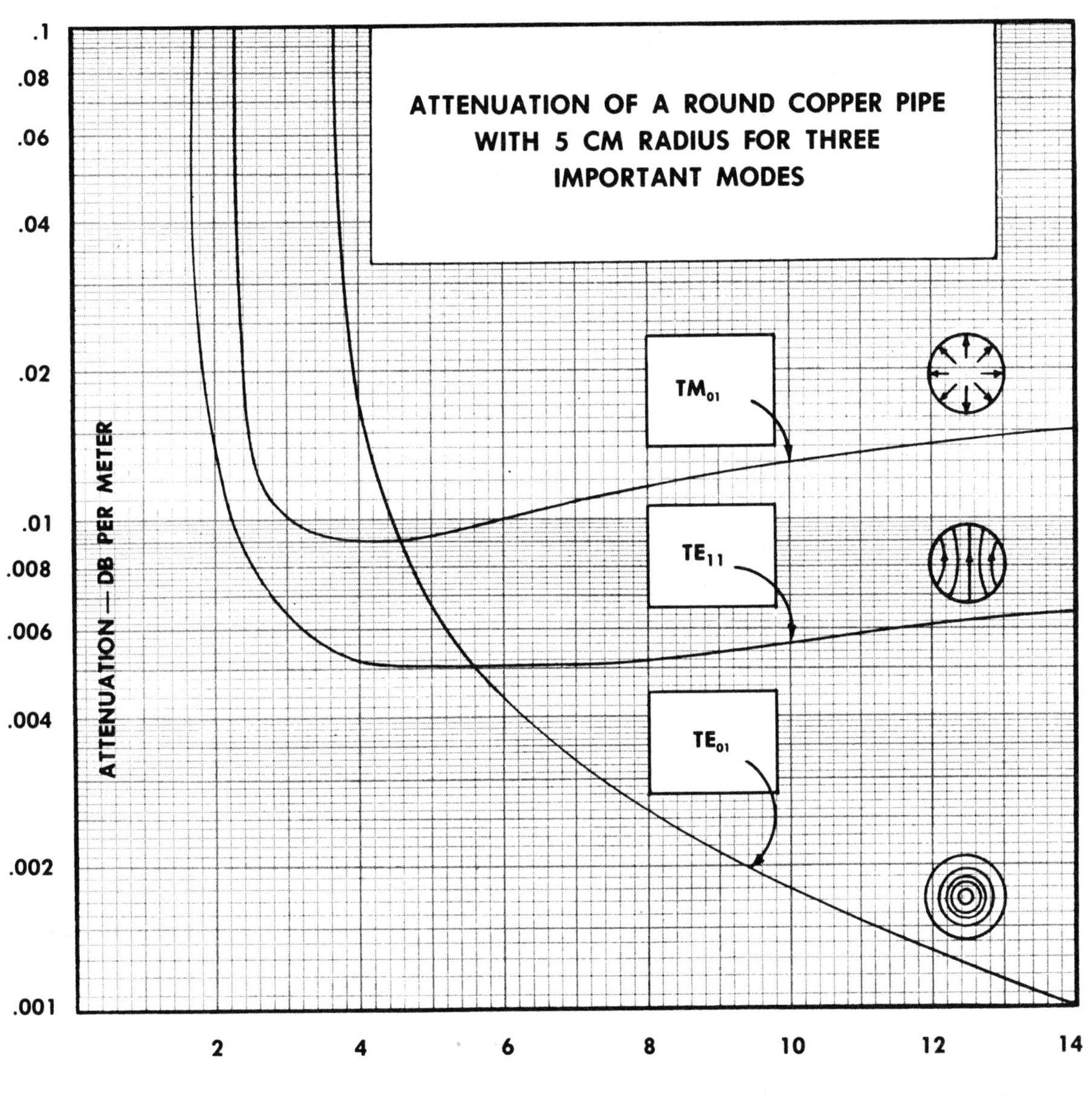

From G. C. Southworth, Principles and Applications of Waveguide Transmission, copyright 1950, D. Van Nostrand Co., Inc., Princeton, N. J.

Reference Table of Rigid Rectangular Waveguide Data and Fittings

EIA WG Designation WR( )	Recommended Operating Range for TE_{10} Mode: Frequency (GHz/sec)	Recommended Operating Range for TE_{10} Mode: Wavelength (cm)	Cut-off for TE_{10} Mode: Frequency (GHz/sec)	Cut-off for TE_{10} Mode: Wavelength (cm)	Range in $\frac{2\lambda}{\lambda c}$	Range in $\frac{\lambda g}{\lambda}$	Theoretical cw power rating lowest to highest frequency megawatts	Theoretical attenuation lowest to highest frequency (db/100 ft.)	Material Alloy	JAN WG Designation RG( )/U	JAN Flange Designation: Choke UG( )/U	JAN Flange Designation: Cover UG( )/U	EIA WG Designation WR( )	Dimensions (inches): Inside	Tol.	Outside	Tol.	Wall Thickness Nominal
2300	0.32-0.49	93.68-61.18	0.256	116.84	1.60-1.05	1.68-1.17	153.0-212.0	.051-.031	Alum.				2300	23.000-11.500	±.020	23.250-11.750	±.020	0.125
2100	0.35-0.53	85.65-56.56	0.281	106.68	1.62-1.06	1.68-1.18	120.0-173.0	.054-.034	Alum.				2100	21.000-10.500	±.020	21.250-10.750	±.020	0.125
1800	0.41-0.625	73.11-47.96	0.328	91.44	1.60-1.05	1.67-1.18	93.4-131.9	.056-.038	Alum.	201			1800	18.000-9.000	±.020	18.250-9.250	±.020	0.125
1500	0.49-0.75	61.18-39.97	0.393	76.20	1.61-1.05	1.62-1.17	67.6-93.3	.069-.050	Alum.	202			1500	15.000-7.500	±.015	15.250-7.750	±.015	0.125
1150	0.64-0.96	46.84-31.23	0.513	58.42	1.60-1.07	1.82-1.18	35.0-53.8	.128-.075	Alum.	203			1150	11.500-5.750	±.015	11.750-6.000	±.015	0.125
975	0.75-1.12	39.95-26.76	0.605	49.53	1.61-1.08	1.70-1.19	27.0-38.5	.137-.095	Alum.	204			975	9.750-4.875	±.010	10.000-5.125	±.010	0.125
770	0.96-1.45	31.23-20.67	0.766	39.12	1.60-1.06	1.66-1.18	17.2-24.1	.201-.136	Alum.	205			770	7.700-3.850	±.005	7.950-4.100	±.005	0.125
650	1.12-1.70	26.76-17.63	0.908	33.02	1.62-1.07	1.70-1.18	11.9-17.2	.317-.212 .269-.178	Brass Alum.	69 103		417A 418A	650	6.500-3.250	±.005	6.660-3.410	±.005	0.080
510	1.45-2.20	20.67-13.62	1.157	25.91	1.60-1.05	1.67-1.18	7.5-10.7						510	5.100-2.550	±.005	5.260-2.710	±.005	0.080
430	1.70-2.60	17.63-11.53	1.372	21.84	1.61-1.06	1.70-1.18	5.2-7.5	.588-.385 .501-.330	Brass Alum.	104 105		435A 437A	430	4.300-2.150	±.005	4.460-2.310	±.005	0.080
340	2.20-3.30	13.63-9.08	1.736	17.27	1.58-1.05	1.78-1.22	3.1-4.5	.877-.572 .751-.492	Brass Alum.	112 113		553 554	340	3.400-1.700	±.005	3.560-1.860	±.005	0.080
284	2.60-3.95	11.53-7.59	2.078	14.43	1.60-1.05	1.67-1.17	2.2-3.2	1.102-.752 .940-.641	Brass Alum.	48 75	54A 585	53 584	284	2.840-1.340	±.005	3.000-1.500	±.005	0.080
229	3.30-4.90	9.08-6.12	2.577	11.63	1.56-1.05	1.62-1.17	1.6-2.2						229	2.290-1.145	±.005	2.418-1.273	±.005	0.064
187	3.95-5.85	7.59-5.12	3.152	9.510	1.60-1.08	1.67-1.19	1.4-2.0	2.08-1.44 1.77-1.12	Brass Alum.	49 95	148B 406A	149A 407	187	1.872-0.872	±.005	2.000-1.000	±.005	0.064
159	4.90-7.05	6.12-4.25	3.711	8.078	1.51-1.05	1.52-1.19	0.79-1.0						159	1.590-0.795	±.004	1.718-0.923	±.004	0.064
137	5.85-8.20	5.12-3.66	4.301	6.970	1.47-1.05	1.48-1.17	0.56-0.71	2.87-2.30 2.45-1.94	Brass Alum.	50 106	343A 440A	344 441	137	1.372-0.622	±.004	1.500-0.750	±.004	0.064
112	7.05-10.00	4.25-2.99	5.259	5.700	1.49-1.05	1.51-1.17	0.35-0.46	4.12-3.21 3.50-2.74	Brass Alum.	51 68	52A 137A	51 138	112	1.122-0.497	±.004	1.250-0.625	±.004	0.064
90	8.20-12.40	3.66-2.42	6.557	4.572	1.60-1.06	1.68-1.18	0.20-0.29	6.45-4.48 5.49-3.83	Brass Alum.	52 67	40A 136A	39 135	90	0.900-0.400	±.003	1.000-0.500	±.003	0.050
75	10.00-15.00	2.99-2.00	7.868	3.810	1.57-1.05	1.64-1.17	0.17-0.23						75	0.750-0.375	±.003	0.850-0.475	±.003	0.050
62	12.4-18.00	2.42-1.66	9.486	3.160	1.53-1.05	1.55-1.18	0.12-0.16	9.51-8.31 — — 6.14-5.36	Brass Alum. Silver	91 — 107	541 — —	419 — —	62	0.622-0.311	±.0025	0.702-0.391	±.003	0.040
51	15.00-22.00	2.00-1.36	11.574	2.590	1.54-1.05	1.58-1.18	0.080-0.107						51	0.510-0.255	±.0025	0.590-0.335	±.003	0.040
42	18.00-26.50	1.66-1.13	14.047	2.134	1.56-1.06	1.60-1.18	0.043-0.058	20.7-14.8 17.6-12.6 13.3-9.5	Brass Alum. Silver	53 121 66	596 598 —	595 597 —	42	0.420-0.170	±.0020	0.500-0.250	±.003	0.040
34	22.00-33.00	1.36-0.91	17.328	1.730	1.57-1.05	1.62-1.18	0.034-0.048						34	0.340-0.170	±.0020	0.420-0.250	±.003	0.040
28	26.50-40.00	1.13-0.75	21.081	1.422	1.59-1.05	1.65-1.17	0.022-0.031	— — — — 21.9-15.0	Brass Alum. Silver	— — 96	600 — —	599 — —	28	0.280-0.140	±.0015	0.360-0.220	±.002	0.040
22	33.00-50.00	0.91-0.60	26.342	1.138	1.60-1.05	1.67-1.17	0.014-0.020	— — 31.0-20.9	Brass Silver	— 97		383 —	22	0.224-0.112	±.0010	0.304-0.192	±.002	0.040
19	40.00-60.00	0.75-0.50	31.357	0.956	1.57-1.05	1.63-1.16	0.011-0.015						19	0.188-0.094	±.0010	0.268-0.174	±.002	0.040
15	50.00-75.00	0.60-0.40	39.863	0.752	1.60-1.06	1.67-1.17	0.0063-0.0090	— — 52.9-39.1	Brass Silver	— 98		385 —	15	0.148-0.074	±.0010	0.228-0.154	±.002	0.040
12	60.00-90.00	0.50-0.33	48.350	0.620	1.61-1.06	1.68-1.18	0.0042-0.0060	— — 93.3-52.2	Brass Silver	— 99		387 —	12	0.122-0.061	±.0005	0.202-0.141	±.002	0.040
10	75.00-110.00	0.40-0.27	59.010	0.508	1.57-1.06	1.61-1.18	0.0030-0.0041						10	0.100-0.050	±.0005	0.180-0.130	±.002	0.040
8	90.00-140.00	0.333-0.214	73.840	.406	1.64-1.05	1.75-1.17	0.0018-0.0026	152-99	Silver	138	—	—	8	0.080-0.040	±0.0003	0.156 DIA	±.001	—
7	110.00-170.00	0.272-0.176	90.840	.330	1.64-1.06	1.77-1.18	0.0012-0.0017	163-137	Silver	136	—	—	7	0.065-0.0325	±0.00025	0.156 DIA	±.001	—
5	140.00-220.00	0.214-0.136	115.750	.259	1.65-1.05	1.78-1.17	0.00071-0.00107	308-193	Silver	135	—	—	5	0.051-0.0255	±0.00025	0.156 DIA	±.001	—
4	170.00-260.00	0.176-0.115	137.520	.218	1.61-1.05	1.69-1.17	0.00052-0.00075	384-254	Silver	137	—	—	4	0.043-0.0215	±0.00020	0.156 DIA	±.001	—
3	220.00-325.00	0.136-0.092	173.280	.173	1.57-1.06	1.62-1.18	0.00035-0.00047	512-348	Silver	139	—	—	3	0.034-0.0170	±0.00020	0.156 DIA	±.001	—

Courtesy of Microwave Development Laboratories, Inc., Natick, Mass.

WAVEGUIDE MULTIPLICATION SCALING FACTORS

TO DETERMINE THE SCALING FACTOR, FIND WHERE THE KNOWN WAVEGUIDE ON THE HORIZONTAL SCALE INTERSECTS THE UNKNOWN WAVEGUIDE ON THE VERTICAL SCALE. EXAMPLE. TO GO FROM WR90 TO WR187, USE SCALE FACTOR 2.078 (INDICATED IN BOLD TYPE ON THE CHART.)

EIA Waveguide WR( )	2300	2100	1800	1500	1150	975	770	650	510	430	340	284	229	187	159	137	112	90	75	62	51	42	34	28	22	19	15	12	10	EIA Waveguide WR( )
2300	1	1.095	1.278	1.533	2.000	2.359	2.987	3.538	4.510	5.349	6.765	8.098	10.044	12.299	14.465	16.788	20.536	25.555	30.667	36.977	45.098	54.762	67.647	82.143	102.678	122.340	155.405	188.524	230.000	**2300**
2100	.9130	1	1.167	1.400	1.826	2.154	2.727	3.231	4.118	4.884	6.176	7.394	9.170	11.230	13.207	15.328	18.750	23.333	28.000	33.762	41.176	50.000	61.765	75.000	93.750	111.702	141.892	172.131	210.000	**2100**
1800	.7826	.8571	1	1.200	1.565	1.846	2.338	2.769	3.529	4.186	5.294	6.338	7.860	9.626	11.321	13.139	16.071	20.000	24.000	28.939	35.294	42.857	52.941	64.286	80.357	95.745	121.622	147.541	180.000	**1800**
1500	.6522	.7143	.8333	1	1.304	1.538	1.948	2.308	2.941	3.488	4.412	5.282	6.550	8.021	9.434	10.949	13.393	16.667	20.000	24.116	29.412	35.714	44.118	53.571	66.964	79.787	101.351	122.951	150.000	**1500**
1150	.5000	.5476	.6389	.7667	1	1.179	1.493	1.769	2.255	2.674	3.382	4.049	5.022	6.150	7.233	8.394	10.268	12.778	15.333	18.489	22.549	27.380	33.823	41.071	51.339	61.170	77.703	94.262	115.000	**1150**
975	.4239	.4643	.5417	.6500	.8478	1	1.266	1.500	1.912	2.267	2.868	3.433	4.258	5.214	6.132	7.117	8.705	10.833	13.000	15.675	19.118	23.214	28.676	34.821	43.527	51.862	65.878	79.918	97.500	**975**
770	.3348	.3667	.4278	.5133	.6696	.7897	1	1.185	1.510	1.791	2.265	2.711	3.362	4.118	4.843	5.620	6.875	8.555	10.267	12.379	15.098	18.333	22.647	27.500	34.375	40.957	52.027	63.115	77.000	**770**
650	.2826	.3095	.3611	.4333	.5652	.6667	.8441	1	1.274	1.512	1.912	2.289	2.838	3.476	4.088	4.744	5.803	7.222	8.667	10.450	12.745	15.476	19.118	23.214	29.018	34.574	43.919	53.279	65.000	**650**
510	.2217	.2428	.2833	.3400	.4435	.5231	.6623	.7846	1	1.186	1.500	1.796	2.227	2.727	3.207	3.723	4.553	5.667	6.800	8.199	10.000	12.143	15.000	18.214	22.768	27.128	34.459	41.803	51.000	**510**
430	.1869	.2047	.2389	.2867	.3739	.4410	.5584	.6615	.8431	1	1.265	1.514	1.878	2.299	2.704	3.139	3.839	4.778	5.733	6.913	8.431	10.238	12.647	15.357	19.196	22.872	29.054	35.246	43.000	**430**
340	.1478	.1619	.1889	.2267	.2956	.3487	.4415	.5231	.6666	.7907	1	1.197	1.485	1.818	2.138	2.482	3.036	3.778	4.533	5.466	6.667	8.095	10.000	12.143	15.178	18.085	22.973	27.869	34.000	**340**
284	.1235	.1352	.1578	.1893	.2469	.2913	.3688	.4369	.5569	.6605	.8353	1	1.240	1.519	1.786	2.073	2.536	3.155	3.787	4.566	5.569	6.762	8.353	10.143	12.678	15.106	19.189	23.279	28.400	**284**
229	.0996	.1090	.1272	.1527	.1991	.2349	.2974	.3523	.4490	.5325	.6735	.8063	1	1.224	1.440	1.671	2.045	2.544	3.053	3.682	4.490	5.452	6.735	8.178	10.223	12.181	15.473	18.770	22.900	**229**
187	.0813	.0890	.1039	.1247	.1626	.1918	.2428	.2877	.3667	.4349	.5500	.6584	.8166	1	1.176	1.365	1.670	**2.078**	2.493	3.006	3.667	4.452	5.500	6.678	8.348	9.947	12.635	15.328	18.700	**187**
159	.0691	.0757	.0883	.1060	.1383	.1631	.2065	.2246	.3118	.3698	.4676	.5598	.6943	.8503	1	1.160	1.420	1.767	2.120	2.556	3.118	3.786	4.676	5.678	7.098	8.457	10.743	13.033	15.900	**159**
137	.0596	.0652	.0761	.0913	.1191	.1405	.1779	.2108	.2686	.3186	.4029	.4824	.5982	.7326	.8616	1	1.223	1.522	1.827	2.202	2.686	3.262	4.029	4.893	6.116	7.287	9.257	11.229	13.700	**137**
112	.0487	.0533	.0622	.0747	.0974	.1149	.1454	.1723	.2196	.2605	.3294	.3944	.4891	.5989	.7044	.8175	1	1.244	1.493	1.801	2.196	2.667	3.294	4.000	5.000	5.957	7.567	9.180	11.200	**112**
90	.0391	.0428	.0500	.0600	.0783	.0923	.1169	.1385	.1765	.2093	.2647	.3169	.3930	.4813	.5660	.6569	.8036	1	1.200	1.447	1.765	2.143	2.647	3.214	4.018	4.787	6.081	7.377	9.000	**90**
75	.0326	.0357	.0417	.0500	.0652	.0769	.0974	.1154	.1471	.1744	.2206	.2641	.3275	.4011	.4717	.5474	.6696	.8333	1	1.206	1.470	1.786	2.206	2.678	3.348	3.989	5.067	6.147	7.500	**75**
62	.0270	.0296	.0346	.0415	.0541	.0638	.0808	.0957	.1220	.1446	.1829	.2190	.2716	.3326	.3912	.4540	.5553	.6911	.8293	1	1.220	1.481	1.829	2.221	2.777	3.308	4.203	5.098	6.220	**62**
51	.0222	.0243	.0283	.0340	.0443	.0523	.0662	.0785	.1000	.1186	.1500	.1796	.2227	.2727	.3207	.3723	.4553	.5667	.6800	.8199	1	1.214	1.500	1.821	2.277	2.713	3.446	4.180	5.100	**51**
42	.0183	.0200	.0233	.0280	.0365	.0431	.0545	.0646	.0823	.0977	.1235	.1479	.1834	.2246	.2642	.3066	.3750	.4667	.5600	.6752	.8235	1	1.235	1.500	1.875	2.234	2.838	3.443	4.200	**42**
34	.0148	.0162	.0189	.0227	.0296	.0349	.0441	.0523	.0667	.0791	.1000	.1197	.1485	.1818	.2131	.2482	.3436	.3778	.4533	.5466	.6667	.8095	1	1.214	1.518	1.808	2.297	2.787	3.400	**34**
28	.0122	.0133	.0156	.0187	.0243	.0287	.0364	.0431	.0549	.0651	.0823	.0986	.1223	.1497	.1761	.2044	.2500	.3111	.3733	.4502	.5490	.6667	.8235	1	1.250	1.489	1.892	2.295	2.800	**28**
22	.0097	.0107	.0124	.0149	.0195	.0230	.0291	.0345	.0439	.0521	.0659	.0789	.0978	.1198	.1409	.1635	.2000	.2489	.2987	.3601	.4392	.5333	.6588	.8000	1	1.191	1.513	1.836	2.240	**22**
19	.0082	.0089	.0104	.0125	.0163	.0193	.0244	.0289	.0369	.0437	.0553	.0662	.0821	.1005	.1182	.1372	.1678	.2089	.2507	.3022	.3686	.4476	.5529	.6714	.8393	1	1.270	1.541	1.880	**19**
15	.0064	.0070	.0082	.0099	.0129	.0152	.0192	.0228	.0290	.0344	.0435	.0521	.0646	.0791	.0931	.1080	.1321	.1644	.1973	.2379	.2902	.3524	.4353	.5286	.6607	.7872	1	1.213	1.480	**15**
12	.0053	.0058	.0068	.0081	.0106	.0125	.0158	.0188	.0239	.0284	.0359	.0429	.0533	.0652	.0767	.0890	.1089	.1355	.1627	.1961	.2392	.2905	.3588	.4357	.5446	.6489	.8243	1	1.220	**12**
10	.0043	.0048	.0056	.0067	.0087	.0103	.0130	.0154	.0196	.0232	.0294	.0352	.0437	.0535	.0629	.0730	.8928	.1111	.1333	.1608	.1961	.2381	.2941	.3571	.4464	.5319	.6757	.8197	1	**10**
	2300	**2100**	**1800**	**1500**	**1150**	**975**	**770**	**650**	**510**	**430**	**340**	**284**	**229**	**187**	**159**	**137**	**112**	**90**	**75**	**62**	**51**	**42**	**34**	**28**	**22**	**19**	**15**	**12**	**10**	

Courtesy of Microwave Development Laboratories, Inc., Natick, Mass.

TABLES OF CONSTANTS FOR STANDARD RECTANGULAR WAVEGUIDES

M. MICHAEL BRADY

Summary

Tables of wavelength and waveguide wavelength and pertinent related ratios are presented of 36 standard rigid hollow metal rectangular waveguides of approximately two-to-one dimension ratio. The effects ascribed to corner radii have been included in the computations and the waveguides are assumed to be operated in "typical" air of $\epsilon_r = 1.00064$. Thus the inaccuracies associated with the customary idealizations of perfectly-rectangular waveguides operated in a vacuum have been eliminated. A comprehensive discussion of errors effected by waveguide attenuation, waveguide deformation, and parameter deviation is given.

Background

Customarily, tabulations of constants for rectangular waveguides[1, 2, 3, 4] have listed free-space and waveguide wavelengths and their related ratios and have been based on the idealizations of perfectly rectangular waveguide cross sections operated in a lossless medium having a relative dielectric constant of unity. Commercially available rectangular waveguides seldom can be considered as perfectly rectangular[5] and the majority of practical waveguide systems are operated in air or with an internal gas whose dielectric constant is greater than that of free space. Thus the usefulness of such tabulations is restricted in that they do not accurately represent the physical situation. The tabulations of constants presented here are for standard rectangular waveguides operated in air and thus can be regarded as accurately representing the physical situation.

Basis of Tables

In free space, wavelength λ is directly proportional to the speed of electromagnetic waves c and inversely proportional to the frequency involved: $\lambda = c/f$. In media whose dielectric constant is greater than that of free space, the speed of electromagnetic waves becomes

$$c/\sqrt{\epsilon_r}$$

where ϵ_r is the relative dielectric constant. If f is stated in Hertz and c in centimeters per second, then λ is in centimeters. In a rectangular waveguide operated above its cutoff frequency in the dominant TE_{10} mode, the waveguide wavelength λ_g is given by

$$\lambda_g = \lambda \left[\epsilon_r - (\lambda/\lambda_c)^2 \right]^{-1/2} \tag{1}$$

where the waveguide cutoff wavelength λ_c, measured in the same units as λ, is twice the effective width of the waveguide. In a perfectly rectangular waveguide, it is simply equal to twice the broad dimension a: $\lambda_c = 2a$.

Commercially available waveguides have inside cross sections with corner radii, and their walls may be deformed. The waveguides treated here are considered to be standard rectangular waveguides having rectangular cross sections with standard corner radii; deformations are deviations from the standards and will thus be treated separately as errors.

Kerns and Grandy[6] have derived an expression for the wave impedance in a rectangular waveguide with filleted corners, from which the waveguide wavelength λ_g' is

$$\lambda_g' = \lambda_g \left[1 + (\lambda_g/2a)^2 \, (r^2/ab) \, (4 - \pi) \right] \tag{2}$$

where λ_g is the waveguide wavelength for a perfectly rectangular waveguide having the same dimensions a and b, and r is the corner radius in the filleted waveguide. For the purpose of the computations carried out here, it is somewhat simpler to assume that the effect of the filleted corners is to modify the cutoff wavelength to λ_c' and then compute values of λ_g' for tabulation from (1). It can be shown[7, 8, 9] that the properties of a waveguide having a rectangular cross section with round corners are equal to those of a waveguide having a perfectly rectangular cross section of the same height and same total area as shown in Figure 1. The broad dimension of the equivalent perfectly rectangular cross section is

$$a' = a - \frac{(4 - \pi)\, r^2}{b} \tag{3}$$

The corrected cutoff wavelength λ_c' is then

$$\lambda_c' = 2a' = \lambda_c - \frac{2r^2}{b} (4 - \pi) \tag{4}$$

Equations (2) and (4) are equivalent for small differences

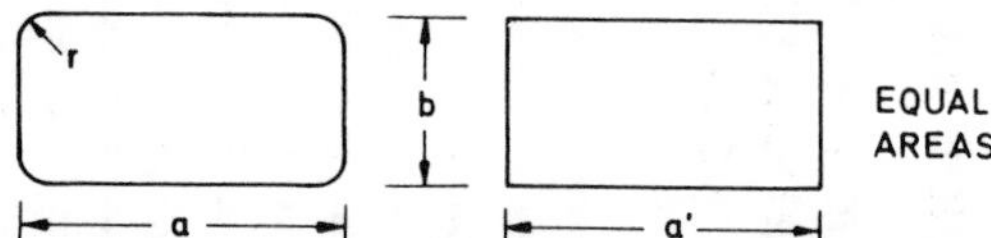

Figure 1 – Standard and equivalent waveguide cross sections

between the primed and unprimed wavelengths[10].

It has been pointed out[11] that laboratory work is seldom done in a vacuum and that only a very small proportion of waveguide devices are produced for operation in a vacuum. It is then more useful to assume a "typical" value for ϵ_r than to assume that it is unity.

The relative dielectric constant of air is given directly by the radio refractive index, which is a function of the characteristics and amounts present of the constituent gases and vapors. Assuming unity permeability and neglecting conductivity:

$$\epsilon_r = (1 + 10^{-6}N)^2 \tag{5}$$

where N is the radio refractive index. The radio refractive index equation has been reviewed in the literature[12]: in summary, careful examinations[13, 14] and experimental verifications[15] indicate that the Smith and Weintraub constants[16] are sufficiently accurate to warrant their being adopted as standards. With these constants, the equation for the radio refractive index is:

$$N = \frac{77.6}{T}\left[\rho + \frac{4810e}{T}\right] \qquad (6)$$

where T is the temperature in degrees Kelvin (T = °C + 273), ρ is the pressure in millibars, and e is the partial pressure of water vapor in millibars. The dispersion of N can be expected to be largest at frequencies near the water-vapor resonance at 22.5 GHz and the oxygen resonance frequencies around 60 GHz and at 119 GHz[17].

Although there is no standard laboratory air, for the purposes of the tabulations presented here, air at 20°C, 760 mm pressure, and 9° dew-point temperature will be considered as typical. Equations (6) and (5) give the relative dielectric constant of this "typical" air as ϵ_r = 1.0006364. This will be rounded off to 1.00064 in the computations that follow.

This relative dielectric constant will affect the waveguide wavelengths computed according to (1), the cutoff frequencies corresponding to the cutoff wavelengths, and the wavelengths in air corresponding to the tabulated frequencies.

The Tabulations

Waveguide nomenclature varies greatly from country to country[18]: even the nomenclature for a single rectangular waveguide can be excessive. For example, the 1.0-by-0.5 inch outside dimensioned rectangular waveguide is included in all present-day nomenclature systems and thus has an IEC number, three RG numbers, one WR number, a WG number, four British Joint Service numbers, three NATO numbers, a Japanese number, a French number, and two commonly-used band-letter designations. Except for the IEC and EIA numbers, none contain any information on the waveguide itself. The 36 rectangular waveguides classified by the IEC, EIA, and RCSC are listed in Table 1 along with cross-references to other classification systems. The major dimensions and, with few exceptions, the corner radii, agree between the systems. For the sake of consistency, the most recent IEC[19] metric dimensions and corner radii are assumed to take precedence and are used in the tabulations.

The constants tabulated are divided into "theoretical" and "physical" constants.

The theoretical constants are the free-space wavelength and the waveguide wavelength assuming a perfectly rectangular cross section and a vacuum dielectric. These values of λ_g will agree with earlier tabulations based on the accepted speed of light of 299792.5 ± 0.4 km/sec.

The physical constants tabulated are the TEM wavelength in air λ, the waveguide wavelength λ_g for the physical waveguide in air computed using (1), (3) and (4), the ratios λ/λ_c, $1/\lambda_g$, λ_g/λ, λ/λ_g, and λ_g and its reciprocal in English units.

The computations of the "physical" constants have been made assuming the following conditions:

a) Air dielectric with μ_r = 1.00000, ϵ_r = 1.00064.
b) Waveguide walls of infinite conductivity. The variety of waveguide materials in use makes tabulations based on a specific material too specialized.
c) Rectangular cross section of zero dimensional tolerance with dimensions and corner radii as specified in the IEC metric specifications.
d) Plane parallel waveguide walls with no slots, flange connections, or other obstructions.
e) Monochromatic frequency known with requisite accuracy.
f) Speed of light c = 299792.5 ± 0.4 km/sec[20,21,22].
g) One inch = 2.54000 centimeters.

The frequency ranges tabulated for the various waveguide sizes generally exceed or, for the higher frequencies, agree with the broadest presently recommended operating range. For the most part, the ranges are in agreement with previous tabulations.

The tables were computed on a Univac 1107 computer. The programming was such that all the significant figures of c = 299792.5 km/sec were used. Rounding off in the fourth or fifth decimal place follows the convention that the place is unchanged if the following place is from 0 to 4 and is otherwise increased by one.

Accuracies and Errors

39

The conditions assumed for computation are not always met in practice. For small deviations from the variables in (1), a valid error expression can be obtained by partial differentiation with respect to each variable; a useful procedure is given in the following section. The common deviations are as follows.

a) The dielectric may be air whose relative dielectric constant is different than the 1.00064 assumed. Dielectric constants for air are best computed using (5) and (6) or tables of the radio refractive index[12, 14] and the difference from 1.00064 treated as an error. The general effect of dielectric materials is presented by Moreno[23]. Glasser[24] has presented a set of approximate curves for λ_g as a function of dielectric constant.

b) The finite conductivity of physical waveguide walls tends to reduce the waveguide wavelength. Lewin[25] states that the waveguide wavelength λ_g' in a waveguide of attenuation constant α is

$$2\pi/\lambda_g' = \alpha + 2\pi/\lambda_g \qquad (7)$$

where λ_g is the waveguide wavelength in lossless waveguide. Defining $\lambda_g' = \lambda_g + \Delta\lambda_g$, solving (6) for the ratio $\Delta\lambda_g/\lambda_g$, expanding the resultant expression in a series, and assuming that $\Delta\lambda_g/\lambda_g$ is so small that the series can be approximated by its first term gives:

$$\Delta\lambda_g/\lambda_g = -\alpha\lambda_g/2\pi \qquad (8)$$

The phase shift per unit length in a waveguide is

$$\text{Phase shift per unit length} = -\frac{2\pi}{\lambda_g}\frac{\Delta\lambda_g}{\lambda_g} \text{ radians}$$

TABLE 1 – NOMENCLATURE AND CHARACTERISTICS OF 36 STANDARD RECTANGULAR WAVEGUIDES

Nomenclature										Characteristics									
IEC	AMERICAN RG–( )/U				EIA	G.B. RCSC	JAPAN	FRANCE	BAND LETTERS AND CODES IN USE	MECHANICAL					ELECTRICAL				
										INSIDE DIM.		OUTSIDE DIM. (c)				Recommended Freq. Range for TE_{01} Mode		Attenuation	
153 IEC-R ( )	Copper or Brass (a)	Aluminum	Magnesium	Silver	WR-( )	WG -( )	WRJ ( )	CCTU GU ( )		Width a in.	Height b in.	Width in.	Height in.	Dia. in. (f)	Cutoff Freq. MHz (g)	from GHz	to GHz	Computed Value dB/meter	At Freq. of GHz
3		290			2300	0.0			P	23.000	11.500	23.250	11.750		256.5046	0.32	0.49	0.00078	0.386
4		291			2100	0			J, N	21.000	10.500	21.250	10.750		280.9343	0.35	0.53	0.00090	0.422
5		201			1800	1			J	18.000	9.000	18.250	9.250		327.7583	0.41	0.62	0.00113	0.49
6		202			1500	2			H	15.000	7.500	15.250	7.750		393.3131	0.49	0.75	0.00149	0.59
8		203			1150	3			F	11.500	5.750	11.750	6.000		513.0267	0.64	0.98	0.00222	0.77
9		204			975	4	1		E	9.750	4.875	10.000	5.125		605.1054	0.76	1.15	0.00284	0.91
12		205			770	5			D	7.700	3.850	7.970	4.100		766.2235	0.96	1.46	0.00405	1.15
14	69	103	206		650	6	1.4		L	6.500	3.250	6.660	3.410		907.7035	1.14	1.73	0.00522	1.36
18	337	338	339		510	7				5.100	2.5500	5.260	2.710		1156.9429	1.45	2.20	0.00749	1.74
22	104	105	207		430	8	2		LS, M, R	4.300	2.1500	4.460	2.310		1372.2704	1.72	2.61	0.00970	2.06
26	112	113	208		340	9A	2.6		MS	3.400	1.7000	3.560	1.860		1735.7340	2.17	3.30	0.0138	2.61
32	48	75	167		284	10	3		S	2.8400	1.3400	3.000	1.500		2078.2336	2.60	3.95	0.0189	3.12
35								P7		2.613	1.1614	2.7705	1.3189		2259.1980	2.82	4.29	0.0223	3.39
40	340	341	342		229	11A	4		SC	2.2900	1.1450	2.418	1.273		2577.9246	3.22	4.90	0.0249	3.87
41								P6		2.2441	0.9972	2.4016	1.1547		2631.1703	3.29	5.00	0.0280	3.39
48	49	95	168		187	12	5		C, G, H	1.8720	0.8720	2.000	1.000		3153.0286	3.94	5.99	0.0355	4.73
58	343	344	345		159	13	6		C, CA	1.5900	0.7950	1.718	0.923		3712.5356	4.64	7.05	0.0431	5.57
70	50	106	169		137	14	7		A,C,G,J,XB,XN	1.3720	0.6220	1.500	0.750		4304.1025	5.38	8.17	0.0576	6.46
84	51	68	170		112	15	9		B,H,W,XB,XL	1.1220	0.4970	1.250	0.625		5266.0611	6.57	9.99	0.0794	7.89
100	52	67	171		90	16	10	0	X, XS	0.9000	0.4000	1.000	0.500		6570.5860	8.20	12.5	0.110	9.84
120	346	347	348		75	17	120		M, XG	0.7500	0.3750	0.850	0.475		7889.9412	9.84	15.0	0.133	11.8
140	91	349	172	107	62	18	140		G, KU, P, U, Y	0.6220	0.3110	0.702	0.391		9495.1201	11.9	18.0	0.176	14.2
180	352	351	350		51	19	180			0.5100	0.2550	0.590	0.335		11586.691	14.5	22.0	0.238	17.4
220	53	121	173	66	42	20	220		K	0.4200	0.1700	0.500	0.250		14088.529	17.6	26.7	0.370	21.1
260	354	355	356		34	21	260			0.3400	0.1700	0.420	0.250		17415.732	21.7	33.0	0.435	26.1
320	271			96	28	22	320		A,KA,R,T,U,V	0.2800	0.1400	0.360	0.220	0.4331	21184.834	26.4	40.0	0.583	31.6
400	272			97	22	23	400		B,Q,V	0.2440	0.1120	0.304	0.192	0.4331	26461.666	32.9	50.1	0.815	39.5
500					19	24	500		F	0.1880	0.0940	0.268	0.174	0.2953	31595.916	39.2	59.6	1.060	47.1
620	273			98	15	25	620		M,V,W	0.1480	0.0740	0.228	0.154	0.2953	40058.509	49.8	75.8	1.52	59.9
740	274			99	12	26	740		E,Z	0.1220	0.0610	0.202	0.141	0.2953	48549.10	60.5	91.9	2.03	72.6
900					10	27	900		W	0.1000	0.0500	0.180	0.130	0.2953	59350.75	73.8	112	2.74	88.6
1200	278			138	8	28	1200		F,N	0.0800	0.0400	0.160 (d)	0.120	0.1575	74440.66	92.2	140	3.82	111.0
1400	276			136	7	29				0.0650	0.0325			0.1575	91227.28	114	173	5.21	136.3
1800	275			135	5	30			A, G	0.0510	0.0255	(e)		0.1575	116475.52	145	220	7.50	174.0
2200	277			137	4	31				0.0430	0.0215			0.1575	137938.66	172	261	9.70	206.0
2600				139	3	32			R	0.0340	0.0170			0.1575	174438.49	217	330	13.76	260.5

So (8) can be interpreted as indicating that the phase shift per unit length caused by an attenuation of α nepers per unit length is approximately equal to $-\alpha$. Most waveguide attenuations are stated in dB per unit length. Rewriting (8) using 1 neper = 8.68688 dB gives

$$\Delta\lambda_g/\lambda_g = -1.82633 \times 10^{-2}\alpha\lambda_g \qquad (9)$$

where α is now in dB per unit length.

An expression for the propagation constant γ valid for all frequencies in rectangular waveguides operating in the TE_{mo} mode has been given by Käch[26] as

$$\gamma = \sqrt{\gamma_o^2 + (1-j)\frac{\mu_m}{\mu}\delta\left(\frac{m^2 2\pi^2}{a^3} + \frac{k^2}{b}\right)} \qquad (10)$$

where

$$\delta = \sqrt{\pi f \mu_m \sigma_m}$$

is the skin depth,

$$k = \omega\sqrt{\mu\epsilon}$$

is the wave number, the subscript m refers to the metal, and $\gamma_o = k^2 - (m\pi/a)^2$ as in the notation of Kerns and Hedberg[27]. The attenuation constant is found from (10) by separating it into real and imaginary parts and approximating for frequencies lower than, equal to, and greater than cutoff frequency[28]. Above cutoff frequency for the TE_{10} mode:

$$\alpha = \sqrt{\frac{\pi\mu_m}{2\mu^2 c\sigma_m}}\left[\frac{2}{a^{3/2}}\;\frac{\frac{a}{2b}\left(\frac{f}{fc}\right)^{3/2} + \left(\frac{f}{fc}\right)^{-1/2}}{\sqrt{\frac{f}{fc}^2 - 1}}\right] \qquad (11)$$

The quantity $(\pi\mu_m/2\mu^2 c\sigma_m)^{1/2} = (R_s/\eta)(c/2f)^{1/2}$ where η is the TEM wave impedance and $R_s = 1/\sigma_m\delta$ is the surface resistivity. This quantity is customarily normalized to free space and copper waveguide:

$$\pi\mu_m/2\mu^2 c\sigma_m = \frac{R_s}{\eta}\sqrt{\frac{C}{2f}} = K\sqrt{\epsilon_r}\sqrt{\frac{\rho}{\rho_o}}$$

so

$$\alpha = K\sqrt{\epsilon_r}\sqrt{\frac{\rho}{\rho_o}}\left[\frac{1}{b\sqrt{a}}\;\frac{\left(\frac{f}{fc}\right)^2 + \left(\frac{2b}{a}\right)}{\sqrt{\frac{f}{fc}}\sqrt{\left(\frac{f}{fc}\right)^2 - 1}}\right] \qquad (12)$$

where ρ is the resistivity of the non-magnetic wall material, ρ_o is the resistivity of copper = 1.7241×10^{-8} ohm-meter, and the constant K depends on the constants used in the derivation and on the units used for the a and b dimensions. If a and b are in meters such that the equation is dimentionally self-consistent, K is approximately 7.357×10^{-5}. The values of K stated by (or derived from the work of) four different authors are given in Table 2A[29,30,31,32].

If the average of these values is assumed, and the a and b dimensions in (12) are stated in millimeters, K = 2.32655. However, the consensus of opinion in precision waveguide work is that the constants in the attenuation expression should not be lumped together and assigned a single value, but rather should be evaluated for each particular application[33]. The resistivities of common waveguide metals[34] are given in Table 2B.

Cox and Rupp[35] have presented a thorough practical discussion of waveguide losses as functions of material, surface roughness, and oxidation. Kibler[36] has shown that a finite conductivity in waveguide walls tends to produce a cutoff region instead of a singular cutoff frequency. For the present purposes, these effects are considered to be too specialized to particular materials to allow their being included as tabulated parameters.

c) Slightly displaced or non-parallel walls can easily be treated using the differential of (1). Young[37] has presented general expressions for the change in waveguide wavelength when any of the four waveguide walls are deformed by a small amount:

Due to top-wall deformation:

$$\Delta\lambda_g/\lambda_g = (\lambda_g/2a)^2(\cos 2\pi x/a)(\Delta S_{top}/ab) \qquad (13)$$

Due to side-wall deformation:

$$\Delta\lambda_g/\lambda_g = (\lambda_g/2a)^2(\Delta S_{side}/ab) \qquad (14)$$

where, as shown in Figure 2A, ΔS_{top} and ΔS_{side} are the incremental changes in cross sectional area due to the deformations and x is the distance to the top-wall deformation as measured from the center of the wall. For the

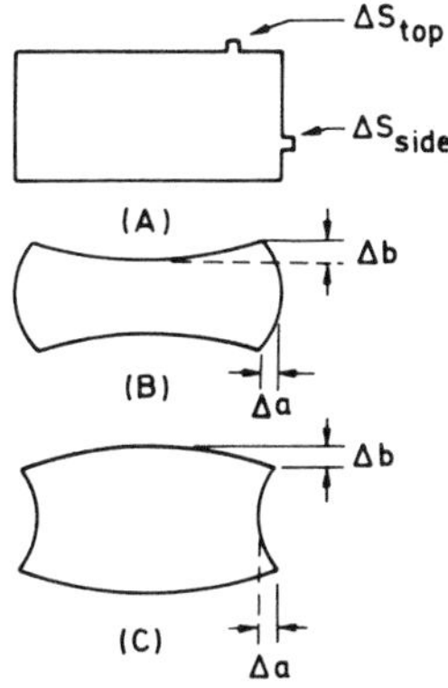

Figure 2 — Waveguide deformations in general (A), evacuated waveguide (B), and pressurized waveguide (C).

particular case of incremental waveguide deformations caused by evacuated or pressurized operation, Young gives:

$$\frac{\Delta\lambda_g}{\lambda_g} = \pm\left(\frac{\lambda_g}{a}\right)^2\left(\left|\frac{\Delta a}{a}\right| + \frac{1}{3}\left|\frac{\Delta b}{b}\right|\right) \qquad (15)$$

41

where the plus sign is taken for evacuated waveguide and the minus sign for pressurized waveguide and where a and b are the incremental deformations as shown in Figures 2B and 2C. According to Virgile[38], $\Delta a/\Delta b$ can be set equal to a constant, in which case (13) becomes:

$$\frac{\Delta\lambda_g}{\lambda_g} = \pm \left(\frac{\lambda_g}{a}\right)^2 \left(\frac{bC}{a} + \frac{1}{3}\right)\left(\frac{\Delta b}{b}\right) \qquad (16)$$

The constant C is equal to k_3/k_2 of Virgile's Table II and is, for the ten waveguide sizes presented there, as listed in Table 3. Waveguide component manufacturing methods may well distort the standard waveguide stock used. Schepis[39] has presented a complete treatment of the stresses and deformations caused by shrink fitting, one of the more common component manufacturing methods to cause deformations in cross section.

TABLE 2

Author	Reference No.	K X 10^{-5}
IEC	27	7.35962
Moreno	28	7.35112
Matthaei, Young & Jones	29	7.35614
Ramo, Whinnery & Van Duzer	30	7.36222

Table 2A) Constant K in Equation (12)

Metal	Resistivity ohm-meter X10^{-8}	Conductivity %IACS
Aluminum	2.83	60.9
Brass (Cu90 Zn10)	4.22	40.9
Brass (Cu66 Zn34)	7.00	24.6
Coin Silver	2.10	82.0
Copper	1.724	100.0
Magnesium	4.60	37.5
Silver	1.62	106.4
Tellurium Copper	1.90	91.0

Table 2B) Resistivity and Conductivity of Common Waveguide Metals. Conductivity is stated in % of International Annealed Copper Standard; the recriprocal of this figure X 100 can be used directly for ρ/ρ_o in Equation (12). Figures quoted are from MIL-HDBK 216 of 4 January 1962.

TABLE 3

Waveguide size	C
R 14 (WR 650)	–0.2325
R 22 (WR 430)	–0.2119
R 26 (WR 340)	–0.2176
R 32 (WR 284)	–0.2093
R 48 (WR 187)	–0.2105
R 70 (WR 137)	–0.2045
R 84 (WR 112)	–0.2005
R 100 (WR 90)	–0.1128
R 140 (WR 62)	–0.2142
R 220 (WR 42)	–0.1666

Constant C = k_3/k_2 from Virgile's[38] Table II

d) Slight obstructions can be treated by using the differential of (1) or by applying Young's equations (13) and (14). The effect of a slot, as in the slotted section used for vswr measurements, is to slightly increase the waveguide wavelength[40]. The general problem of multiple flange joints has been treated by Kienlin & Kürzl[41] on a reflection basis. Kerns and Grandy[6] have treated a number of obstructions, including the transition between a perfectly rectangular and filleted rectangular waveguides; the latter has been measured by Anson and Beatty[42].

e) For tabulation, it is usually sufficient to state frequency to four or five significant figures; frequency being the independent variable implies that there is zero error in the tabulated frequencies. There is, however, error in any practical measured frequency: accuracies of from parts in 10^4 to parts in 10^9 or better can be attained in the microwave region.

f) Some waveguide constant tabulations[1,2] have used a value of c that is most likely Michelson's 1927 optical rotating mirror value corrected by Birge to vacuum of 299776 ± 1 km/sec. As recommended by the XIIth General Assembly of the URSI in 1957, the value of c in vacuum of 299792.5 km/sec has been used here. Extensive and independent studies in the USA[20] and the USSR[21] in 1962 indicated that the accuracy in this value of c was one part in 10^9. Froome and Essen have thoroughly substantiated this value in their 1969 monograph[22]. Thus, for the tabulations presented here, c is regarded as being free of error.

g) Some waveguide equipment may be constructed using the older "larger" inch: 1 inch = 2.54001 centimeters.

The computations tabulated in Tables 4 through 39 were made on a Univac 1107 computer operating in the double precision mode. Although ten tabulated results are to four and five decimal places, ten to twelve decimal places were retained in all computation. The speed of electromagnetic waves is given to seven significant figures, and the longest waveguide wavelength tabulated is given to seven significant figures. The computer accuracy is then more than sufficient for the arithmetic operations involved in the tabulations. For all practical purposes, the tables can be considered to be free of computational error.

Error Evaluation

Deviations from the tabulated values of λ and λ_g and their related rations depend on the deviations in the pertinent parameters ϵ_r, f, and a' used in computing the tables. Additional errors in λ_g and its related ratios arise from waveguide attenuation (Eq. 12) and waveguide deformations (Eqs. 13, 14, 15 and 16).

To find the per-unit error in λ_g due to deviations in the parameters used in computation, (1) and (4) are combined and rewritten to read:

$$\lambda_g = \left[\frac{\epsilon_r}{2} - \frac{1}{4a'^2}\right]^{-1/2} \qquad (17)$$

Neglecting the second-order terms in the Taylor expansion, the first-order per-unit error in λ_g is then:

$$\frac{d\lambda_g}{\lambda_g} = \frac{1}{\rho\text{-}\epsilon_r}\left[\frac{d\epsilon_r}{2} - \epsilon_r\frac{d\lambda}{\lambda} + \rho\frac{da'}{a'}\right] \quad (18)$$

where ρ is defined as the square of the λ/λ_c ratio. From (3) and (4): $da'/a' = 2da/\lambda_c$. Because $\lambda = c/f$ and the speed of electromagnetic waves is regarded as being constant to far better than four decimal places, the per-unit error in λ_g is simply the negative of the per-unit error in f: $d\lambda/\lambda = -df/f$. The relative dielectric constant used in computation is 1.00064. Equation (18) then becomes:

$$\frac{d\lambda_g}{\lambda_g} = \frac{1}{1.00064\text{-}\rho}\left[\frac{d\epsilon_r}{2} - 1.00064\frac{df}{f} + \frac{2\rho}{\lambda_c}da\right] + \frac{\Delta\lambda_g}{\lambda_g} \quad (19)$$

where $\Delta\lambda_g/\lambda_g$ is the attenuation and/or deformation error from (12) and/or (13-16). The parameters in (19) are given in Tables 4 - 39.

Example: For IEC-R 48 (WR-187) waveguide, the parameters of interest from Table 19 for a frequency of 4.75 GHz are:

λ_c = 9.50504 cm

λ_g = 8.4349 cm

$\rho^{1/2}$ = (λ/λ_c) = 0.66380

da = $\pm$0.095 mm

α = 0.0355 dB/meter for Cu guide at 4.73 GHz

For illustration assume:

1) The waveguide is operated at ambient pressure and is not submitted to deformation. The $\Delta\lambda_g/\lambda_g$ term in (19) will then be entirely due to attenuation.

2) The waveguide is operated at a lower temperature and pressure than that assumed as typical for computing the tables: 0^oC, 1000 mb pressure, dew-point temperature of -60^oC result in ϵ_r = 1.00056.

3) Most laboratory-type counter frequency meters have accuracies of the order of one part in 10^7. Assume that the frequency of 4.75 GHz is known to one part in 10^5.

Equation (19) then yields:

$$d\lambda/\lambda_g = 4.719 \times 10^{-6} \pm 1.798 \times 10^{-6}$$
$$\pm 1.595 \times 10^{-4} - 5.469 \times 10^{-5}$$

Thus λ_g is: λ_g = 8.4349, +0.0009, −0.0017 cm

Note that the tolerance in the waveguide a dimension is the greatest single contributor to $d\lambda_g/\lambda_g$: it is responsible for an inaccuracy in λ_g of $\pm$0.0013 cm.

Acknowledgements

Discussions with L. Lewin, S. B. Cohn, and T. Saad at the 1969 G-MTT Microwave Symposium were valuable in delineating the problems involved. The comments and constructive criticism of D. M. Kerns and R. W. Beatty of the National Bureau of Standards contributed greatly to the correctness of the presentation. The tabulations are the result of computations programmed, run, and meticulously checked by C. Hansson of the Norwegian Computing Center in Oslo.

References

1. Sperry Gyroscope Co., "Tables of Constants for Rectangular Waveguides (in Decimal Frequencies), "**IRE Trans** Vol. MTT-4, No. 3, 12 page supplement (1956).

2. id., **The Microwave Engineers' Handbook** 1963, Horizon-House-Microwave, Inc., Dedham, Massachusetts.

3. Booth, A. E., Microwave Data Tables, Iliffe & Sons Ltd., London, 1959, Tables 12 through 20.

4. Brady, M. M. and M. Vånar, "Tables of Constants for Rectangular Waveguides," **The Microwave Engineers' Handbook**, 1965 edition pp. 290-312, 1966 edition pp. 340-362, Horizon-House Microwave, Inc., Dedham, Massachusetts.

5. Waveguide sections made by broaching or electroforming can have very sharp inside corners. The free-space and waveguide wavelengths tabulated in the second and third columns of tables 4 through 39 can be interpreted as applying to such waveguides filled with lossless media of unity relative dielectric constant.

6. Kerns, D. M. and W. T. Grandy, "Perturbation Theorems for Waveguide Junctions, with Applications," **IEEE Trans.**, Vol. MTT-14, No. 2, pp. 85-92 (February 1966).

7. Valenzuela, G. R., "The Cutoff Wavelengths of Composite Waveguides," **IRE Trans** Vol. MTT-9, No. 4, pp. 363-364, (July 1961).

8. Cohn, S. B., "Microwave Coupling by Large Apertures," **Proc. IRE** Vol. 40, No. 6, pp. 696-699 (June 1952).

9. Brady, M. M., "Cutoff Wavelengths and Frequencies of Standard Rectangular Waveguides," **Electronics Letters** Vol. 5, No. 17, pp. 410-412 (21 August 1969).

10. Define $\lambda_g = \lambda_g(1 + \Delta\lambda_g/\lambda_g)$, $\lambda_c = \lambda_c(1 + \Delta\lambda_c/\lambda_c)$. Taking the differential of (1) with ϵ_r = 1 and λ a constant, and considering the per-unit errors to be so small that they may be set equal to the resulting differentials results in $\Delta\lambda_g/\lambda_g = -(\lambda_g/\lambda_c)^2 \Delta\lambda_c/\lambda_c$, which also follows from combining (2) and (4).

11. Cohn, S. B., "Confusion and Misconceptions in Microwave Engineering," **The Microwave Journal**, Vol. 11, No. 9, pp. 20-22 (September 1968).

12. Brady, M. M., "Note on the Presentation of the Radio Refractive Index as a Function of Meteorological Parameters," **Radio Science** (New Series) Vol. 2, No. 12, pp. 1523-1524 (December 1967).

13. Bean, B. R., "The Radio Refractive Index of Air," **Proc. IRE** Vo. 50, No. 3, pp. 90-91 (march 1962).

14. Bean, B. R. and E. J. Dutton, Radio Meteorology, NBS Monograph 92, U. S. Government Printing Office, Washington, D.C., 1966, and Dover Publications, Inc., New York, 1968.

15. Boudouris, G., "On the Index of Refraction of Air, The Absorption and Dispersion of Centimeter Waves by Gases," **J. Research NBS** (Radio Prop.) Vol. 67D, No. 6, pp. 631-684 (1963).

16. Smith, E. K. and S. Weintraub, "The Constants in the Equation for Atmospheric Refractive Index at Radio Frequencies," **Proc. IRE** Vol. 41, No. 8, pp. 1035-1037 (August 1953).

17. A thorough discussion of oxygen absorption has been given by: Reber, E. E., R. L. Mitchell and C. J. Carter, "Oxygen Absorption in the Earth's Atmosphere," **Microwave J.**, Vol. 12, No. 11, pp. 75-81 (November 1969).

18. Brady, M. M., "Worldwide Specs on Rectangular Waveguide and Flanges," **MicroWaves** Vol. 6, No. 7, pp. 33-38 (July 1967).

19. International Electrotechnical Commission, Hollow Metallic Waveguides, Part 5: Relevant specifications for rectangular waveguides with circular outside cross section (1968) and Amendment No. 1 to Publication 153-2 Part 2: Relevant specifications for ordinary rectangular waveguides (July 1968), IEC, Geneva, 1968.

20. McNish, A. G., "The Speed of Light," **IRE Trans.** Vol. I-11, No. 3-4, pp. 138-148 (1962).

21. Karatashev, A. I., "Problem of the Most Probable Speed of Propagation of Electromagnetic Waves (Speed of Light)," **Izmeritel'naya Tekhnika** Vol. 3, pp. 59-60 (1962).

22. In a 156-page monograph, Froome and Essen give a comprehensive treatment of the speed of light: Froome, K. E. and L. Essen, The Velocity of Light and Radio Waves, Academic Press, New York and London, 1969.

23. Moreno, T., Microwave Transmission Design Data, McGraw-Hill Book Co., New York, 1948, and Dover Publications Inc., New York, 1958, pp. 185-197.

24. Glasser, R., "Charts Speed Design of Dielectric-Filled Waveguides," **MicroWaves** Vol. 4, No. 4, pp. 57-59 (September 1965).

25. Lewin, L., "A Note on the Effect of Waveguide Losses on Guide Wavelength," **Proc IEE** Vol. 109 Part B, No. 43, p. 40 (January 1962).

26. Käch, A., "Die Ausbreitung der gedämpften H_{om}-Welle in der Umgebung der Grenzfrequenz," **Helvetica physica acta** (Basel) Vol. 20, No. 3, pp. 341-356 (3 August 1947), Eq. 43.

27. Kerns, D. M. and R. W. Hedberg, "Propagation Constant in Rectangular Waveguide of Finite Conductivity," **J. Applied Physics** Vol. 25, No. 12, pp. 1550-1551 (December 1954).

28. Käch, A., op. cit., Equations 48 and 50.

29. International Electrotechnical Commission, Hollow Metallic Waveguides, Part 1: General requirements and measuring methods, Publication 153-1, IEC, Geneva, 1964, p. 23.

30. Moreno, T., op. cit., p. 131.

31. Matthaei, G. L., L. Young, and E. M. T. Jones, Microwave Filters, Impedance-Matching Networks, and Coupling Structures, McGraw-Hill Book Co., New York, 1964, Section 5.06: "Special Properties of Waveguides" pp. 197-202.

32. Ramo, S., J. R. Whinnery, and T. Van Duzer, Fields and Waves in Communication Electronics, John Wiley & Sons, Inc., New York, 1967, P. 423.

33. See, for example, Beatty, R. W. and B. C. Yates, "A Graph of Return Loss Versus Frequency for Wuarter-Wavelength Short-Circuited Waveguide Impedance Standards," **IEEE Trans.** Vol. MTT-17, No. 5, pp. 282-284 (May 1960).

34. Numerous references on metal conductivity are available, not all of which agree. The most commonly available are:

Chemical Rubber Publishing Co., Handbook of Chemistry and Physics, Cleveland, various editions, pp. 2588-2595.

Ministry of Defense, "Defence Specification DEF-5351, Specification for Tubing, Waveguide," London: Her Majesty's Stationery Office, 1960, p. 8.

Department of Defense, "MIL-HDBK-216, RF Transmission Lines and Fittings," Defense Supply Agency, Washington, D. C., January 1962, Table 6. c of Section 6.

N. Marcuvitz (editor), "Waveguide Handbook," New York: McGraw-Hill Book Co., 1951 (Rad Lab Series Vol. 10) and Dover Publications Inc., New York, 1965, Table 1.2 p. 21.

ITT, "Reference Data For Radio Engineers," 5th edition, Howard W. Sams & Co., Inc., New York: 1968, Tables 12-14 of Section 4-21.

35. R. M. Cox and W. E. Rupp, "Fight Waveguide Losses Five Ways," **MicroWaves** Vol.5, No. 8, pp. 32-40 (August 1966).

36. Young, L., "Incremental Phase Shift Due to Changes in Cross Section of Rectangular Waveguides," **The Microwave Journal** Vol. 9, No. 5, pp. 45-46 (May 1966).

37. Kibler, L. U., "The Cutoff Region of a Rectangular Waveguide with Losses, Its Properties and Uses," **Bell System Technical Journal** Vol. 48, No. 7, pp. 2221-2258 (September 1969).

38. Virgile, L. G., "Deflection of Waveguide Subjected to Internal Pressure," **IRE Trans** Vol. MTT-5, No. 4, pp.247-250 (October 1957).

39. Schepis, A. J., "On the Theory of Shrink Fits with Application to Waveguide Pressure Seals," **Bell System Technical Journal** Vol. 41, No. 5, pp. 885-907 (May 1962).

40. Ginzton, E. L., Microwave Measurements, McGraw-Hill Book Co., New York, 1957, pp. 239-241.

41. von Kienlin, U. and A. Kürzl, "Reflexionen an Hohlleiter-Flanschverbin-dungen," **NTZ** Vol. 11, No. 11, pp. 561-568 (November 1958).

42. Anson, W. J., R. W. Beatty, D. M. Kerns, and W. T. Grandy, "Investigations of the Reflection from a Junction of An Ideal Rectangular Waveguide with one Having Rounded Inside Corners," 1962 PGMTT Symposium, Boulder, Colorado, paper 3.2, Symposium Digest pp. 27-31.

Notes for Tables 1 and 4 through 39

a) RG-271/U through RG-277/U are silver plated,

b) RCSC precision waveguides come in WG-22 through WG-32 inside dimensions, have a round outer profile, and are designated by the suffix P.

c) Outside dimensions for IEC-R 3 through 12 are under consideration by the IEC. The dimensions given are EIA and RCSC dimensions.

d) Outside dimensions for IEC-R1200 are not yet final; RCSC method standard is given.

e) Rectangular outside dimensions for IEC-R 1400 through 2600 are not yet standardized by the IEC or other authorities. Circular outside cross sections have been standardized for these sizes.

f) Outside diameters given are IEC. RCSC diameters are 0.438 in. for WG-22P and 23P, 0.313 in. for WG-24P through 27P, and 0.188 in. for WG-28P through 32P. EIA diameter is 0.156 in. for WR-3 through WR-8.

h) Tolerance is presently under consideration by the IEC. Tolerance, if given, is EIA. Tolerances in inches are not converted into metric tolerances.

j) Corner radius is presently under consideration by the IEC. Radius given is converted from original RCSC inch specification.

TABLE 4

IEC-R 3 | Brit: WG-0.0 | Amer: WR-2300, RG-290/U

Outside dimensions: 23.276 X 11.876 ±0.020 inches (c,h)
593.8 X 301.7 millimeters

Inside dimensions: 23.00 X 11.500 ±0.20 inches (h)
584.2 X 292.10 millimeters
corner radius: 1.5 millimeters
a/b: 2.000

Cutoff:	Rectangle in Vacuum	Waveguide in Air
Wavelength:	116.84000cm	116.83868cm
Frequency:	256.58379 MHz	256.50463 MHz

f (MHz)	THEORETICAL λ (cm)	THEORETICAL λ_g (cm)	PHYSICAL λ (cm)	λ_g (cm)	λ/λ_c	$1/\lambda_g$ (1/cm)	λ_g/λ	λ/λ_g	λ_g (in)	$1/\lambda_g$ (1/in)
275	109.0155	302.9945	108.9806	301.9482	.93274	.00331	2.77066	.36092	118.87723	.00841
280	107.0687	267.4507	107.0345	266.7115	.91609	.00375	2.49183	.40131	105.00452	.00952
285	105.1903	241.6600	105.1567	241.1002	.90002	.00415	2.29277	.43615	94.92135	.01054
290	103.3767	221.8267	103.3437	221.3824	.88450	.00452	2.14220	.46681	87.15841	.01147
295	101.6246	205.9481	101.5921	205.5833	.86951	.00486	2.02362	.49416	80.93831	.01236
300	99.9308	192.8544	99.8989	192.5472	.85502	.00519	1.92742	.51883	75.80598	.01319
305	98.2926	181.8101	98.2612	181.5462	.84100	.00551	1.84759	.54125	71.47490	.01399
310	96.7073	172.3265	96.6763	172.0962	.82743	.00581	1.78013	.56176	67.75441	.01476
315	95.1722	164.0643	95.1418	163.8606	.81430	.00610	1.72228	.58063	64.51205	.01550
320	93.6852	156.7796	93.6552	156.5974	.80158	.00639	1.67206	.59806	61.65253	.01622
325	92.2438	150.2917	92.2143	150.1274	.78925	.00666	1.62803	.61424	59.10527	.01692
330	90.8462	144.4640	90.8172	144.3145	.77729	.00693	1.58907	.62930	56.81675	.01760
335	89.4903	139.1905	89.4617	139.0536	.76569	.00719	1.55434	.64336	54.74552	.01827
340	88.1743	134.3878	88.1461	134.2617	.75443	.00745	1.52317	.65652	52.85892	.01892
345	86.8964	129.9890	86.8686	129.8722	.74349	.00770	1.49504	.66888	51.13079	.01956
350	85.6550	125.9402	85.6276	125.8314	.73287	.00795	1.46952	.68049	49.53993	.02019
355	84.4486	122.1967	84.4216	122.0951	.72255	.00819	1.44625	.69144	48.06893	.02080
360	83.2757	118.7218	83.2491	118.6265	.71251	.00843	1.42496	.70177	46.70333	.02141
365	82.1349	115.4845	82.1087	115.3948	.70275	.00867	1.40539	.71155	45.43103	.02201
370	81.0250	112.4588	80.9991	112.3741	.69326	.00890	1.38735	.72080	44.24179	.02260
375	79.9447	109.6225	79.9191	109.5423	.68401	.00913	1.37066	.72957	43.12689	.02319
380	78.8928	106.9564	78.8675	106.8803	.67501	.00936	1.35519	.73791	42.07885	.02376
385	77.8682	104.4442	77.8433	104.3717	.66625	.00958	1.34079	.74583	41.09122	.02434
390	76.8699	102.0714	76.8453	102.0023	.65770	.00980	1.32737	.75337	40.15839	.02490
395	75.8968	99.8256	75.8726	99.7596	.64938	.01002	1.31483	.76055	39.27544	.02546
400	74.9481	97.6960	74.9242	97.6327	.64126	.01024	1.30309	.76741	38.43809	.02602
405	74.0228	95.6726	73.9992	95.6120	.63334	.01046	1.29207	.77395	37.64252	.02657
410	73.1201	93.7471	73.0967	93.6889	.62562	.01067	1.28171	.78021	36.88538	.02711
415	72.2392	91.9117	72.2161	91.8557	.61808	.01089	1.27196	.78619	36.16366	.02765
420	71.3792	90.1597	71.3563	90.1057	.61073	.01110	1.26276	.79192	35.47470	.02819
425	70.5394	88.4849	70.5168	88.4329	.60354	.01131	1.25407	.79741	34.81608	.02872
430	69.7192	86.8819	69.6969	86.8316	.59652	.01152	1.24585	.80267	34.18567	.02925
435	68.9178	85.3456	68.8958	85.2970	.58967	.01172	1.23806	.80772	33.58150	.02978
440	68.1347	83.8717	68.1129	83.8246	.58297	.01193	1.23067	.81256	33.00181	.03030
445	67.3691	82.4559	67.3476	82.4103	.57641	.01213	1.22366	.81722	32.44501	.03082
450	66.6206	81.0947	66.5992	81.0505	.57001	.01234	1.21699	.82170	31.90964	.03134
455	65.8885	79.7846	65.8674	79.7417	.56375	.01254	1.21064	.82601	31.39437	.03185
460	65.1723	78.5226	65.1514	78.4809	.55762	.01274	1.20459	.83016	30.89797	.03236
465	64.4715	77.3057	64.4509	77.2652	.55162	.01294	1.19882	.83415	30.41935	.03287
470	63.7856	76.1315	63.7652	76.0920	.54575	.01314	1.19331	.83800	29.95748	.03338
475	63.1142	74.9974	63.0940	74.9590	.54001	.01334	1.18805	.84171	29.51140	.03389
480	62.4568	73.9013	62.4368	73.8639	.53438	.01354	1.18302	.84530	29.08026	.03439
485	61.8129	72.8412	61.7931	72.8047	.52888	.01374	1.17820	.84875	28.66326	.03489
490	61.1821	71.8151	61.1626	71.7795	.52348	.01393	1.17358	.85209	28.25963	.03539
495	60.5641	70.8213	60.5448	70.7865	.51819	.01413	1.16916	.85532	27.86871	.03588
500	59.9585	69.8582	59.9393	69.8242	.51301	.01432	1.16491	.85843	27.48984	.03638
505	59.3649	68.9242	59.3459	68.8910	.50793	.01452	1.16084	.86145	27.12243	.03687
510	58.7828	68.0180	58.7640	67.9854	.50295	.01471	1.15692	.86436	26.76592	.03736
515	58.2121	67.1381	58.1935	67.1063	.49807	.01490	1.15316	.86718	26.41980	.03785
520	57.6524	66.2835	57.6340	66.2523	.49328	.01509	1.14954	.86992	26.08358	.03834
525	57.1033	65.4529	57.0851	65.4223	.48858	.01529	1.14605	.87256	25.75682	.03882

TABLE 5

IEC-R 4 | Brit: WG-0 | Amer: WR-2100, RG-291/U

Outside dimensions: 21.376 X 10.876 ±0.020 inches (c,h)
543.0 X 276.30 millimeters

Inside dimensions: 21.00 X 10.500 ±0.20 inches
533.4 X 266.70 millimeters
corner radius: 1.5 millimeters
a/b: 2.000

Cutoff:	Rectangle in Vacuum	Waveguide in Air
Wavelength:	106.68000cm	106.67855cm
Frequency:	281.02034 MHz	280.93427 MHz

f (MHz)	THEORETICAL λ (cm)	THEORETICAL λ_g (cm)	PHYSICAL λ (cm)	λ_g (cm)	λ/λ_c	$1/\lambda_g$ (1/cm)	λ_g/λ	λ/λ_g	λ_g (in)	$1/\lambda_g$ (1/in)
300	99.9308	285.4834	99.8989	284.4444	.93645	.00352	2.84732	.35121	111.98597	.00893
305	98.2926	252.8966	98.2612	252.1561	.92110	.00397	2.56618	.38968	99.27406	.01007
310	96.7073	229.0725	96.6763	228.5087	.90624	.00438	2.36365	.42308	89.96406	.01112
315	95.1722	210.6593	95.1418	210.2103	.89185	.00476	2.20944	.45260	82.75996	.01208
320	93.6852	195.8651	93.6552	195.4956	.87792	.00512	2.08740	.47907	76.96678	.01299
325	92.2438	183.6332	92.2143	183.3215	.86441	.00545	1.98799	.50302	72.17382	.01386
330	90.8462	173.2946	90.8172	173.0265	.85132	.00578	1.90522	.52487	68.12068	.01468
335	89.4903	164.4024	89.4617	164.1682	.83861	.00609	1.83507	.54494	64.63316	.01547
340	88.1743	156.6451	88.1461	156.4379	.82628	.00639	1.77476	.56346	61.58970	.01624
345	86.8964	149.7978	86.8686	149.6125	.81430	.00668	1.72229	.58062	58.90257	.01698
350	85.6550	143.6940	85.6276	143.5267	.80267	.00697	1.67617	.59660	56.50658	.01770
355	84.4486	138.2067	84.4216	138.0545	.79136	.00724	1.63530	.61151	54.35219	.01840
360	83.2757	133.2377	83.2491	133.0984	.78037	.00751	1.59880	.62547	52.40094	.01908
365	82.1349	128.7095	82.1087	128.5811	.76968	.00778	1.56599	.63857	50.62249	.01975
370	81.0250	124.5599	80.9991	124.4410	.75928	.00804	1.53633	.65090	48.99251	.02041
375	79.9447	120.7383	79.9191	120.6277	.74916	.00829	1.50937	.66253	47.49123	.02106
380	78.8928	117.2034	78.8675	117.1001	.73930	.00854	1.48477	.67351	46.10240	.02169
385	77.8682	113.9207	77.8433	113.8238	.72970	.00879	1.46222	.68389	44.81253	.02232
390	76.8699	110.8614	76.8453	110.7702	.72034	.00903	1.44147	.69374	43.61030	.02293
395	75.8968	108.0009	75.8726	107.9148	.71123	.00927	1.42232	.70308	42.48613	.02354
400	74.9481	105.3184	74.9242	105.2369	.70234	.00950	1.40458	.71196	41.43187	.02414
405	74.0228	102.7962	73.9992	102.7189	.69366	.00974	1.38811	.72040	40.44050	.02473
410	73.1201	100.4187	73.0967	100.3452	.68521	.00997	1.37277	.72845	39.50598	.02531
415	72.2392	98.1726	72.2161	98.1025	.67695	.01019	1.35846	.73613	38.62303	.02589
420	71.3792	96.0461	71.3563	95.9792	.66889	.01042	1.34507	.74346	37.78707	.02646
425	70.5394	94.0289	70.5168	93.9649	.66102	.01064	1.33252	.75046	36.99404	.02703
430	69.7192	92.1120	69.6969	92.0506	.65334	.01086	1.32073	.75716	36.24038	.02759
435	68.9178	90.2872	68.8958	90.2283	.64583	.01108	1.30963	.76357	35.52293	.02815
440	68.1347	88.5475	68.1129	88.4908	.63849	.01130	1.29918	.76972	34.83888	.02870
445	67.3691	86.8863	67.3476	86.8317	.63131	.01152	1.28931	.77561	34.18570	.02925
450	66.6206	85.2980	66.5992	85.2453	.62430	.01173	1.27997	.78127	33.56115	.02980
455	65.8885	83.7773	65.8674	83.7265	.61744	.01194	1.27114	.78670	32.96319	.03034

Courtesy of M. Brady

460	65.1723	82.3197	65.1514	82.2706	.61073	.01216	1.26276	.79192	32.38998	.03087
465	64.4715	80.9209	64.4509	80.8733	.60416	.01237	1.25481	.79694	31.83988	.03141
470	63.7856	79.5770	63.7652	79.5309	.59773	.01257	1.24725	.80177	31.31138	.03194
475	63.1142	78.2845	63.0940	78.2399	.59144	.01278	1.24005	.80642	30.80309	.03246
480	62.4568	77.0404	62.4368	76.9970	.58528	.01299	1.23320	.81090	30.31378	.03299
485	61.8129	75.8415	61.7931	75.7994	.57925	.01319	1.22666	.81522	29.84230	.03351
490	61.1821	74.6854	61.1626	74.6445	.57334	.01340	1.22043	.81939	29.38750	.03403
495	60.5641	73.5695	60.5448	73.5297	.56754	.01360	1.21447	.82341	28.94870	.03454
500	59.9585	72.4916	59.9393	72.4528	.56187	.01380	1.20877	.82729	28.52473	.03506
505	59.3649	71.4496	59.3459	71.4118	.55631	.01400	1.20332	.83104	28.11488	.03557
510	58.7828	70.4415	58.7640	70.4046	.55085	.01420	1.19809	.83466	27.71837	.03608
515	58.2121	69.4656	58.1935	69.4296	.54550	.01440	1.19308	.83817	27.33450	.03658
520	57.6524	68.5202	57.6340	68.4851	.54026	.01460	1.18828	.84155	26.96264	.03709
525	57.1033	67.6038	57.0851	67.5695	.53511	.01480	1.18366	.84483	26.60217	.03759
530	56.5646	66.7149	56.5465	66.6814	.53006	.01500	1.17923	.84801	26.25253	.03809
535	56.0360	65.8523	56.0181	65.8195	.52511	.01519	1.17497	.85109	25.91320	.03859
540	55.5171	65.0146	55.4994	64.9826	.52025	.01539	1.17087	.85407	25.58369	.03909
545	55.0078	64.2008	54.9902	64.1694	.51548	.01558	1.16692	.85695	25.26354	.03958
550	54.5077	63.4096	54.4903	63.3789	.51079	.01578	1.16312	.85975	24.95233	.04008
555	54.0167	62.6402	53.9994	62.6101	.50619	.01597	1.15946	.86247	24.64965	.04057
560	53.5344	61.8915	53.5173	61.8620	.50167	.01617	1.15593	.86511	24.35513	.04106
565	53.0606	61.1627	53.0436	61.1338	.49723	.01636	1.15252	.86767	24.06842	.04155
570	52.5952	60.4529	52.5784	60.4245	.49287	.01655	1.14923	.87015	23.78918	.04204
575	52.1378	59.7613	52.1211	59.7335	.48858	.01674	1.14605	.87256	23.51711	.04252

TABLE 6

IEC-R 5 — Brit: WG-1 — Amer: WR-1800, RG-201/U

Outside dimensions: 18.250 X 9.250 ±0.015 inches (c,h)
463.6 X 234.95 millimeters

Inside dimensions: 18.000 X 9.000 ±0.015 inches
457.2 X 228.60 millimeters
corner radius: 1.5 millimeters
a/b: 2.000

Cutoff:	Rectangle in Vacuum	Waveguide in Air
Wavelength:	91.44000cm	91.43831cm
Frequency:	327.85706 MHz	327.75828 MHz

	THEORETICAL		PHYSICAL							
f (MHz)	λ (cm)	λ_g (cm)	λ (cm)	λ_g (cm)	$\frac{\lambda}{\lambda_c}$	$1/\lambda_g$ (1/cm)	$\frac{\lambda_g}{\lambda}$	$\frac{\lambda}{\lambda_g}$	λ_g (in)	$1/\lambda_g$ (1/in)
375	79.9447	164.6944	79.9191	164.3960	.87402	.00608	2.05703	.48614	64.72284	.01545
380	78.8928	156.0451	78.8675	155.7861	.86252	.00642	1.97529	.50626	61.33313	.01630
385	77.8682	148.5382	77.8433	148.3104	.85132	.00674	1.90524	.52487	58.38991	.01713
390	76.8699	141.9404	76.8453	141.7376	.84041	.00706	1.84445	.54217	55.80219	.01792
395	75.8968	136.0800	75.8726	135.8978	.82977	.00736	1.79113	.55831	53.50306	.01869
400	74.9481	130.8280	74.9242	130.6629	.81940	.00765	1.74394	.57342	51.44209	.01944
405	74.0228	126.0849	73.9992	125.9342	.80928	.00794	1.70183	.58760	49.58039	.02017
410	73.1201	121.7726	73.0967	121.6342	.79941	.00822	1.66402	.60096	47.88748	.02088
415	72.2392	117.8290	72.2161	117.7012	.78978	.00850	1.62985	.61355	46.33905	.02158
420	71.3792	114.2038	71.3563	114.0852	.78038	.00877	1.59881	.62547	44.91544	.02226
425	70.5394	110.8559	70.5168	110.7454	.77120	.00903	1.57048	.63675	43.60056	.02294
430	69.7192	107.7514	69.6969	107.6480	.76223	.00929	1.54452	.64745	42.38112	.02360
435	68.9178	104.8618	68.8958	104.7648	.75347	.00955	1.52063	.65762	41.24597	.02424
440	68.1347	102.1632	68.1129	102.0718	.74491	.00980	1.49857	.66730	40.18575	.02488
445	67.3691	99.6353	67.3476	99.5489	.73654	.01005	1.47814	.67653	39.19249	.02552
450	66.6206	97.2605	66.5992	97.1787	.72835	.01029	1.45916	.68533	38.25935	.02614
455	65.8885	95.0240	65.8674	94.9464	.72035	.01053	1.44148	.69373	37.38046	.02675
460	65.1723	92.9127	65.1514	92.8388	.71252	.01077	1.42497	.70177	36.55070	.02736
465	64.4715	90.9152	64.4509	90.8447	.70486	.01101	1.40952	.70946	35.76564	.02796
470	63.7856	89.0216	63.7652	88.9543	.69736	.01124	1.39503	.71683	35.02137	.02855
475	63.1142	87.2232	63.0940	87.1587	.69002	.01147	1.38141	.72390	34.31446	.02914
480	62.4568	85.5121	62.4368	85.4503	.68283	.01170	1.36859	.73068	33.64185	.02972
485	61.8129	83.8815	61.7931	83.8222	.67579	.01193	1.35650	.73719	33.00085	.03030
490	61.1821	82.3252	61.1626	82.2682	.66889	.01216	1.34507	.74345	32.38904	.03087
495	60.5641	80.8378	60.5448	80.7828	.66214	.01238	1.33427	.74948	31.80427	.03144
500	59.9585	79.4143	59.9393	79.3613	.65552	.01260	1.32403	.75527	31.24459	.03201
505	59.3649	78.0501	59.3459	77.9990	.64903	.01282	1.31431	.76085	30.70825	.03256
510	58.7828	76.7414	58.7640	76.6919	.64266	.01304	1.30508	.76623	30.19367	.03312
515	58.2121	75.4844	58.1935	75.4365	.63642	.01326	1.29630	.77142	29.69942	.03367
520	57.6524	74.2758	57.6340	74.2294	.63030	.01347	1.28795	.77643	29.22419	.03422
525	57.1033	73.1126	57.0851	73.0676	.62430	.01369	1.27998	.78126	28.76679	.03476
530	56.5646	71.9920	56.5465	71.9484	.61841	.01390	1.27237	.78593	28.32613	.03530
535	56.0360	70.9114	56.0181	70.8691	.61263	.01411	1.26511	.79044	27.90122	.03584
540	55.5171	69.8687	55.4994	69.8275	.60696	.01432	1.25817	.79481	27.49115	.03638
545	55.0078	68.8615	54.9902	68.8215	.60139	.01453	1.25152	.79903	27.09506	.03691
550	54.5077	67.8879	54.4903	67.8490	.59592	.01474	1.24516	.80311	26.71220	.03744
555	54.0167	66.9462	53.9994	66.9083	.59056	.01495	1.23906	.80707	26.34183	.03796
560	53.5344	66.0346	53.5173	65.9976	.58528	.01515	1.23320	.81090	25.98331	.03849
565	53.0606	65.1515	53.0436	65.1155	.58010	.01536	1.22758	.81461	25.63601	.03901
570	52.5952	64.2956	52.5784	64.2604	.57501	.01556	1.22218	.81821	25.29937	.03953
575	52.1378	63.4654	52.1211	63.4310	.57001	.01577	1.21699	.82170	24.97285	.04004
580	51.6884	62.6597	51.6718	62.6261	.56510	.01597	1.21200	.82508	24.65596	.04056
585	51.2466	61.8774	51.2302	61.8446	.56027	.01617	1.20719	.82837	24.34825	.04107
590	50.8123	61.1173	50.7960	61.0852	.55552	.01637	1.20256	.83156	24.04928	.04158
595	50.3853	60.3784	50.3692	60.3470	.55085	.01657	1.19809	.83466	23.75865	.04209
600	49.9654	59.6598	49.9494	59.6290	.54626	.01677	1.19379	.83767	23.47598	.04260
605	49.5525	58.9605	49.5366	58.9304	.54175	.01697	1.18963	.84060	23.20093	.04310
610	49.1463	58.2798	49.1306	58.2502	.53731	.01717	1.18562	.84344	22.93316	.04360
615	48.7467	57.6168	48.7312	57.5878	.53294	.01736	1.18174	.84621	22.67235	.04411
620	48.3536	56.9707	48.3882	56.9423	.52864	.01756	1.17800	.84890	22.41823	.04461
625	47.9668	56.3410	47.9515	56.3131	.52441	.01776	1.17438	.85152	22.17050	.04510
630	47.5861	55.7268	47.5709	55.6994	.52025	.01795	1.17087	.85406	21.92892	.04560
635	47.2114	55.1277	47.1963	55.1008	.51615	.01815	1.16748	.85655	21.69323	.04610
640	46.8426	54.5429	46.8276	54.5165	.51212	.01834	1.16420	.85896	21.46320	.04659
645	46.4795	53.9720	46.4646	53.9461	.50815	.01854	1.16102	.86132	21.23862	.04708
650	46.1219	53.4145	46.1072	53.3890	.50424	.01873	1.15793	.86361	21.01928	.04758
655	45.7698	52.8697	45.7552	52.8446	.50039	.01892	1.15494	.86584	20.80498	.04807
660	45.4231	52.3373	45.4086	52.3126	.49660	.01912	1.15204	.86802	20.59553	.04855
665	45.0816	51.8168	45.0672	51.7925	.49287	.01931	1.14923	.87015	20.39076	.04904
670	44.7451	51.3077	44.7308	51.2839	.48919	.01950	1.14650	.87222	20.19050	.04953
675	44.4137	50.8098	44.3995	50.7863	.48557	.01969	1.14385	.87424	19.99459	.05001

TABLE 7

IEC-R 6 | Brit: WG-2 | Amer: WR-1500, RG-202/U

Outside dimensions: 15.250 X 7.750 ±0.10 inches (c,h)
387.6 X 196.85 millimeters

Inside dimensions: 15.000 X 7.500 ±0.010 inches (h)
381.0 X 190.50 millimeters
corner radius: 1.5 millimeters
a/b: 2.000

Cutoff:	Rectangle in Vacuum	Waveguide in Air
Wavelength:	76.20000cm	76.19797cm
Frequency:	393.42848 MHz	393.31311 MHz

f (MHz)	THEORETICAL λ (cm)	λ_g (cm)	λ (cm)	λ_g (cm)	$\frac{\lambda}{\lambda_c}$	PHYSICAL $1/\lambda_g$ (1/cm)	$\frac{\lambda_g}{\lambda}$	$\frac{\lambda}{\lambda_g}$	λ_g (in)	$1/\lambda_g$ (1/in)
450	66.6206	137.2454	66.5992	137.0003	.87403	.00730	2.05708	.48612	53.93712	.01854
455	65.8885	131.1666	65.8674	130.9490	.86442	.00764	1.98807	.50300	51.55471	.01940
460	65.1723	125.7746	65.1514	125.5795	.85503	.00796	1.92750	.51881	49.44074	.02023
465	64.4715	120.9480	64.4509	120.7715	.84583	.00828	1.87385	.53366	47.54784	.02103
470	63.7856	116.5934	63.7652	116.4327	.83684	.00859	1.82596	.54766	45.83964	.02182
475	63.1142	112.6379	63.0940	112.4906	.82803	.00889	1.78290	.56088	44.28762	.02258
480	62.4568	109.0234	62.4368	108.8876	.81940	.00918	1.74396	.57341	42.86912	.02333
485	61.8129	105.7030	61.7931	105.5772	.81095	.00947	1.70856	.58529	41.56583	.02406
490	61.1821	102.6386	61.1626	102.5215	.80268	.00975	1.67621	.59658	40.36270	.02478
495	60.5641	99.7984	60.5448	99.6890	.79457	.01003	1.64653	.60734	39.24765	.02548
500	59.9585	97.1561	59.9393	97.0536	.78663	.01030	1.61920	.61759	38.21009	.02617
505	59.3649	94.6896	59.3459	94.5932	.77884	.01057	1.59393	.62738	37.24141	.02685
510	58.7828	92.3799	58.7640	92.2890	.77120	.01084	1.57050	.63674	36.33423	.02752
515	58.2121	90.2110	58.1935	90.1249	.76371	.01110	1.54871	.64570	35.48226	.02818
520	57.6524	88.1689	57.6340	88.0873	.75637	.01135	1.52839	.65428	34.68004	.02884
525	57.1033	86.2417	57.0851	86.1641	.74917	.01161	1.50940	.66252	33.92287	.02948
530	56.5646	84.4188	56.5465	84.3449	.74210	.01186	1.49160	.67042	33.20665	.03011
535	56.0360	82.6911	56.0181	82.6206	.73516	.01210	1.47489	.67802	32.52778	.03074
540	55.5171	81.0505	55.4994	80.9830	.72836	.01235	1.45917	.68532	31.88308	.03136
545	55.0078	79.4898	54.9902	79.4252	.72168	.01259	1.44435	.69235	31.26977	.03198
550	54.5077	78.0027	54.4903	77.9408	.71511	.01283	1.43036	.69912	30.68536	.03259
555	54.0167	76.5836	53.9994	76.5241	.70867	.01307	1.41713	.70565	30.12762	.03319
560	53.5344	75.2274	53.5173	75.1702	.70234	.01330	1.40460	.71195	29.59457	.03379
565	53.0606	73.9296	53.0436	73.8744	.69613	.01354	1.39271	.71802	29.08443	.03438
570	52.5952	72.6860	52.5784	72.6328	.69002	.01377	1.38142	.72389	28.59559	.03497
575	52.1378	71.4929	52.1211	71.4416	.68402	.01400	1.37068	.72956	28.12661	.03555
580	51.6884	70.3471	51.6718	70.2974	.67813	.01423	1.36046	.73505	27.67616	.03613
585	51.2466	69.2454	51.2302	69.1973	.67233	.01445	1.35071	.74035	27.24305	.03671
590	50.8123	68.1850	50.7960	68.1385	.66663	.01468	1.34141	.74548	26.82619	.03728
595	50.3853	67.1635	50.3692	67.1184	.66103	.01490	1.33253	.75045	26.42458	.03784
600	49.9654	66.1785	49.9494	66.1348	.65552	.01512	1.32403	.75527	26.03732	.03841
605	49.5525	65.2279	49.5366	65.1854	.65010	.01534	1.31590	.75903	25.66356	.03897
610	49.1463	64.3098	49.1306	64.2685	.64478	.01556	1.30811	.76446	25.30254	.03952
615	48.7467	63.4222	48.7312	63.3820	.63953	.01578	1.30065	.76885	24.95355	.04007
620	48.3536	62.5636	48.3382	62.5245	.63438	.01599	1.29348	.77311	24.61593	.04062
625	47.9668	61.7324	47.9515	61.6943	.62930	.01621	1.28660	.77724	24.28909	.04117
630	47.5861	60.9271	47.5709	60.8900	.62431	.01642	1.27998	.78126	23.97245	.04171
635	47.2114	60.1466	47.1963	60.1104	.61939	.01664	1.27362	.78516	23.66550	.04226
640	46.8426	59.3894	46.8276	59.3541	.61455	.01685	1.26750	.78895	23.36775	.04279
645	46.4795	58.6546	46.4646	58.6201	.60979	.01706	1.26161	.79264	23.07876	.04333
650	46.1219	57.9409	46.1072	57.9072	.60510	.01727	1.25593	.79623	22.79811	.04386
655	45.7698	57.2474	45.7552	57.2145	.60048	.01748	1.25045	.79971	22.52540	.04439
660	45.4231	56.5733	45.4086	56.5411	.59593	.01769	1.24516	.80311	22.26026	.04492
665	45.0816	55.9175	45.0672	55.8860	.59145	.01789	1.24006	.80641	22.00236	.04545
670	44.7451	55.2793	44.7308	55.2485	.58703	.01810	1.23513	.80963	21.75138	.04597
675	44.4137	54.6580	44.3995	54.6278	.58269	.01831	1.23037	.81276	21.50700	.04650
680	44.0871	54.0527	44.0730	54.0231	.57840	.01851	1.22576	.81582	21.26895	.04702
685	43.7653	53.4629	43.7513	53.4339	.57418	.01871	1.22131	.81879	21.03696	.04754
690	43.4482	52.8879	43.4343	52.8594	.57002	.01892	1.21700	.82169	20.81079	.04805
695	43.1356	52.3270	43.1218	52.2991	.56592	.01912	1.21282	.82452	20.59018	.04857
700	42.8275	51.7797	42.8138	51.7523	.56188	.01932	1.20878	.82728	20.37493	.04908
705	42.5238	51.2455	42.5102	51.2186	.55789	.01952	1.20486	.82997	20.16482	.04959
710	42.2243	50.7239	42.2108	50.6975	.55396	.01972	1.20106	.83260	19.95965	.05010
715	41.9290	50.2144	41.9156	50.1884	.55009	.01992	1.19737	.83516	19.75923	.05061
720	41.6378	49.7165	41.6245	49.6910	.54627	.02012	1.19379	.83767	19.56339	.05112
725	41.3507	49.2298	41.3375	49.2047	.54250	.02032	1.19032	.84011	19.37195	.05162
730	41.0675	48.7539	41.0543	48.7293	.53879	.02052	1.18695	.84250	19.18475	.05212
735	40.7881	48.2884	40.7750	48.2642	.53512	.02072	1.18367	.84483	19.00165	.05263
740	40.5125	47.8330	40.4995	47.8091	.53150	.02092	1.18049	.84711	18.82249	.05313
745	40.2406	47.3872	40.2277	47.3637	.52794	.02111	1.17739	.84934	18.64714	.05363
750	39.9723	46.9508	39.9595	46.9277	.52442	.02131	1.17438	.85151	18.47548	.05413
755	39.7076	46.5234	39.6949	46.5007	.52094	.02151	1.17145	.85364	18.30736	.05462
760	39.4464	46.1048	39.4338	46.0824	.51752	.02170	1.16860	.85572	18.14268	.05512
765	39.1886	45.6946	39.1760	45.6726	.51413	.02189	1.16583	.85776	17.98132	.05561
770	38.9341	45.2926	38.9216	45.2709	.51080	.02209	1.16313	.85975	17.82317	.05611
775	38.6829	44.8985	38.6705	44.8771	.50750	.02228	1.16050	.86170	17.66814	.05660
780	38.4349	44.5120	38.4226	44.4909	.50425	.02248	1.15794	.86361	17.51611	.05709
785	38.1901	44.1330	38.1779	44.1122	.50104	.02267	1.15544	.86547	17.36701	.05758
790	37.9484	43.7612	37.9363	43.7406	.49786	.02286	1.15300	.86730	17.22073	.05807
795	37.7097	43.3963	37.6977	43.3761	.49473	.02305	1.15063	.86909	17.07719	.05856
800	37.4741	43.0382	37.4621	43.0182	.49164	.02325	1.14831	.87084	16.93631	.05904

TABLE 8

IEC-R 8 | Brit: WG-3 | Amer: WR-1150, RG-203/U

Outside dimensions: 11.750 X 6.000 ±0.010 inches (c,h)
298.45 X 152.40 millimeters

Inside dimensions: 11.500 X 5.750 ±0.10 inches (h)
292.10 X 146.05 millimeters
corner radius: 1.5 millimeters
a/b: 2.000

Cutoff:	Rectangle in Vacuum	Waveguide in Air
Wavelength:	58.42000cm	58.41735cm
Frequency:	513.16757 MHz	513.02666 MHz

f (MHz)	THEORETICAL λ (cm)	λ_g (cm)	λ (cm)	λ_g (cm)	$\frac{\lambda}{\lambda_c}$	PHYSICAL $1/\lambda_g$ (1/cm)	$\frac{\lambda_g}{\lambda}$	$\frac{\lambda}{\lambda_g}$	λ_g (in)	$1/\lambda_g$ (1/in)
575	52.1378	115.5752	52.1211	115.3423	.89222	.00867	2.21297	.45188	45.41037	.02202
580	51.6884	110.9133	51.6718	110.7047	.88453	.00903	2.14246	.46675	43.58452	.02294
585	51.2466	106.7398	51.2302	106.5512	.87697	.00939	2.07985	.48080	41.94930	.02384
590	50.8123	102.9740	50.7960	102.8025	.86954	.00973	2.02383	.49411	40.47341	.02471
595	50.3853	99.5532	50.3692	99.3961	.86223	.01006	1.97335	.50675	39.13232	.02555
600	49.9654	96.4272	49.9494	96.2825	.85504	.01039	1.92760	.51878	37.90649	.02638
605	49.5525	93.5555	49.5366	93.4216	.84798	.01070	1.88591	.53025	36.78014	.02719
610	49.1463	90.9051	49.1306	90.7806	.84103	.01102	1.84774	.54120	35.74038	.02798
615	48.7467	88.4486	48.7312	88.3324	.83419	.01132	1.81265	.55168	34.77653	.02876
620	48.3536	86.1633	48.3382	86.0544	.82746	.01162	1.78026	.56172	33.87970	.02952
625	47.9668	84.0299	47.9515	83.9276	.82084	.01192	1.75026	.57134	33.04237	.03026

47

f (MHz)	λ (cm)	λg (cm)	λ (cm)	λg (cm)	λ/λc	1/λg (1/cm)	λg/λ	λ/λg	λg (in)	1/λg (1/in)
630	47.5861	82.0322	47.5709	81.9358	.81433	.01220	1.72239	.58059	32.25818	.03100
635	47.2114	80.1561	47.1963	80.0650	.80792	.01249	1.69643	.58947	31.52167	.03172
640	46.8426	78.3898	46.8276	78.3035	.80160	.01277	1.67217	.59803	30.82814	.03244
645	46.4795	76.7227	46.4646	76.6408	.79539	.01305	1.64944	.60626	30.17353	.03314
650	46.1219	75.1459	46.1072	75.0679	.78927	.01332	1.62812	.61421	29.55429	.03384
655	45.7698	73.6513	45.7552	73.5770	.78325	.01359	1.60806	.62187	28.96731	.03452
660	45.4231	72.2320	45.4086	72.1610	.77731	.01386	1.58915	.62927	28.40985	.03520
665	45.0816	70.8818	45.0672	70.8139	.77147	.01412	1.57130	.63642	27.87949	.03587
670	44.7451	69.5953	44.7308	69.5302	.76571	.01438	1.55441	.64333	27.37408	.03653
675	44.4137	68.3674	44.3995	68.3049	.76004	.01464	1.53842	.65002	26.89170	.03719
680	44.0871	67.1939	44.0730	67.1338	.75445	.01490	1.52324	.65650	26.43064	.03783
685	43.7653	66.0708	43.7513	66.0130	.74894	.01515	1.50882	.66277	25.98936	.03848
690	43.4482	64.9945	43.4343	64.9388	.74352	.01540	1.49511	.66885	25.56647	.03911
695	43.1356	63.9619	43.1218	63.9082	.73817	.01565	1.48204	.67475	25.16071	.03974
700	42.8275	62.9701	42.8138	62.9182	.73290	.01589	1.46958	.68047	24.77094	.04037
705	42.5238	62.0164	42.5102	61.9662	.72770	.01614	1.45768	.68602	24.39614	.04099
710	42.2243	61.0983	42.2108	61.0498	.72257	.01638	1.44631	.69142	24.03536	.04161
715	41.9290	60.2139	41.9156	60.1668	.71752	.01662	1.43543	.69666	23.68773	.04222
720	41.6378	59.3609	41.6245	59.3153	.71254	.01686	1.42501	.70175	23.35248	.04282
725	41.3507	58.5376	41.3375	58.4934	.70762	.01710	1.41502	.70670	23.02888	.04342
730	41.0675	57.7423	41.0543	57.6993	.70278	.01733	1.40544	.71152	22.71627	.04402
735	40.7881	56.9734	40.7750	56.9316	.69800	.01756	1.39624	.71621	22.41402	.04461
740	40.5125	56.2294	40.4995	56.1888	.69328	.01780	1.38739	.72078	22.12159	.04520
745	40.2406	55.5091	40.2277	55.4696	.68863	.01803	1.37889	.72522	21.83844	.04579
750	39.9723	54.8112	39.9595	54.7728	.68404	.01826	1.37071	.72955	21.56409	.04637
755	39.7076	54.1346	39.6949	54.0971	.67951	.01849	1.36282	.73377	21.29809	.04695
760	39.4464	53.4782	39.4338	53.4417	.67504	.01871	1.35523	.73788	21.04002	.04753
765	39.1886	52.8410	39.1760	52.8053	.67062	.01894	1.34790	.74190	20.78950	.04810
770	38.9341	52.2221	38.9216	52.1873	.66627	.01916	1.34083	.74581	20.54617	.04867
775	38.6829	51.6206	38.6705	51.5866	.66197	.01938	1.33400	.74962	20.30968	.04924
780	38.4349	51.0357	38.4226	51.0025	.65773	.01961	1.32741	.75335	20.07971	.04980
785	38.1901	50.4667	38.1779	50.4342	.65354	.01983	1.32103	.75698	19.85598	.05036
790	37.9484	49.9128	37.9363	49.8810	.64940	.02005	1.31486	.76053	19.63821	.05092
795	37.7097	49.3735	37.6977	49.3424	.64532	.02027	1.30890	.76400	19.42613	.05148
800	37.4741	48.8480	37.4621	48.8175	.64128	.02048	1.30312	.76739	19.21950	.05203
805	37.2413	48.3358	37.2294	48.3060	.63730	.02070	1.29752	.77070	19.01809	.05258
810	37.0114	47.8363	36.9996	47.8071	.63337	.02092	1.29210	.77394	18.82169	.05313
815	36.7844	47.3491	36.7726	47.3204	.62948	.02113	1.28684	.77710	18.63009	.05368
820	36.5601	46.8735	36.5484	46.8455	.62564	.02135	1.28174	.78019	18.44309	.05422
825	36.3385	46.4093	36.3269	46.3817	.62185	.02156	1.27679	.78321	18.26052	.05476
830	36.1196	45.9559	36.1080	45.9288	.61810	.02177	1.27198	.78617	18.08221	.05530
835	35.9033	45.5128	35.8918	45.4863	.61440	.02198	1.26732	.78907	17.90799	.05584
840	35.6896	45.0798	35.6782	45.0538	.61075	.02220	1.26278	.79190	17.73771	.05638
845	35.4784	44.6565	35.4671	44.6309	.60713	.02241	1.25838	.79468	17.57122	.05691
850	35.2697	44.2425	35.2584	44.2173	.60356	.02262	1.25409	.79739	17.40838	.05744
855	35.0635	43.8374	35.0522	43.8126	.60003	.02282	1.24992	.80005	17.24907	.05797
860	34.8596	43.4409	34.8484	43.4166	.59654	.02303	1.24587	.80265	17.09315	.05850
865	34.6581	43.0528	34.6470	43.0289	.59309	.02324	1.24192	.80520	16.94052	.05903
870	34.4589	42.6728	34.4479	42.6493	.58969	.02345	1.23808	.80770	16.79105	.05956
875	34.2620	42.3006	34.2510	42.2774	.58632	.02365	1.23434	.81015	16.64465	.06008
880	34.0673	41.9358	34.0564	41.9130	.58298	.02386	1.23069	.81255	16.50119	.06060
885	33.8749	41.5784	33.8640	41.5559	.57969	.02406	1.22714	.81490	16.36060	.06112
890	33.6846	41.2280	33.6738	41.2059	.57643	.02427	1.22368	.81721	16.22278	.06164
895	33.4964	40.8844	33.4857	40.8626	.57321	.02447	1.22030	.81947	16.08763	.06216
900	33.3103	40.5474	33.2996	40.5259	.57003	.02468	1.21701	.82169	15.95508	.06268
905	33.1262	40.2167	33.1156	40.1956	.56688	.02488	1.21379	.82386	15.82504	.06319
910	32.9442	39.8923	32.9337	39.8715	.56377	.02508	1.21066	.82600	15.69743	.06370
915	32.7642	39.5739	32.7537	39.5533	.56068	.02528	1.20760	.82809	15.57218	.06422
920	32.5861	39.2613	32.5757	39.2410	.55764	.02548	1.20461	.83014	15.44922	.06473
925	32.4100	38.9543	32.3996	38.9344	.55462	.02568	1.20169	.83216	15.32849	.06524
930	32.2358	38.6529	32.2254	38.6332	.55164	.02588	1.19884	.83414	15.20990	.06575
935	32.0634	38.3567	32.0531	38.3373	.54869	.02608	1.19605	.83608	15.09341	.06625
940	31.8928	38.0657	31.8826	38.0465	.54577	.02628	1.19333	.83799	14.97895	.06676
945	31.7241	37.7798	31.7139	37.7608	.54289	.02648	1.19067	.83986	14.86647	.06727
950	31.5571	37.4987	31.5470	37.4800	.54003	.02668	1.18807	.84170	14.75591	.06777
955	31.3919	37.2224	31.3818	37.2039	.53720	.02688	1.18552	.84351	14.64721	.06827
960	31.2284	36.9507	31.2184	36.9324	.53440	.02708	1.18303	.84528	14.54033	.06877
965	31.0666	36.6835	31.0566	36.6654	.53163	.02727	1.18060	.84703	14.43521	.06928
970	30.9064	36.4206	30.8966	36.4028	.52889	.02747	1.17822	.84874	14.33182	.06977
975	30.7479	36.1620	30.7381	36.1444	.52618	.02767	1.17588	.85042	14.23009	.07027
980	30.5911	35.9076	30.5813	35.8902	.52350	.02786	1.17360	.85208	14.13000	.07077
985	30.4358	35.6572	30.4261	35.6400	.52084	.02806	1.17136	.85371	14.03149	.07127
990	30.2821	35.4107	30.2724	35.3937	.51821	.02825	1.16917	.85530	13.93453	.07176
995	30.1299	35.1680	30.1203	35.1512	.51560	.02845	1.16703	.85688	13.83907	.07226
1000	29.9792	34.9291	29.9697	34.9125	.51303	.02864	1.16493	.85842	13.74509	.07275
1005	29.8301	34.6938	29.8206	34.6774	.51047	.02884	1.16287	.85994	13.65253	.07325
1010	29.6824	34.4621	29.6729	34.4459	.50795	.02903	1.16085	.86144	13.56137	.07374
1015	29.5362	34.2339	29.5268	34.2178	.50544	.02922	1.15887	.86291	13.47158	.07423
1020	29.3914	34.0090	29.3820	33.9931	.50297	.02942	1.15694	.86435	13.38311	.07472
1025	29.2480	33.7874	29.2387	33.7717	.50051	.02961	1.15503	.86577	13.29595	.07521
1030	29.1061	33.5691	29.0968	33.5535	.49808	.02980	1.15317	.86717	13.21005	.07570
1035	28.9655	33.3539	28.9562	33.3385	.49568	.03000	1.15134	.86855	13.12539	.07619
1040	28.8262	33.1417	28.8170	33.1265	.49329	.03019	1.14955	.86991	13.04193	.07668
1045	28.6883	32.9326	28.6791	32.9175	.49093	.03038	1.14779	.87124	12.95966	.07716
1050	28.5517	32.7264	28.5425	32.7115	.48860	.03057	1.14606	.87255	12.87854	.07765

TAPLE 9

IEC-R 9 Brit: WG-4 Amer: WR-975, RG-204/U

Outside dimensions: 10.000 X 5.125 ±0.010 inches (c,h)
254.00 X 130.18 millimeters

Inside dimensions: 9.750 X 4.875 ±0.010 inches (h)
247.65 X 123.82 millimeters
corner radius: 1.2 millimeters
a/b: 2.000

Cutoff: Ractangle in Vacuum Waveguide in Air

Wavelength: 49.53000cm 49.52800cm
Frequency: 605.27457 MHz 605.10538 MHz

f (MHz)	THEORETICAL λ (cm)	THEORETICAL λ_g (cm)	PHYSICAL λ (cm)	PHYSICAL λ_g (cm)	$\frac{\lambda}{\lambda_c}$	$1/\lambda_g$ (1/cm)	$\frac{\lambda_g}{\lambda}$	$\frac{\lambda}{\lambda_g}$	λ_g (in)	$1/\lambda_g$ (1/in)
700	42.8275	85.2583	42.8138	85.1203	.86444	.01175	1.98815	.50298	33.51192	.02984
705	42.5238	82.9348	42.5102	82.8063	.85831	.01208	1.94792	.51337	32.60091	.03067
710	42.2243	80.7768	42.2108	80.6567	.85226	.01240	1.91081	.52334	31.75462	.03149
715	41.9290	78.7653	41.9156	78.6528	.84630	.01271	1.87646	.53292	30.96566	.03229
720	41.6378	76.8844	41.6245	76.7785	.84042	.01302	1.84455	.54214	30.22777	.03308
725	41.3507	75.1202	41.3375	75.0204	.83463	.01333	1.81483	.55102	29.53560	.03386
730	41.0675	73.4612	41.0543	73.3668	.82891	.01363	1.78707	.55958	28.88458	.03462
735	40.7881	71.8971	40.7750	71.8077	.82327	.01393	1.76107	.56784	28.27073	.03537
740	40.5125	70.4191	40.4995	70.3342	.81771	.01422	1.73667	.57582	27.69061	.03611
745	40.2406	69.0195	40.2277	68.9387	.81222	.01451	1.71371	.58353	27.14121	.03684
750	39.9723	67.6916	39.9595	67.6145	.80681	.01479	1.69207	.59099	26.61987	.03757
755	39.7076	66.4293	39.6949	66.3556	.80146	.01507	1.67164	.59821	26.12427	.03828
760	39.4464	65.2274	39.4338	65.1569	.79619	.01535	1.65231	.60521	25.65232	.03898
765	39.1886	64.0811	39.1760	64.0135	.79099	.01562	1.63400	.61200	25.20218	.03968
770	38.9341	62.9862	38.9216	62.9214	.78585	.01589	1.61662	.61858	24.77221	.04037
775	38.6829	61.9391	38.6705	61.8767	.78078	.01616	1.60010	.62496	24.36092	.04105

780	38.4349	60.9361	38.4226	60.8762	.77578	.01643	1.58438	.63116	23.96690	.04172
785	38.1901	59.9744	38.1779	59.9166	.77083	.01669	1.56941	.63718	23.58922	.04239
790	37.9484	59.0510	37.9363	58.9953	.76596	.01695	1.55512	.64304	23.22651	.04305
795	37.7097	58.1636	37.6977	58.1098	.76114	.01721	1.54147	.64873	22.87788	.04371
800	37.4741	57.3098	37.4621	57.2578	.75638	.01746	1.52842	.65427	22.54244	.04436
805	37.2413	56.4875	37.2294	56.4372	.75168	.01772	1.51593	.65966	22.21936	.04501
810	37.0114	55.6948	36.9996	55.6461	.74704	.01797	1.50396	.66491	21.90790	.04565
815	36.7844	54.9299	36.7726	54.8827	.74246	.01822	1.49249	.67002	21.60737	.04628
820	36.5601	54.1913	36.5484	54.1455	.73793	.01847	1.48148	.67500	21.31713	.04691
825	36.3385	53.4775	36.3269	53.4330	.73346	.01872	1.47090	.67986	21.03662	.04754
830	36.1196	52.7870	36.1080	52.7438	.72904	.01896	1.46072	.68459	20.76529	.04816
835	35.9033	52.1187	35.8918	52.0767	.72468	.01920	1.45094	.68921	20.50264	.04877
840	35.6896	51.4713	35.6782	51.4305	.72036	.01944	1.44151	.69372	20.24822	.04939
845	35.4784	50.8439	35.4671	50.8041	.71610	.01968	1.43243	.69811	20.00161	.05000
850	35.2697	50.2353	35.2584	50.1965	.71189	.01992	1.42367	.70241	19.76241	.05060
855	35.0635	49.6446	35.0522	49.6068	.70773	.02016	1.41523	.70660	19.53025	.05120
860	34.8596	49.0710	34.8484	49.0342	.70361	.02039	1.40707	.71070	19.30480	.05180
865	34.6581	48.5137	34.6470	48.4777	.69954	.02063	1.39919	.71470	19.08573	.05240
870	34.4589	47.9719	34.4479	47.9368	.69552	.02086	1.39157	.71861	18.87274	.05299
875	34.2620	47.4448	34.2510	47.4105	.69155	.02109	1.38421	.72244	18.66556	.05357
880	34.0673	46.9319	34.0564	46.8984	.68762	.02132	1.37708	.72618	18.46393	.05416
885	33.8749	46.4325	33.8640	46.3997	.68373	.02155	1.37018	.72983	18.26760	.05474
890	33.6846	45.9459	33.6738	45.9139	.67989	.02178	1.36349	.73341	18.07634	.05532
895	33.4964	45.4718	33.4857	45.4404	.67610	.02201	1.35701	.73691	17.88993	.05590
900	33.3103	45.0095	33.2996	44.9788	.67234	.02223	1.35073	.74034	17.70818	.05647
905	33.1262	44.5585	33.1156	44.5285	.66862	.02246	1.34464	.74370	17.53089	.05704
910	32.9442	44.1185	32.9337	44.0890	.66495	.02268	1.33872	.74698	17.35788	.05761
915	32.7642	43.6889	32.7537	43.6600	.66132	.02290	1.33298	.75020	17.18899	.05818
920	32.5861	43.2694	32.5757	43.2411	.65772	.02313	1.32740	.75335	17.02404	.05874
925	32.4100	42.8595	32.3996	42.8317	.65417	.02335	1.32198	.75644	16.86289	.05930
930	32.2358	42.4590	32.2254	42.4317	.65065	.02357	1.31671	.75947	16.70540	.05986
935	32.0634	42.0674	32.0531	42.0406	.64717	.02379	1.31159	.76243	16.55142	.06042
940	31.8928	41.6844	31.8826	41.6581	.64373	.02400	1.30661	.76534	16.40083	.06097
945	31.7241	41.3097	31.7139	41.2839	.64032	.02422	1.30176	.76819	16.25351	.06153
950	31.5571	40.9431	31.5470	40.9177	.63695	.02444	1.29704	.77099	16.10933	.06208
955	31.3919	40.5842	31.3818	40.5592	.63362	.02466	1.29244	.77373	15.96820	.06262
960	31.2284	40.2327	31.2184	40.2082	.63032	.02487	1.28796	.77642	15.83000	.06317
965	31.0666	39.8885	31.0566	39.8644	.62705	.02509	1.28360	.77906	15.69463	.06372
970	30.9064	39.5512	30.8966	39.5275	.62382	.02530	1.27935	.78165	15.56200	.06426
975	30.7479	39.2207	30.7381	39.1973	.62062	.02551	1.27520	.78419	15.43201	.06480
980	30.5911	38.8966	30.5813	38.8737	.61745	.02572	1.27116	.78668	15.30459	.06534
985	30.4358	38.5789	30.4261	38.5563	.61432	.02594	1.26721	.78913	15.17964	.06588
990	30.2821	38.2673	30.2724	38.2450	.61122	.02615	1.26336	.79154	15.05709	.06641
995	30.1299	37.9616	30.1203	37.9396	.60815	.02636	1.25961	.79390	14.93686	.06695
1000	29.9792	37.6616	29.9697	37.6400	.60511	.02657	1.25594	.79622	14.81889	.06748
1005	29.8301	37.3671	29.8206	37.3459	.60209	.02678	1.25235	.79850	14.70309	.06801
1010	29.6824	37.0781	29.6729	37.0571	.59911	.02699	1.24885	.80074	14.58941	.06854
1015	29.5362	36.7943	29.5268	36.7736	.59616	.02719	1.24543	.80293	14.47778	.06907
1020	29.3914	36.5155	29.3820	36.4951	.59324	.02740	1.24209	.80510	14.36815	.06960
1025	29.2480	36.2416	29.2387	36.2215	.59035	.02761	1.23882	.80722	14.26044	.07012
1030	29.1061	35.9726	29.0968	35.9527	.58748	.02781	1.23563	.80931	14.15461	.07065
1035	28.9655	35.7081	28.9562	35.6885	.58464	.02802	1.23250	.81136	14.05061	.07117
1040	28.8262	35.4482	28.8170	35.4289	.58183	.02823	1.22944	.81338	13.94838	.07169
1045	28.6883	35.1926	28.6791	35.1736	.57905	.02843	1.22645	.81536	13.84787	.07221
1050	28.5517	34.9414	28.5425	34.9225	.57629	.02863	1.22353	.81731	13.74903	.07273
1055	28.4164	34.6942	28.4073	34.6756	.57356	.02884	1.22066	.81923	13.65183	.07325
1060	28.2823	34.4511	28.2733	34.4328	.57085	.02904	1.21786	.82111	13.55621	.07377
1065	28.1495	34.2119	28.1405	34.1938	.56817	.02925	1.21511	.82297	13.46213	.07428
1070	28.0180	33.9766	28.0090	33.9587	.56552	.02945	1.21242	.82480	13.36956	.07480
1075	27.8877	33.7449	27.8788	33.7273	.56289	.02965	1.20978	.82659	13.27845	.07531
1080	27.7586	33.5169	27.7497	33.4995	.56028	.02985	1.20720	.82836	13.18877	.07582
1085	27.6306	33.2925	27.6218	33.2752	.55770	.03005	1.20467	.83010	13.10047	.07633
1090	27.5039	33.0714	27.4951	33.0544	.55514	.03025	1.20219	.83181	13.01353	.07684
1095	27.3783	32.8537	27.3696	32.8369	.55261	.03045	1.19976	.83350	12.92791	.07735
1100	27.2539	32.6393	27.2451	32.6227	.55010	.03065	1.19738	.83516	12.84358	.07786
1105	27.1305	32.4281	27.1219	32.4117	.54761	.03085	1.19504	.83679	12.76050	.07837
1110	27.0083	32.2201	26.9997	32.2038	.54514	.03105	1.19275	.83840	12.67865	.07887
1115	26.8872	32.0150	26.8786	31.9989	.54270	.03125	1.19050	.83999	12.59799	.07938
1120	26.7672	31.8129	26.7586	31.7970	.54027	.03145	1.18829	.84155	12.51851	.07988
1125	26.6482	31.6138	26.6397	31.5980	.53787	.03165	1.18612	.84308	12.44016	.08038
1130	26.5303	31.4174	26.5218	31.4018	.53549	.03185	1.18400	.84459	12.36292	.08089
1135	26.4134	31.2239	26.4050	31.2084	.53313	.03204	1.18191	.84609	12.28678	.08139
1140	26.2976	31.0330	26.2892	31.0177	.53079	.03224	1.17987	.84755	12.21169	.08189
1145	26.1828	30.8447	26.1744	30.8296	.52848	.03244	1.17786	.84900	12.13765	.08239
1150	26.0689	30.6591	26.0606	30.6441	.52618	.03263	1.17588	.85043	12.06462	.08289
1155	25.9561	30.4760	25.9478	30.4612	.52390	.03283	1.17394	.85183	11.99258	.08338
1160	25.8442	30.2953	25.8359	30.2807	.52164	.03302	1.17204	.85322	11.92152	.08388
1165	25.7333	30.1171	25.7250	30.1026	.51940	.03322	1.17017	.85458	11.85140	.08438
1170	25.6233	29.9412	25.6151	29.9268	.51718	.03341	1.16833	.85592	11.78222	.08487
1175	25.5143	29.7676	25.5061	29.7534	.51498	.03361	1.16652	.85725	11.71394	.08537
1180	25.4061	29.5963	25.3980	29.5822	.51280	.03380	1.16475	.85856	11.64655	.08586
1185	25.2989	29.4273	25.2909	29.4133	.51064	.03400	1.16300	.85984	11.58003	.08636
1190	25.1926	29.2603	25.1846	29.2465	.50849	.03419	1.16129	.86111	11.51437	.08685
1195	25.0872	29.0955	25.0792	29.0818	.50636	.03439	1.15960	.86237	11.44954	.08734
1200	24.9827	28.9328	24.9747	28.9192	.50425	.03458	1.15794	.86360	11.38553	.08783

TABLE 10

IEC-R 12 Brit: WG-5 Amer: WR-770, RG-205/U

Outside dimensions: 7.950 X 4.100 ±0.008 inches (c,h)
201.93 X 104.14 millimeters

Inside dimensions: 7.700 X 3.850 ±0.008 inches (h)
195.58 X 97.79 millimeters
corner radius: 1.2 millimeters
a/b: 2.000

Cutoff: Rectangle in Vacuum Waveguide in Air

Wavelength: 39.11600cm 39.11347cm
Frequency: 766.41911 MHz 766.22350 MHz

	THEORETICAL		PHYSICAL							
f (MHz)	λ (cm)	λ_g (cm)	λ (cm)	λ_g (cm)	$\frac{\lambda}{\lambda_c}$	$1/\lambda_g$ (1/cm)	$\frac{\lambda_g}{\lambda}$	$\frac{\lambda}{\lambda_g}$	λ_g (in)	$1/\lambda_g$ (1/in)
850	35.2697	81.5625	35.2584	81.3896	.90144	.01229	2.30837	.43321	32.04316	.03121
860	34.8596	76.8442	34.8484	76.6968	.89096	.01304	2.20087	.45437	30.19561	.03312
870	34.4589	72.8171	34.4479	72.6894	.88072	.01376	2.11013	.47391	28.61787	.03494
880	34.0673	69.3263	34.0564	69.2139	.87071	.01445	2.03233	.49205	27.24958	.03670
890	33.6846	66.2613	33.6738	66.1614	.86093	.01511	1.96477	.50896	26.04778	.03839
900	33.3103	63.5414	33.2996	63.4516	.85136	.01576	1.90547	.52480	24.98094	.04003
910	32.9442	61.1056	32.9337	61.0243	.84200	.01639	1.85294	.53968	24.02531	.04162
920	32.5861	58.9073	32.5757	58.8331	.83285	.01700	1.80604	.55370	23.16266	.04317
930	32.2358	56.9099	32.2254	56.8418	.82390	.01759	1.76388	.56693	22.37866	.04469
940	31.8928	55.0842	31.8826	55.0213	.81513	.01817	1.72575	.57946	21.66193	.04616
950	31.5571	53.4067	31.5470	53.3483	.80655	.01874	1.69107	.59134	21.00327	.04761
960	31.2284	51.8581	31.2184	51.8037	.79815	.01930	1.65940	.60263	20.39516	.04903
970	30.9064	50.4226	30.8966	50.3717	.78992	.01985	1.63033	.61337	19.83138	.05043
980	30.5911	49.0869	30.5813	49.0391	.78186	.02039	1.60357	.62361	19.30674	.05180
990	30.2821	47.8398	30.2724	47.7948	.77396	.02092	1.57883	.63338	18.81686	.05314
1000	29.9792	46.6719	29.9697	46.6294	.76622	.02145	1.55589	.64272	18.35803	.05447

1010	29.6824	45.5750	29.6729	45.5348	.75864	.02196	1.53456	.65165	17.92707	.05578
1020	29.3914	44.5421	29.3820	44.5039	.75120	.02247	1.51467	.66021	17.52123	.05707
1030	29.1061	43.5672	29.0968	43.5309	.74391	.02297	1.49607	.66842	17.13815	.05835
1040	28.8262	42.6450	28.8170	42.6104	.73675	.02347	1.47866	.67629	16.77575	.05961
1050	28.5517	41.7709	28.5425	41.7378	.72974	.02396	1.46230	.68385	16.43222	.06086
1060	28.2823	40.9408	28.2733	40.9091	.72285	.02444	1.44692	.69112	16.10596	.06209
1070	28.0180	40.1511	28.0090	40.1207	.71610	.02492	1.43242	.69812	15.79557	.06331
1080	27.7586	39.3986	27.7497	39.3694	.70947	.02540	1.41873	.70485	15.49978	.06452
1090	27.5039	38.6804	27.4951	38.6524	.70296	.02587	1.40579	.71134	15.21747	.06571
1100	27.2539	37.9941	27.2451	37.9670	.69657	.02634	1.39353	.71760	14.94765	.06690
1110	27.0083	37.3372	26.9997	37.3111	.69029	.02680	1.38191	.72364	14.68942	.06808
1120	26.7672	36.7077	26.7586	36.6826	.68413	.02726	1.37087	.72946	14.44195	.06924
1130	26.5303	36.1038	26.5218	36.0795	.67807	.02772	1.36037	.73509	14.20453	.07040
1140	26.2976	35.5238	26.2892	35.5003	.67213	.02817	1.35038	.74053	13.97649	.07155
1150	26.0689	34.9661	26.0606	34.9433	.66628	.02862	1.34085	.74580	13.75721	.07269
1160	25.8442	34.4293	25.8359	34.4072	.66054	.02906	1.33176	.75089	13.54616	.07382
1170	25.6233	33.9122	25.6151	33.8908	.65489	.02951	1.32308	.75581	13.34282	.07495
1180	25.4061	33.4135	25.3980	33.3927	.64934	.02995	1.31478	.76059	13.14674	.07606
1190	25.1926	32.9323	25.1846	32.9121	.64389	.03038	1.30683	.76521	12.95750	.07718
1200	24.9827	32.4674	24.9747	32.4477	.63852	.03082	1.29922	.76969	12.77470	.07828
1210	24.7762	32.0180	24.7683	31.9989	.63324	.03125	1.29193	.77404	12.59800	.07938
1220	24.5732	31.5833	24.5653	31.5647	.62805	.03168	1.28493	.77825	12.42704	.08047
1230	24.3734	31.1625	24.3656	31.1443	.62295	.03211	1.27821	.78234	12.26154	.08156
1240	24.1768	30.7548	24.1691	30.7371	.61792	.03253	1.27175	.78632	12.10121	.08264
1250	23.9834	30.3596	23.9757	30.3423	.61298	.03296	1.26554	.79018	11.94578	.08371
1260	23.7931	29.9762	23.7854	29.9593	.60811	.03338	1.25957	.79392	11.79501	.08478
1270	23.6057	29.6041	23.5982	29.5876	.60333	.03380	1.25381	.79757	11.64868	.08585
1280	23.4213	29.2428	23.4138	29.2267	.59861	.03422	1.24827	.80111	11.50656	.08691
1290	23.2397	28.8917	23.2323	28.8759	.59397	.03463	1.24292	.80456	11.36847	.08796
1300	23.0610	28.5503	23.0536	28.5349	.58940	.03504	1.23776	.80791	11.23422	.08901
1310	22.8849	28.2183	22.8776	28.2032	.58490	.03546	1.23279	.81117	11.10362	.09006
1320	22.7116	27.8952	22.7043	27.8804	.58047	.03587	1.22798	.81435	10.97653	.09110
1330	22.5408	27.5806	22.5336	27.5661	.57611	.03628	1.22333	.81744	10.85279	.09214
1340	22.3726	27.2741	22.3654	27.2599	.57181	.03668	1.21884	.82045	10.73225	.09318
1350	22.2069	26.9755	22.1997	26.9615	.56757	.03709	1.21450	.82339	10.61478	.09421
1360	22.0436	26.6843	22.0365	26.6706	.56340	.03749	1.21029	.82625	10.50026	.09524
1370	21.8827	26.4004	21.8757	26.3869	.55929	.03790	1.20622	.82903	10.38855	.09626
1380	21.7241	26.1233	21.7171	26.1101	.55523	.03830	1.20228	.83175	10.27956	.09728
1390	21.5678	25.8528	21.5609	25.8399	.55124	.03870	1.19846	.83441	10.17317	.09830
1400	21.4137	25.5887	21.4069	25.5760	.54730	.03910	1.19475	.83699	10.06929	.09931
1410	21.2619	25.3307	21.2551	25.3182	.54342	.03950	1.19116	.83952	9.96781	.10032
1420	21.1121	25.0787	21.1054	25.0664	.53959	.03989	1.18768	.84198	9.86865	.10133
1430	20.9645	24.8323	20.9578	24.8202	.53582	.04029	1.18429	.84439	9.77172	.10234
1440	20.8189	24.5913	20.8123	24.5794	.53210	.04068	1.18101	.84674	9.67694	.10334
1450	20.6753	24.3557	20.6687	24.3440	.52843	.04108	1.17782	.84903	9.58423	.10434
1460	20.5337	24.1251	20.5272	24.1136	.52481	.04147	1.17471	.85127	9.49353	.10533
1470	20.3940	23.8994	20.3875	23.8881	.52124	.04186	1.17170	.85346	9.40475	.10633
1480	20.2562	23.6785	20.2498	23.6673	.51772	.04225	1.16877	.85560	9.31784	.10732
1490	20.1203	23.4621	20.1139	23.4511	.51424	.04264	1.16592	.85769	9.23272	.10831
1500	19.9862	23.2502	19.9798	23.2394	.51082	.04303	1.16314	.85974	9.14935	.10930
1510	19.8538	23.0425	19.8475	23.0319	.50743	.04342	1.16044	.86174	9.06766	.11028
1520	19.7232	22.8390	19.7169	22.8285	.50409	.04380	1.15782	.86370	8.98760	.11126
1530	19.5943	22.6395	19.5880	22.6292	.50080	.04419	1.15526	.86561	8.90912	.11224
1540	19.4670	22.4439	19.4608	22.4337	.49755	.04458	1.15276	.86748	8.83216	.11322
1550	19.3415	22.2521	19.3353	22.2420	.49434	.04496	1.15033	.86931	8.75668	.11420

TABLE 11

IEC-R 14 | Birt: WG-6 | Amer: WR-650, RG-69/U, RG-103/U, RG-206/U

Outside dimensions: 6.660 X 3.410 ±0.008 inches
169.16 X 86.61 ±0.20 millimeters

Inside dimensions: 6.500 X 3.250 ±0.0130 inches
165.10 X 82.55 ±0.33 millimeters
corner radius: 1.2 millimeters
a/b: 2.000

Cutoff: Rectangle in Vacuum | Waveguide in Air

Wavelength: 33.02000cm | 33.01702cm
Frequency: 907.91187 MHz | 907.70350 MHz

	THEORETICAL		PHYSICAL							
f (GHz)	λ (cm)	λ_g (cm)	λ (cm)	λ_g (cm)	$\frac{\lambda}{\lambda_c}$	$1/\lambda_g$ (1/cm)	$\frac{\lambda_g}{\lambda}$	$\frac{\lambda}{\lambda_g}$	λ_g (in)	$1/\lambda_g$ (1/in)
1.000	29.9792	71.5220	29.9697	71.3689	.90770	.01401	2.38137	.41993	28.09800	.03559
1.010	29.6824	67.7515	29.6729	67.6191	.89872	.01479	2.27881	.43882	26.62168	.03756
1.020	29.3914	64.4907	29.3820	64.3746	.88991	.01553	2.19095	.45642	25.34432	.03946
1.030	29.1061	61.6335	29.0968	61.5304	.88127	.01625	2.11468	.47288	24.22457	.04128
1.040	28.8262	59.1023	28.8170	59.0098	.87279	.01695	2.04774	.48834	23.23221	.04304
1.050	28.5517	56.8389	28.5425	56.7552	.86448	.01762	1.98844	.50291	22.34458	.04475
1.060	28.2823	54.7987	28.2733	54.7225	.85632	.01827	1.93549	.51667	21.54430	.04642
1.070	28.0180	52.9470	28.0090	52.8772	.84832	.01891	1.88786	.52970	20.81780	.04804
1.080	27.7586	51.2562	27.7497	51.1918	.84047	.01953	1.84477	.54207	20.15427	.04962
1.090	27.5039	49.7041	27.4951	49.6444	.83276	.02014	1.80557	.55384	19.54503	.05116
1.100	27.2539	48.2723	27.2451	48.2168	.82519	.02074	1.76974	.56506	18.98298	.05268
1.110	27.0083	46.9461	26.9997	46.8942	.81775	.02132	1.73684	.57576	18.46227	.05416
1.120	26.7672	45.7128	26.7586	45.6641	.81045	.02190	1.70652	.58599	17.97801	.05562
1.130	26.5303	44.5621	26.5218	44.5163	.80328	.02246	1.67848	.59578	17.52609	.05706
1.140	26.2976	43.4849	26.2892	43.4417	.79623	.02302	1.65246	.60516	17.10303	.05847
1.150	26.0689	42.4738	26.0606	42.4328	.78931	.02357	1.62824	.61416	16.70584	.05986
1.160	25.8442	41.5220	25.8359	41.4832	.78250	.02411	1.60564	.62280	16.33198	.06123
1.170	25.6233	40.6241	25.6151	40.5872	.77581	.02464	1.58450	.63111	15.97920	.06258
1.180	25.4061	39.7750	25.3980	39.7398	.76924	.02516	1.56468	.63911	15.64559	.06392
1.190	25.1926	38.9704	25.1846	38.9368	.76278	.02568	1.54606	.64681	15.32945	.06523
1.200	24.9827	38.2065	24.9747	38.1744	.75642	.02620	1.52852	.65423	15.02930	.06654
1.210	24.7762	37.4800	24.7683	37.4493	.75017	.02670	1.51198	.66138	14.74381	.06783
1.220	24.5732	36.7879	24.5653	36.7584	.74402	.02720	1.49635	.66829	14.47181	.06910
1.230	24.3734	36.1275	24.3656	36.0992	.73797	.02770	1.48156	.67496	14.21227	.07036
1.240	24.1768	35.4965	24.1691	35.4692	.73202	.02819	1.46755	.68141	13.96426	.07161
1.250	23.9834	34.8927	23.9757	34.8664	.72616	.02868	1.45424	.68765	13.72693	.07285
1.260	23.7931	34.3142	23.7854	34.2888	.72040	.02916	1.44159	.69368	13.49954	.07408
1.270	23.6057	33.7593	23.5982	33.7348	.71473	.02964	1.42955	.69952	13.28141	.07529
1.280	23.4213	33.2264	23.4138	33.2027	.70914	.03012	1.41808	.70518	13.07191	.07650
1.290	23.2397	32.7140	23.2323	32.6911	.70365	.03059	1.40714	.71066	12.87050	.07770
1.300	23.0610	32.2209	23.0536	32.1987	.69823	.03106	1.39669	.71598	12.67665	.07889
1.310	22.8849	31.7459	22.8776	31.7244	.69290	.03152	1.38670	.72114	12.48990	.08006
1.320	22.7116	31.2879	22.7043	31.2670	.68765	.03198	1.37714	.72614	12.30984	.08124
1.330	22.5408	30.8459	22.5336	30.8256	.68248	.03244	1.36798	.73100	12.13606	.08240
1.340	22.3726	30.4190	22.3654	30.3992	.67739	.03290	1.35921	.73572	11.96820	.08355
1.350	22.2069	30.0063	22.1997	29.9871	.67237	.03335	1.35079	.74031	11.80594	.08470
1.360	22.0436	29.6071	22.0365	29.5884	.66743	.03380	1.34270	.74477	11.64897	.08584
1.370	21.8827	29.2207	21.8757	29.2024	.66256	.03424	1.33493	.74910	11.49701	.08698
1.380	21.7241	28.8463	21.7171	28.8285	.65776	.03469	1.32745	.75332	11.34979	.08811
1.390	21.5678	28.4833	21.5609	28.4660	.65302	.03513	1.32026	.75743	11.20708	.08923
1.400	21.4137	28.1313	21.4069	28.1144	.64836	.03557	1.31333	.76142	11.06864	.09035
1.410	21.2619	27.7896	21.2551	27.7731	.64376	.03601	1.30666	.76531	10.93427	.09146
1.420	21.1121	27.4578	21.1054	27.4416	.63923	.03644	1.30022	.76910	10.80378	.09256
1.430	20.9645	27.1353	20.9578	27.1195	.63476	.03687	1.29400	.77279	10.67697	.09366
1.440	20.8189	26.8218	20.8123	26.8063	.63035	.03730	1.28801	.77639	10.55368	.09475

1.450	20.6753	26.5169	20.6687	26.5017	.62600	.03773	1.28221	.77990	10.43375	.09584
1.460	20.5337	26.2201	20.5272	26.2052	.62171	.03816	1.27661	.78332	10.31703	.09693
1.470	20.3940	25.9311	20.3875	25.9166	.61749	.03859	1.27120	.78666	10.20337	.09801
1.480	20.2562	25.6496	20.2498	25.6353	.61331	.03901	1.26596	.78992	10.09266	.09908
1.490	20.1203	25.3752	20.1139	25.3613	.60920	.03943	1.26088	.79309	9.98475	.10015
1.500	19.9862	25.1077	19.9798	25.0940	.60514	.03985	1.25597	.79620	9.87954	.10122
1.510	19.8538	24.8468	19.8475	24.8334	.60113	.04027	1.25121	.79922	9.77692	.10228
1.520	19.7232	24.5922	19.7169	24.5790	.59717	.04069	1.24660	.80218	9.67678	.10334
1.530	19.5943	24.3437	19.5880	24.3307	.59327	.04110	1.24212	.80507	9.57902	.10439
1.540	19.4670	24.1009	19.4608	24.0892	.58942	.04151	1.23778	.80790	9.48356	.10545
1.550	19.3415	23.8638	19.3353	23.8514	.58562	.04193	1.23357	.81066	9.39030	.10649
1.560	19.2175	23.6321	19.2113	23.6199	.58186	.04234	1.22948	.81335	9.29916	.10754
1.570	19.0951	23.4056	19.0890	23.3935	.57816	.04275	1.22550	.81599	9.21006	.10858
1.580	18.9742	23.1841	18.9681	23.1722	.57450	.04316	1.22164	.81857	9.12293	.10961
1.590	18.8549	22.9674	18.8488	22.9557	.57088	.04356	1.21789	.82110	9.03769	.11065
1.600	18.7370	22.7554	18.7310	22.7439	.56731	.04397	1.21424	.82356	8.95429	.11168
1.610	18.6207	22.5478	18.6147	22.5365	.56379	.04437	1.21068	.82598	8.87265	.11271
1.620	18.5057	22.3446	18.4998	22.3335	.56031	.04478	1.20723	.82834	8.79271	.11373
1.630	18.3922	22.1456	18.3863	22.1346	.55687	.04518	1.20387	.83066	8.71442	.11475
1.640	18.2800	21.9506	18.2742	21.9398	.55348	.04558	1.20059	.83292	8.63773	.11577
1.650	18.1692	21.7596	18.1634	21.7489	.55012	.04598	1.19740	.83514	8.56257	.11679
1.660	18.0598	21.5723	18.0540	21.5618	.54681	.04638	1.19429	.83731	8.48890	.11780
1.670	17.9516	21.3887	17.9459	21.3784	.54354	.04678	1.19127	.83944	8.41667	.11881
1.680	17.8448	21.2086	17.8391	21.1984	.54030	.04717	1.18831	.84153	8.34584	.11982
1.690	17.7392	21.0320	17.7335	21.0220	.53710	.04757	1.18544	.84357	8.27636	.12083
1.700	17.6349	20.8587	17.6292	20.8488	.53394	.04796	1.18263	.84557	8.20819	.12183
1.710	17.5317	20.6887	17.5261	20.6789	.53082	.04836	1.17989	.84754	8.14129	.12283
1.720	17.4298	20.5217	17.4242	20.5121	.52773	.04875	1.17722	.84946	8.07562	.12383
1.730	17.3290	20.3578	17.3235	20.3483	.52468	.04914	1.17461	.85135	8.01114	.12483
1.740	17.2295	20.1969	17.2239	20.1875	.52167	.04954	1.17206	.85320	7.94783	.12582
1.750	17.1310	20.0388	17.1255	20.0295	.51869	.04993	1.16957	.85501	7.88564	.12681
1.760	17.0337	19.8835	17.0282	19.8743	.51574	.05032	1.16714	.85679	7.82454	.12780
1.770	16.9374	19.7309	16.9320	19.7218	.51283	.05071	1.16477	.85854	7.76451	.12879
1.780	16.8423	19.5809	16.8369	19.5720	.50995	.05109	1.16245	.86025	7.70550	.12978
1.790	16.7482	19.4335	16.7428	19.4247	.50710	.05148	1.16018	.86194	7.64750	.13076
1.800	16.6551	19.2886	16.6498	19.2798	.50428	.05187	1.15796	.86359	7.59048	.13174
1.810	16.5631	19.1460	16.5578	19.1374	.50149	.05225	1.15579	.86521	7.53441	.13272
1.820	16.4721	19.0058	16.4668	18.9973	.49874	.05264	1.15367	.86680	7.47926	.13370
1.830	16.3821	18.8680	16.3769	18.8595	.49601	.05302	1.15160	.86836	7.42501	.13468
1.840	16.2931	18.7323	16.2879	18.7240	.49332	.05341	1.14956	.86989	7.37163	.13566
1.850	16.2050	18.5988	16.1998	18.5906	.49065	.05379	1.14758	.87140	7.31911	.13663
1.860	16.1179	18.4674	16.1127	18.4593	.48801	.05417	1.14563	.87288	7.26742	.13760
1.870	16.0317	18.3381	16.0266	18.3300	.48540	.05456	1.14373	.87433	7.21654	.13857
1.880	15.9464	18.2108	15.9413	18.2028	.48282	.05494	1.14186	.87576	7.16645	.13954

TABLE 12

IEC-R 18

Brit: WG-7

Amer: WR-510, RG-337/U, RG-338/U, RG-339/U

Outside dimensions: 5.260 X 2.710 ±0.008 inches
133.60 X 68.83 ±0.20 millimeters

Inside dimensions: 5.100 X 2.5500 ±0.0102 inches
129.54 X 64.77 ±0.26 millimeters
corner radius: 1.2 millimeters
a/b: 2.000

Cutoff:	Rectangle in Vacuum	Waveguide in Air
Wavelength:	25.90800cm	25.90418cm
Frequency:	1157.14260 MHz	1156.94290 MHz

	THEORETICAL		PHYSICAL							
f (GHz)	λ (cm)	λ_g (cm)	λ (cm)	λ_g (cm)	$\frac{\lambda}{\lambda_c}$	$1/\lambda_g$ (1/cm)	$\frac{\lambda_g}{\lambda}$	$\frac{\lambda}{\lambda_g}$	λ_g (in)	$1/\lambda_g$ (1/in)
1.300	23.0610	50.6004	23.0536	50.5202	.88996	.01979	2.19143	.45632	19.88985	.05028
1.310	22.8849	48.8180	22.8776	48.7449	.88316	.02051	2.13068	.46933	19.19092	.05211
1.320	22.7116	47.1999	22.7043	47.1329	.87647	.02122	2.07595	.48171	18.55625	.05389
1.330	22.5408	45.7221	22.5336	45.6603	.86988	.02190	2.02632	.49351	17.97648	.05563
1.340	22.3726	44.3652	22.3654	44.3079	.86339	.02257	1.98109	.50477	17.44405	.05733
1.350	22.2069	43.1135	22.1997	43.0601	.85699	.02322	1.93966	.51555	16.95278	.05899
1.360	22.0436	41.9538	22.0365	41.9039	.85069	.02386	1.90157	.52588	16.49759	.06061
1.370	21.8827	40.8754	21.8757	40.8285	.84448	.02449	1.86639	.53579	16.07422	.06221
1.380	21.7241	39.8689	21.7171	39.8249	.83836	.02511	1.83380	.54532	15.67908	.06378
1.390	21.5678	38.9268	21.5609	38.8852	.83233	.02572	1.80351	.55448	15.30914	.06532
1.400	21.4137	38.0424	21.4069	38.0030	.82639	.02631	1.77527	.56330	14.96180	.06684
1.410	21.2619	37.2098	21.2551	37.1725	.82053	.02690	1.74887	.57180	14.63483	.06833
1.420	21.1121	36.4243	21.1054	36.3888	.81475	.02748	1.72415	.58000	14.32629	.06980
1.430	20.9645	35.6815	20.9578	35.6476	.80905	.02805	1.70092	.58792	14.03448	.07125
1.440	20.8189	34.9775	20.8123	34.9452	.80343	.02862	1.67907	.59557	13.75794	.07269
1.450	20.6753	34.3092	20.6687	34.2782	.79789	.02917	1.65846	.60297	13.49536	.07410
1.460	20.5337	33.6735	20.5272	33.6438	.79243	.02972	1.63899	.61013	13.24560	.07550
1.470	20.3940	33.0678	20.3875	33.0394	.78704	.03027	1.62057	.61707	13.00763	.07688
1.480	20.2562	32.4899	20.2498	32.4626	.78172	.03080	1.60311	.62379	12.78053	.07824
1.490	20.1203	31.9377	20.1139	31.9113	.77647	.03134	1.58653	.63031	12.56351	.07960
1.500	19.9862	31.4092	19.9798	31.3838	.77130	.03186	1.57078	.63663	12.35583	.08093
1.510	19.8538	30.9028	19.8475	30.8783	.76619	.03239	1.55578	.64276	12.15682	.08226
1.520	19.7232	30.4170	19.7169	30.3934	.76115	.03290	1.54149	.64872	11.96590	.08357
1.530	19.5943	29.9505	19.5880	29.9276	.75617	.03341	1.52785	.65451	11.78253	.08487
1.540	19.4670	29.5019	19.4608	29.4798	.75126	.03392	1.51483	.66014	11.60621	.08616
1.550	19.3415	29.0702	19.3353	29.0487	.74641	.03442	1.50237	.66561	11.43651	.08744
1.560	19.2175	28.6542	19.2113	28.6334	.74163	.03492	1.49045	.67094	11.27301	.08871
1.570	19.0951	28.2531	19.0890	28.2329	.73691	.03542	1.47902	.67612	11.11533	.08997
1.580	18.9742	27.8660	18.9681	27.8464	.73224	.03591	1.46806	.68117	10.96315	.09121
1.590	18.8549	27.4921	18.8488	27.4730	.72764	.03640	1.45754	.68609	10.81615	.09245
1.600	18.7370	27.1306	18.7310	27.1120	.72309	.03688	1.44744	.69088	10.67403	.09369
1.610	18.6207	26.7808	18.6147	26.7628	.71860	.03737	1.43772	.69554	10.53653	.09491
1.620	18.5057	26.4422	18.4998	26.4246	.71416	.03784	1.42837	.70010	10.40340	.09612
1.630	18.3922	26.1142	18.3863	26.0970	.70978	.03832	1.41937	.70454	10.27441	.09733
1.640	18.2800	25.7961	18.2742	25.7794	.70545	.03879	1.41070	.70887	10.14935	.09853
1.650	18.1692	25.4875	18.1634	25.4712	.70118	.03926	1.40233	.71310	10.02803	.09972
1.660	18.0598	25.1880	18.0540	25.1721	.69695	.03973	1.39426	.71722	9.91026	.10091
1.670	17.9516	24.8971	17.9459	24.8815	.69278	.04019	1.38647	.72126	9.79586	.10208
1.680	17.8448	24.6144	17.8391	24.5991	.68866	.04065	1.37894	.72519	9.68469	.10326
1.690	17.7392	24.3394	17.7335	24.3245	.68458	.04111	1.37167	.72904	9.57658	.10442
1.700	17.6349	24.0720	17.6292	24.0574	.68055	.04157	1.36463	.73280	9.47141	.10558
1.710	17.5317	23.8117	17.5261	23.7974	.67657	.04202	1.35782	.73647	9.36904	.10673
1.720	17.4298	23.5581	17.4242	23.5441	.67264	.04247	1.35123	.74007	9.26934	.10788
1.730	17.3290	23.3111	17.3235	23.2974	.66875	.04292	1.34484	.74358	9.17221	.10903
1.740	17.2295	23.0704	17.2239	23.0569	.66491	.04337	1.33866	.74702	9.07753	.11016
1.750	17.1310	22.8356	17.1255	22.8224	.66111	.04382	1.33265	.75038	8.98520	.11129
1.760	17.0337	22.6066	17.0282	22.5936	.65735	.04426	1.32683	.75367	8.89513	.11242
1.770	16.9374	22.3830	16.9320	22.3703	.65364	.04470	1.32119	.75690	8.80722	.11354
1.780	16.8423	22.1648	16.8369	22.1523	.64997	.04514	1.31570	.76005	8.72139	.11466
1.790	16.7482	21.9517	16.7428	21.9394	.64634	.04558	1.31038	.76314	8.63756	.11577
1.800	16.6551	21.7434	16.6498	21.7314	.64275	.04602	1.30520	.76617	8.55565	.11688
1.810	16.5631	21.5398	16.5578	21.5280	.63919	.04645	1.30017	.76913	8.47559	.11799
1.820	16.4721	21.3408	16.4668	21.3292	.63568	.04688	1.29528	.77203	8.39731	.11909
1.830	16.3821	21.1461	16.3769	21.1347	.63221	.04732	1.29052	.77488	8.32075	.12018
1.840	16.2931	20.9557	16.2879	20.9444	.62877	.04775	1.28589	.77767	8.24584	.12127
1.850	16.2050	20.7693	16.1998	20.7582	.62537	.04817	1.28139	.78040	8.17253	.12236
1.860	16.1179	20.5868	16.1127	20.5759	.62201	.04860	1.27700	.78309	8.10075	.12345

1.870	16.0317	20.4081	16.0266	20.3974	.61869	.04903	1.27272	.78572	8.03047	.12453
1.880	15.9464	20.2331	15.9413	20.2225	.61540	.04945	1.26856	.78830	7.96162	.12560
1.890	15.8620	20.0616	15.8570	20.0511	.61214	.04987	1.26450	.79083	7.89415	.12668
1.900	15.7786	19.8935	15.7735	19.8832	.60892	.05029	1.26054	.79331	7.82803	.12775
1.910	15.6959	19.7287	15.6909	19.7185	.60573	.05071	1.25668	.79574	7.76321	.12881
1.920	15.6142	19.5670	15.6092	19.5571	.60257	.05113	1.25292	.79814	7.69964	.12988
1.930	15.5333	19.4085	15.5283	19.3987	.59945	.05155	1.24925	.80048	7.63729	.13094
1.940	15.4532	19.2530	15.4483	19.2433	.59636	.05197	1.24566	.80279	7.57611	.13199
1.950	15.3740	19.1004	15.3691	19.0908	.59330	.05238	1.24216	.80505	7.51608	.13305
1.960	15.2955	18.9506	15.2906	18.9412	.59028	.05280	1.23874	.80727	7.45716	.13410
1.970	15.2179	18.8035	15.2130	18.7942	.58728	.05321	1.23540	.80945	7.39931	.13515
1.980	15.1410	18.6591	15.1362	18.6499	.58431	.05362	1.23214	.81159	7.34250	.13619
1.990	15.0649	18.5173	15.0601	18.5082	.58138	.05403	1.22895	.81370	7.28670	.13724
2.000	14.9896	18.3779	14.9848	18.3690	.57847	.05444	1.22584	.81577	7.23188	.13828
2.010	14.9150	18.2410	14.9103	18.2322	.57559	.05485	1.22279	.81780	7.17802	.13931
2.020	14.8412	18.1064	14.8365	18.0977	.57274	.05526	1.21981	.81980	7.12508	.14035
2.030	14.7681	17.9742	14.7634	17.9655	.56992	.05566	1.21690	.82176	7.07304	.14138
2.040	14.6957	17.8441	14.6910	17.8356	.56713	.05607	1.21405	.82369	7.02188	.14241
2.050	14.6240	17.7162	14.6193	17.7078	.56436	.05647	1.21126	.82559	6.97157	.14344
2.060	14.5530	17.5904	14.5484	17.5821	.56162	.05688	1.20853	.82745	6.92208	.14447
2.070	14.4827	17.4667	14.4781	17.4585	.55891	.05728	1.20585	.82929	6.87341	.14549
2.080	14.4131	17.3449	14.4085	17.3368	.55622	.05768	1.20323	.83109	6.82551	.14651
2.090	14.3441	17.2251	14.3396	17.2171	.55356	.05808	1.20067	.83287	6.77838	.14753
2.100	14.2758	17.1072	14.2713	17.0993	.55093	.05848	1.19816	.83461	6.73200	.14854
2.110	14.2082	16.9911	14.2036	16.9833	.54831	.05888	1.19570	.83633	6.68633	.14956
2.120	14.1412	16.8769	14.1366	16.8691	.54573	.05928	1.19329	.83802	6.64138	.15057
2.130	14.0748	16.7644	14.0703	16.7567	.54317	.05968	1.19093	.83968	6.59711	.15158
2.140	14.0090	16.6535	14.0045	16.6459	.54063	.06007	1.18861	.84132	6.55352	.15259
2.150	13.9438	16.5444	13.9394	16.5369	.53811	.06047	1.18634	.84293	6.51058	.15360
2.160	13.8793	16.4369	13.8748	16.4294	.53562	.06087	1.18412	.84451	6.46827	.15460
2.170	13.8153	16.3309	13.8109	16.3236	.53315	.06126	1.18193	.84607	6.42659	.15560
2.180	13.7519	16.2265	13.7476	16.2192	.53071	.06166	1.17979	.84761	6.38552	.15660
2.190	13.6892	16.1237	13.6848	16.1164	.52828	.06205	1.17769	.84912	6.34505	.15760
2.200	13.6269	16.0222	13.6226	16.0151	.52588	.06244	1.17563	.85061	6.30515	.15860
2.210	13.5653	15.9223	13.5609	15.9152	.52350	.06283	1.17361	.85207	6.26582	.15960
2.220	13.5042	15.8237	13.4998	15.8167	.52115	.06322	1.17162	.85352	6.22705	.16059
2.230	13.4436	15.7265	13.4393	15.7196	.51881	.06361	1.16967	.85494	6.18881	.16158
2.240	13.3836	15.6307	13.3793	15.6238	.51649	.06400	1.16776	.85634	6.15110	.16257
2.250	13.3241	15.5362	13.3198	15.5293	.51420	.06439	1.16588	.85772	6.11391	.16356
2.260	13.2652	15.4429	13.2609	15.4362	.51192	.06478	1.16403	.85908	6.07723	.16455
2.270	13.2067	15.3509	13.2025	15.3442	.50967	.06517	1.16222	.86042	6.04104	.16553
2.280	13.1488	15.2602	13.1446	15.2535	.50743	.06556	1.16044	.86174	6.00533	.16652
2.290	13.0914	15.1706	13.0872	15.1640	.50522	.06595	1.15869	.86304	5.97010	.16750
2.300	13.0345	15.0822	13.0303	15.0757	.50302	.06633	1.15698	.86432	5.93533	.16848
2.310	12.9780	14.9950	12.9739	14.9886	.50084	.06672	1.15529	.86559	5.90101	.16946
2.320	12.9221	14.9089	12.9180	14.9025	.49868	.06710	1.15363	.86683	5.86713	.17044
2.330	12.8666	14.8239	12.8625	14.8176	.49654	.06749	1.15200	.86806	5.83369	.17142
2.340	12.8116	14.7400	12.8075	14.7337	.49442	.06787	1.15039	.86927	5.80067	.17239
2.350	12.7571	14.6572	12.7530	14.6509	.49232	.06826	1.14882	.87046	5.76808	.17337

TABLE 13

IEC-R 22   Brit: WG-8   Amer: WR-430, RG-104/U, RG-105/U, RG-207/U

Outside dimensions: 4.460 X 2.310 ±0.008 inches; 113.28 X 58.67 ±0.20 millimeters

Inside dimensions: 4.300 X 2.1500 ±0.0086 inches; 109.22 X 54.61 ±0.22 millimeters; corner radius: 1.2 millimeters; a/b: 2.000

Cutoff:	Rectangle in Vacuum	Waveguide in Air
Wavelength:	21.84400cm	21.83947cm
Frequency:	1372.42490 MHz	1372.27040 MHz

	THEORETICAL		PHYSICAL							
f (GHz)	λ (cm)	λ_g (cm)	λ (cm)	λ_g (cm)	$\frac{\lambda}{\lambda_c}$	$1/\lambda_g$ (1/cm)	$\frac{\lambda_g}{\lambda}$	$\frac{\lambda}{\lambda_g}$	λ_g (in)	$1/\lambda_g$ (1/in)
1.500	19.9862	49.5237	19.9798	49.4387	.91485	.02023	2.47444	.40413	19.46406	.05138
1.510	19.8538	47.6071	19.8475	47.5304	.90879	.02104	2.39479	.41757	18.71276	.05344
1.520	19.7232	45.8863	19.7169	45.8166	.90281	.02183	2.32372	.43034	18.03802	.05544
1.530	19.5943	44.3299	19.5880	44.2660	.89691	.02259	2.25985	.44251	17.42758	.05738
1.540	19.4670	42.9130	19.4608	42.8542	.89108	.02333	2.20208	.45412	16.87174	.05927
1.550	19.3415	41.6158	19.3353	41.5614	.88534	.02406	2.14951	.46522	16.36275	.06111
1.560	19.2175	40.4222	19.2113	40.3716	.87966	.02477	2.10145	.47586	15.89433	.06292
1.570	19.0951	39.3190	19.0890	39.2717	.87406	.02546	2.05730	.48607	15.46131	.06468
1.580	18.9742	38.2951	18.9681	38.2509	.86853	.02614	2.01659	.49589	15.05940	.06640
1.590	18.8549	37.3416	18.8488	37.2999	.86306	.02681	1.97890	.50533	14.68501	.06810
1.600	18.7370	36.4505	18.7310	36.4112	.85767	.02746	1.94390	.51443	14.33511	.06976
1.610	18.6207	35.6152	18.6147	35.5781	.85234	.02811	1.91129	.52321	14.00711	.07139
1.620	18.5057	34.8302	18.4998	34.7949	.84708	.02874	1.88083	.53168	13.69879	.07300
1.630	18.3922	34.0905	18.3863	34.0570	.84188	.02936	1.85230	.53987	13.40825	.07458
1.640	18.2800	33.3918	18.2742	33.3599	.83675	.02998	1.82552	.54779	13.13381	.07614
1.650	18.1692	32.7305	18.1634	32.7000	.83168	.03058	1.80032	.55546	12.87403	.07768
1.660	18.0598	32.1033	18.0540	32.0742	.82667	.03118	1.77657	.56288	12.62763	.07919
1.670	17.9516	31.5074	17.9459	31.4795	.82172	.03177	1.75413	.57008	12.39350	.08069
1.680	17.8448	30.9402	17.8391	30.9134	.81683	.03235	1.73290	.57707	12.17062	.08217
1.690	17.7392	30.3994	17.7335	30.3736	.81199	.03292	1.71278	.58385	11.95813	.08363
1.700	17.6349	29.8830	17.6292	29.8583	.80722	.03349	1.69368	.59043	11.75522	.08507
1.710	17.5317	29.3893	17.5261	29.3654	.80250	.03405	1.67552	.59683	11.56119	.08650
1.720	17.4298	28.9166	17.4242	28.8935	.79783	.03461	1.65824	.60305	11.37541	.08791
1.730	17.3290	28.4634	17.3235	28.4411	.79322	.03516	1.64177	.60910	11.19729	.08931
1.740	17.2295	28.0284	17.2239	28.0069	.78866	.03571	1.62604	.61499	11.02633	.09069
1.750	17.1310	27.6104	17.1255	27.5896	.78415	.03625	1.61102	.62072	10.86204	.09206
1.760	17.0337	27.2084	17.0282	27.1882	.77970	.03678	1.59665	.62631	10.70401	.09342
1.770	16.9374	26.8212	16.9320	26.8016	.77529	.03731	1.58290	.63175	10.55183	.09477
1.780	16.8423	26.4481	16.8369	26.4291	.77094	.03784	1.56971	.63706	10.40515	.09611
1.790	16.7482	26.0882	16.7428	26.0697	.76663	.03836	1.55707	.64223	10.26365	.09743
1.800	16.6551	25.7406	16.6498	25.7226	.76237	.03888	1.54492	.64728	10.12703	.09875
1.810	16.5631	25.4048	16.5578	25.3873	.75816	.03939	1.53325	.65221	9.99500	.10005
1.820	16.4721	25.0800	16.4668	25.0630	.75399	.03990	1.52203	.65702	9.86731	.10134
1.830	16.3821	24.7657	16.3769	24.7491	.74987	.04041	1.51122	.66172	9.74373	.10263
1.840	16.2931	24.4612	16.2879	24.4451	.74580	.04091	1.50082	.66630	9.62404	.10391
1.850	16.2050	24.1662	16.1998	24.1504	.74177	.04141	1.49078	.67079	9.50804	.10517
1.860	16.1179	23.8801	16.1127	23.8647	.73778	.04190	1.48111	.67517	9.39554	.10643
1.870	16.0317	23.6024	16.0266	23.5874	.73383	.04240	1.47177	.67946	9.28636	.10768
1.880	15.9464	23.3328	15.9413	23.3181	.72993	.04289	1.46275	.68365	9.18035	.10893
1.890	15.8620	23.0709	15.8570	23.0565	.72607	.04337	1.45403	.68774	9.07735	.11016
1.900	15.7786	22.8162	15.7735	22.8021	.72225	.04386	1.44560	.69176	8.97722	.11139
1.910	15.6959	22.5686	15.6909	22.5548	.71847	.04434	1.43744	.69568	8.87983	.11261
1.920	15.6142	22.3275	15.6092	22.3141	.71472	.04481	1.42955	.69952	8.78506	.11383
1.930	15.5333	22.0929	15.5283	22.0797	.71102	.04529	1.42190	.70329	8.69279	.11504
1.940	15.4532	21.8643	15.4483	21.8514	.70736	.04576	1.41449	.70697	8.60290	.11624
1.950	15.3740	21.6416	15.3691	21.6289	.70373	.04623	1.40730	.71058	8.51530	.11744
1.960	15.2955	21.4244	15.2906	21.4119	.70014	.04670	1.40033	.71412	8.42990	.11863
1.970	15.2179	21.2126	15.2130	21.2004	.69658	.04717	1.39357	.71758	8.34660	.11981
1.980	15.1410	21.0059	15.1362	20.9939	.69307	.04763	1.38700	.72098	8.26531	.12099
1.990	15.0649	20.8041	15.0601	20.7923	.68958	.04809	1.38062	.72431	8.18596	.12216
2.000	14.9896	20.6071	14.9848	20.5955	.68614	.04855	1.37442	.72758	8.10847	.12333
2.010	14.9150	20.4146	14.9103	20.4032	.68272	.04901	1.36840	.73078	8.03276	.12449

2.020	14.8412	20.2265	14.8365	20.2153	.67934	.04947	1.36254	.73392	7.95878	.12565
2.030	14.7681	20.0426	14.7634	20.0316	.67600	.04992	1.35684	.73701	7.88645	.12680
2.040	14.6957	19.8627	14.6910	19.8519	.67268	.05037	1.35130	.74003	7.81571	.12795
2.050	14.6240	19.6868	14.6193	19.6761	.66940	.05082	1.34590	.74300	7.74651	.12909
2.060	14.5530	19.5146	14.5484	19.5041	.66615	.05127	1.34064	.74591	7.67880	.13023
2.070	14.4827	19.3461	14.4781	19.3358	.66293	.05172	1.33552	.74877	7.61251	.13136
2.080	14.4131	19.1810	14.4085	19.1709	.65975	.05216	1.33053	.75158	7.54759	.13249
2.090	14.3441	19.0194	14.3396	19.0094	.65659	.05261	1.32566	.75434	7.48401	.13362
2.100	14.2758	18.8610	14.2713	18.8512	.65346	.05305	1.32092	.75705	7.42172	.13474
2.110	14.2082	18.7058	14.2036	18.6961	.65037	.05349	1.31629	.75971	7.36067	.13586
2.120	14.1412	18.5537	14.1366	18.5441	.64730	.05393	1.31178	.76233	7.30082	.13697
2.130	14.0748	18.4045	14.0703	18.3950	.64426	.05436	1.30737	.76489	7.24214	.13808
2.140	14.0090	18.2582	14.0045	18.2488	.64125	.05480	1.30307	.76742	7.18458	.13919
2.150	13.9438	18.1146	13.9394	18.1054	.63827	.05523	1.29887	.76990	7.12812	.14029
2.160	13.8793	17.9737	13.8748	17.9647	.63531	.05566	1.29477	.77234	7.07271	.14139
2.170	13.8153	17.8355	13.8109	17.8265	.63238	.05610	1.29076	.77474	7.01832	.14248
2.180	13.7519	17.6997	13.7476	17.6909	.62948	.05653	1.28684	.77710	6.96493	.14358
2.190	13.6892	17.5665	13.6848	17.5577	.62661	.05695	1.28301	.77942	6.91250	.14467
2.200	13.6269	17.4355	13.6226	17.4269	.62376	.05738	1.27927	.78170	6.86100	.14575
2.210	13.5653	17.3069	13.5609	17.2984	.62094	.05781	1.27561	.78394	6.81041	.14683
2.220	13.5042	17.1806	13.4998	17.1722	.61814	.05823	1.27203	.78615	6.76070	.14791
2.230	13.4436	17.0564	13.4393	17.0481	.61537	.05866	1.26853	.78832	6.71185	.14899
2.240	13.3836	16.9343	13.3793	16.9261	.61262	.05908	1.26510	.79045	6.66383	.15006
2.250	13.3241	16.8143	13.3198	16.8062	.60990	.05950	1.26174	.79256	6.61662	.15113
2.260	13.2652	16.6963	13.2609	16.6883	.60720	.05992	1.25846	.79462	6.57019	.15220
2.270	13.2067	16.5802	13.2025	16.5723	.60452	.06034	1.25524	.79666	6.52453	.15327
2.280	13.1488	16.4660	13.1446	16.4582	.60187	.06076	1.25209	.79866	6.47961	.15433
2.290	13.0914	16.3537	13.0872	16.3460	.59924	.06118	1.24900	.80064	6.43542	.15539
2.300	13.0345	16.2431	13.0303	16.2355	.59664	.06159	1.24598	.80258	6.39193	.15645
2.310	12.9788	16.1343	12.9739	16.1268	.59406	.06201	1.24302	.80449	6.34912	.15750
2.320	12.9221	16.0272	12.9180	16.0197	.59150	.06242	1.24011	.80638	6.30698	.15855
2.330	12.8666	15.9218	12.8625	15.9144	.58896	.06284	1.23727	.80823	6.26550	.15960
2.340	12.8116	15.8179	12.8075	15.8106	.58644	.06325	1.23448	.81006	6.22465	.16065
2.350	12.7571	15.7157	12.7530	15.7084	.58394	.06366	1.23174	.81186	6.18442	.16170
2.360	12.7031	15.6149	12.6990	15.6078	.58147	.06407	1.22905	.81363	6.14479	.16274
2.370	12.6495	15.5157	12.6454	15.5086	.57902	.06448	1.22642	.81538	6.10575	.16378
2.380	12.5963	15.4179	12.5923	15.4109	.57658	.06489	1.22384	.81710	6.06729	.16482
2.390	12.5436	15.3216	12.5396	15.3146	.57417	.06530	1.22130	.81880	6.02938	.16585
2.400	12.4914	15.2266	12.4874	15.2197	.57178	.06570	1.21881	.82047	5.99202	.16689
2.410	12.4395	15.1330	12.4355	15.1262	.56941	.06611	1.21637	.82212	5.95520	.16792
2.420	12.3881	15.0408	12.3842	15.0340	.56705	.06652	1.21397	.82374	5.91890	.16895
2.430	12.3371	14.9498	12.3332	14.9431	.56472	.06692	1.21162	.82534	5.88311	.16998
2.440	12.2866	14.8601	12.2826	14.8534	.56241	.06732	1.20930	.82692	5.84781	.17100
2.450	12.2364	14.7716	12.2325	14.7650	.56011	.06773	1.20703	.82848	5.81301	.17203
2.460	12.1867	14.6843	12.1828	14.6778	.55783	.06813	1.20480	.83001	5.77867	.17305
2.470	12.1373	14.5983	12.1335	14.5918	.55558	.06853	1.20261	.83153	5.74481	.17407
2.480	12.0884	14.5133	12.0845	14.5069	.55333	.06893	1.20045	.83302	5.71140	.17509
2.490	12.0399	14.4295	12.0360	14.4232	.55111	.06933	1.19834	.83449	5.67843	.17611
2.500	11.9917	14.3468	11.9879	14.3406	.54891	.06973	1.19626	.83594	5.64590	.17712
2.510	11.9439	14.2652	11.9401	14.2590	.54672	.07013	1.19421	.83737	5.61379	.17813
2.520	11.8965	14.1847	11.8927	14.1785	.54455	.07053	1.19220	.83878	5.58210	.17914
2.530	11.8495	14.1052	11.8457	14.0991	.54240	.07093	1.19023	.84018	5.55082	.18015
2.540	11.8029	14.0267	11.7991	14.0206	.54026	.07132	1.18828	.84155	5.51993	.18116
2.550	11.7566	13.9492	11.7528	13.9432	.53815	.07172	1.18637	.84291	5.48944	.18217
2.560	11.7106	13.8727	11.7069	13.8667	.53604	.07212	1.18449	.84425	5.45933	.18317
2.570	11.6651	13.7971	11.6613	13.7912	.53396	.07251	1.18264	.84557	5.42960	.18418
2.580	11.6199	13.7225	11.6161	13.7166	.53189	.07290	1.18082	.84687	5.40023	.18518
2.590	11.5750	13.6487	11.5713	13.6429	.52983	.07330	1.17903	.84815	5.37123	.18618
2.600	11.5305	13.5759	11.5268	13.5701	.52780	.07369	1.17727	.84942	5.34257	.18718
2.610	11.4863	13.5040	11.4826	13.4982	.52577	.07408	1.17554	.85068	5.31427	.18817
2.620	11.4425	13.4329	11.4388	13.4272	.52377	.07448	1.17383	.85191	5.28630	.18917
2.630	11.3990	13.3626	11.3953	13.3570	.52178	.07487	1.17215	.85313	5.25866	.19016
2.640	11.3558	13.2932	11.3521	13.2876	.51980	.07526	1.17050	.85434	5.23135	.19116
2.650	11.3129	13.2246	11.3093	13.2191	.51784	.07565	1.16887	.85553	5.20436	.19215
2.660	11.2704	13.1568	11.2668	13.1513	.51589	.07604	1.16726	.85670	5.17769	.19314
2.670	11.2282	13.0898	11.2246	13.0843	.51396	.07643	1.16569	.85786	5.15132	.19413
2.680	11.1863	13.0236	11.1827	13.0181	.51204	.07682	1.16413	.85901	5.12525	.19511
2.690	11.1447	12.9581	11.1411	12.9527	.51014	.07720	1.16260	.86014	5.09948	.19610
2.700	11.1034	12.8933	11.0999	12.8880	.50825	.07759	1.16109	.86126	5.07400	.19708
2.710	11.0625	12.8293	11.0589	12.8240	.50637	.07798	1.15961	.86236	5.04881	.19807
2.720	11.0218	12.7660	11.0183	12.7607	.50451	.07837	1.15814	.86345	5.02390	.19905
2.730	10.9814	12.7034	10.9779	12.6981	.50266	.07875	1.15670	.86453	4.99926	.20003
2.740	10.9413	12.6414	10.9378	12.6362	.50083	.07914	1.15528	.86559	4.97489	.20101
2.750	10.9015	12.5802	10.8981	12.5750	.49901	.07952	1.15388	.86664	4.95079	.20199
2.760	10.8620	12.5196	10.8586	12.5145	.49720	.07991	1.15250	.86768	4.92695	.20297
2.770	10.8228	12.4597	10.8194	12.4546	.49540	.08029	1.15114	.86871	4.90337	.20394
2.780	10.7839	12.4004	10.7805	12.3953	.49362	.08068	1.14979	.86972	4.88004	.20492
2.790	10.7453	12.3417	10.7418	12.3367	.49185	.08106	1.14847	.87072	4.85696	.20589
2.800	10.7069	12.2836	10.7035	12.2787	.49010	.08144	1.14717	.87171	4.83411	.20686

TABLE 14

IEC-R 26

Brit: WG-9A

Amer: WR-340, RG-112/U, RG-113/U, RG-208/U

Outside dimensions: 3.560 X 1.860 ±0.007 inches
90.42 X 47.24 ±0.17 millimeters

Inside dimensions: 3.400 X 1.7000 ±0.0068 inches
86.36 X 43.18 ±0.17 millimeters
corner radius: 1.2 millimeters
a/b: 2.000

Cutoff: Rectangle in Vacuum / Waveguide in Air
Wavelength: 17.27200cm / 17.26627cm
Frequency: 1735.71390 MHz / 1735.73400 MHz

f (GHz)	THEORETICAL λ (cm)	THEORETICAL λ_g (cm)	PHYSICAL λ (cm)	PHYSICAL λ_g (cm)	$\frac{\lambda}{\lambda_c}$	$1/\lambda_g$ (1/cm)	$\frac{\lambda_g}{\lambda}$	$\frac{\lambda}{\lambda_g}$	λ_g (in)	$1/\lambda_g$ (1/in)
1.950	15.3740	33.7336	15.3691	33.7038	.89012	.02967	2.19296	.45600	13.26920	.07536
1.975	15.1794	31.8151	15.1745	31.7889	.87885	.03146	2.09489	.47735	12.51533	.07990
2.000	14.9896	30.1715	14.9848	30.1482	.86787	.03317	2.01191	.49704	11.86937	.08425
2.025	14.8046	28.7423	14.7998	28.7213	.85715	.03482	1.94065	.51529	11.30761	.08844
2.050	14.6240	27.4843	14.6193	27.4652	.84670	.03641	1.87869	.53229	10.81306	.09248
2.075	14.4478	26.3654	14.4432	26.3479	.83650	.03795	1.82424	.54817	10.37318	.09640
2.100	14.2758	25.3616	14.2713	25.3454	.82654	.03945	1.77597	.56307	9.97849	.10022
2.125	14.1079	24.4541	14.1034	24.4391	.81682	.04092	1.73285	.57708	9.62168	.10393
2.150	13.9438	23.6284	13.9394	23.6143	.80732	.04235	1.69407	.59029	9.29698	.10756
2.175	13.7836	22.8728	13.7792	22.8595	.79804	.04375	1.65899	.60278	8.99981	.11111
2.200	13.6269	22.1777	13.6226	22.1652	.78897	.04512	1.62709	.61459	8.72645	.11459
2.225	13.4738	21.5354	13.4695	21.5235	.78011	.04646	1.59794	.62580	8.47383	.11801
2.250	13.3241	20.9395	13.3198	20.9282	.77144	.04778	1.57120	.63645	8.23945	.12137
2.275	13.1777	20.3845	13.1735	20.3738	.76296	.04908	1.54658	.64659	8.02117	.12467
2.300	13.0345	19.8660	13.0303	19.8558	.75467	.05036	1.52382	.65625	7.81723	.12792
2.325	12.8943	19.3801	12.8902	19.3703	.74655	.05163	1.50272	.66546	7.62610	.13113
2.350	12.7571	18.9235	12.7530	18.9141	.73861	.05287	1.48310	.67426	7.44649	.13429
2.375	12.6228	18.4933	12.6188	18.4842	.73084	.05410	1.46482	.68268	7.27726	.13741
2.400	12.4914	18.0871	12.4874	18.0783	.72322	.05531	1.44773	.69074	7.11745	.14050
2.425	12.3626	17.7026	12.3586	17.6942	.71577	.05652	1.43173	.69846	6.96621	.14355
2.450	12.2364	17.3380	12.2325	17.3299	.70846	.05770	1.41671	.70586	6.82280	.14657

53

2.475	12.1128	16.9917	12.1090	16.9838	.70131	.05888	1.40258	.71297	6.68654	.14955
2.500	11.9917	16.6621	11.9879	16.6545	.69429	.06004	1.38928	.71980	6.55687	.15251
2.525	11.8730	16.3479	11.8692	16.3405	.68742	.06120	1.37672	.72636	6.43327	.15544
2.550	11.7566	16.0480	11.7528	16.0408	.68068	.06234	1.36485	.73268	6.31528	.15835
2.575	11.6424	15.7613	11.6387	15.7543	.67407	.06347	1.35361	.73876	6.20247	.16123
2.600	11.5305	15.4868	11.5268	15.4800	.66759	.06460	1.34296	.74462	6.09449	.16408
2.625	11.4207	15.2237	11.4170	15.2171	.66123	.06572	1.33285	.75027	5.99099	.16692
2.650	11.3129	14.9713	11.3093	14.9648	.65499	.06682	1.32323	.75572	5.89167	.16973
2.675	11.2072	14.7288	11.2036	14.7225	.64887	.06792	1.31409	.76099	5.79626	.17253
2.700	11.1034	14.4956	11.0999	14.4894	.64286	.06902	1.30537	.76607	5.70451	.17530
2.725	11.0016	14.2711	10.9980	14.2651	.63697	.07010	1.29706	.77098	5.61618	.17806
2.750	10.9015	14.0548	10.8981	14.0489	.63118	.07118	1.28912	.77572	5.53107	.18080
2.775	10.8033	13.8462	10.7999	13.8405	.62549	.07225	1.28154	.78031	5.44900	.18352
2.800	10.7069	13.6448	10.7035	13.6392	.61991	.07332	1.27428	.78476	5.36977	.18623
2.825	10.6121	13.4503	10.6087	13.4448	.61442	.07438	1.26734	.78906	5.29324	.18892
2.850	10.5190	13.2623	10.5157	13.2569	.60903	.07543	1.26068	.79322	5.21925	.19160
2.875	10.4276	13.0804	10.4242	13.0751	.60373	.07648	1.25430	.79726	5.14767	.19426
2.900	10.3377	12.9042	10.3344	12.8990	.59853	.07753	1.24817	.80117	5.07837	.19691
2.925	10.2493	12.7336	10.2460	12.7285	.59341	.07856	1.24229	.80497	5.01122	.19955
2.950	10.1625	12.5682	10.1592	12.5632	.58838	.07960	1.23663	.80865	4.94613	.20218
2.975	10.0771	12.4077	10.0738	12.4028	.58344	.08063	1.23119	.81222	4.88299	.20479
3.000	9.9931	12.2520	9.9899	12.2471	.57858	.08165	1.22595	.81569	4.82170	.20740
3.025	9.9105	12.1007	9.9073	12.0959	.57380	.08267	1.22091	.81906	4.76218	.20999
3.050	9.8293	11.9537	9.8261	11.9490	.56909	.08369	1.21605	.82234	4.70434	.21257
3.075	9.7493	11.8108	9.7462	11.8062	.56447	.08470	1.21136	.82552	4.64811	.21514
3.100	9.6707	11.6718	9.6676	11.6673	.55991	.08571	1.20684	.82861	4.59341	.21770
3.125	9.5934	11.5365	9.5903	11.5321	.55543	.08671	1.20247	.83162	4.54018	.22026
3.150	9.5172	11.4048	9.5142	11.4004	.55103	.08772	1.19826	.83455	4.48836	.22280
3.175	9.4423	11.2765	9.4393	11.2722	.54669	.08871	1.19418	.83739	4.43787	.22533
3.200	9.3685	11.1515	9.3655	11.1472	.54242	.08971	1.19024	.84017	4.38867	.22786
3.225	9.2959	11.0296	9.2929	11.0254	.53821	.09070	1.18643	.84286	4.34071	.23038
3.250	9.2244	10.9107	9.2214	10.9066	.53407	.09169	1.18274	.84549	4.29393	.23289
3.275	9.1540	10.7947	9.1510	10.7906	.53000	.09267	1.17917	.84805	4.24828	.23539
3.300	9.0846	10.6815	9.0817	10.6775	.52598	.09366	1.17571	.85055	4.20373	.23788
3.325	9.0163	10.5709	9.0134	10.5670	.52203	.09463	1.17236	.85298	4.16023	.24037
3.350	8.9490	10.4630	8.9462	10.4590	.51813	.09561	1.16911	.85535	4.11773	.24285
3.375	8.8827	10.3574	8.8799	10.3536	.51429	.09658	1.16596	.85766	4.07621	.24533
3.400	8.8174	10.2543	8.8146	10.2505	.51051	.09756	1.16290	.85992	4.03563	.24779
3.425	8.7531	10.1535	8.7503	10.1497	.50678	.09853	1.15993	.86212	3.99594	.25025
3.450	8.6896	10.0548	8.6869	10.0511	.50311	.09949	1.15705	.86427	3.95713	.25271
3.475	8.6271	9.9583	8.6244	9.9547	.49949	.10046	1.15425	.86636	3.91916	.25516
3.500	8.5655	9.8639	8.5628	9.8603	.49592	.10142	1.15153	.86841	3.88199	.25760
3.525	8.5048	9.7714	8.5020	9.7679	.49241	.10238	1.14888	.87041	3.84561	.26004

TABLE 15

IEC-R 32 — Brit: WG-10 — Amer: WR-284, RG-48/U, RG-75/U, RG-167/U

Outside dimensions: 3.000 X 1.500 ±0.006 inches
76.20 X 38.10 ±0.14 millimeters

Inside dimensions: 2.8400 X 1.3400 ±0.0057 inches
72.14 X 34.04 ±0.14 millimeters
corner radius: 1.2 millimeters
a/b: 2.1194

Cutoff:	Rectangle in Vacuum	Waveguide in Air
Wavelength:	14.42800cm	14.42074cm
Frequency:	2077.85210 MHz	2078.23360 MHz

	THEORETICAL		PHYSICAL							
f (GHz)	λ (cm)	λ_g (cm)	λ (cm)	λ_g (cm)	$\frac{\lambda}{\lambda_c}$	$1/\lambda_g$ (1/cm)	$\frac{\lambda_g}{\lambda}$	$\frac{\lambda}{\lambda_g}$	λ_g (in)	$1/\lambda_g$ (1/in)
2.350	12.7571	27.3100	12.7530	27.3036	.88435	.03663	2.14095	.46708	10.74944	.09303
2.375	12.6228	26.0625	12.6188	26.0561	.87505	.03838	2.06487	.48429	10.25832	.09748
2.400	12.4914	24.9608	12.4874	24.9546	.86593	.04007	1.99839	.50040	9.82463	.10178
2.425	12.3626	23.9784	12.3586	23.9723	.85700	.04171	1.93972	.51554	9.43790	.10596
2.450	12.2364	23.0949	12.2325	23.0890	.84826	.04331	1.88751	.52980	9.09014	.11001
2.475	12.1128	22.2948	12.1090	22.2889	.83969	.04487	1.84069	.54327	8.77515	.11396
2.500	11.9917	21.5654	11.9879	21.5596	.83129	.04638	1.79846	.55603	8.48805	.11781
2.525	11.8730	20.8969	11.8692	20.8912	.82306	.04787	1.76013	.56814	8.22490	.12158
2.550	11.7566	20.2811	11.7528	20.2756	.81499	.04932	1.72517	.57965	7.98251	.12527
2.575	11.6424	19.7114	11.6387	19.7060	.80708	.05075	1.69314	.59062	7.75827	.12889
2.600	11.5305	19.1823	11.5268	19.1770	.79932	.05215	1.66369	.60107	7.54999	.13245
2.625	11.4207	18.6891	11.4170	18.6838	.79171	.05352	1.63649	.61106	7.35584	.13595
2.650	11.3129	18.2278	11.3093	18.2227	.78424	.05488	1.61130	.62062	7.17428	.13939
2.675	11.2072	17.7952	11.2036	17.7901	.77691	.05621	1.58789	.62977	7.00399	.14278
2.700	11.1034	17.3883	11.0999	17.3834	.76972	.05753	1.56609	.63853	6.84384	.14612
2.725	11.0016	17.0047	10.9980	16.9998	.76265	.05882	1.54571	.64695	6.69285	.14941
2.750	10.9015	16.6422	10.8981	16.6374	.75572	.06011	1.52664	.65503	6.55017	.15267
2.775	10.8033	16.2990	10.7999	16.2942	.74891	.06137	1.50874	.66280	6.41505	.15588
2.800	10.7069	15.9733	10.7035	15.9686	.74223	.06262	1.49191	.67028	6.28685	.15906
2.825	10.6121	15.6637	10.6087	15.6591	.73566	.06386	1.47606	.67748	6.16499	.16221
2.850	10.5190	15.3689	10.5157	15.3644	.72920	.06509	1.46109	.68442	6.04896	.16532
2.875	10.4276	15.0877	10.4242	15.0833	.72286	.06630	1.44694	.69111	5.93830	.16840
2.900	10.3377	14.8192	10.3344	14.8148	.71663	.06750	1.43355	.69757	5.83261	.17145
2.925	10.2493	14.5624	10.2460	14.5581	.71051	.06869	1.42085	.70380	5.73152	.17447
2.950	10.1625	14.3164	10.1592	14.3122	.70449	.06987	1.40879	.70983	5.63471	.17747
2.975	10.0771	14.0806	10.0738	14.0764	.69857	.07104	1.39732	.71565	5.54189	.18044
3.000	9.9931	13.8542	9.9899	13.8500	.69274	.07220	1.38641	.72129	5.45277	.18339
3.025	9.9105	13.6366	9.9073	13.6325	.68702	.07335	1.37600	.72674	5.36713	.18632
3.050	9.8293	13.4272	9.8261	13.4232	.68139	.07450	1.36608	.73202	5.28473	.18922
3.075	9.7493	13.2257	9.7462	13.2217	.67585	.07563	1.35659	.73714	5.20539	.19211
3.100	9.6707	13.0313	9.6676	13.0274	.67040	.07676	1.34753	.74210	5.12891	.19497
3.125	9.5934	12.8439	9.5903	12.8400	.66503	.07788	1.33885	.74691	5.05512	.19782
3.150	9.5172	12.6629	9.5142	12.6590	.65976	.07899	1.33054	.75157	4.98387	.20065
3.175	9.4423	12.4879	9.4393	12.4842	.65456	.08010	1.32258	.75610	4.91502	.20346
3.200	9.3685	12.3188	9.3655	12.3150	.64945	.08120	1.31493	.76049	4.84844	.20625
3.225	9.2959	12.1550	9.2929	12.1514	.64441	.08230	1.30759	.76476	4.78400	.20903
3.250	9.2244	11.9965	9.2214	11.9928	.63946	.08338	1.30054	.76891	4.72159	.21179
3.275	9.1540	11.8428	9.1510	11.8392	.63458	.08447	1.29375	.77294	4.66110	.21454
3.300	9.0846	11.6938	9.0817	11.6902	.62977	.08554	1.28722	.77687	4.60244	.21728
3.325	9.0163	11.5492	9.0134	11.5456	.62503	.08661	1.28094	.78068	4.54553	.22000
3.350	8.9490	11.4087	8.9462	11.4053	.62037	.08768	1.27488	.78439	4.49026	.22270
3.375	8.8827	11.2723	8.8799	11.2689	.61577	.08874	1.26903	.78800	4.43657	.22540
3.400	8.8174	11.1398	8.8146	11.1363	.61125	.08980	1.26340	.79152	4.38439	.22808
3.425	8.7531	11.0108	8.7503	11.0074	.60678	.09085	1.25795	.79494	4.33364	.23075
3.450	8.6896	10.8853	8.6869	10.8820	.60239	.09189	1.25270	.79828	4.28425	.23341
3.475	8.6271	10.7632	8.6244	10.7599	.59805	.09294	1.24762	.80153	4.23618	.23606
3.500	8.5655	10.6442	8.5628	10.6410	.59378	.09398	1.24270	.80470	4.18936	.23870
3.525	8.5048	10.5283	8.5020	10.5251	.58957	.09501	1.23795	.80779	4.14374	.24133
3.550	8.4449	10.4153	8.4422	10.4121	.58542	.09604	1.23335	.81080	4.09927	.24395
3.575	8.3858	10.3052	8.3831	10.3020	.58132	.09707	1.22890	.81374	4.05590	.24655
3.600	8.3276	10.1977	8.3249	10.1945	.57729	.09809	1.22458	.81661	4.01359	.24915
3.625	8.2701	10.0927	8.2675	10.0896	.57331	.09911	1.22040	.81941	3.97229	.25174
3.650	8.2135	9.9903	8.2109	9.9872	.56938	.10013	1.21634	.82214	3.93197	.25433
3.675	8.1576	9.8902	8.1550	9.8872	.56551	.10114	1.21241	.82481	3.89259	.25690
3.700	8.1025	9.7925	8.0999	9.7894	.56168	.10215	1.20859	.82741	3.85411	.25946
3.725	8.0481	9.6969	8.0455	9.6939	.55792	.10316	1.20488	.82996	3.81650	.26202
3.750	7.9945	9.6035	7.9919	9.6005	.55420	.10416	1.20128	.83245	3.77973	.26457
3.775	7.9415	9.5121	7.9390	9.5092	.55053	.10516	1.19778	.83488	3.74377	.26711

3.800	7.8893	9.4227	7.8868	9.4198	.54690	.10616	1.19438	.83725	3.70858	.26964
3.825	7.8377	9.3352	7.8352	9.3323	.54333	.10715	1.19108	.83958	3.67415	.27217
3.850	7.7868	9.2496	7.7843	9.2467	.53980	.10815	1.18786	.84185	3.64044	.27469
3.875	7.7366	9.1657	7.7341	9.1629	.53632	.10914	1.18474	.84407	3.60743	.27721
3.900	7.6870	9.0836	7.6845	9.0807	.53288	.11012	1.18169	.84624	3.57510	.27971
3.925	7.6380	9.0031	7.6356	9.0003	.52949	.11111	1.17873	.84837	3.54342	.28221
3.950	7.5897	8.9242	7.5873	8.9214	.52614	.11209	1.17584	.85045	3.51237	.28471
3.975	7.5419	8.8469	7.5395	8.8441	.52283	.11307	1.17303	.85249	3.48194	.28720
4.000	7.4948	8.7711	7.4924	8.7683	.51956	.11405	1.17029	.85449	3.45210	.28968
4.025	7.4483	8.6967	7.4459	8.6940	.51633	.11502	1.16763	.85644	3.42283	.29216
4.050	7.4023	8.6238	7.3999	8.6211	.51314	.11599	1.16502	.85835	3.39413	.29463
4.075	7.3569	8.5522	7.3545	8.5495	.51000	.11697	1.16249	.86023	3.36596	.29709
4.100	7.3120	8.4819	7.3097	8.4793	.50689	.11793	1.16001	.86206	3.33831	.29955
4.125	7.2677	8.4130	7.2654	8.4104	.50381	.11890	1.15760	.86386	3.31117	.30201
4.150	7.2239	8.3453	7.2216	8.3427	.50078	.11987	1.15524	.86562	3.28452	.30446
4.175	7.1807	8.2788	7.1784	8.2762	.49778	.12083	1.15294	.86735	3.25835	.30690

TABLE 16

IEC-R 35

Outside dimensions: 2.7705 X 1.3189 ±0.006 inches
70.37 X 33.50 ±0.15 millimeters

Inside dimensions: 2.613 X 1.1614 ±0.0056 inches
66.37 X 29.500 ±0.14 millimeters
corner radius: 1.2 millimeters
a/b: 2.2498

Cutoff:	Rectangle in Vacuum	Waveguide in Air
Wavelength:	13.27400cm	13.26562cm
Frequency:	2258.49400 MHz	2259.19800 MHz

	THEORETICAL		PHYSICAL							
f (GHz)	λ (cm)	λ_g (cm)	λ (cm)	λ_g (cm)	$\frac{\lambda}{\lambda_c}$	$1/\lambda_g$ (1/cm)	$\frac{\lambda_g}{\lambda}$	$\frac{\lambda}{\lambda_g}$	λ_g (in)	$1/\lambda_g$ (1/in)
2.500	11.9917	27.9655	11.9879	27.9754	.90368	.03575	2.33364	.42851	11.01392	.09079
2.550	11.7566	25.3217	11.7528	25.3276	.88596	.03948	2.15502	.46403	9.97148	.10029
2.600	11.5305	23.2740	11.5268	23.2774	.86892	.04296	2.01942	.49519	9.16433	.10912
2.650	11.3129	21.6261	11.3093	21.6279	.85253	.04624	1.91239	.52290	8.51490	.11744
2.700	11.1034	20.2618	11.0999	20.2625	.83674	.04935	1.82547	.54780	7.97735	.12535
2.750	10.9015	19.1075	10.8981	19.1073	.82153	.05234	1.75328	.57036	7.52258	.13293
2.800	10.7069	18.1138	10.7035	18.1131	.80686	.05521	1.69227	.59092	7.13113	.14023
2.850	10.5190	17.2463	10.5157	17.2452	.79270	.05799	1.63995	.60978	6.78943	.14729
2.900	10.3377	16.4801	10.3344	16.4786	.77903	.06068	1.59455	.62714	6.48766	.15414
2.950	10.1625	15.7967	10.1592	15.7951	.76583	.06331	1.55475	.64319	6.21853	.16081
3.000	9.9931	15.1821	9.9899	15.1803	.75307	.06587	1.51957	.65808	5.97649	.16732
3.050	9.8293	14.6254	9.8261	14.6234	.74072	.06838	1.48822	.67194	5.75725	.17369
3.100	9.6707	14.1179	9.6676	14.1158	.72877	.07084	1.46011	.68488	5.55741	.17994
3.150	9.5172	13.6528	9.5142	13.6506	.71721	.07326	1.43476	.69698	5.37425	.18607
3.200	9.3685	13.2243	9.3655	13.2221	.70600	.07563	1.41178	.70832	5.20554	.19210
3.250	9.2244	12.8279	9.2214	12.8256	.69514	.07797	1.39085	.71898	5.04947	.19804
3.300	9.0846	12.4598	9.0817	12.4575	.68461	.08027	1.37171	.72902	4.90452	.20389
3.350	8.9490	12.1167	8.9462	12.1144	.67439	.08255	1.35414	.73848	4.76943	.20967
3.400	8.8174	11.7959	8.8146	11.7935	.66447	.08479	1.33795	.74741	4.64313	.21537
3.450	8.6896	11.4951	8.6869	11.4927	.65484	.08701	1.32300	.75586	4.52469	.22101
3.500	8.5655	11.2122	8.5628	11.2099	.64549	.08921	1.30914	.76386	4.41333	.22659
3.550	8.4449	10.9456	8.4422	10.9433	.63639	.09138	1.29626	.77145	4.30837	.23211
3.600	8.3276	10.6938	8.3249	10.6914	.62755	.09353	1.28427	.77865	4.20922	.23757
3.650	8.2135	10.4554	8.2109	10.4530	.61896	.09567	1.27307	.78550	4.11536	.24299
3.700	8.1025	10.2293	8.0999	10.2269	.61059	.09778	1.26260	.79202	4.02634	.24836
3.750	7.9945	10.0144	7.9919	10.0121	.60245	.09988	1.25278	.79823	3.94176	.25369
3.800	7.8893	9.8099	7.8868	9.8076	.59453	.10196	1.24355	.80415	3.86126	.25898
3.850	7.7868	9.6150	7.7843	9.6127	.58680	.10403	1.23488	.80980	3.78453	.26423
3.900	7.6870	9.4289	7.6845	9.4266	.57928	.10608	1.22670	.81519	3.71127	.26945
3.950	7.5897	9.2510	7.5873	9.2488	.57195	.10812	1.21899	.82035	3.64125	.27463
4.000	7.4948	9.0808	7.4924	9.0785	.56480	.11015	1.21170	.82529	3.57422	.27978
4.050	7.4023	8.9176	7.3999	8.9154	.55783	.11217	1.20479	.83002	3.50999	.28490
4.100	7.3120	8.7611	7.3097	8.7588	.55102	.11417	1.19825	.83455	3.44836	.28999
4.150	7.2239	8.6107	7.2216	8.6085	.54439	.11616	1.19205	.83889	3.38918	.29506
4.200	7.1379	8.4661	7.1356	8.4640	.53790	.11815	1.18615	.84306	3.33227	.30010
4.250	7.0539	8.3270	7.0517	8.3249	.53158	.12012	1.18055	.84706	3.27750	.30511
4.300	6.9719	8.1930	6.9697	8.1909	.52539	.12209	1.17521	.85091	3.22475	.31010
4.350	6.8918	8.0638	6.8896	8.0617	.51936	.12404	1.17013	.85461	3.17389	.31507
4.400	6.8135	7.9391	6.8113	7.9370	.51345	.12599	1.16528	.85817	3.12481	.32002
4.450	6.7369	7.8187	6.7348	7.8167	.50768	.12793	1.16064	.86159	3.07742	.32495
4.500	6.6621	7.7024	6.6599	7.7003	.50204	.12986	1.15622	.86489	3.03162	.32986
4.550	6.5888	7.5899	6.5867	7.5878	.49653	.13179	1.15199	.86807	2.98733	.33475
4.600	6.5172	7.4810	6.5151	7.4790	.49113	.13371	1.14793	.87113	2.94447	.33962

TABLE 17

IEC-R 40 Brit: WG-11A

Amer: WR-229, RG-340/U, RG-341/U, RG-342/U

Outside dimensions: 2.418 X 1.273 ±0.005 inches
61.42 X 32.33 ±0.12 millimeters

Inside dimensions: 2.2900 X 1.1450 ±0.0046 inches
58.17 X 29.083 ±0.12 millimeters
corner radius: 1.2 millimeters
a/b: 2.000

Cutoff:	Rectangle in Vacuum	Waveguide in Air
Wavelength:	11.63400cm	11.62550cm
Frequency:	2576.86520 MHz	2577.92460 MHz

	THEORETICAL		PHYSICAL							
f (GHz)	λ (cm)	λ_g (cm)	λ (cm)	λ_g (cm)	$\frac{\lambda}{\lambda_c}$	$1/\lambda_g$ (1/cm)	$\frac{\lambda_g}{\lambda}$	$\frac{\lambda}{\lambda_g}$	λ_g (in)	$1/\lambda_g$ (1/in)
3.000	9.9931	19.5158	9.9899	19.5234	.85931	.05122	1.95431	.51169	7.68636	.13010
3.050	9.8293	18.3736	9.8261	18.3793	.84522	.05441	1.87045	.53463	7.23593	.13820
3.100	9.6707	17.3964	9.6676	17.4006	.83159	.05747	1.79988	.55559	6.85064	.14597
3.150	9.5172	16.5476	9.5142	16.5507	.81839	.06042	1.73958	.57485	6.51601	.15347
3.200	9.3685	15.8010	9.3655	15.8032	.80560	.06328	1.68738	.59263	6.22175	.16073
3.250	9.2244	15.1374	9.2214	15.1390	.79321	.06605	1.64172	.60912	5.96025	.16778
3.300	9.0846	14.5425	9.0817	14.5435	.78119	.06876	1.60141	.62445	5.72580	.17465
3.350	8.9490	14.0049	8.9462	14.0055	.76953	.07140	1.56554	.63876	5.51399	.18136
3.400	8.8174	13.5160	8.8146	13.5163	.75821	.07398	1.53339	.65215	5.32137	.18792
3.450	8.6896	13.0688	8.6869	13.0687	.74722	.07652	1.50442	.66471	5.14517	.19436
3.500	8.5655	12.6575	8.5628	12.6572	.73655	.07901	1.47817	.67651	4.98316	.20068
3.550	8.4449	12.2776	8.4422	12.2772	.72618	.08145	1.45427	.68763	4.83353	.20689
3.600	8.3276	11.9253	8.3249	11.9247	.71609	.08386	1.43241	.69813	4.69475	.21300
3.650	8.2135	11.5974	8.2109	11.5965	.70628	.08623	1.41234	.70804	4.56557	.21903
3.700	8.1025	11.2910	8.0999	11.2901	.69674	.08857	1.39385	.71744	4.44492	.22498
3.750	7.9945	11.0040	7.9919	11.0030	.68745	.09088	1.37677	.72634	4.33189	.23085
3.800	7.8893	10.7345	7.8868	10.7333	.67840	.09317	1.36093	.73479	4.22572	.23665
3.850	7.7868	10.4805	7.7843	10.4793	.66959	.09543	1.34621	.74283	4.12572	.24238
3.900	7.6870	10.2409	7.6845	10.2396	.66101	.09766	1.33249	.75047	4.03133	.24806
3.950	7.5897	10.0141	7.5873	10.0128	.65264	.09987	1.31968	.75776	3.94203	.25368
4.000	7.4948	9.7991	7.4924	9.7978	.64448	.10206	1.30769	.76471	3.85739	.25924

55

4.050	7.4023	9.5950	7.3999	9.5936	.63652	.10424	1.29644	.77134	3.77700	.26476
4.100	7.3120	9.4008	7.3097	9.3993	.62876	.10639	1.28588	.77768	3.70053	.27023
4.150	7.2239	9.2158	7.2216	9.2143	.62119	.10853	1.27593	.78374	3.62767	.27566
4.200	7.1379	9.0392	7.1356	9.0377	.61379	.11065	1.26655	.78954	3.55813	.28105
4.250	7.0539	8.8704	7.0517	8.8689	.60657	.11275	1.25770	.79510	3.49169	.28639
4.300	6.9719	8.7090	6.9697	8.7074	.59952	.11484	1.24932	.80043	3.42811	.29171
4.350	6.8918	8.5542	6.8896	8.5527	.59263	.11692	1.24139	.80555	3.36719	.29698
4.400	6.8135	8.4058	6.8113	8.4043	.58589	.11899	1.23387	.81046	3.30876	.30223
4.450	6.7369	8.2633	6.7348	8.2617	.57931	.12104	1.22673	.81517	3.25265	.30744
4.500	6.6621	8.1263	6.6599	8.1247	.57287	.12308	1.21995	.81971	3.19872	.31263
4.550	6.5888	7.9945	6.5867	7.9929	.56658	.12511	1.21349	.82407	3.14682	.31778
4.600	6.5172	7.8676	6.5151	7.8660	.56042	.12713	1.20734	.82827	3.09684	.32291
4.650	6.4472	7.7452	6.4451	7.7436	.55439	.12914	1.20147	.83231	3.04865	.32801
4.700	6.3786	7.6271	6.3765	7.6255	.54849	.13114	1.19587	.83621	3.00216	.33309
4.750	6.3114	7.5131	6.3094	7.5115	.54272	.13313	1.19052	.83997	2.95727	.33815
4.800	6.2457	7.4029	6.2437	7.4013	.53707	.13511	1.18540	.84359	2.91389	.34318
4.850	6.1813	7.2963	6.1793	7.2947	.53153	.13709	1.18051	.84709	2.87194	.34820
4.900	6.1182	7.1932	6.1163	7.1916	.52611	.13905	1.17582	.85047	2.83135	.35319
4.950	6.0564	7.0934	6.0545	7.0918	.52079	.14101	1.17133	.85373	2.79203	.35816
5.000	5.9958	6.9966	5.9939	6.9950	.51558	.14296	1.16701	.85689	2.75394	.36312
5.050	5.9365	6.9028	5.9346	6.9012	.51048	.14490	1.16287	.85994	2.71700	.36805
5.100	5.8783	6.8117	5.8764	6.8102	.50548	.14684	1.15890	.86289	2.68116	.37297

TABLE 18

IEC-R 41

Outside dimensions: 2.4016 X 1.1547 ±0.006 inches
61.00 X 29.330 ±0.15 millimeters

Inside dimensions: 2.2441 X 0.9972 ±0.0048 inches
57.00 X 25.330 ±0.12 millimeters
corner radius: 1.2 millimeters
a/b: 2.2503

Cutoff: Rectangle in Vacuum / Waveguide in Air

Wavelength: 11.40000cm 11.39024cm
Frequency: 2629.75880 MHz 2631.17030 MHz

	THEORETICAL					PHYSICAL				
f (GHz)	λ (cm)	λ_g (cm)	λ (cm)	λ_g (cm)	$\frac{\lambda}{\lambda_c}$	$1/\lambda_g$ (1/cm)	$\frac{\lambda_g}{\lambda}$	$\frac{\lambda}{\lambda_g}$	λ_g (in)	$1/\lambda_g$ (1/in)
3.100	9.6707	18.2638	9.6676	18.2757	.84876	.05472	1.89040	.52899	7.19515	.13898
3.150	9.5172	17.2887	9.5142	17.2982	.83529	.05781	1.81815	.55001	6.81032	.14684
3.200	9.3685	16.4424	9.3655	16.4501	.82224	.06079	1.75645	.56933	6.47641	.15441
3.250	9.2244	15.6986	9.2214	15.7048	.80959	.06367	1.70308	.58717	6.18299	.16173
3.300	9.0846	15.0379	9.0817	15.0429	.79732	.06648	1.65640	.60372	5.92242	.16885
3.350	8.9490	14.4457	8.9462	14.4499	.78542	.06920	1.61520	.61912	5.68893	.17578
3.400	8.8174	13.9110	8.8146	13.9143	.77387	.07187	1.57855	.63349	5.47808	.18255
3.450	8.6896	13.4248	8.6869	13.4275	.76266	.07447	1.54572	.64695	5.28641	.18916
3.500	8.5655	12.9801	8.5628	12.9823	.75176	.07703	1.51614	.65957	5.11115	.19565
3.550	8.4449	12.5714	8.4422	12.5732	.74117	.07953	1.48933	.67144	4.95006	.20202
3.600	8.3276	12.1940	8.3249	12.1953	.73088	.08200	1.46492	.68263	4.80131	.20828
3.650	8.2135	11.8440	8.2109	11.8450	.72087	.08442	1.44260	.69319	4.66339	.21444
3.700	8.1025	11.5182	8.0999	11.5190	.71113	.08681	1.42211	.70318	4.53504	.22051
3.750	7.9945	11.2141	7.9919	11.2146	.70165	.08917	1.40324	.71264	4.41518	.22649
3.800	7.8893	10.9291	7.8868	10.9294	.69241	.09150	1.38580	.72161	4.30292	.23240
3.850	7.7868	10.6615	7.7843	10.6616	.68342	.09379	1.36962	.73013	4.19748	.23824
3.900	7.6870	10.4095	7.6845	10.4094	.67466	.09607	1.35459	.73823	4.09820	.24401
3.950	7.5897	10.1716	7.5873	10.1714	.66612	.09831	1.34059	.74594	4.00449	.24972
4.000	7.4948	9.9466	7.4924	9.9462	.65779	.10054	1.32751	.75329	3.91584	.25537
4.050	7.4023	9.7333	7.3999	9.7328	.64967	.10274	1.31526	.76030	3.83183	.26097
4.100	7.3120	9.5307	7.3097	9.5302	.64175	.10493	1.30378	.76700	3.75205	.26652
4.150	7.2239	9.3381	7.2216	9.3375	.63402	.10710	1.29299	.77340	3.67616	.27202
4.200	7.1379	9.1545	7.1356	9.1538	.62647	.10924	1.28283	.77953	3.60386	.27748
4.250	7.0539	8.9793	7.0517	8.9786	.61910	.11138	1.27325	.78539	3.53487	.28290
4.300	6.9719	8.8120	6.9697	8.8111	.61190	.11349	1.26421	.79101	3.46894	.28827
4.350	6.8918	8.6518	6.8896	8.6509	.60487	.11559	1.25565	.79640	3.40587	.29361
4.400	6.8135	8.4983	6.8113	8.4974	.59799	.11768	1.24755	.80157	3.34544	.29891
4.450	6.7369	8.3512	6.7348	8.3502	.59127	.11976	1.23986	.80654	3.28747	.30418
4.500	6.6621	8.2098	6.6599	8.2088	.58470	.12182	1.23257	.81131	3.23182	.30942
4.550	6.5888	8.0740	6.5867	8.0729	.57828	.12387	1.22563	.81590	3.17832	.31463
4.600	6.5172	7.9433	6.5151	7.9422	.57199	.12591	1.21903	.82032	3.12684	.31981
4.650	6.4472	7.8174	6.4451	7.8163	.56584	.12794	1.21275	.82458	3.07727	.32496
4.700	6.3786	7.6960	6.3765	7.6949	.55982	.12996	1.20675	.82867	3.02948	.33009
4.750	6.3114	7.5789	6.3094	7.5778	.55393	.13197	1.20103	.83262	2.98337	.33519
4.800	6.2457	7.4659	6.2437	7.4647	.54816	.13396	1.19556	.83643	2.93885	.34027
4.850	6.1813	7.3566	6.1793	7.3554	.54251	.13595	1.19033	.84011	2.89583	.34532
4.900	6.1182	7.2509	6.1163	7.2497	.53697	.13794	1.18532	.84365	2.85422	.35036
4.950	6.0564	7.1487	6.0545	7.1475	.53155	.13991	1.18053	.84708	2.81396	.35537
5.000	5.9958	7.0497	5.9939	7.0484	.52623	.14188	1.17593	.85039	2.77497	.36036
5.050	5.9365	6.9537	5.9346	6.9525	.52102	.14383	1.17152	.85359	2.73720	.36534
5.100	5.8783	6.8607	5.8764	6.8594	.51592	.14578	1.16728	.85669	2.70057	.37029
5.150	5.8212	6.7704	5.8194	6.7692	.51091	.14773	1.16322	.85968	2.66503	.37523
5.200	5.7652	6.6828	5.7634	6.6815	.50599	.14967	1.15931	.86258	2.63053	.38015

TABLE 19

IEC-R 48 Brit: WG-12 Amer: WR-187, RG-49/U, RG-95/U, RG-168/U

Outside dimensions: 2.000 X 1.000 ±0.004 inches
50.80 X 25.40 ±0.095 millimeters

Inside dimensions: 1.8720 X 0.8720 ±0.0037 inches
47.55 X 22.149 ±0.095 millimeters
corner radius: 0.8 millimeters
a/b: 2.1468

Cutoff: Rectangle in Vacuum / Waveguide in Air

Wavelength: 9.51000cm 9.50504cm
Frequency: 3152.39220 MHz 3153.02860 MHz

	THEORETICAL					PHYSICAL				
f (GHz)	λ (cm)	λ_g (cm)	λ (cm)	λ_g (cm)	$\frac{\lambda}{\lambda_c}$	$1/\lambda_g$ (1/cm)	$\frac{\lambda_g}{\lambda}$	$\frac{\lambda}{\lambda_g}$	λ_g (in)	$1/\lambda_g$ (1/in)
3.600	8.3276	17.2442	8.3249	17.2411	.87584	.05800	2.07102	.48285	6.78782	.14732
3.650	8.2135	16.2947	8.2109	16.2915	.86384	.06138	1.98414	.50400	6.41397	.15591
3.700	8.1025	15.4762	8.0999	15.4730	.85217	.06463	1.91027	.52349	6.09173	.16416
3.750	7.9945	14.7609	7.9919	14.7577	.84081	.06776	1.84658	.54154	5.81011	.17211
3.800	7.8893	14.1286	7.8868	14.1253	.82974	.07079	1.79102	.55834	5.56116	.17982
3.850	7.7868	13.5641	7.7843	13.5609	.81897	.07374	1.74208	.57403	5.33896	.18730
3.900	7.6870	13.0562	7.6845	13.0530	.80847	.07661	1.69861	.58872	5.13898	.19459
3.950	7.5897	12.5957	7.5873	12.5926	.79824	.07941	1.65971	.60252	4.95773	.20171
4.000	7.4948	12.1758	7.4924	12.1727	.78826	.08215	1.62468	.61551	4.79242	.20866
4.050	7.4023	11.7907	7.3999	11.7877	.77853	.08483	1.59295	.62777	4.64082	.21548
4.100	7.3120	11.4358	7.3097	11.4328	.76903	.08747	1.56407	.63936	4.50111	.22217
4.150	7.2239	11.1073	7.2216	11.1044	.75977	.09005	1.53766	.65034	4.37180	.22874
4.200	7.1379	10.8021	7.1356	10.7992	.75072	.09260	1.51342	.66076	4.25165	.23520
4.250	7.0539	10.5175	7.0517	10.5146	.74189	.09511	1.49108	.67065	4.13962	.24157
4.300	6.9719	10.2512	6.9697	10.2485	.73326	.09758	1.47043	.68007	4.03482	.24784
4.350	6.8918	10.0015	6.8896	9.9987	.72483	.10001	1.45128	.68905	3.93651	.25403
4.400	6.8135	9.7665	6.8113	9.7638	.71660	.10242	1.43348	.69760	3.84402	.26014

f (GHz)	λ (cm)	λ_g (cm)	λ (cm)	λ_g (cm)	λ/λ_c	$1/\lambda_g$ (1/cm)	λ_g/λ	λ/λ_g	λ_g (in)	$1/\lambda_g$ (1/in)
4.450	6.7369	9.5450	6.7348	9.5423	.70855	.10480	1.41687	.70578	3.75681	.26618
4.500	6.6621	9.3356	6.6599	9.3330	.70067	.10715	1.40136	.71359	3.67439	.27215
4.550	6.5888	9.1372	6.5867	9.1347	.69297	.10947	1.38683	.72107	3.59633	.27806
4.600	6.5172	8.9491	6.5151	8.9465	.68544	.11178	1.37319	.72823	3.52226	.28391
4.650	6.4472	8.7702	6.4451	8.7677	.67807	.11406	1.36037	.73510	3.45184	.28970
4.700	6.3786	8.5998	6.3765	8.5974	.67086	.11631	1.34828	.74168	3.38479	.29544
4.750	6.3114	8.4374	6.3094	8.4349	.66380	.11855	1.33688	.74801	3.32084	.30113
4.800	6.2457	8.2822	6.2437	8.2798	.65688	.12078	1.32611	.75409	3.25976	.30677
4.850	6.1813	8.1338	6.1793	8.1314	.65011	.12298	1.31591	.75993	3.20135	.31237
4.900	6.1182	7.9916	6.1163	7.9893	.64348	.12517	1.30624	.76555	3.14540	.31792
4.950	6.0564	7.8554	6.0545	7.8531	.63698	.12734	1.29707	.77097	3.09176	.32344
5.000	5.9958	7.7246	5.9939	7.7223	.63061	.12950	1.28835	.77619	3.04027	.32892
5.050	5.9365	7.5988	5.9346	7.5966	.62436	.13164	1.28006	.78121	2.99079	.33436
5.100	5.8783	7.4779	5.8764	7.4757	.61824	.13377	1.27216	.78607	2.94319	.33977
5.150	5.8212	7.3615	5.8194	7.3593	.61224	.13588	1.26462	.79075	2.89736	.34514
5.200	5.7652	7.2492	5.7634	7.2471	.60635	.13799	1.25743	.79527	2.85318	.35049
5.250	5.7103	7.1410	5.7085	7.1389	.60058	.14008	1.25056	.79964	2.81057	.35580
5.300	5.6565	7.0364	5.6547	7.0344	.59491	.14216	1.24399	.80386	2.76943	.36108
5.350	5.6036	6.9355	5.6018	6.9334	.58935	.14423	1.23771	.80795	2.72968	.36634
5.400	5.5517	6.8378	5.5499	6.8358	.58389	.14629	1.23168	.81190	2.69125	.37158
5.450	5.5008	6.7433	5.4990	6.7413	.57854	.14834	1.22591	.81572	2.65405	.37678
5.500	5.4508	6.6518	5.4490	6.6498	.57328	.15038	1.22037	.81943	2.61804	.38197
5.550	5.4017	6.5632	5.3999	6.5612	.56811	.15241	1.21505	.82301	2.58314	.38713
5.600	5.3534	6.4772	5.3517	6.4752	.56304	.15443	1.20994	.82649	2.54931	.39226
5.650	5.3061	6.3938	5.3044	6.3919	.55806	.15645	1.20502	.82986	2.51648	.39738
5.700	5.2595	6.3128	5.2578	6.3109	.55316	.15846	1.20029	.83313	2.48462	.40248
5.750	5.2138	6.2342	5.2121	6.2323	.54835	.16045	1.19574	.83630	2.45367	.40755
5.800	5.1688	6.1578	5.1672	6.1559	.54363	.16245	1.19135	.83938	2.42359	.41261
5.850	5.1247	6.0835	5.1230	6.0816	.53898	.16443	1.18712	.84237	2.39435	.41765
5.900	5.0812	6.0112	5.0796	6.0094	.53441	.16641	1.18304	.84528	2.36590	.42267
5.950	5.0385	5.9409	5.0369	5.9391	.52992	.16838	1.17911	.84810	2.33821	.42768
6.000	4.9965	5.8724	4.9949	5.8706	.52550	.17034	1.17531	.85084	2.31125	.43267
6.050	4.9552	5.8056	4.9537	5.8039	.52116	.17230	1.17163	.85351	2.28499	.43764
6.100	4.9146	5.7406	4.9131	5.7389	.51689	.17425	1.16809	.85610	2.25940	.44260
6.150	4.8747	5.6772	4.8731	5.6755	.51269	.17620	1.16465	.85862	2.23445	.44754
6.200	4.8354	5.6154	4.8338	5.6137	.50855	.17814	1.16133	.86108	2.21011	.45247
6.250	4.7967	5.5551	4.7951	5.5534	.50448	.18007	1.15812	.86347	2.18636	.45738
6.300	4.7586	5.4962	4.7571	5.4945	.50048	.18200	1.15501	.86579	2.16318	.46228
6.350	4.7211	5.4387	4.7196	5.4370	.49654	.18393	1.15200	.86806	2.14055	.46717
6.400	4.6843	5.3825	4.6828	5.3808	.49266	.18584	1.14907	.87027	2.11844	.47205

TABLE 20

IEC-R 58 — Brit: WG-13 — Amer: WR-159, RG-343/U, RG-344/U, RG-345/U

Outside dimensions: 1.718 X 0.923 ±0.003 inches
43.64 X 23.44 ±0.081 millimeters

Inside dimensions: 1.5900 X 0.7950 ±0.0032 inches
40.39 X 20.193 ±0.081 millimeters
corner radius: 0.8 millimeters
a/b: 2.000

Cutoff:	Rectangle in Vacuum	Waveguide in Air
Wavelength:	8.07800cm	8.07256cm
Frequency:	3711.22180 MHz	3712.53560 MHz

f (GHz)	THEORETICAL λ (cm)	THEORETICAL λ_g (cm)	PHYSICAL λ (cm)	λ_g (cm)	λ/λ_c	$1/\lambda_g$ (1/cm)	λ_g/λ	λ/λ_g	λ_g (in)	$1/\lambda_g$ (1/in)
4.300	6.9719	13.8037	6.9697	13.8071	.86338	.07243	1.98102	.50479	5.43587	.18396
4.350	6.8918	13.2113	6.8896	13.2139	.85346	.07568	1.91796	.52139	5.20233	.19222
4.400	6.8135	12.6835	6.8113	12.6855	.84376	.07883	1.86242	.53694	4.99428	.20023
4.450	6.7369	12.2092	6.7348	12.2107	.83428	.08190	1.81308	.55155	4.80735	.20801
4.500	6.6621	11.7798	6.6599	11.7809	.82501	.08488	1.76893	.56531	4.63816	.21560
4.550	6.5888	11.3887	6.5867	11.3895	.81594	.08780	1.72915	.57832	4.48405	.22301
4.600	6.5172	11.0304	6.5151	11.0309	.80707	.09065	1.69311	.59063	4.34286	.23026
4.650	6.4472	10.7005	6.4451	10.7007	.79839	.09345	1.66029	.60230	4.21289	.23737
4.700	6.3786	10.3954	6.3765	10.3954	.78990	.09620	1.63027	.61340	4.09269	.24434
4.750	6.3114	10.1121	6.3094	10.1120	.78159	.09889	1.60268	.62395	3.98109	.25119
4.800	6.2457	9.8482	6.2437	9.8479	.77344	.10155	1.57725	.63401	3.87711	.25792
4.850	6.1813	9.6014	6.1793	9.6009	.76547	.10416	1.55372	.64362	3.77990	.26456
4.900	6.1182	9.3700	6.1163	9.3694	.75766	.10673	1.53189	.65279	3.68875	.27109
4.950	6.0564	9.1524	6.0545	9.1517	.75001	.10927	1.51157	.66157	3.60305	.27754
5.000	5.9958	8.9473	5.9939	8.9466	.74251	.11177	1.49260	.66997	3.52227	.28391
5.050	5.9365	8.7535	5.9346	8.7527	.73516	.11425	1.47487	.67803	3.44596	.29019
5.100	5.8783	8.5701	5.8764	8.5692	.72795	.11670	1.45825	.68576	3.37372	.29641
5.150	5.8212	8.3961	5.8194	8.3952	.72088	.11912	1.44263	.69318	3.30518	.30256
5.200	5.7652	8.2307	5.7634	8.2297	.71395	.12151	1.42793	.70031	3.24005	.30864
5.250	5.7103	8.0733	5.7085	8.0722	.70715	.12388	1.41407	.70718	3.17805	.31466
5.300	5.6565	7.9231	5.6547	7.9221	.70048	.12623	1.40098	.71378	3.11893	.32062
5.350	5.6036	7.7798	5.6018	7.7787	.69393	.12856	1.38860	.72015	3.06248	.32653
5.400	5.5517	7.6427	5.5499	7.6416	.68751	.13086	1.37688	.72628	3.00849	.33239
5.450	5.5008	7.5114	5.4990	7.5103	.68120	.13315	1.36575	.73220	2.95680	.33820
5.500	5.4508	7.3856	5.4490	7.3844	.67501	.13542	1.35518	.73791	2.90725	.34397
5.550	5.4017	7.2648	5.3999	7.2636	.66893	.13767	1.34512	.74343	2.85968	.34969
5.600	5.3534	7.1487	5.3517	7.1475	.66295	.13991	1.33555	.74876	2.81398	.35537
5.650	5.3061	7.0370	5.3044	7.0358	.65709	.14213	1.32642	.75391	2.77001	.36101
5.700	5.2595	6.9295	5.2578	6.9283	.65132	.14434	1.31771	.75889	2.72768	.36661
5.750	5.2138	6.8259	5.2121	6.8247	.64566	.14653	1.30939	.76371	2.68689	.37218
5.800	5.1688	6.7260	5.1672	6.7247	.64009	.14870	1.30143	.76838	2.64754	.37771
5.850	5.1247	6.6295	5.1230	6.6283	.63462	.15087	1.29382	.77291	2.60955	.38321
5.900	5.0812	6.5363	5.0796	6.5350	.62924	.15302	1.28652	.77729	2.57284	.38868
5.950	5.0385	6.4461	5.0369	6.4449	.62396	.15516	1.27953	.78154	2.53735	.39411
6.000	4.9965	6.3589	4.9949	6.3576	.61876	.15729	1.27281	.78566	2.50300	.39952
6.050	4.9552	6.2744	4.9537	6.2732	.61364	.15941	1.26637	.78966	2.46975	.40490
6.100	4.9146	6.1926	4.9131	6.1913	.60861	.16152	1.26017	.79354	2.43752	.41025
6.150	4.8747	6.1132	4.8731	6.1119	.60366	.16361	1.25421	.79731	2.40627	.41558
6.200	4.8354	6.0362	4.8338	6.0349	.59880	.16570	1.24848	.80097	2.37596	.42088
6.250	4.7967	5.9615	4.7951	5.9602	.59401	.16778	1.24296	.80453	2.34653	.42616
6.300	4.7586	5.8888	4.7571	5.8876	.58929	.16985	1.23764	.80799	2.31794	.43142
6.350	4.7211	5.8183	4.7196	5.8170	.58465	.17191	1.23251	.81135	2.29016	.43665
6.400	4.6843	5.7497	4.6828	5.7484	.58008	.17396	1.22756	.81462	2.26314	.44186
6.450	4.6479	5.6829	4.6465	5.6816	.57559	.17601	1.22278	.81781	2.23686	.44706
6.500	4.6122	5.6179	4.6107	5.6166	.57116	.17804	1.21817	.82090	2.21128	.45223
6.550	4.5770	5.5546	4.5755	5.5534	.56680	.18007	1.21371	.82392	2.18637	.45738
6.600	4.5423	5.4930	4.5409	5.4917	.56251	.18209	1.20940	.82685	2.16210	.46251
6.650	4.5082	5.4329	4.5067	5.4316	.55828	.18411	1.20523	.82972	2.13844	.46763
6.700	4.4745	5.3743	4.4731	5.3731	.55411	.18611	1.20120	.83250	2.11538	.47273
6.750	4.4414	5.3172	4.4399	5.3159	.55001	.18811	1.19729	.83522	2.09288	.47781
6.800	4.4087	5.2614	4.4073	5.2601	.54596	.19011	1.19351	.83787	2.07092	.48288
6.850	4.3765	5.2069	4.3751	5.2057	.54198	.19210	1.18984	.84045	2.04949	.48793
6.900	4.3448	5.1538	4.3434	5.1525	.53805	.19408	1.18628	.84297	2.02856	.49296
6.950	4.3136	5.1018	4.3122	5.1006	.53418	.19606	1.18284	.84543	2.00811	.49798
7.000	4.2827	5.0511	4.2814	5.0498	.53036	.19803	1.17949	.84782	1.98813	.50299
7.050	4.2524	5.0015	4.2510	5.0002	.52660	.19999	1.17624	.85016	1.96859	.50798
7.100	4.2224	4.9529	4.2211	4.9517	.52289	.20195	1.17309	.85245	1.94949	.51295
7.150	4.1929	4.9055	4.1916	4.9042	.51924	.20391	1.17003	.85468	1.93080	.51792
7.200	4.1638	4.8590	4.1625	4.8578	.51563	.20585	1.16705	.85686	1.91252	.52287
7.250	4.1351	4.8135	4.1337	4.8123	.51207	.20780	1.16416	.85899	1.89462	.52781
7.300	4.1067	4.7690	4.1054	4.7678	.50857	.20974	1.16134	.86107	1.87710	.53274
7.350	4.0788	4.7254	4.0775	4.7242	.50511	.21167	1.15861	.86310	1.85993	.53765
7.400	4.0512	4.6827	4.0500	4.6815	.50169	.21361	1.15595	.86509	1.84312	.54256
7.450	4.0241	4.6409	4.0228	4.6397	.49833	.21553	1.15336	.86704	1.82665	.54745

TABLE 21

IEC-R 70 — Brit: WG-14 — Amer: WR-137, RG-50/U, RG-106/U, RG-169/U

Outside dimensions: 1.500 X 0.750 ±0.003 inches
38.10 X 19.05 ±0.070 millimeters

Inside dimensions: 1.3720 X 0.6220 ±0.0028 inches
34.85 X 15.799 ±0.070 millimeters
corner radius: 0.8 millimeters
a/b: 2.2058

Cutoff:	Rectangle in Vacuum	Waveguide in Air
Wavelength:	6.97000cm	6.96305cm
Frequency:	4301.18360 MHz	4304.10250 MHz

	THEORETICAL		PHYSICAL							
f (GHz)	λ (cm)	λ_g (cm)	λ (cm)	λ_g (cm)	$\frac{\lambda}{\lambda_c}$	$1/\lambda_g$ (1/cm)	$\frac{\lambda_g}{\lambda}$	$\frac{\lambda}{\lambda_g}$	λ_g (in)	$1/\lambda_g$ (1/in)
4.900	6.1182	12.7718	6.1163	12.7900	.87839	.07819	2.09115	.47821	5.03544	.19859
4.950	6.0564	12.2366	6.0545	12.2523	.86952	.08162	2.02368	.49415	4.82374	.20731
5.000	5.9958	11.7590	5.9939	11.7726	.86082	.08494	1.96409	.50914	4.63489	.21575
5.050	5.9365	11.3292	5.9346	11.3411	.85230	.08817	1.91103	.52328	4.46502	.22396
5.100	5.8783	10.9397	5.8764	10.9502	.84394	.09132	1.86342	.53665	4.31111	.23196
5.150	5.8212	10.5845	5.8194	10.5938	.83575	.09439	1.82044	.54932	4.17079	.23976
5.200	5.7652	10.2588	5.7634	10.2671	.82771	.09740	1.78143	.56135	4.04215	.24739
5.250	5.7103	9.9587	5.7085	9.9660	.81983	.10034	1.74582	.57280	3.92364	.25487
5.300	5.6565	9.6809	5.6547	9.6875	.81209	.10323	1.71319	.58371	3.81398	.26219
5.350	5.6036	9.4228	5.6018	9.4287	.80451	.10606	1.68316	.59412	3.71210	.26939
5.400	5.5517	9.1822	5.5499	9.1875	.79706	.10884	1.65543	.60407	3.61713	.27646
5.450	5.5008	8.9571	5.4990	8.9619	.78974	.11158	1.62973	.61360	3.52831	.28342
5.500	5.4508	8.7459	5.4490	8.7503	.78256	.11428	1.60584	.62273	3.44499	.29028
5.550	5.4017	8.5473	5.3999	8.5512	.77551	.11694	1.58357	.63148	3.36662	.29703
5.600	5.3534	8.3599	5.3517	8.3635	.76859	.11957	1.56277	.63989	3.29272	.30370
5.650	5.3061	8.1829	5.3044	8.1861	.76179	.12216	1.54328	.64797	3.22289	.31028
5.700	5.2595	8.0152	5.2578	8.0181	.75511	.12472	1.52499	.65574	3.15675	.31678
5.750	5.2138	7.8561	5.2121	7.8587	.74854	.12725	1.50778	.66323	3.09399	.32321
5.800	5.1688	7.7048	5.1672	7.7072	.74209	.12975	1.49157	.67044	3.03433	.32956
5.850	5.1247	7.5607	5.1230	7.5629	.73574	.13222	1.47626	.67739	2.97752	.33585
5.900	5.0812	7.4233	5.0796	7.4253	.72951	.13468	1.46178	.68410	2.92334	.34207
5.950	5.0385	7.2920	5.0369	7.2938	.72338	.13710	1.44807	.69057	2.87159	.34824
6.000	4.9965	7.1664	4.9949	7.1681	.71735	.13951	1.43507	.69683	2.82208	.35435
6.050	4.9552	7.0462	4.9537	7.0477	.71142	.14189	1.42272	.70288	2.77467	.36040
6.100	4.9146	6.9308	4.9131	6.9322	.70559	.14425	1.41097	.70873	2.72921	.36641
6.150	4.8747	6.8201	4.8731	6.8213	.69985	.14660	1.39978	.71440	2.68556	.37236
6.200	4.8354	6.7137	4.8338	6.7148	.69421	.14893	1.38912	.71988	2.64361	.37827
6.250	4.7967	6.6113	4.7951	6.6122	.68866	.15123	1.37894	.72519	2.60324	.38414
6.300	4.7586	6.5126	4.7571	6.5135	.68319	.15353	1.36922	.73034	2.56437	.38996
6.350	4.7211	6.4176	4.7196	6.4183	.67781	.15580	1.35992	.73534	2.52690	.39574
6.400	4.6843	6.3258	4.6828	6.3265	.67252	.15806	1.35102	.74018	2.49075	.40149
6.450	4.6479	6.2372	4.6465	6.2378	.66730	.16031	1.34249	.74488	2.45584	.40719
6.500	4.6122	6.1516	4.6107	6.1522	.66217	.16254	1.33432	.74945	2.42211	.41286
6.550	4.5770	6.0688	4.5755	6.0693	.65711	.16476	1.32647	.75388	2.38948	.41850
6.600	4.5423	5.9887	4.5409	5.9891	.65214	.16697	1.31893	.75819	2.35790	.42411
6.650	4.5082	5.9111	4.5067	5.9114	.64723	.16917	1.31168	.76238	2.32731	.42968
6.700	4.4745	5.8358	4.4731	5.8361	.64240	.17135	1.30471	.76645	2.29767	.43522
6.750	4.4414	5.7629	4.4399	5.7631	.63764	.17352	1.29800	.77041	2.26892	.44074
6.800	4.4087	5.6921	4.4073	5.6922	.63296	.17568	1.29154	.77427	2.24102	.44622
6.850	4.3765	5.6233	4.3751	5.6234	.62834	.17783	1.28531	.77802	2.21394	.45168
6.900	4.3448	5.5565	4.3434	5.5566	.62378	.17997	1.27930	.78168	2.18762	.45712
6.950	4.3136	5.4916	4.3122	5.4916	.61930	.18210	1.27350	.78524	2.16204	.46253
7.000	4.2827	5.4284	4.2814	5.4284	.61487	.18422	1.26790	.78870	2.13716	.46791
7.050	4.2524	5.3669	4.2510	5.3669	.61051	.18633	1.26249	.79208	2.11295	.47327
7.100	4.2224	5.3071	4.2211	5.3070	.60621	.18843	1.25726	.79538	2.08938	.47861
7.150	4.1929	5.2488	4.1916	5.2487	.60197	.19052	1.25221	.79859	2.06642	.48393
7.200	4.1638	5.1921	4.1625	5.1919	.59779	.19261	1.24731	.80172	2.04405	.48922
7.250	4.1351	5.1367	4.1337	5.1365	.59367	.19469	1.24258	.80478	2.02224	.49450
7.300	4.1067	5.0827	4.1054	5.0825	.58960	.19675	1.23799	.80776	2.00098	.49976
7.350	4.0788	5.0300	4.0775	5.0298	.58559	.19882	1.23354	.81067	1.98023	.50499
7.400	4.0512	4.9786	4.0500	4.9783	.58164	.20087	1.22923	.81352	1.95997	.51021
7.450	4.0241	4.9284	4.0228	4.9281	.57773	.20292	1.22505	.81629	1.94020	.51541
7.500	3.9972	4.8794	3.9960	4.8790	.57388	.20496	1.22100	.81900	1.92088	.52059
7.550	3.9708	4.8314	3.9695	4.8311	.57008	.20699	1.21706	.82165	1.90201	.52576
7.600	3.9446	4.7846	3.9434	4.7843	.56633	.20902	1.21324	.82424	1.88356	.53091
7.650	3.9189	4.7388	3.9176	4.7384	.56263	.21104	1.20952	.82677	1.86553	.53604
7.700	3.8934	4.6940	3.8922	4.6936	.55897	.21306	1.20592	.82925	1.84788	.54116
7.750	3.8683	4.6502	3.8671	4.6498	.55537	.21506	1.20241	.83166	1.83062	.54626
7.800	3.8435	4.6073	3.8423	4.6069	.55181	.21707	1.19900	.83403	1.81373	.55135
7.850	3.8190	4.5653	3.8178	4.5649	.54829	.21906	1.19568	.83634	1.79719	.55642
7.900	3.7948	4.5242	3.7936	4.5237	.54482	.22106	1.19245	.83861	1.78099	.56148
7.950	3.7710	4.4839	3.7698	4.4834	.54140	.22304	1.18931	.84082	1.76513	.56653
8.000	3.7474	4.4444	3.7462	4.4439	.53801	.22503	1.18625	.84299	1.74958	.57156
8.050	3.7241	4.4057	3.7229	4.4052	.53467	.22700	1.18327	.84511	1.73435	.57658
8.100	3.7011	4.3678	3.7000	4.3673	.53137	.22897	1.18037	.84719	1.71942	.58159
8.150	3.6784	4.3306	3.6773	4.3301	.52811	.23094	1.17754	.84923	1.70477	.58659
8.200	3.6560	4.2942	3.6548	4.2936	.52489	.23290	1.17478	.85122	1.69041	.59157
8.250	3.6338	4.2584	3.6327	4.2578	.52171	.23486	1.17209	.85317	1.67632	.59655
8.300	3.6120	4.2233	3.6108	4.2227	.51857	.23681	1.16947	.85509	1.66249	.60151
8.350	3.5903	4.1888	3.5892	4.1883	.51546	.23876	1.16691	.85696	1.64892	.60646
8.400	3.5690	4.1550	3.5678	4.1544	.51239	.24071	1.16442	.85880	1.63560	.61140
8.450	3.5478	4.1218	3.5467	4.1212	.50936	.24265	1.16198	.86060	1.62252	.61633
8.500	3.5270	4.0891	3.5258	4.0886	.50637	.24458	1.15960	.86237	1.60967	.62124
8.550	3.5063	4.0571	3.5052	4.0565	.50340	.24652	1.15728	.86410	1.59705	.62615
8.600	3.4860	4.0256	3.4848	4.0250	.50048	.24845	1.15501	.86580	1.58465	.63105
8.650	3.4658	3.9947	3.4647	3.9941	.49758	.25037	1.15279	.86746	1.57247	.63594

TABLE 22

IEC-R 84 — Brit: WG-15 — Amer: WR-112, RG-51/U, RG-68/U, RG-170/U

Outside dimensions: 1.250 X 0.625 ±0.002 inches
31.75 X 15.88 ±0.057 millimeters

Inside dimensions: 1.220 X 0.4970 ±0.0023 inches
28.499 X 12.624 ±0.057 millimeters
corner radius: 0.8 millimeters
a/b: 2.4547

Cutoff:	Rectangle in Vacuum	Waveguide in Air
Wavelength:	5.69980cm	5.69110cm
Frequency:	5259.70210 MHz	5266.06110 MHz

	THEORETICAL		PHYSICAL							
f (GHz)	λ (cm)	λ_g (cm)	λ (cm)	λ_g (cm)	$\frac{\lambda}{\lambda_c}$	$1/\lambda_g$ (1/cm)	$\frac{\lambda_g}{\lambda}$	$\frac{\lambda}{\lambda_g}$	λ_g (in)	$1/\lambda_g$ (1/in)
6.000	4.9965	10.3837	4.9949	10.4168	.87768	.09600	2.08546	.47951	4.10109	.24384
6.050	4.9552	10.0277	4.9537	10.0572	.87042	.09943	2.03025	.49255	3.95952	.25256
6.100	4.9146	9.7033	4.9131	9.7299	.86329	.10278	1.98041	.50495	3.83065	.26105
6.150	4.8747	9.4062	4.8731	9.4302	.85627	.10604	1.93515	.51676	3.71269	.26935
6.200	4.8354	9.1327	4.8338	9.1545	.84936	.10924	1.89385	.52802	3.60414	.27746
6.250	4.7967	8.8799	4.7951	8.8997	.84257	.11236	1.85598	.53880	3.50382	.28540
6.300	4.7586	8.6451	4.7571	8.6632	.83588	.11543	1.82112	.54911	3.41073	.29319

6.350	4.7211	8.4263	4.7196	8.4430	.82930	.11844	1.78891	.55900	3.32402	.30084
6.400	4.6843	8.2218	4.6828	8.2372	.82282	.12140	1.75905	.56849	3.24299	.30836
6.450	4.6479	8.0301	4.6465	8.0443	.81644	.12431	1.73127	.57761	3.16704	.31575
6.500	4.6122	7.8498	4.6107	7.8630	.81016	.12718	1.70537	.58638	3.09566	.32303
6.550	4.5770	7.6799	4.5755	7.6921	.80398	.13000	1.68115	.59483	3.02840	.33021
6.600	4.5423	7.5194	4.5409	7.5308	.79789	.13279	1.65844	.60297	2.96487	.33728
6.650	4.5082	7.3674	4.5067	7.3780	.79189	.13554	1.63712	.61083	2.90474	.34427
6.700	4.4745	7.2233	4.4731	7.2332	.78598	.13825	1.61704	.61841	2.84770	.35116
6.750	4.4414	7.0863	4.4399	7.0955	.78016	.14093	1.59811	.62574	2.79352	.35797
6.800	4.4087	6.9558	4.4073	6.9645	.77442	.14358	1.58022	.63282	2.74194	.36471
6.850	4.3765	6.8315	4.3751	6.8396	.76877	.14621	1.56329	.63968	2.69276	.37137
6.900	4.3448	6.7127	4.3434	6.7204	.76320	.14880	1.54725	.64631	2.64581	.37796
6.950	4.3136	6.5991	4.3122	6.6063	.75771	.15137	1.53201	.65274	2.60091	.38448
7.000	4.2827	6.4904	4.2814	6.4971	.75229	.15391	1.51753	.65896	2.55793	.39094
7.050	4.2524	6.3861	4.2510	6.3925	.74696	.15643	1.50375	.66500	2.51672	.39734
7.100	4.2224	6.2860	4.2211	6.2920	.74170	.15893	1.49061	.67086	2.47717	.40369
7.150	4.1929	6.1898	4.1916	6.1955	.73651	.16141	1.47808	.67655	2.43916	.40998
7.200	4.1638	6.0972	4.1625	6.1026	.73140	.16386	1.46611	.68208	2.40260	.41622
7.250	4.1351	6.0081	4.1337	6.0132	.72635	.16630	1.45466	.68744	2.36741	.42240
7.300	4.1067	5.9222	4.1054	5.9270	.72138	.16872	1.44371	.69266	2.33348	.42854
7.350	4.0788	5.8393	4.0775	5.8439	.71647	.17112	1.43321	.69773	2.30076	.43464
7.400	4.0512	5.7593	4.0500	5.7637	.71163	.17350	1.42314	.70267	2.26916	.44069
7.450	4.0241	5.6820	4.0228	5.6861	.70685	.17587	1.41348	.70747	2.23863	.44670
7.500	3.9972	5.6072	3.9960	5.6111	.70214	.17822	1.40420	.71215	2.20911	.45267
7.550	3.9708	5.5348	3.9695	5.5386	.69749	.18055	1.39528	.71670	2.18053	.45860
7.600	3.9446	5.4647	3.9434	5.4683	.69290	.18287	1.38670	.72114	2.15286	.46450
7.650	3.9189	5.3968	3.9176	5.4002	.68837	.18518	1.37844	.72546	2.12605	.47036
7.700	3.8934	5.3309	3.8922	5.3341	.68390	.18747	1.37047	.72967	2.10004	.47618
7.750	3.8683	5.2670	3.8671	5.2700	.67949	.18975	1.36280	.73378	2.07481	.48197
7.800	3.8435	5.2049	3.8423	5.2078	.67514	.19202	1.35540	.73779	2.05031	.48773
7.850	3.8190	5.1446	3.8178	5.1473	.67084	.19428	1.34825	.74170	2.02651	.49346
7.900	3.7948	5.0859	3.7936	5.0886	.66659	.19652	1.34135	.74552	2.00337	.49916
7.950	3.7710	5.0289	3.7698	5.0314	.66240	.19875	1.33467	.74925	1.98087	.50483
8.000	3.7474	4.9734	3.7462	4.9758	.65826	.20097	1.32822	.75288	1.95898	.51047
8.050	3.7241	4.9194	3.7229	4.9217	.65417	.20318	1.32198	.75644	1.93766	.51609
8.100	3.7011	4.8668	3.7000	4.8689	.65013	.20538	1.31594	.75991	1.91690	.52167
8.150	3.6784	4.8155	3.6773	4.8176	.64614	.20757	1.31009	.76330	1.89667	.52724
8.200	3.6560	4.7655	3.6548	4.7675	.64220	.20976	1.30443	.76662	1.87695	.53278
8.250	3.6338	4.7167	3.6327	4.7186	.63831	.21193	1.29893	.76986	1.85772	.53829
8.300	3.6120	4.6691	3.6108	4.6709	.63447	.21409	1.29360	.77303	1.83895	.54379
8.350	3.5903	4.6227	3.5892	4.6244	.63067	.21624	1.28843	.77614	1.82064	.54926
8.400	3.5690	4.5774	3.5678	4.5790	.62691	.21839	1.28342	.77917	1.80275	.55471
8.450	3.5478	4.5331	3.5467	4.5346	.62320	.22053	1.27854	.78214	1.78528	.56014
8.500	3.5270	4.4898	3.5258	4.4913	.61954	.22265	1.27381	.78505	1.76821	.56554
8.550	3.5063	4.4474	3.5052	4.4489	.61591	.22478	1.26921	.78789	1.75152	.57093
8.600	3.4860	4.4061	3.4848	4.4074	.61233	.22689	1.26474	.79068	1.73521	.57630
8.650	3.4658	4.3656	3.4647	4.3669	.60879	.22900	1.26039	.79340	1.71925	.58165
8.700	3.4459	4.3260	3.4448	4.3272	.60529	.23110	1.25616	.79608	1.70363	.58698
8.750	3.4262	4.2872	3.4251	4.2884	.60184	.23319	1.25205	.79869	1.68834	.59230
8.800	3.4067	4.2493	3.4056	4.2504	.59842	.23527	1.24804	.80126	1.67338	.59759
8.850	3.3875	4.2121	3.3864	4.2131	.59504	.23735	1.24414	.80377	1.65872	.60287
8.900	3.3685	4.1757	3.3674	4.1767	.59169	.23942	1.24034	.80623	1.64436	.60814
8.950	3.3496	4.1400	3.3486	4.1409	.58839	.24149	1.23663	.80865	1.63029	.61339
9.000	3.3310	4.1050	3.3300	4.1059	.58512	.24355	1.23302	.81102	1.61650	.61862
9.050	3.3126	4.0707	3.3116	4.0716	.58189	.24561	1.22950	.81334	1.60298	.62384
9.100	3.2944	4.0371	3.2934	4.0379	.57869	.24765	1.22607	.81561	1.58972	.62904
9.150	3.2764	4.0041	3.2754	4.0049	.57553	.24970	1.22272	.81785	1.57672	.63423
9.200	3.2586	3.9717	3.2576	3.9725	.57240	.25173	1.21945	.82004	1.56396	.63940
9.250	3.2410	3.9399	3.2400	3.9406	.56930	.25377	1.21626	.82219	1.55144	.64456
9.300	3.2236	3.9087	3.2225	3.9094	.56624	.25579	1.21315	.82430	1.53915	.64971
9.350	3.2063	3.8781	3.2053	3.8788	.56322	.25781	1.21011	.82637	1.52708	.65485
9.400	3.1893	3.8481	3.1883	3.8487	.56022	.25983	1.20714	.82840	1.51523	.65997
9.450	3.1724	3.8185	3.1714	3.8191	.55726	.26184	1.20424	.83040	1.50359	.66508
9.500	3.1557	3.7895	3.1547	3.7901	.55432	.26385	1.20140	.83236	1.49215	.67017
9.550	3.1392	3.7610	3.1382	3.7615	.55142	.26585	1.19863	.83429	1.48091	.67526
9.600	3.1228	3.7330	3.1218	3.7335	.54855	.26785	1.19592	.83618	1.46987	.68033
9.650	3.1067	3.7054	3.1057	3.7059	.54571	.26984	1.19327	.83803	1.45901	.68539
9.700	3.0906	3.6784	3.0897	3.6788	.54289	.27183	1.19068	.83986	1.44834	.69045
9.750	3.0748	3.6517	3.0738	3.6521	.54011	.27381	1.18814	.84165	1.43784	.69549
9.800	3.0591	3.6255	3.0581	3.6259	.53735	.27579	1.18566	.84341	1.42752	.70052
9.850	3.0436	3.5998	3.0426	3.6001	.53463	.27777	1.18323	.84514	1.41736	.70553
9.900	3.0282	3.5744	3.0272	3.5747	.53193	.27974	1.18085	.84684	1.40737	.71054
9.950	3.0130	3.5494	3.0120	3.5498	.52925	.28171	1.17853	.84852	1.39754	.71554
10.000	2.9979	3.5249	2.9970	3.5252	.52661	.28367	1.17625	.85016	1.38786	.72053
10.050	2.9830	3.5007	2.9821	3.5010	.52399	.28563	1.17401	.85178	1.37834	.72551
10.100	2.9682	3.4769	2.9673	3.4772	.52139	.28759	1.17183	.85337	1.36896	.73048
10.150	2.9536	3.4535	2.9527	3.4537	.51882	.28954	1.16968	.85493	1.35972	.73544
10.200	2.9391	3.4304	2.9382	3.4306	.51628	.29149	1.16758	.85647	1.35063	.74040
10.250	2.9248	3.4077	2.9239	3.4078	.51376	.29344	1.16553	.85798	1.34167	.74534
10.300	2.9106	3.3853	2.9097	3.3854	.51127	.29538	1.16351	.85947	1.33285	.75027
10.350	2.8965	3.3632	2.8956	3.3633	.50880	.29732	1.16153	.86093	1.32415	.75520
10.400	2.8826	3.3414	2.8817	3.3416	.50635	.29926	1.15959	.86237	1.31559	.76012
10.450	2.8688	3.3200	2.8679	3.3201	.50393	.30119	1.15769	.86379	1.30714	.76503
10.500	2.8552	3.2989	2.8543	3.2990	.50153	.30312	1.15582	.86519	1.29882	.76993
10.550	2.8416	3.2781	2.8407	3.2782	.49915	.30505	1.15399	.86656	1.29062	.77482
10.600	2.8282	3.2575	2.8273	3.2576	.49680	.30697	1.15219	.86791	1.28253	.77971
10.650	2.8150	3.2373	2.8141	3.2374	.49447	.30889	1.15043	.86924	1.27455	.78459

TABLE 23

IEC-R 100

Brit: WG-16

Amer: WR-90, RG-52/U, RG-67/U, RG-171/U

Outside dimensions: 1.000 X 0.500 ±0.002 inches
25.40 X 12.70 ±0.05 millimeters

Inside dimensions: 0.9000 X 0.4000 ±0.0018 inches
22.860 X 10.160 ±0.046 millimeters
corner radius: 0.8 millimeters
a/b: 2.2500

Cutoff: Rectangle in Vacuum — Waveguide in Air

Wavelength: 4.57200cm — 4.56119cm
Frequency: 6557.14120 MHz — 6570.58600 MHz

f (GHz)	THEORETICAL λ (cm)	THEORETICAL λ_g (cm)	PHYSICAL λ (cm)	λ_g (cm)	$\frac{\lambda}{\lambda_c}$	$1/\lambda_g$ (1/cm)	$\frac{\lambda_g}{\lambda}$	$\frac{\lambda}{\lambda_g}$	λ_g (in)	$1/\lambda_g$ (1/in)
7.500	3.9972	8.2347	3.9960	8.2831	.87608	.12073	2.07287	.48242	3.26106	.30665
7.600	3.9446	7.8023	3.9434	7.8431	.86455	.12750	1.98893	.50278	3.08783	.32385
7.700	3.8934	7.4269	3.8922	7.4619	.85332	.13401	1.91716	.52161	2.93775	.34040
7.800	3.8435	7.0970	3.8423	7.1273	.84238	.14031	1.85498	.53909	2.80603	.35638
7.900	3.7948	6.8040	3.7936	6.8305	.83172	.14640	1.80052	.55539	2.68918	.37186
8.000	3.7474	6.5414	3.7462	6.5648	.82132	.15233	1.75238	.57065	2.58456	.38691
8.100	3.7011	6.3042	3.7000	6.3250	.81118	.15810	1.70948	.58497	2.49017	.40158
8.200	3.6560	6.0886	3.6548	6.1072	.80129	.16374	1.67099	.59845	2.40441	.41590
8.300	3.6120	5.8914	3.6108	5.9082	.79164	.16926	1.63624	.61116	2.32604	.42991
8.400	3.5690	5.7102	3.5678	5.7253	.78221	.17466	1.60470	.62317	2.25405	.44365
8.500	3.5270	5.5428	3.5258	5.5565	.77301	.17997	1.57593	.63454	2.18760	.45712
8.600	3.4860	5.3876	3.4848	5.4001	.76402	.18518	1.54958	.64534	2.12600	.47037
8.700	3.4459	5.2431	3.4448	5.2545	.75524	.19031	1.52535	.65559	2.06870	.48339
8.800	3.4067	5.1082	3.4056	5.1186	.74666	.19536	1.50298	.66534	2.01521	.49623

8.900	3.3685	4.9818	3.3674	4.9914	.73827	.20034	1.48228	.67464	1.95512	.50888
9.000	3.3310	4.8630	3.3300	4.8719	.73007	.20526	1.46305	.68350	1.91808	.52136
9.100	3.2944	4.7512	3.2934	4.7594	.72204	.21011	1.44515	.69197	1.87379	.53368
9.200	3.2586	4.6456	3.2576	4.6532	.71419	.21490	1.42844	.70006	1.83199	.54586
9.300	3.2236	4.5458	3.2225	4.5528	.70651	.21964	1.41281	.70781	1.79245	.55789
9.400	3.1893	4.4511	3.1883	4.4577	.69900	.22433	1.39815	.71523	1.75498	.56981
9.500	3.1557	4.3612	3.1547	4.3673	.69164	.22898	1.38437	.72235	1.71941	.58160
9.600	3.1228	4.2756	3.1218	4.2813	.68444	.23357	1.37141	.72918	1.68556	.59327
9.700	3.0906	4.1941	3.0897	4.1994	.67738	.23813	1.35919	.73573	1.65332	.60484
9.800	3.0591	4.1163	3.0581	4.1213	.67047	.24264	1.34764	.74204	1.62255	.61631
9.900	3.0282	4.0419	3.0272	4.0466	.66370	.24712	1.33673	.74810	1.59314	.62769
10.000	2.9979	3.9707	2.9970	3.9751	.65706	.25156	1.32638	.75393	1.56501	.63897
10.100	2.9682	3.9025	2.9673	3.9066	.65055	.25597	1.31657	.75955	1.53805	.65017
10.200	2.9391	3.8371	2.9382	3.8410	.64418	.26035	1.30725	.76496	1.51219	.66129
10.300	2.9106	3.7742	2.9097	3.7779	.63792	.26470	1.29839	.77019	1.48736	.67233
10.400	2.8826	3.7138	2.8817	3.7172	.63179	.26902	1.28995	.77522	1.46348	.68330
10.500	2.8552	3.6556	2.8543	3.6589	.62577	.27331	1.28191	.78009	1.44051	.69420
10.600	2.8282	3.5996	2.8273	3.6027	.61987	.27757	1.27423	.78479	1.41838	.70503
10.700	2.8018	3.5456	2.8009	3.5485	.61407	.28181	1.26690	.78933	1.39704	.71580
10.800	2.7759	3.4934	2.7750	3.4962	.60839	.28603	1.25990	.79371	1.37645	.72651
10.900	2.7504	3.4431	2.7495	3.4457	.60281	.29022	1.25319	.79796	1.35656	.73716
11.000	2.7254	3.3944	2.7245	3.3969	.59733	.29439	1.24677	.80207	1.33734	.74775
11.100	2.7008	3.3473	2.7000	3.3496	.59194	.29854	1.24062	.80605	1.31876	.75829
11.200	2.6767	3.3017	2.6759	3.3039	.58666	.30267	1.23472	.80990	1.30076	.76878
11.300	2.6530	3.2576	2.6522	3.2597	.58147	.30678	1.22905	.81364	1.28333	.77922
11.400	2.6298	3.2148	2.6289	3.2168	.57637	.31087	1.22361	.81726	1.26644	.78961
11.500	2.6069	3.1733	2.6061	3.1752	.57136	.31495	1.21837	.82077	1.25006	.79996
11.600	2.5844	3.1330	2.5836	3.1348	.56643	.31900	1.21334	.82417	1.23416	.81027
11.700	2.5623	3.0939	2.5615	3.0956	.56159	.32304	1.20849	.82748	1.21873	.82053
11.800	2.5406	3.0559	2.5398	3.0575	.55683	.32707	1.20382	.83069	1.20373	.83075
11.900	2.5193	3.0189	2.5185	3.0204	.55215	.33108	1.19932	.83380	1.18915	.84093
12.000	2.4983	2.9830	2.4975	2.9844	.54755	.33507	1.19498	.83683	1.17498	.85108
12.100	2.4776	2.9480	2.4768	2.9494	.54302	.33905	1.19080	.83977	1.16118	.86119
12.200	2.4573	2.9140	2.4565	2.9153	.53857	.34302	1.18675	.84263	1.14776	.87127
12.300	2.4373	2.8808	2.4366	2.8821	.53419	.34697	1.18285	.84542	1.13468	.88131
12.400	2.4177	2.8485	2.4169	2.8497	.52989	.35091	1.17908	.84812	1.12194	.89132
12.500	2.3983	2.8170	2.3976	2.8192	.52565	.35484	1.17543	.85075	1.10952	.90129
12.600	2.3793	2.7863	2.3785	2.7874	.52148	.35876	1.17190	.85332	1.09740	.91124
12.700	2.3606	2.7564	2.3598	2.7574	.51737	.36266	1.16848	.85581	1.08559	.92116
12.800	2.3421	2.7271	2.3414	2.7281	.51333	.36655	1.16517	.85824	1.07406	.93105
12.900	2.3240	2.6986	2.3232	2.6995	.50935	.37044	1.16197	.86061	1.06280	.94091
13.000	2.3061	2.6707	2.3054	2.6716	.50543	.37431	1.15886	.86292	1.05181	.95074
13.100	2.2885	2.6435	2.2878	2.6443	.50157	.37817	1.15585	.86516	1.04107	.96055
13.200	2.2712	2.6169	2.2704	2.6177	.49777	.38202	1.15293	.86735	1.03057	.97034

TABLE 24

IEC-R 120 | Brit: WG-17 | Amer: WR-75, RG-346/U, RG-347/U, RG-348/U

Outside dimensions: 0.850 X 0.475 ±0.002 inches
21.59 X 12.06 ±0.05 millimeters

Inside dimensions: 0.7500 X 0.3750 ±0.0015 inches
19.050 X 9.525 ±0.038 millimeters
corner radius: 0.8 millimeters
a/b: 2.000

Cutoff: | Rectangle in Vacuum | Waveguide in Air
Wavelength: 3.81000cm 3.79846cm
Frequency: 7868.56950 MHz 7889.94120 MHz

	THEORETICAL		PHYSICAL							
f (GHz)	λ (cm)	λ_g (cm)	λ (cm)	λ_g (cm)	$\frac{\lambda}{\lambda_c}$	$1/\lambda_g$ (1/cm)	$\frac{\lambda_g}{\lambda}$	$\frac{\lambda}{\lambda_g}$	λ_g (in)	$1/\lambda_g$ (1/in)
9.000	3.3310	6.8623	3.3300	6.9177	.87666	.14456	2.07742	.48137	2.72352	.36717
9.100	3.2944	6.5583	3.2934	6.6065	.86703	.15137	2.00601	.49850	2.60099	.38447
9.200	3.2586	6.2887	3.2576	6.3310	.85760	.15795	1.94348	.51454	2.49252	.40120
9.300	3.2236	6.0474	3.2225	6.0848	.84838	.16434	1.88820	.52960	2.39560	.41743
9.400	3.1893	5.8297	3.1883	5.8630	.83936	.17056	1.83894	.54379	2.30828	.43322
9.500	3.1557	5.6319	3.1547	5.6618	.83052	.17662	1.79473	.55719	2.22907	.44862
9.600	3.1228	5.4512	3.1218	5.4782	.82187	.18254	1.75480	.56987	2.15677	.46366
9.700	3.0906	5.2852	3.0897	5.3097	.81340	.18834	1.71853	.58189	2.09042	.47837
9.800	3.0591	5.1319	3.0581	5.1543	.80510	.19401	1.68543	.59332	2.02924	.49280
9.900	3.0282	4.9899	3.0272	5.0104	.79696	.19959	1.65509	.60420	1.97258	.50695
10.000	2.9979	4.8578	2.9970	4.8766	.78899	.20506	1.62717	.61456	1.91991	.52086
10.100	2.9682	4.7345	2.9673	4.7518	.78118	.21045	1.60139	.62446	1.87078	.53454
10.200	2.9391	4.6190	2.9382	4.6350	.77352	.21575	1.57749	.63392	1.82480	.54801
10.300	2.9106	4.5105	2.9097	4.5254	.76601	.22098	1.55528	.64297	1.78164	.56128
10.400	2.8826	4.4084	2.8817	4.4222	.75865	.22613	1.53459	.65164	1.74103	.57437
10.500	2.8552	4.3121	2.8543	4.3249	.75142	.23122	1.51525	.65996	1.70272	.58730
10.600	2.8282	4.2209	2.8273	4.2329	.74433	.23624	1.49714	.66794	1.66650	.60006
10.700	2.8018	4.1346	2.8009	4.1457	.73738	.24121	1.48015	.67561	1.63218	.61268
10.800	2.7759	4.0525	2.7750	4.0630	.73055	.24612	1.46416	.68298	1.59961	.62515
10.900	2.7504	3.9745	2.7495	3.9843	.72385	.25098	1.44911	.69008	1.56863	.63750
11.000	2.7254	3.9001	2.7245	3.9094	.71727	.25579	1.43489	.69692	1.53913	.64972
11.100	2.7008	3.8292	2.7000	3.8379	.71081	.26056	1.42146	.70350	1.51098	.66182
11.200	2.6767	3.7614	2.6759	3.7696	.70446	.26528	1.40874	.70986	1.48409	.67381
11.300	2.6530	3.6965	2.6522	3.7042	.69822	.26996	1.39667	.71599	1.45836	.68570
11.400	2.6298	3.6343	2.6289	3.6416	.69210	.27460	1.38522	.72191	1.43371	.69749
11.500	2.6069	3.5746	2.6061	3.5816	.68608	.27921	1.37433	.72763	1.41007	.70918
11.600	2.5844	3.5174	2.5836	3.5239	.68017	.28377	1.36396	.73316	1.38737	.72079
11.700	2.5623	3.4623	2.5615	3.4685	.67435	.28831	1.35408	.73851	1.36555	.73231
11.800	2.5406	3.4093	2.5398	3.4152	.66864	.29281	1.34466	.74368	1.34455	.74374
11.900	2.5193	3.3582	2.5185	3.3638	.66302	.29728	1.33566	.74870	1.32433	.75510
12.000	2.4983	3.3089	2.4975	3.3143	.65750	.30173	1.32705	.75355	1.30483	.76638
12.100	2.4776	3.2614	2.4768	3.2665	.65206	.30614	1.31882	.75826	1.28602	.77759
12.200	2.4573	3.2155	2.4565	3.2203	.64672	.31053	1.31093	.76282	1.26785	.78874
12.300	2.4373	3.1711	2.4366	3.1757	.64146	.31489	1.30337	.76724	1.25029	.79982
12.400	2.4177	3.1282	2.4169	3.1326	.63629	.31923	1.29611	.77154	1.23330	.81083
12.500	2.3983	3.0866	2.3976	3.0908	.63120	.32354	1.28915	.77571	1.21686	.82179
12.600	2.3793	3.0464	2.3785	3.0504	.62619	.32783	1.28246	.77975	1.20094	.83268
12.700	2.3606	3.0073	2.3598	3.0112	.62126	.33210	1.27602	.78369	1.18550	.84353
12.800	2.3421	2.9695	2.3414	2.9731	.61640	.33634	1.26983	.78751	1.17053	.85431
12.900	2.3240	2.9327	2.3232	2.9362	.61162	.34057	1.26386	.79122	1.15600	.86505
13.000	2.3061	2.8970	2.3054	2.9004	.60692	.34478	1.25812	.79484	1.14189	.87574
13.100	2.2885	2.8624	2.2878	2.8656	.60229	.34897	1.25258	.79835	1.12819	.88638
13.200	2.2712	2.8287	2.2704	2.8318	.59772	.35314	1.24723	.80177	1.11486	.89697
13.300	2.2541	2.7959	2.2534	2.7988	.59323	.35729	1.24208	.80510	1.10191	.90752
13.400	2.2373	2.7640	2.2365	2.7668	.58880	.36143	1.23709	.80835	1.08930	.91802
13.500	2.2207	2.7329	2.2200	2.7356	.58444	.36555	1.23228	.81150	1.07702	.92849
13.600	2.2044	2.7026	2.2037	2.7053	.58014	.36965	1.22763	.81458	1.06506	.93891
13.700	2.1883	2.6731	2.1876	2.6757	.57591	.37374	1.22312	.81758	1.05341	.94930
13.800	2.1724	2.6444	2.1717	2.6468	.57173	.37781	1.21877	.82050	1.04205	.95965
13.900	2.1568	2.6163	2.1561	2.6187	.56762	.38187	1.21455	.82335	1.03097	.96996
14.000	2.1414	2.5890	2.1407	2.5912	.56357	.38592	1.21046	.82613	1.02017	.98023
14.100	2.1262	2.5623	2.1255	2.5644	.55957	.38995	1.20650	.82884	1.00962	.99047
14.200	2.1112	2.5362	2.1105	2.5383	.55563	.39397	1.20266	.83149	.99932	1.00068
14.300	2.0965	2.5107	2.0958	2.5127	.55174	.39798	1.19894	.83407	.98926	1.01086
14.400	2.0819	2.4858	2.0812	2.4877	.54791	.40197	1.19532	.83659	.97943	1.02101
14.500	2.0675	2.4615	2.0669	2.4633	.54413	.40595	1.19182	.83905	.96982	1.03112
14.600	2.0534	2.4377	2.0527	2.4395	.54041	.40992	1.18841	.84146	.96042	1.04121

14.700	2.0394	2.4144	2.0388	2.4161	.53673	.41388	1.18510	.84381	.95123	1.05127
14.800	2.0256	2.3916	2.0250	2.3933	.53310	.41783	1.18189	.84610	.94224	1.06130
14.900	2.0120	2.3694	2.0114	2.3709	.52953	.42177	1.17876	.84835	.93344	1.07130
15.000	1.9986	2.3475	1.9980	2.3491	.52600	.42570	1.17573	.85054	.92483	1.08128
15.100	1.9854	2.3262	1.9847	2.3276	.52251	.42962	1.17277	.85268	.91640	1.09123
15.200	1.9723	2.3052	1.9717	2.3067	.51908	.43353	1.16989	.85478	.90814	1.10116
15.300	1.9594	2.2847	1.9588	2.2861	.51568	.43743	1.16709	.85683	.90004	1.11106
15.400	1.9467	2.2646	1.9461	2.2660	.51233	.44132	1.16437	.85884	.89211	1.12094
15.500	1.9341	2.2449	1.9335	2.2462	.50903	.44520	1.16171	.86080	.88433	1.13080
15.600	1.9217	2.2256	1.9211	2.2268	.50577	.44907	1.15913	.86272	.87671	1.14063
15.700	1.9095	2.2067	1.9089	2.2078	.50254	.45293	1.15661	.86460	.86923	1.15045
15.800	1.8974	2.1881	1.8968	2.1892	.49936	.45679	1.15415	.86644	.86189	1.16024

TABLE 25

IEC-R 140 Brit: WG-18 Amer: WR-62, RG-91/U, RG-349/U, RG-172/U

Outside dimensions: 0.702 X 0.391 ±0.002 inches
17.83 X 9.93 ±0.05 millimeters

Inside dimensions: 0.6220 X 0.3110 ±0.0016 inches
15.799 X 7.899 ±0.031 millimeters
corner radius: 0.4 millimeters
a/b: 2.000

Cutoff: Rectangle in Vacuum Waveguide in Air
Wavelength: 3.15980cm 3.15632cm
Frequency: 9487.70480 MHz 9495.12010 MHz

	THEORETICAL		PHYSICAL							
f (GHz)	λ (cm)	λ_g (cm)	λ (cm)	λ_g (cm)	λ/λ_c	$1/\lambda_g$ (1/cm)	λ_g/λ	λ/λ_g	λ_g (in)	$1/\lambda_g$ (1/in)
11.000	2.7254	5.3859	2.7245	5.3939	.86319	.18539	1.97976	.50511	2.12358	.47090
11.100	2.7008	5.2035	2.7000	5.2106	.85542	.19192	1.92988	.51817	2.05142	.48747
11.200	2.6767	5.0370	2.6759	5.0434	.84778	.19828	1.88478	.53057	1.98559	.50363
11.300	2.6530	4.8843	2.6522	4.8900	.84028	.20450	1.84377	.54237	1.92520	.51943
11.400	2.6298	4.7435	2.6289	4.7486	.83291	.21059	1.80631	.55362	1.86954	.53489
11.500	2.6069	4.6131	2.6061	4.6177	.82566	.21656	1.77193	.56436	1.81801	.55005
11.600	2.5844	4.4919	2.5836	4.4961	.81854	.22241	1.74025	.57463	1.77012	.56493
11.700	2.5623	4.3788	2.5615	4.3827	.81155	.22817	1.71097	.58446	1.72546	.57956
11.800	2.5406	4.2730	2.5398	4.2765	.80467	.23384	1.68380	.59390	1.68367	.59394
11.900	2.5193	4.1737	2.5185	4.1769	.79791	.23941	1.65852	.60295	1.64446	.60810
12.000	2.4983	4.0803	2.4975	4.0832	.79126	.24491	1.63494	.61164	1.60756	.62206
12.100	2.4776	3.9921	2.4768	3.9948	.78472	.25032	1.61288	.62001	1.57277	.63582
12.200	2.4573	3.9088	2.4565	3.9113	.77829	.25567	1.59220	.62806	1.53988	.64940
12.300	2.4373	3.8299	2.4366	3.8322	.77196	.26095	1.57277	.63582	1.50872	.66281
12.400	2.4177	3.7549	2.4169	3.7570	.76574	.26617	1.55448	.64330	1.47915	.67606
12.500	2.3983	3.6837	2.3976	3.6856	.75961	.27132	1.53723	.65052	1.45103	.68917
12.600	2.3793	3.6158	2.3785	3.6176	.75358	.27643	1.52093	.65749	1.42425	.70212
12.700	2.3606	3.5511	2.3598	3.5527	.74765	.28148	1.50550	.66423	1.39870	.71495
12.800	2.3421	3.4892	2.3414	3.4907	.74181	.28647	1.49088	.67075	1.37430	.72765
12.900	2.3240	3.4300	2.3232	3.4314	.73606	.29143	1.47700	.67705	1.35095	.74022
13.000	2.3061	3.3733	2.3054	3.3746	.73039	.29633	1.46381	.68315	1.32858	.75268
13.100	2.2885	3.3189	2.2878	3.3201	.72482	.30119	1.45125	.68906	1.30713	.76504
13.200	2.2712	3.2667	2.2704	3.2678	.71933	.30602	1.43928	.69479	1.28653	.77728
13.300	2.2541	3.2165	2.2534	3.2175	.71392	.31080	1.42787	.70034	1.26673	.78943
13.400	2.2373	3.1681	2.2365	3.1691	.70859	.31555	1.41697	.70573	1.24768	.80149
13.500	2.2207	3.1216	2.2200	3.1225	.70334	.32026	1.40654	.71096	1.22933	.81345
13.600	2.2044	3.0767	2.2037	3.0776	.69817	.32493	1.39657	.71604	1.21163	.82533
13.700	2.1883	3.0334	2.1876	3.0342	.69307	.32958	1.38702	.72097	1.19456	.83713
13.800	2.1724	2.9916	2.1717	2.9923	.68805	.33419	1.37786	.72577	1.17807	.84884
13.900	2.1568	2.9512	2.1561	2.9518	.68310	.33877	1.36907	.73042	1.16214	.86048
14.000	2.1414	2.9121	2.1407	2.9127	.67822	.34333	1.36062	.73496	1.14672	.87205
14.100	2.1262	2.8742	2.1255	2.8748	.67341	.34785	1.35251	.73936	1.13180	.88355
14.200	2.1112	2.8375	2.1105	2.8381	.66867	.35235	1.34471	.74366	1.11735	.89498
14.300	2.0965	2.8020	2.0958	2.8025	.66399	.35683	1.33720	.74783	1.10334	.90634
14.400	2.0819	2.7675	2.0812	2.7680	.65938	.36128	1.32997	.75190	1.08975	.91764
14.500	2.0675	2.7341	2.0669	2.7345	.65484	.36570	1.32299	.75586	1.07656	.92889
14.600	2.0534	2.7016	2.0527	2.7019	.65035	.37011	1.31627	.75972	1.06375	.94007
14.700	2.0394	2.6700	2.0388	2.6703	.64593	.37449	1.30978	.76349	1.05131	.95120
14.800	2.0256	2.6393	2.0250	2.6396	.64156	.37885	1.30351	.76716	1.03921	.96227
14.900	2.0120	2.6094	2.0114	2.6097	.63726	.38319	1.29746	.77074	1.02744	.97329
15.000	1.9986	2.5804	1.9980	2.5806	.63301	.38751	1.29161	.77423	1.01599	.98426
15.100	1.9854	2.5521	1.9847	2.5523	.62882	.39181	1.28595	.77764	1.00484	.99519
15.200	1.9723	2.5245	1.9717	2.5247	.62468	.39609	1.28047	.78096	.99397	1.00606
15.300	1.9594	2.4976	1.9588	2.4978	.62060	.40035	1.27517	.78421	.98339	1.01689
15.400	1.9467	2.4714	1.9461	2.4716	.61657	.40460	1.27003	.78738	.97307	1.02768
15.500	1.9341	2.4459	1.9335	2.4460	.61259	.40883	1.26506	.79048	.96300	1.03842
15.600	1.9217	2.4210	1.9211	2.4211	.60866	.41304	1.26023	.79350	.95318	1.04912
15.700	1.9095	2.3966	1.9089	2.3967	.60478	.41724	1.25555	.79646	.94359	1.05978
15.800	1.8974	2.3729	1.8968	2.3729	.60096	.42142	1.25101	.79935	.93423	1.07040
15.900	1.8855	2.3496	1.8849	2.3497	.59718	.42559	1.24660	.80218	.92508	1.08099
16.000	1.8737	2.3270	1.8731	2.3270	.59345	.42974	1.24232	.80494	.91614	1.09154
16.100	1.8621	2.3048	1.8615	2.3048	.58976	.43388	1.23816	.80765	.90740	1.10205
16.200	1.8506	2.2831	1.8500	2.2831	.58612	.43800	1.23412	.81029	.89886	1.11252
16.300	1.8392	2.2619	1.8386	2.2619	.58252	.44211	1.23019	.81288	.89050	1.12297
16.400	1.8280	2.2411	1.8274	2.2411	.57897	.44621	1.22637	.81541	.88232	1.13338
16.500	1.8169	2.2208	1.8163	2.2208	.57546	.45030	1.22265	.81789	.87431	1.14375
16.600	1.8060	2.2009	1.8054	2.2008	.57200	.45437	1.21904	.82032	.86648	1.15410
16.700	1.7952	2.1814	1.7946	2.1813	.56857	.45843	1.21551	.82270	.85880	1.16442
16.800	1.7845	2.1623	1.7839	2.1622	.56519	.46248	1.21208	.82503	.85128	1.17470
16.900	1.7739	2.1436	1.7734	2.1435	.56184	.46652	1.20874	.82731	.84391	1.18496
17.000	1.7635	2.1253	1.7629	2.1252	.55854	.47055	1.20549	.82954	.83668	1.19519
17.100	1.7532	2.1073	1.7526	2.1072	.55527	.47457	1.20231	.83173	.82960	1.20540
17.200	1.7430	2.0896	1.7424	2.0895	.55204	.47857	1.19922	.83387	.82266	1.21557
17.300	1.7329	2.0724	1.7324	2.0722	.54885	.48257	1.19620	.83598	.81584	1.22572
17.400	1.7229	2.0554	1.7224	2.0553	.54570	.48656	1.19326	.83804	.80916	1.23585
17.500	1.7131	2.0387	1.7126	2.0386	.54258	.49053	1.19039	.84006	.80260	1.24595
17.600	1.7034	2.0224	1.7028	2.0222	.53950	.49450	1.18759	.84204	.79616	1.25603
17.700	1.6937	2.0063	1.6932	2.0062	.53645	.49846	1.18485	.84399	.78984	1.26608
17.800	1.6842	1.9906	1.6837	1.9904	.53343	.50241	1.18218	.84590	.78363	1.27611
17.900	1.6748	1.9751	1.6743	1.9749	.53045	.50635	1.17957	.84777	.77753	1.28612
18.000	1.6655	1.9599	1.6650	1.9597	.52751	.51028	1.17702	.84960	.77154	1.29611
18.100	1.6563	1.9449	1.6558	1.9448	.52459	.51420	1.17453	.85141	.76566	1.30607
18.200	1.6472	1.9302	1.6467	1.9301	.52171	.51812	1.17209	.85317	.75987	1.31602
18.300	1.6382	1.9158	1.6377	1.9156	.51886	.52202	1.16971	.85491	.75418	1.32594
18.400	1.6293	1.9016	1.6288	1.9014	.51604	.52592	1.16739	.85661	.74859	1.33584
18.500	1.6205	1.8876	1.6200	1.8875	.51325	.52981	1.16511	.85829	.74309	1.34573
18.600	1.6118	1.8739	1.6113	1.8737	.51049	.53370	1.16288	.85993	.73769	1.35559
18.700	1.6032	1.8604	1.6027	1.8602	.50776	.53757	1.16070	.86155	.73237	1.36544
18.800	1.5946	1.8471	1.5941	1.8469	.50506	.54144	1.15857	.86313	.72713	1.37527
18.900	1.5862	1.8340	1.5857	1.8338	.50239	.54531	1.15648	.86469	.72198	1.38508
19.000	1.5779	1.8212	1.5774	1.8210	.49974	.54916	1.15444	.86622	.71691	1.39487
19.100	1.5696	1.8085	1.5691	1.8083	.49713	.55301	1.15244	.86772	.71192	1.40465
19.200	1.5614	1.7960	1.5609	1.7958	.49454	.55685	1.15048	.86920	.70701	1.41440

61

TABLE 26

IEC-R 180 | Brit: WG-19 | Amer: WR-51, RG-352/U, RG-351/U, RG-350/U

Outside dimensions: 0.590 X 0.335 ±0.002 inches
14.99 X 8.51 ±0.05 millimeters

Inside dimensions: 0.5100 X 0.2550 ±0.0010 inches
12.954 X 6.477 ±0.026 millimeters
corner radius: 0.4 millimeters
a/b: 2.000

Cutoff: Rectangle in Vacuum | Waveguide in Air
Wavelength: 2.59080cm | 2.58656cm
Frequency: 11571.4256 MHz | 11586.6914 MHz

	THEORETICAL		PHYSICAL							
f (GHz)	λ (cm)	λ_g (cm)	λ (cm)	λ_g (cm)	$\frac{\lambda}{\lambda_c}$	$1/\lambda_g$ (1/cm)	$\frac{\lambda_g}{\lambda}$	$\frac{\lambda}{\lambda_g}$	λ_g (in)	$1/\lambda_g$ (1/in)
13.500	2.2207	4.3113	2.2200	4.3239	.85827	.23127	1.94772	.51342	1.70231	.58744
13.600	2.2044	4.1954	2.2037	4.2069	.85196	.23771	1.90904	.52382	1.65624	.60379
13.700	2.1883	4.0875	2.1876	4.0981	.84574	.24402	1.87335	.53380	1.61342	.61980
13.800	2.1724	3.9869	2.1717	3.9966	.83962	.25021	1.84030	.54339	1.57347	.63554
13.900	2.1568	3.8927	2.1561	3.9017	.83357	.25630	1.80960	.55261	1.53609	.65100
14.000	2.1414	3.8042	2.1407	3.8126	.82762	.26229	1.78100	.56148	1.50101	.66622
14.100	2.1262	3.7210	2.1255	3.7287	.82175	.26819	1.75428	.57004	1.46800	.68120
14.200	2.1112	3.6424	2.1105	3.6496	.81596	.27400	1.72925	.57829	1.43687	.69596
14.300	2.0965	3.5681	2.0958	3.5749	.81026	.27973	1.70575	.58625	1.40743	.71051
14.400	2.0819	3.4978	2.0812	3.5040	.80463	.28538	1.68365	.59395	1.37955	.72489
14.500	2.0675	3.4309	2.0669	3.4368	.79908	.29097	1.66281	.60139	1.35308	.73906
14.600	2.0534	3.3673	2.0527	3.3729	.79361	.29648	1.64313	.60859	1.32791	.75306
14.700	2.0394	3.3068	2.0388	3.3120	.78821	.30193	1.62452	.61557	1.30393	.76691
14.800	2.0256	3.2490	2.0250	3.2539	.78288	.30732	1.60688	.62232	1.28106	.78060
14.900	2.0120	3.1938	2.0114	3.1984	.77763	.31266	1.59014	.62888	1.25921	.79415
15.000	1.9986	3.1409	1.9980	3.1453	.77245	.31794	1.57423	.63523	1.23830	.80756
15.100	1.9854	3.0903	1.9847	3.0944	.76733	.32316	1.55909	.64140	1.21827	.82084
15.200	1.9723	3.0417	1.9717	3.0456	.76228	.32834	1.54467	.64739	1.19906	.83399
15.300	1.9594	2.9950	1.9588	2.9987	.75730	.33347	1.53091	.65321	1.18061	.84702
15.400	1.9467	2.9502	1.9461	2.9537	.75238	.33856	1.51776	.65886	1.16287	.85994
15.500	1.9341	2.9070	1.9335	2.9103	.74753	.34360	1.50520	.66436	1.14580	.87275
15.600	1.9217	2.8654	1.9211	2.8686	.74274	.34860	1.49317	.66972	1.12936	.88546
15.700	1.9095	2.8253	1.9089	2.8283	.73801	.35357	1.48165	.67492	1.11351	.89806
15.800	1.8974	2.7866	1.8968	2.7895	.73333	.35849	1.47060	.67999	1.09821	.91057
15.900	1.8855	2.7492	1.8849	2.7519	.72872	.36338	1.46000	.68493	1.08344	.92299
16.000	1.8737	2.7131	1.8731	2.7156	.72417	.36824	1.44981	.68974	1.06915	.93532
16.100	1.8621	2.6781	1.8615	2.6806	.71967	.37306	1.44002	.69444	1.05534	.94757
16.200	1.8506	2.6442	1.8500	2.6466	.71523	.37785	1.43060	.69901	1.04196	.95973
16.300	1.8392	2.6114	1.8386	2.6137	.71084	.38260	1.42153	.70347	1.02900	.97182
16.400	1.8280	2.5796	1.8274	2.5818	.70651	.38733	1.41279	.70782	1.01644	.98383
16.500	1.8169	2.5488	1.8163	2.5508	.70222	.39203	1.40436	.71207	1.00425	.99576
16.600	1.8060	2.5188	1.8054	2.5208	.69799	.39671	1.39623	.71621	.99243	1.00763
16.700	1.7952	2.4897	1.7946	2.4916	.69381	.40135	1.38839	.72026	.98094	1.01943
16.800	1.7845	2.4614	1.7839	2.4632	.68968	.40597	1.38080	.72422	.96978	1.03117
16.900	1.7739	2.4339	1.7734	2.4357	.68560	.41057	1.37348	.72808	.95892	1.04284
17.000	1.7635	2.4072	1.7629	2.4088	.68157	.41514	1.36639	.73185	.94836	1.05445
17.100	1.7532	2.3812	1.7526	2.3827	.67758	.41969	1.35954	.73554	.93809	1.06600
17.200	1.7430	2.3558	1.7424	2.3573	.67364	.42421	1.35290	.73915	.92808	1.07749
17.300	1.7329	2.3311	1.7324	2.3326	.66975	.42871	1.34647	.74268	.91833	1.08893
17.400	1.7229	2.3070	1.7224	2.3084	.66590	.43320	1.34024	.74613	.90883	1.10032
17.500	1.7131	2.2836	1.7126	2.2849	.66210	.43766	1.33420	.74951	.89956	1.11165
17.600	1.7034	2.2607	1.7028	2.2619	.65833	.44210	1.32834	.75282	.89052	1.12293
17.700	1.6937	2.2383	1.6932	2.2395	.65462	.44652	1.32266	.75605	.88170	1.13417
17.800	1.6842	2.2165	1.6837	2.2177	.65094	.45093	1.31714	.75922	.87309	1.14535
17.900	1.6748	2.1952	1.6743	2.1963	.64730	.45531	1.31178	.76232	.86468	1.15649
18.000	1.6655	2.1743	1.6650	2.1754	.64371	.45968	1.30657	.76536	.85647	1.16759
18.100	1.6563	2.1540	1.6558	2.1550	.64015	.46403	1.30151	.76834	.84843	1.17864
18.200	1.6472	2.1341	1.6467	2.1351	.63663	.46837	1.29659	.77125	.84058	1.18965
18.300	1.6382	2.1146	1.6377	2.1156	.63315	.47269	1.29181	.77411	.83290	1.20062
18.400	1.6293	2.0956	1.6288	2.0965	.62971	.47699	1.28715	.77691	.82539	1.21155
18.500	1.6205	2.0769	1.6200	2.0778	.62631	.48127	1.28262	.77966	.81804	1.22244
18.600	1.6118	2.0587	1.6113	2.0595	.62294	.48555	1.27820	.78235	.81084	1.23329
18.700	1.6032	2.0408	1.6027	2.0416	.61961	.48980	1.27390	.78499	.80379	1.24410
18.800	1.5946	2.0233	1.5941	2.0241	.61631	.49405	1.26972	.78758	.79689	1.25488
18.900	1.5862	2.0062	1.5857	2.0069	.61305	.49828	1.26563	.79012	.79012	1.26563
19.000	1.5779	1.9893	1.5774	1.9901	.60983	.50249	1.26165	.79261	.78349	1.27634
19.100	1.5696	1.9729	1.5691	1.9736	.60663	.50670	1.25777	.79506	.77699	1.28701
19.200	1.5614	1.9567	1.5609	1.9574	.60347	.51089	1.25399	.79746	.77062	1.29766
19.300	1.5533	1.9409	1.5528	1.9415	.60035	.51507	1.25029	.79981	.76437	1.30827
19.400	1.5453	1.9253	1.5448	1.9259	.59725	.51923	1.24669	.80212	.75824	1.31885
19.500	1.5374	1.9100	1.5369	1.9106	.59419	.52339	1.24317	.80440	.75222	1.32940
19.600	1.5296	1.8951	1.5291	1.8956	.59116	.52753	1.23973	.80663	.74631	1.33992
19.700	1.5218	1.8804	1.5213	1.8809	.58816	.53166	1.23638	.80882	.74051	1.35042
19.800	1.5141	1.8659	1.5136	1.8664	.58519	.53578	1.23310	.81097	.73482	1.36088
19.900	1.5065	1.8517	1.5060	1.8522	.58225	.53989	1.22989	.81308	.72923	1.37132
20.000	1.4990	1.8378	1.4985	1.8383	.57933	.54399	1.22676	.81516	.72373	1.38173
20.100	1.4915	1.8241	1.4910	1.8246	.57645	.54808	1.22370	.81720	.71833	1.39211
20.200	1.4841	1.8106	1.4836	1.8111	.57360	.55215	1.22070	.81920	.71303	1.40247
20.300	1.4768	1.7974	1.4763	1.7978	.57077	.55622	1.21777	.82117	.70781	1.41280
20.400	1.4696	1.7844	1.4691	1.7848	.56798	.56028	1.21491	.82311	.70269	1.42311
20.500	1.4624	1.7716	1.4619	1.7720	.56520	.56433	1.21210	.82501	.69764	1.43340
20.600	1.4553	1.7590	1.4548	1.7594	.56246	.56837	1.20936	.82689	.69268	1.44366
20.700	1.4483	1.7467	1.4478	1.7470	.55974	.57240	1.20667	.82873	.68781	1.45390
20.800	1.4413	1.7345	1.4408	1.7348	.55705	.57642	1.20404	.83054	.68301	1.46411
20.900	1.4344	1.7225	1.4340	1.7228	.55439	.58044	1.20146	.83232	.67829	1.47431
21.000	1.4276	1.7107	1.4271	1.7110	.55175	.58444	1.19894	.83407	.67364	1.48448
21.100	1.4208	1.6991	1.4204	1.6994	.54913	.58844	1.19647	.83579	.66906	1.49463
21.200	1.4141	1.6877	1.4137	1.6880	.54654	.59242	1.19405	.83749	.66456	1.50476
21.300	1.4075	1.6764	1.4070	1.6767	.54398	.59640	1.19167	.83916	.66012	1.51487
21.400	1.4009	1.6654	1.4005	1.6656	.54143	.60038	1.18935	.84080	.65576	1.52496
21.500	1.3944	1.6544	1.3939	1.6547	.53892	.60434	1.18706	.84241	.65145	1.53503
21.600	1.3879	1.6437	1.3875	1.6439	.53642	.60830	1.18483	.84401	.64722	1.54508
21.700	1.3815	1.6331	1.3811	1.6333	.53395	.61225	1.18263	.84557	.64304	1.55511
21.800	1.3752	1.6227	1.3748	1.6229	.53150	.61619	1.18048	.84711	.63893	1.56513
21.900	1.3689	1.6124	1.3685	1.6126	.52907	.62013	1.17837	.84863	.63487	1.57512
22.000	1.3627	1.6022	1.3623	1.6024	.52667	.62405	1.17630	.85012	.63088	1.58510
22.100	1.3565	1.5922	1.3561	1.5924	.52428	.62798	1.17427	.85159	.62694	1.59506
22.200	1.3504	1.5824	1.3500	1.5826	.52192	.63189	1.17227	.85304	.62305	1.60500
22.300	1.3444	1.5727	1.3439	1.5728	.51958	.63580	1.17032	.85447	.61922	1.61493
22.400	1.3384	1.5631	1.3379	1.5632	.51726	.63970	1.16839	.85588	.61544	1.62484
22.500	1.3324	1.5536	1.3320	1.5538	.51496	.64360	1.16651	.85726	.61172	1.63474
22.600	1.3265	1.5443	1.3261	1.5444	.51269	.64749	1.16465	.85863	.60805	1.64461
22.700	1.3207	1.5351	1.3202	1.5352	.51043	.65137	1.16283	.85997	.60442	1.65448
22.800	1.3149	1.5260	1.3145	1.5261	.50819	.65525	1.16104	.86129	.60084	1.66433
22.900	1.3091	1.5171	1.3087	1.5172	.50597	.65912	1.15929	.86260	.59732	1.67416
23.000	1.3034	1.5082	1.3030	1.5083	.50377	.66298	1.15756	.86389	.59383	1.68398
23.100	1.2978	1.4995	1.2974	1.4996	.50159	.66684	1.15587	.86515	.59040	1.69378
23.200	1.2922	1.4909	1.2918	1.4910	.49943	.67070	1.15420	.86640	.58700	1.70357
23.300	1.2867	1.4824	1.2863	1.4825	.49728	.67454	1.15256	.86763	.58365	1.71334
23.400	1.2812	1.4740	1.2808	1.4741	.49516	.67839	1.15095	.86885	.58035	1.72310
23.500	1.2757	1.4657	1.2753	1.4658	.49305	.68223	1.14937	.87005	.57708	1.73285

TABLE 27

IEC-R 220 | Brit: WG-20 | Amer: WR-42, RG-53/U, RG-121/U, RG-173/U

Outside dimensions: 0.500 X 0.250 ±0.002 inches
12.70 X 6.35 ±0.05 millimeters

Inside dimensions: 0.4200 X 0.1700 ±0.0008 inches
10.668 X 4.318 ±0.021 millimeters
corner radius: 0.4 millimeters

Cutoff:	Rectangle in Vacuum	Waveguide in Air
Wavelength:	2.13360cm	2.12724cm
Frequency:	14051.0170 MHz	14088.5292 MHz

f	THEORETICAL		PHYSICAL							
f (GHz)	λ (cm)	λ_g (cm)	λ (cm)	λ_g (cm)	$\frac{\lambda}{\lambda_c}$	$1/\lambda_g$ (1/cm)	$\frac{\lambda_g}{\lambda}$	$\frac{\lambda}{\lambda_g}$	λ_g (in)	$1/\lambda_g$ (1/in)
16.000	1.8737	3.9173	1.8731	3.9496	.88053	.25319	2.10861	.47425	1.55498	.64310
16.100	1.8621	3.8142	1.8615	3.8439	.87506	.26015	2.06501	.48426	1.51336	.66078
16.200	1.8506	3.7182	1.8500	3.7457	.86966	.26697	2.02473	.49389	1.47469	.67811
16.300	1.8392	3.6286	1.8386	3.6541	.86433	.27366	1.98741	.50317	1.43863	.69511
16.400	1.8280	3.5447	1.8274	3.5684	.85906	.28024	1.95270	.51211	1.40488	.71180
16.500	1.8169	3.4659	1.8163	3.4880	.85385	.28670	1.92033	.52074	1.37322	.72821
16.600	1.8060	3.3917	1.8054	3.4123	.84871	.29305	1.89007	.52908	1.34344	.74436
16.700	1.7952	3.3216	1.7946	3.3410	.84362	.29931	1.86169	.53715	1.31534	.76026
16.800	1.7845	3.2554	1.7839	3.2735	.83860	.30548	1.83503	.54495	1.28879	.77592
16.900	1.7739	3.1926	1.7734	3.2096	.83364	.31156	1.80993	.55251	1.26364	.79137
17.000	1.7635	3.1329	1.7629	3.1490	.82874	.31756	1.78624	.55983	1.23977	.80660
17.100	1.7532	3.0761	1.7526	3.0914	.82389	.32348	1.76385	.56694	1.21707	.82165
17.200	1.7430	3.0221	1.7424	3.0364	.81910	.32933	1.74266	.57384	1.19545	.83651
17.300	1.7329	2.9704	1.7324	2.9841	.81437	.33511	1.72255	.58053	1.17483	.85119
17.400	1.7229	2.9211	1.7224	2.9340	.80969	.34083	1.70345	.58704	1.15513	.86571
17.500	1.7131	2.8739	1.7126	2.8861	.80506	.34648	1.68529	.59337	1.13628	.88007
17.600	1.7034	2.8286	1.7028	2.8403	.80048	.35208	1.66799	.59952	1.11822	.89428
17.700	1.6937	2.7852	1.6932	2.7963	.79596	.35761	1.65149	.60551	1.10091	.90834
17.800	1.6842	2.7435	1.6837	2.7541	.79149	.36310	1.63574	.61135	1.08428	.92227
17.900	1.6748	2.7034	1.6743	2.7135	.78707	.36853	1.62068	.61703	1.06830	.93607
18.000	1.6655	2.6648	1.6650	2.6744	.78270	.37392	1.60627	.62256	1.05292	.94974
18.100	1.6563	2.6275	1.6558	2.6368	.77837	.37925	1.59246	.62796	1.03810	.96330
18.200	1.6472	2.5917	1.6467	2.6005	.77410	.38454	1.57923	.63322	1.02382	.97674
18.300	1.6382	2.5570	1.6377	2.5655	.76986	.38979	1.56653	.63836	1.01003	.99007
18.400	1.6293	2.5236	1.6288	2.5317	.76568	.39500	1.55432	.64337	.99672	1.00329
18.500	1.6205	2.4912	1.6200	2.4990	.76154	.40016	1.54259	.64826	.98385	1.01642
18.600	1.6118	2.4599	1.6113	2.4674	.75745	.40529	1.53131	.65304	.97140	1.02944
18.700	1.6032	2.4296	1.6027	2.4367	.75340	.41038	1.52044	.65770	.95935	1.04237
18.800	1.5946	2.4002	1.5941	2.4071	.74939	.41544	1.50997	.66226	.94767	1.05522
18.900	1.5862	2.3717	1.5857	2.3783	.74542	.42046	1.49987	.66672	.93636	1.06797
19.000	1.5779	2.3441	1.5774	2.3505	.74150	.42545	1.49013	.67108	.92538	1.08064
19.100	1.5696	2.3172	1.5691	2.3234	.73762	.43041	1.48072	.67535	.91472	1.09323
19.200	1.5614	2.2912	1.5609	2.2971	.73378	.43533	1.47163	.67952	.90437	1.10574
19.300	1.5533	2.2658	1.5528	2.2716	.72998	.44023	1.46285	.68360	.89431	1.11818
19.400	1.5453	2.2412	1.5448	2.2467	.72621	.44509	1.45435	.68759	.88454	1.13054
19.500	1.5374	2.2172	1.5369	2.2226	.72249	.44993	1.44612	.69150	.87502	1.14283
19.600	1.5296	2.1939	1.5291	2.1990	.71880	.45474	1.43816	.69533	.86576	1.15505
19.700	1.5218	2.1712	1.5213	2.1761	.71515	.45953	1.43044	.69908	.85675	1.16721
19.800	1.5141	2.1490	1.5136	2.1538	.71154	.46429	1.42296	.70276	.84796	1.17930
19.900	1.5065	2.1274	1.5060	2.1321	.70797	.46903	1.41571	.70636	.83940	1.19133
20.000	1.4990	2.1064	1.4985	2.1109	.70443	.47374	1.40867	.70989	.83105	1.20330
20.100	1.4915	2.0858	1.4910	2.0902	.70092	.47843	1.40184	.71335	.82291	1.21520
20.200	1.4841	2.0658	1.4836	2.0700	.69745	.48309	1.39521	.71674	.81496	1.22706
20.300	1.4768	2.0462	1.4763	2.0503	.69402	.48774	1.38876	.72007	.80720	1.23885
20.400	1.4696	2.0271	1.4691	2.0310	.69061	.49236	1.38250	.72333	.79962	1.25060
20.500	1.4624	2.0084	1.4619	2.0122	.68725	.49696	1.37641	.72653	.79221	1.26229
20.600	1.4553	1.9901	1.4548	1.9938	.68391	.50155	1.37048	.72967	.78497	1.27393
20.700	1.4483	1.9722	1.4478	1.9759	.68061	.50611	1.36472	.73275	.77790	1.28552
20.800	1.4413	1.9548	1.4408	1.9583	.67733	.51065	1.35911	.73578	.77097	1.29706
20.900	1.4344	1.9377	1.4340	1.9411	.67409	.51518	1.35365	.73875	.76420	1.30856
21.000	1.4276	1.9209	1.4271	1.9242	.67088	.51969	1.34833	.74166	.75757	1.32001
21.100	1.4208	1.9045	1.4204	1.9077	.66770	.52418	1.34314	.74452	.75108	1.33141
21.200	1.4141	1.8885	1.4137	1.8916	.66455	.52865	1.33809	.74734	.74473	1.34278
21.300	1.4075	1.8728	1.4070	1.8758	.66143	.53311	1.33316	.75010	.73850	1.35409
21.400	1.4009	1.8573	1.4005	1.8603	.65834	.53755	1.32836	.75281	.73240	1.36537
21.500	1.3944	1.8422	1.3939	1.8451	.65528	.54197	1.32367	.75548	.72642	1.37661
21.600	1.3879	1.8274	1.3875	1.8302	.65225	.54638	1.31909	.75810	.72056	1.38781
21.700	1.3815	1.8129	1.3811	1.8156	.64924	.55078	1.31463	.76067	.71481	1.39897
21.800	1.3752	1.7987	1.3748	1.8013	.64626	.55516	1.31027	.76320	.70917	1.41009
21.900	1.3689	1.7847	1.3685	1.7872	.64331	.55952	1.30601	.76569	.70364	1.42118
22.000	1.3627	1.7709	1.3623	1.7735	.64039	.56387	1.30185	.76814	.69821	1.43223
22.100	1.3565	1.7575	1.3561	1.7599	.63749	.56821	1.29779	.77054	.69288	1.44325
22.200	1.3504	1.7443	1.3500	1.7466	.63462	.57253	1.29381	.77291	.68765	1.45423
22.300	1.3444	1.7313	1.3439	1.7336	.63177	.57684	1.28993	.77524	.68251	1.46518
22.400	1.3384	1.7185	1.3379	1.7208	.62895	.58114	1.28613	.77753	.67746	1.47610
22.500	1.3324	1.7060	1.3320	1.7082	.62616	.58543	1.28242	.77978	.67250	1.48698
22.600	1.3265	1.6936	1.3261	1.6958	.62339	.58970	1.27878	.78199	.66763	1.49783
22.700	1.3207	1.6815	1.3202	1.6836	.62064	.59396	1.27523	.78417	.66284	1.50866
22.800	1.3149	1.6696	1.3145	1.6717	.61792	.59821	1.27175	.78632	.65813	1.51945
22.900	1.3091	1.6579	1.3087	1.6599	.61522	.60245	1.26834	.78843	.65350	1.53021
23.000	1.3034	1.6464	1.3030	1.6483	.61254	.60667	1.26500	.79051	.64895	1.54095
23.100	1.2978	1.6351	1.2974	1.6370	.60989	.61089	1.26174	.79256	.64447	1.55166
23.200	1.2922	1.6239	1.2918	1.6258	.60726	.61509	1.25854	.79457	.64007	1.56234
23.300	1.2867	1.6130	1.2863	1.6148	.60466	.61929	1.25540	.79656	.63573	1.57299
23.400	1.2812	1.6022	1.2808	1.6039	.60207	.62347	1.25233	.79851	.63147	1.58362
23.500	1.2757	1.5915	1.2753	1.5933	.59951	.62764	1.24932	.80044	.62727	1.59422
23.600	1.2703	1.5811	1.2699	1.5828	.59697	.63181	1.24636	.80233	.62313	1.60479
23.700	1.2649	1.5708	1.2645	1.5724	.59445	.63596	1.24347	.80420	.61906	1.61534
23.800	1.2596	1.5606	1.2592	1.5622	.59196	.64011	1.24063	.80604	.61506	1.62587
23.900	1.2544	1.5506	1.2540	1.5522	.58948	.64424	1.23785	.80785	.61111	1.63637
24.000	1.2491	1.5408	1.2487	1.5423	.58702	.64837	1.23512	.80964	.60722	1.64685
24.100	1.2440	1.5311	1.2436	1.5326	.58459	.65248	1.23244	.81140	.60339	1.65731
24.200	1.2388	1.5216	1.2384	1.5230	.58217	.65659	1.22981	.81313	.59961	1.66774
24.300	1.2337	1.5121	1.2333	1.5136	.57977	.66069	1.22723	.81484	.59589	1.67815
24.400	1.2287	1.5029	1.2283	1.5043	.57740	.66478	1.22470	.81653	.59223	1.68854
24.500	1.2236	1.4937	1.2233	1.4951	.57504	.66886	1.22221	.81819	.58861	1.69891
24.600	1.2187	1.4847	1.2183	1.4860	.57270	.67294	1.21977	.81983	.58505	1.70926
24.700	1.2137	1.4758	1.2133	1.4771	.57039	.67700	1.21737	.82144	.58153	1.71959
24.800	1.2088	1.4670	1.2085	1.4683	.56809	.68106	1.21502	.82303	.57807	1.72990
24.900	1.2040	1.4584	1.2036	1.4596	.56580	.68511	1.21271	.82460	.57465	1.74018
25.000	1.1992	1.4498	1.1988	1.4511	.56354	.68915	1.21043	.82615	.57128	1.75045
25.100	1.1944	1.4414	1.1940	1.4426	.56130	.69319	1.20820	.82768	.56796	1.76070
25.200	1.1897	1.4331	1.1893	1.4343	.55907	.69722	1.20601	.82918	.56467	1.77093
25.300	1.1850	1.4249	1.1846	1.4260	.55686	.70124	1.20385	.83067	.56144	1.78114
25.400	1.1803	1.4168	1.1799	1.4179	.55467	.70525	1.20173	.83213	.55824	1.79134
25.500	1.1757	1.4088	1.1753	1.4099	.55249	.70926	1.19965	.83358	.55509	1.80152
25.600	1.1711	1.4009	1.1707	1.4020	.55033	.71326	1.19760	.83500	.55198	1.81167
25.700	1.1665	1.3932	1.1661	1.3942	.54819	.71725	1.19559	.83641	.54890	1.82182
25.800	1.1620	1.3855	1.1616	1.3865	.54607	.72124	1.19360	.83780	.54587	1.83194
25.900	1.1575	1.3779	1.1571	1.3789	.54396	.72522	1.19166	.83917	.54287	1.84205
26.000	1.1530	1.3704	1.1527	1.3714	.54187	.72919	1.18974	.84052	.53992	1.85214
26.100	1.1486	1.3630	1.1483	1.3640	.53979	.73316	1.18785	.84185	.53700	1.86221
26.200	1.1442	1.3557	1.1439	1.3566	.53773	.73712	1.18600	.84317	.53411	1.87227

f (GHz)	λ (cm)	λ_g (cm)	λ (cm)	λ_g (cm)	λ/λ_c	$1/\lambda_g$ (1/cm)	λ_g/λ	λ/λ_g	λ_g (in)	$1/\lambda_g$ (1/in)
26.300	1.1399	1.3485	1.1395	1.3494	.53569	.74107	1.18417	.84447	.53126	1.88232
26.400	1.1356	1.3413	1.1352	1.3422	.53366	.74502	1.18238	.84576	.52844	1.89235
26.500	1.1313	1.3343	1.1309	1.3352	.53164	.74896	1.18061	.84702	.52566	1.90236
26.600	1.1270	1.3273	1.1267	1.3282	.52964	.75290	1.17887	.84827	.52291	1.91236
26.700	1.1228	1.3205	1.1225	1.3213	.52766	.75683	1.17715	.84951	.52020	1.92234
26.800	1.1186	1.3137	1.1183	1.3145	.52569	.76075	1.17546	.85073	.51752	1.93231
26.900	1.1145	1.3069	1.1141	1.3078	.52374	.76467	1.17380	.85193	.51486	1.94227
27.000	1.1103	1.3003	1.1100	1.3011	.52180	.76859	1.17217	.85312	.51224	1.95221
27.100	1.1062	1.2937	1.1059	1.2945	.51987	.77249	1.17056	.85429	.50965	1.96214
27.200	1.1022	1.2872	1.1018	1.2880	.51796	.77640	1.16897	.85545	.50709	1.97205
27.300	1.0981	1.2808	1.0978	1.2816	.51606	.78030	1.16741	.85660	.50455	1.98195
27.400	1.0941	1.2745	1.0938	1.2752	.51418	.78419	1.16587	.85773	.50205	1.99184
27.500	1.0902	1.2682	1.0898	1.2689	.51231	.78808	1.16435	.85885	.49957	2.00171
27.600	1.0862	1.2620	1.0859	1.2627	.51045	.79196	1.16285	.85995	.49712	2.01157
27.700	1.0823	1.2558	1.0819	1.2565	.50861	.79584	1.16138	.86104	.49470	2.02142
27.800	1.0784	1.2498	1.0780	1.2505	.50678	.79971	1.15993	.86212	.49231	2.03126
27.900	1.0745	1.2438	1.0742	1.2444	.50497	.80358	1.15850	.86319	.48994	2.04108
28.000	1.0707	1.2378	1.0703	1.2385	.50316	.80744	1.15709	.86424	.48759	2.05090
28.100	1.0669	1.2320	1.0665	1.2326	.50137	.81130	1.15570	.86528	.48527	2.06070
28.200	1.0631	1.2261	1.0628	1.2268	.49959	.81515	1.15433	.86631	.48298	2.07049

TABLE 28

IEC-R 260 — Brit: WG-21 — Amer: WG-34, RG-354/U, RG-355/U, RG-356/U

Outside dimensions: 0.420 X 0.250 ±0.002 inches
10.67 X 6.35 ±0.05 millimeters

Inside dimensions: 0.3400 X 0.1700 ±0.0008 inches
8.636 X 4.318 ±0.02 millimeters
corner radius: 0.4 millimeters
a/b: 2.000

Cutoff: Rectangle in Vacuum — Waveguide in Air
Wavelength: 1.72720cm — 1.72084cm
Frequency: 17357.1390 MHz — 17415.7320 MHz

	THEORETICAL		PHYSICAL							
f (GHz)	λ (cm)	λ_g (cm)	λ (cm)	λ_g (cm)	λ/λ_c	$1/\lambda_g$ (1/cm)	λ_g/λ	λ/λ_g	λ_g (in)	$1/\lambda_g$ (1/in)
20.000	1.4990	3.0171	1.4985	3.0463	.87079	.32827	2.03290	.49191	1.19932	.83381
20.250	1.4805	2.8742	1.4800	2.8993	.86004	.34491	1.95900	.51046	1.14145	.87608
20.500	1.4624	2.7484	1.4619	2.7702	.84955	.36098	1.89491	.52773	1.09064	.91689
20.750	1.4448	2.6365	1.4443	2.6557	.83931	.37655	1.83872	.54386	1.04555	.95643
21.000	1.4276	2.5362	1.4271	2.5531	.82932	.39168	1.78900	.55897	1.00517	.99485
21.250	1.4108	2.4454	1.4103	2.4606	.81956	.40641	1.74467	.57318	.96873	1.03228
21.500	1.3944	2.3628	1.3939	2.3765	.81003	.42079	1.70485	.58656	.93561	1.06882
21.750	1.3784	2.2873	1.3779	2.2996	.80072	.43486	1.66888	.59921	.90534	1.10455
22.000	1.3627	2.2178	1.3623	2.2289	.79162	.44865	1.63620	.61117	.87753	1.13956
22.250	1.3474	2.1535	1.3470	2.1637	.78273	.46217	1.60638	.62252	.85185	1.17391
22.500	1.3324	2.0939	1.3320	2.1033	.77403	.47545	1.57904	.63330	.82805	1.20765
22.750	1.3178	2.0385	1.3173	2.0470	.76553	.48852	1.55388	.64355	.80591	1.24084
23.000	1.3034	1.9866	1.3030	1.9945	.75721	.50138	1.53065	.65332	.78523	1.27351
23.250	1.2894	1.9380	1.2890	1.9453	.74906	.51406	1.50913	.66263	.76586	1.30571
23.500	1.2757	1.8923	1.2753	1.8991	.74109	.52657	1.48913	.67153	.74768	1.33748
23.750	1.2623	1.8493	1.2619	1.8556	.73329	.53891	1.47051	.68004	.73055	1.36883
24.000	1.2491	1.8087	1.2487	1.8145	.72566	.55110	1.45311	.68818	.71439	1.39980
24.250	1.2363	1.7703	1.2359	1.7757	.71817	.56315	1.43682	.69598	.69910	1.43041
24.500	1.2236	1.7338	1.2233	1.7389	.71085	.57508	1.42154	.70346	.68461	1.46069
24.750	1.2113	1.6992	1.2109	1.7039	.70367	.58687	1.40718	.71064	.67084	1.49066
25.000	1.1992	1.6662	1.1988	1.6707	.69663	.59855	1.39365	.71754	.65775	1.52033
25.250	1.1873	1.6348	1.1869	1.6390	.68973	.61013	1.38089	.72417	.64528	1.54972
25.500	1.1757	1.6048	1.1753	1.6098	.68297	.62159	1.36883	.73055	.63337	1.57885
25.750	1.1642	1.5761	1.1639	1.5799	.67634	.63297	1.35742	.73669	.62199	1.60773
26.000	1.1530	1.5487	1.1527	1.5522	.66984	.64424	1.34661	.74261	.61111	1.63638
26.250	1.1421	1.5224	1.1417	1.5257	.66346	.65543	1.33635	.74831	.60067	1.66480
26.500	1.1313	1.4971	1.1309	1.5003	.65720	.66654	1.32659	.75381	.59066	1.69301
26.750	1.1207	1.4729	1.1204	1.4759	.65106	.67757	1.31732	.75912	.58105	1.72102
27.000	1.1103	1.4496	1.1100	1.4524	.64503	.68852	1.30848	.76425	.57181	1.74884
27.250	1.1002	1.4271	1.0998	1.4298	.63911	.69940	1.30005	.76920	.56291	1.77647
27.500	1.0902	1.4055	1.0898	1.4090	.63330	.71021	1.29201	.77399	.55435	1.80393
27.750	1.0803	1.3846	1.0800	1.3871	.62759	.72095	1.28432	.77862	.54608	1.83122
28.000	1.0707	1.3645	1.0703	1.3668	.62199	.73164	1.27697	.78310	.53811	1.85836
28.250	1.0612	1.3450	1.0609	1.3472	.61649	.74226	1.26993	.78744	.53041	1.88534
28.500	1.0519	1.3262	1.0516	1.3283	.61108	.75282	1.26319	.79165	.52296	1.91217
28.750	1.0428	1.3080	1.0424	1.3100	.60576	.76333	1.25673	.79572	.51576	1.93887
29.000	1.0338	1.2904	1.0334	1.2923	.60054	.77379	1.25052	.79966	.50879	1.96543
29.250	1.0249	1.2734	1.0246	1.2752	.59541	.78420	1.24457	.80349	.50204	1.99186
29.500	1.0162	1.2568	1.0159	1.2586	.59036	.79456	1.23884	.80721	.49550	2.01817
29.750	1.0077	1.2408	1.0074	1.2424	.58540	.80487	1.23333	.81081	.48915	2.04436
30.000	.9993	1.2252	.9990	1.2268	.58052	.81513	1.22803	.81431	.48299	2.07044
30.250	.9910	1.2101	.9907	1.2116	.57573	.82536	1.22293	.81771	.47701	2.09640
30.500	.9829	1.1954	.9826	1.1968	.57101	.83554	1.21801	.82101	.47120	2.12226
30.750	.9749	1.1811	.9746	1.1825	.56637	.84568	1.21327	.82422	.46554	2.14802
31.000	.9671	1.1672	.9668	1.1685	.56180	.85578	1.20870	.82734	.46005	2.17368
31.250	.9593	1.1537	.9590	1.1549	.55730	.86584	1.20428	.83037	.45470	2.19924
31.500	.9517	1.1405	.9514	1.1417	.55288	.87587	1.20002	.83332	.44950	2.22471
31.750	.9442	1.1277	.9439	1.1288	.54853	.88586	1.19590	.83619	.44443	2.25009
32.000	.9369	1.1151	.9366	1.1163	.54424	.89582	1.19192	.83898	.43948	2.27539
32.250	.9296	1.1030	.9293	1.1041	.54002	.90575	1.18806	.84171	.43467	2.30060
32.500	.9224	1.0911	.9221	1.0921	.53587	.91564	1.18433	.84436	.42997	2.32574
32.750	.9154	1.0795	.9151	1.0805	.53178	.92551	1.18073	.84694	.42539	2.35079
33.000	.9085	1.0681	.9082	1.0691	.52775	.93534	1.17723	.84945	.42092	2.37577
33.250	.9016	1.0571	.9013	1.0580	.52378	.94515	1.17384	.85190	.41655	2.40068
33.500	.8949	1.0463	.8946	1.0472	.51987	.95493	1.17056	.85429	.41228	2.42552
33.750	.8883	1.0357	.8880	1.0366	.51602	.96468	1.16737	.85663	.40812	2.45028
34.000	.8817	1.0254	.8815	1.0263	.51223	.97440	1.16428	.85890	.40404	2.47499
34.250	.8753	1.0153	.8750	1.0162	.50849	.98410	1.16128	.86112	.40006	2.49962
34.500	.8690	1.0055	.8687	1.0063	.50480	.99378	1.15837	.86328	.39617	2.52420
34.750	.8627	.9958	.8624	.9966	.50117	1.00343	1.15554	.86539	.39236	2.54871
35.000	.8565	.9864	.8563	.9871	.49759	1.01306	1.15280	.86746	.38863	2.57317
35.250	.8505	.9771	.8502	.9778	.49406	1.02266	1.15012	.86947	.38498	2.59756
35.500	.8445	.9681	.8442	.9688	.49058	1.03225	1.14753	.87144	.38140	2.62190
35.750	.8386	.9592	.8383	.9599	.48715	1.04181	1.14500	.87336	.37790	2.64619
36.000	.8328	.9505	.8325	.9512	.48377	1.05135	1.14255	.87524	.37447	2.67043
36.250	.8270	.9420	.8267	.9426	.48043	1.06087	1.14016	.87707	.37111	2.69461
36.500	.8213	.9337	.8211	.9343	.47714	1.07037	1.13783	.87887	.36782	2.71874
36.750	.8158	.9255	.8155	.9261	.47390	1.07985	1.13556	.88062	.36459	2.74283
37.000	.8102	.9175	.8100	.9180	.47070	1.08932	1.13336	.88234	.36142	2.76686
37.250	.8048	.9096	.8046	.9101	.46754	1.09876	1.13120	.88401	.35831	2.79085
37.500	.7994	.9019	.7992	.9024	.46442	1.10819	1.12911	.88565	.35527	2.81480
37.750	.7942	.8943	.7939	.8948	.46134	1.11760	1.12707	.88726	.35227	2.83870
38.000	.7889	.8868	.7887	.8873	.45831	1.12699	1.12507	.88883	.34934	2.86256
38.250	.7838	.8795	.7835	.8800	.45531	1.13637	1.12313	.89037	.34646	2.88638
38.500	.7787	.8724	.7784	.8728	.45236	1.14573	1.12123	.89187	.34362	2.91015
38.750	.7737	.8653	.7734	.8657	.44944	1.15508	1.11939	.89335	.34084	2.93389
39.000	.7687	.8584	.7685	.8588	.44656	1.16441	1.11758	.89479	.33811	2.95759
39.250	.7638	.8516	.7636	.8520	.44371	1.17372	1.11582	.89620	.33543	2.98125
39.500	.7590	.8449	.7587	.8453	.44090	1.18302	1.11410	.89759	.33279	3.00487
39.750	.7542	.8383	.7540	.8387	.43813	1.19231	1.11242	.89894	.33020	3.02846
40.000	.7495	.8319	.7492	.8322	.43539	1.20158	1.11077	.90027	.32765	3.05201
40.250	.7448	.8255	.7446	.8259	.43269	1.21084	1.10917	.90158	.32515	3.07553

f (GHz)	λ (cm)	λ_g (cm)	λ (cm)	λ_g (cm)	$\frac{\lambda}{\lambda_c}$	$1/\lambda_g$ (1/cm)	$\frac{\lambda_g}{\lambda}$	$\frac{\lambda}{\lambda_g}$	λ_g (in)	$1/\lambda_g$ (1/in)
40.500	.7402	.8193	.7400	.8196	.43002	1.22009	1.10760	.90285	.32268	3.09902
40.750	.7357	.8131	.7355	.8135	.42738	1.22932	1.10607	.90410	.32026	3.12247
41.000	.7312	.8071	.7310	.8074	.42477	1.23854	1.10457	.90533	.31788	3.14589
41.250	.7268	.8011	.7265	.8014	.42220	1.24775	1.10310	.90653	.31553	3.16928
41.500	.7224	.7953	.7222	.7956	.41966	1.25694	1.10167	.90771	.31322	3.19263
41.750	.7181	.7895	.7178	.7898	.41714	1.26613	1.10027	.90887	.31095	3.21596
42.000	.7138	.7839	.7136	.7841	.41466	1.27530	1.09889	.91001	.30871	3.23926
42.250	.7096	.7783	.7093	.7785	.41221	1.28446	1.09755	.91112	.30651	3.26253

TABLE 29

IEC-R 320, IEC-P 320   Brit: WG-22, WG-22P   Amer: WR-28, RG-96/U, RG-271/U

Outside dimensions: 0.360 X 0.220 ±0.002 inches
9.14 X 5.59 ±0.05 millimeters or
0.4331 - 0.0007, + 0.000 inch diameter
11.000 - 0.018, + 0.000 millimeter diameter

Inside dimensions: 0.2800 X 0.1400 ±0.008 inches
7.112 X 3.556 ±0.020 millimeters
corner radius: 0.4 millimeters
a/b: 2.000

Cutoff: Rectangle in Vacuum   Waveguide in Air
Wavelength: 1.42240cm   1.41468cm
Frequency: 21076.5260 MHz   21184.8340 MHz

f	THEORETICAL λ	λ_g	PHYSICAL λ	λ_g	$\frac{\lambda}{\lambda_c}$	$1/\lambda_g$	$\frac{\lambda_g}{\lambda}$	$\frac{\lambda}{\lambda_g}$	λ_g	$1/\lambda_g$
(GHz)	(cm)	(cm)	(cm)	(cm)		(1/cm)			(in)	(1/in)
24.000	1.2491	2.6115	1.2487	2.6558	.88270	.37654	2.12676	.47020	1.04557	.95641
24.250	1.2363	2.4996	1.2359	2.5383	.87360	.39397	2.05384	.48689	.99932	1.00068
24.500	1.2236	2.4000	1.2233	2.4341	.86469	.41083	1.98986	.50255	.95830	1.04351
24.750	1.2113	2.3106	1.2109	2.3409	.85595	.42719	1.93319	.51728	.92161	1.08506
25.000	1.1992	2.2297	1.1988	2.2568	.84739	.44310	1.88259	.53118	.88852	1.12547
25.250	1.1873	2.1560	1.1869	2.1805	.83900	.45861	1.83711	.54433	.85846	1.16487
25.500	1.1757	2.0886	1.1753	2.1108	.83078	.47376	1.79597	.55680	.83101	1.20335
25.750	1.1642	2.0265	1.1639	2.0467	.82271	.48858	1.75855	.56865	.80580	1.24100
26.000	1.1530	1.9692	1.1527	1.9876	.81480	.50311	1.72437	.57992	.78254	1.27790
26.250	1.1421	1.9159	1.1417	1.9329	.80704	.51736	1.69299	.59067	.76098	1.31410
26.500	1.1313	1.8663	1.1309	1.8820	.79943	.53136	1.66408	.60093	.74093	1.34966
26.750	1.1207	1.8200	1.1204	1.8344	.79196	.54513	1.63735	.61074	.72222	1.38463
27.000	1.1103	1.7765	1.1100	1.7899	.78462	.55868	1.61256	.62013	.70469	1.41906
27.250	1.1002	1.7357	1.0998	1.7481	.77743	.57204	1.58950	.62913	.68824	1.45298
27.500	1.0902	1.6972	1.0898	1.7088	.77036	.58521	1.56799	.63776	.67276	1.48642
27.750	1.0803	1.6608	1.0800	1.6717	.76342	.59820	1.54787	.64605	.65814	1.51943
28.000	1.0707	1.6264	1.0703	1.6366	.75660	.61103	1.52901	.65402	.64432	1.55202
28.250	1.0612	1.5937	1.0609	1.6033	.74991	.62371	1.51130	.66168	.63122	1.58423
28.500	1.0519	1.5627	1.0516	1.5717	.74333	.63625	1.49463	.66906	.61878	1.61608
28.750	1.0428	1.5332	1.0424	1.5417	.73686	.64865	1.47892	.67617	.60695	1.64758
29.000	1.0338	1.5050	1.0334	1.5130	.73051	.66093	1.46407	.68303	.59568	1.67875
29.250	1.0249	1.4782	1.0246	1.4857	.72427	.67308	1.45003	.68964	.58492	1.70962
29.500	1.0162	1.4524	1.0159	1.4596	.71813	.68512	1.43672	.69603	.57465	1.74020
29.750	1.0077	1.4278	1.0074	1.4346	.71210	.69705	1.42410	.70220	.56481	1.77051
30.000	.9993	1.4042	.9990	1.4107	.70616	.70888	1.41210	.70816	.55538	1.80056
30.250	.9910	1.3816	.9907	1.3877	.70033	.72061	1.40069	.71393	.54634	1.83035
30.500	.9829	1.3598	.9826	1.3657	.69458	.73225	1.38982	.71952	.53766	1.85992
30.750	.9749	1.3389	.9746	1.3444	.68894	.74380	1.37945	.72493	.52931	1.88925
31.000	.9671	1.3188	.9668	1.3240	.68338	.75527	1.36956	.73016	.52127	1.91838
31.250	.9593	1.2993	.9590	1.3044	.67791	.76665	1.36010	.73524	.51353	1.94729
31.500	.9517	1.2806	.9514	1.2854	.67253	.77796	1.35105	.74016	.50607	1.97601
31.750	.9442	1.2625	.9439	1.2671	.66724	.78919	1.34239	.74494	.49887	2.00455
32.000	.9369	1.2451	.9366	1.2494	.66203	.80036	1.33409	.74957	.49191	2.03290
32.250	.9296	1.2282	.9293	1.2324	.65689	.81145	1.32613	.75407	.48518	2.06108
32.500	.9224	1.2118	.9221	1.2158	.65184	.82248	1.31849	.75845	.47867	2.08910
32.750	.9154	1.1960	.9151	1.1998	.64687	.83345	1.31115	.76269	.47238	2.11696
33.000	.9085	1.1806	.9082	1.1843	.64196	.84436	1.30409	.76682	.46627	2.14466
33.250	.9016	1.1658	.9013	1.1693	.63714	.85521	1.29730	.77083	.46036	2.17222
33.500	.8949	1.1513	.8946	1.1547	.63238	.86600	1.29076	.77474	.45462	2.19964
33.750	.8883	1.1373	.8880	1.1406	.62770	.87674	1.28446	.77854	.44905	2.22692
34.000	.8817	1.1237	.8815	1.1268	.62308	.88743	1.27839	.78223	.44364	2.25407
34.250	.8753	1.1105	.8750	1.1135	.61854	.89807	1.27253	.78583	.43839	2.28110
34.500	.8690	1.0976	.8687	1.1005	.61405	.90866	1.26688	.78934	.43328	2.30800
34.750	.8627	1.0851	.8624	1.0879	.60964	.91921	1.26142	.79276	.42831	2.33478
35.000	.8565	1.0729	.8563	1.0756	.60528	.92971	1.25615	.79609	.42347	2.36145
35.250	.8505	1.0610	.8502	1.0636	.60099	.94016	1.25105	.79933	.41876	2.38802
35.500	.8445	1.0495	.8442	1.0520	.59676	.95058	1.24612	.80249	.41417	2.41447
35.750	.8386	1.0382	.8383	1.0406	.59258	.96095	1.24134	.80558	.40970	2.44082

TABLE 30

IEC-R 400, IEC-P 400   Brit: WG-23, WG-23P   Amer: WR-22, RG-97/U, RG-272/U

Outside dimensions: 0.304 X 0.192 ±0.002 inches
7.72 X 4.88 ±0.05 millimeters or
0.4331 - 0.0007, + 0.000 inch diameter
11.000 - 0.018, + 0.000 millimeter diameter

Inside dimensions: 0.2240 X 0.1120 ±0.0008 inches
5.690 X 2.845 ±0.020 millimeters
corner radius: 0.3 millimeters
a/b: 2.000

Cutoff: Rectangle in Vacuum   Waveguide in Air
Wavelength: 1.13800cm   1.13257cm
Frequency: 26343.8050 MHz   26461.6660 MHz

f	THEORETICAL λ	λ_g	PHYSICAL λ	λ_g	$\frac{\lambda}{\lambda_c}$	$1/\lambda_g$	$\frac{\lambda_g}{\lambda}$	$\frac{\lambda}{\lambda_g}$	λ_g	$1/\lambda_g$
(GHz)	(mm)	(mm)	(mm)	(mm)		(1/mm)			(in/10)	(10/in)
33.000	90.8462	150.8412	90.8172	151.9514	.80187	.00658	1.67316	.59767	59.82338	.01672
33.500	89.4903	144.8672	89.4617	145.8461	.78990	.00686	1.63026	.61340	57.41973	.01742
34.000	88.1743	139.4755	88.1461	140.3451	.77828	.00713	1.59219	.62807	55.25400	.01810
34.500	86.8964	134.5764	86.8686	135.3540	.76700	.00739	1.55815	.64179	53.28899	.01877
35.000	85.6550	130.0984	85.6276	130.7978	.75605	.00765	1.52752	.65466	51.49520	.01942
35.500	84.4486	125.9839	84.4216	126.6162	.74540	.00790	1.49981	.66675	49.84890	.02006
36.000	83.2757	122.1859	83.2491	122.7601	.73505	.00815	1.47461	.67814	48.33074	.02069
36.500	82.1349	118.6654	82.1087	119.1889	.72498	.00839	1.45160	.68889	46.92478	.02131
37.000	81.0250	115.3898	80.9991	115.8690	.71518	.00863	1.43050	.69906	45.61773	.02192
37.500	79.9447	112.3320	79.9191	112.7720	.70564	.00887	1.41108	.70868	44.39843	.02252
38.000	78.8928	109.4685	78.8675	109.8738	.69636	.00910	1.39314	.71780	43.25740	.02312
38.500	77.8682	106.7795	77.8433	107.1539	.68732	.00933	1.37653	.72646	42.18657	.02370
39.000	76.8699	104.2478	76.8453	104.5946	.67850	.00956	1.36111	.73470	41.17897	.02428
39.500	75.8968	101.8587	75.8726	102.1806	.66992	.00979	1.34674	.74253	40.22858	.02486
40.000	74.9481	99.5992	74.9242	99.8986	.66154	.01001	1.33333	.75000	39.33017	.02543
40.500	74.0228	97.4579	73.9992	97.7370	.65337	.01023	1.32079	.75713	38.47915	.02599
41.000	73.1201	95.4248	73.0967	95.6856	.64541	.01045	1.30903	.76393	37.67148	.02655
41.500	72.2392	93.4912	72.2161	93.7351	.63763	.01067	1.29798	.77043	36.90359	.02710
42.000	71.3792	91.6491	71.3563	91.8777	.63004	.01088	1.28759	.77664	36.17233	.02765
42.500	70.5394	89.8915	70.5168	90.1061	.62263	.01110	1.27780	.78260	35.47486	.02819
43.000	69.7192	88.2123	69.6969	88.4140	.61539	.01131	1.26855	.78830	34.80866	.02873
43.500	68.9178	86.6057	68.8958	86.7955	.60831	.01152	1.25981	.79377	34.17147	.02926
44.000	68.1347	85.0666	68.1129	85.2456	.60140	.01173	1.25153	.79902	33.56125	.02980
44.500	67.3691	83.5906	67.3476	83.7594	.59464	.01194	1.24369	.80406	32.97615	.03032
45.000	66.6206	82.1734	66.5992	82.3329	.58804	.01215	1.23624	.80890	32.41451	.03085
45.500	65.8885	80.8112	65.8674	80.9620	.58158	.01235	1.22917	.81356	31.87481	.03137

f (GHz)	λ (mm)	λ_g (mm)	λ (mm)	λ_g (mm)	λ/λ_c	$1/\lambda_g$ (1/mm)	λ_g/λ	λ/λ_g	λ_g (in/10)	$1/\lambda_g$ (10/in)
46.000	65.1723	79.5006	65.1514	79.6434	.57525	.01256	1.22243	.81804	31.35565	.03189
46.500	64.4715	78.2384	64.4509	78.3737	.56907	.01276	1.21602	.82235	30.85579	.03241
47.000	63.7856	77.0218	63.7652	77.1501	.56301	.01296	1.20991	.82651	30.37406	.03292
47.500	63.1142	75.8481	63.0940	75.9699	.55709	.01316	1.20407	.83051	29.90941	.03343
48.000	62.4568	74.7149	62.4368	74.8306	.55128	.01336	1.19850	.83438	29.46086	.03394
48.500	61.8129	73.6199	61.7931	73.7299	.54560	.01356	1.19317	.83810	29.02750	.03445
49.000	61.1821	72.5610	61.1626	72.6656	.54003	.01376	1.18807	.84170	28.60852	.03495
49.500	60.5641	71.5364	60.5448	71.6360	.53458	.01396	1.18319	.84517	28.20315	.03546
50.000	59.9585	70.5442	59.9393	70.6391	.52923	.01416	1.17851	.84853	27.81066	.03596

TABLE 31

IEC-R 500, IEC-P 500 Brit: WG-24, WG-24P Amer: WR-19

Outside dimensions: 0.268 X 0.174 ±0.002 inches
6.81 X 4.42 ±0.05 millimeters or
0.2953 - 0.0006, + 0.000 inch diameter
7.500 - 0.015, + 0.000 millimeter diameter

Inside dimensions: 0.1880 X 0.0940 ±0.0008 inches
4.775 X 2.388 ±0.020 millimeters
corner radius: 0.3 millimeters
a/b: 2.000

Cutoff:	Rectangle in Vacuum	Waveguide in Air
Wavelength:	9.550cm	9.4853cm
Frequency:	31391.8850 MHz	31595.9160 MHz

f	THEORETICAL λ	λ_g	PHYSICAL λ	λ_g	λ/λ_c	$1/\lambda_g$	λ_g/λ	λ/λ_g	λ_g	$1/\lambda_g$
(GHz)	(mm)	(mm)	(mm)	(mm)		(1/mm)			(in/10)	(10/in)
40.000	74.9481	120.9323	74.9242	122.1455	.78990	.00819	1.63025	.61340	48.08876	.02079
40.500	74.0228	117.1565	73.9992	118.2562	.78015	.00846	1.59807	.62575	46.55756	.02148
41.000	73.1201	113.6728	73.0967	114.6743	.77063	.00872	1.56880	.63743	45.14735	.02215
41.500	72.2392	110.4450	72.2161	111.3608	.76135	.00898	1.54205	.64849	43.84284	.02281
42.000	71.3792	107.4429	71.3563	108.2836	.75228	.00924	1.51750	.65898	42.63132	.02346
42.500	70.5394	104.6411	70.5168	105.4155	.74343	.00949	1.49490	.66894	41.50215	.02410
43.000	69.7192	102.0181	69.6969	102.7336	.73479	.00973	1.47401	.67842	40.44631	.02472
43.500	68.9178	99.5555	68.8958	100.2186	.72634	.00998	1.45464	.68746	39.45612	.02534
44.000	68.1347	97.2374	68.1129	97.8535	.71809	.01022	1.43664	.69607	38.52500	.02596
44.500	67.3691	95.0502	67.3476	95.6240	.71002	.01046	1.41986	.70430	37.64725	.02656
45.000	66.6206	92.9818	66.5992	93.5175	.70213	.01069	1.40418	.71216	36.81792	.02716
45.500	65.8885	91.0219	65.8674	91.5230	.69442	.01093	1.38950	.71968	36.03268	.02775
46.000	65.1723	89.1612	65.1514	89.6309	.68687	.01116	1.37573	.72689	35.28774	.02834
46.500	64.4715	87.3916	64.4509	87.8325	.67948	.01139	1.36278	.73379	34.57974	.02892
47.000	63.7856	85.7058	63.7652	86.1205	.67225	.01161	1.35059	.74042	33.90572	.02949
47.500	63.1142	84.0973	63.0940	84.4881	.66518	.01184	1.33908	.74678	33.26302	.03006
48.000	62.4568	82.5605	62.4368	82.9292	.65825	.01206	1.32821	.75289	32.64928	.03063
48.500	61.8129	81.0902	61.7931	81.4385	.65146	.01228	1.31792	.75877	32.06239	.03119
49.000	61.1821	79.6816	61.1626	80.0111	.64481	.01250	1.30817	.76443	31.50044	.03175
49.500	60.5641	78.3306	60.5448	78.6427	.63830	.01272	1.29892	.76987	30.96170	.03230
50.000	59.9585	77.0334	59.9393	77.3293	.63192	.01293	1.29013	.77512	30.44463	.03285
50.500	59.3649	75.7864	59.3459	76.0674	.62566	.01315	1.28176	.78017	29.94779	.03339
51.000	58.7828	74.5866	58.7640	74.8536	.61953	.01336	1.27380	.78505	29.46992	.03393
51.500	58.2121	73.4309	58.1935	73.6850	.61351	.01357	1.26621	.78976	29.00984	.03447
52.000	57.6524	72.3169	57.6340	72.5588	.60761	.01378	1.25896	.79431	28.56646	.03501
52.500	57.1033	71.2420	57.0851	71.4726	.60183	.01399	1.25204	.79870	28.13881	.03554
53.000	56.5646	70.2040	56.5465	70.4240	.59615	.01420	1.24542	.80294	27.72597	.03607
53.500	56.0360	69.2009	56.0181	69.4109	.59058	.01441	1.23908	.80705	27.32713	.03659
54.000	55.5171	68.2308	55.4994	68.4314	.58511	.01461	1.23301	.81102	26.94151	.03712
54.500	55.0078	67.2918	54.9902	67.4837	.57974	.01482	1.22720	.81487	26.56839	.03764
55.000	54.5077	66.3825	54.4903	66.5661	.57447	.01502	1.22161	.81859	26.20713	.03816
55.500	54.0167	65.5012	53.9994	65.6770	.56930	.01523	1.21626	.82220	25.85710	.03867
56.000	53.5344	64.6467	53.5173	64.8151	.56421	.01543	1.21111	.82569	25.51776	.03919
56.500	53.0606	63.8174	53.0436	63.9789	.55922	.01563	1.20616	.82908	25.18856	.03970
57.000	52.5952	63.0124	52.5784	63.1673	.55431	.01583	1.20139	.83237	24.86902	.04021
57.500	52.1378	62.2303	52.1211	62.3791	.54949	.01603	1.19681	.83556	24.55868	.04072
58.000	51.6884	61.4702	51.6718	61.6131	.54476	.01623	1.19239	.83865	24.25712	.04123
58.500	51.2466	60.7311	51.2302	60.8684	.54010	.01643	1.18813	.84166	23.96392	.04173
59.000	50.8123	60.0119	50.7960	60.1440	.53552	.01663	1.18403	.84457	23.67872	.04223
59.500	50.3853	59.3120	50.3692	59.4390	.53102	.01682	1.18007	.84741	23.40117	.04273
60.000	49.9654	58.6303	49.9494	58.7526	.52660	.01702	1.17624	.85017	23.13093	.04323

TABLE 32

IEC-R 620, IEC-P 620 Brit: WG-25, WG-25P Amer: WR-15, RG-98/U, RG-273/U

Outside dimensions: 0.228 X 0.154 ±0.002 inches
5.79 X 3.91 ±0.05 millimeters or
0.2953 - 0.0006, + 0.000 inch diameter
7.500 - 0.015, + 0.000 millimeter diameter

Inside dimensions: 0.1480 X 0.0740 ±0.0008 inches
3.759 X 1.880 ±0.020 millimeters
corner radius: 0.2 millimeters
a/b: 2.000

Cutoff:	Rectangle in Vacuum	Waveguide in Air
Wavelength:	7.5180cm	7.4815cm
Frequency:	39876.6290 MHz	40058.5090 MHz

f	THEORETICAL λ	λ_g	PHYSICAL λ	λ_g	λ/λ_c	$1/\lambda_g$	λ_g/λ	λ/λ_g	λ_g	$1/\lambda_g$
(GHz)	(mm)	(mm)	(mm)	(mm)		(1/mm)			(in/10)	(10/in)
50.000	59.9585	99.3882	59.9393	100.1312	.80117	.00999	1.67054	.59861	39.42172	.02537
50.500	59.3649	96.7524	59.3459	97.4357	.79324	.01026	1.64183	.60908	38.36051	.02607
51.000	58.7828	94.2923	58.7640	94.9230	.78546	.01053	1.61532	.61907	37.37126	.02676
51.500	58.2121	91.9893	58.1935	92.5731	.77784	.01080	1.59078	.62862	36.44610	.02744
52.000	57.6524	89.8269	57.6340	90.3689	.77036	.01107	1.56798	.63776	35.57833	.02811
52.500	57.1033	87.7914	57.0851	88.2959	.76302	.01133	1.54674	.64652	34.76218	.02877
53.000	56.5646	85.8707	56.5465	86.3414	.75582	.01158	1.52691	.65492	33.99268	.02942
53.500	56.0360	84.0542	56.0181	84.4944	.74876	.01184	1.50834	.66298	33.26551	.03006
54.000	55.5171	82.3328	55.4994	82.7453	.74182	.01209	1.49092	.67073	32.57688	.03070
54.500	55.0078	80.6984	54.9902	81.0856	.73502	.01233	1.47455	.67817	31.92348	.03132
55.000	54.5077	79.1438	54.4903	79.5080	.72834	.01258	1.45912	.68534	31.30237	.03195
55.500	54.0167	77.6627	53.9994	78.0058	.72177	.01282	1.44457	.69225	30.71095	.03256
56.000	53.5344	76.2494	53.5173	76.5732	.71533	.01306	1.43081	.69890	30.14692	.03317
56.500	53.0606	74.8989	53.0436	75.2048	.70900	.01330	1.41779	.70532	29.60820	.03377
57.000	52.5952	73.6066	52.5784	73.8961	.70278	.01353	1.40545	.71152	29.09295	.03437
57.500	52.1378	72.3684	52.1211	72.6427	.69667	.01377	1.39373	.71750	28.59949	.03497
58.000	51.6884	71.1806	51.6718	71.4408	.69066	.01400	1.38259	.72328	28.12632	.03555
58.500	51.2466	70.0399	51.2302	70.2871	.68476	.01423	1.37199	.72887	27.67208	.03614
59.000	50.8123	68.9432	50.7960	69.1782	.67896	.01446	1.36188	.73428	27.23553	.03672
59.500	50.3853	67.8878	50.3692	68.1115	.67325	.01468	1.35225	.73951	26.81554	.03729
60.000	49.9654	66.8711	49.9494	67.0842	.66764	.01491	1.34304	.74458	26.41110	.03786
60.500	49.5525	65.8908	49.5366	66.0940	.66212	.01513	1.33424	.74949	26.02125	.03843
61.000	49.1463	64.9447	49.1306	65.1387	.65670	.01535	1.32583	.75425	25.64515	.03899
61.500	48.7467	64.0310	48.7312	64.2163	.65136	.01557	1.31777	.75886	25.28199	.03955
62.000	48.3536	63.1477	48.3382	63.3249	.64610	.01579	1.31004	.76334	24.93106	.04011
62.500	47.9668	62.2934	47.9515	62.4628	.64094	.01601	1.30263	.76768	24.59167	.04066
63.000	47.5861	61.4663	47.5709	61.6285	.63585	.01623	1.29551	.77190	24.26321	.04121
63.500	47.2114	60.6651	47.1963	60.8206	.63084	.01644	1.28867	.77599	23.94510	.04176
64.000	46.8426	59.8884	46.8276	60.0375	.62591	.01666	1.28210	.77997	23.63682	.04231
64.500	46.4795	59.1351	46.4646	59.2782	.62106	.01687	1.27577	.78384	23.33786	.04285

f (GHz)	λ (mm)	λ_g (mm)	λ (mm)	λ_g (mm)	λ/λ_c	$1/\lambda_g$ (1/mm)	λ_g/λ	λ/λ_g	λ_g (in/10)	$1/\lambda_g$ (10/in)
65.000	46.1219	58.4040	46.1072	58.5413	.61628	.01708	1.26968	.78760	23.04776	.04339
65.500	45.7698	57.6940	45.7552	57.8259	.61158	.01729	1.26381	.79126	22.76610	.04392
66.000	45.4231	57.0041	45.4086	57.1309	.60695	.01750	1.25815	.79482	22.49248	.04446
66.500	45.0816	56.3334	45.0672	56.4554	.60238	.01771	1.25269	.79828	22.22652	.04499
67.000	44.7451	55.6811	44.7308	55.7984	.59789	.01792	1.24743	.80165	21.96788	.04552
67.500	44.4137	55.0462	44.3995	55.1592	.59346	.01813	1.24234	.80493	21.71621	.04605
68.000	44.0871	54.4281	44.0730	54.5369	.58910	.01834	1.23742	.80813	21.47123	.04657
68.500	43.7653	53.8261	43.7513	53.9309	.58480	.01854	1.23267	.81125	21.23264	.04710
69.000	43.4482	53.2393	43.4343	53.3404	.58056	.01875	1.22807	.81429	21.00016	.04762
69.500	43.1356	52.6673	43.1218	52.7648	.57638	.01895	1.22362	.81725	20.77354	.04814
70.000	42.8275	52.1094	42.8138	52.2035	.57226	.01916	1.21931	.82013	20.55255	.04866
70.500	42.5238	51.5651	42.5102	51.6559	.56821	.01936	1.21514	.82295	20.33696	.04917
71.000	42.2243	51.0337	42.2108	51.1214	.56420	.01956	1.21110	.82570	20.12654	.04969
71.500	41.9290	50.5149	41.9156	50.5996	.56026	.01976	1.20718	.82838	19.92111	.05020
72.000	41.6378	50.0081	41.6245	50.0900	.55637	.01996	1.20338	.83100	19.72046	.05071
72.500	41.3507	49.5129	41.3375	49.5920	.55253	.02016	1.19969	.83355	19.52441	.05122
73.000	41.0675	49.0288	41.0543	49.1053	.54875	.02036	1.19611	.83605	19.33281	.05173
73.500	40.7881	48.5555	40.7750	48.6295	.54501	.02056	1.19263	.83848	19.14547	.05223
74.000	40.5125	48.0925	40.4995	48.1641	.54133	.02076	1.18925	.84087	18.96226	.05274
74.500	40.2406	47.6395	40.2277	47.7088	.53770	.02096	1.18597	.84319	18.78301	.05324
75.000	39.9723	47.1962	39.9595	47.2633	.53411	.02116	1.18278	.84547	18.60760	.05374

TABLE 33

IEC-R 740, IEC-P 740   Brit: WG-26, WG-26P   Amer: WR-12, RG-99/U, RG-274/U

Outside dimensions: 0.202 X 0.141 ±0.002 inches
5.13 X 3.58 ±0.05 millimeters or
0.2953 - 0.0006, + 0.000 inch diameter
7.500 - 0.015, + 0.000 millimeter diameter

Inside dimensions: 0.1220 X 0.610 ±0.0008 inches
3.099 X 1.549 ±0.020 millimeters
corner radius: 0.15 millimeters
a/b: 2.000

Cutoff:	Rectangle in Vacuum	Waveguide in Air
Wavelength:	6.1980mm	6.1731mm
Frequency:	48369.2330 MHz	48549.0980 MHz

f	THEORETICAL λ	λ_g	PHYSICAL λ	λ_g	λ/λ_c	$1/\lambda_g$	λ_g/λ	λ/λ_g	λ_g	$1/\lambda_g$
(GHz)	(mm)	(mm)	(mm)	(mm)		(1/mm)			(in/10)	(10/in)
60.000	49.9654	84.4430	49.9494	84.9801	.80915	.01177	1.70132	.58778	33.45673	.02989
60.500	49.5525	82.4943	49.5366	82.9937	.80246	.01205	1.67540	.59687	32.67467	.03060
61.000	49.1463	80.6600	49.1306	81.1254	.79589	.01233	1.65122	.60561	31.93915	.03131
61.500	48.7467	78.9292	48.7312	79.3640	.78942	.01260	1.62861	.61402	31.24568	.03200
62.000	48.3536	77.2924	48.3382	77.6995	.78305	.01287	1.60742	.62212	30.59037	.03269
62.500	47.9668	75.7412	47.9515	76.1233	.77679	.01314	1.58751	.62992	29.96980	.03337
63.000	47.5861	74.2685	47.5709	74.6277	.77062	.01340	1.56877	.63744	29.38097	.03404
63.500	47.2114	72.8677	47.1963	73.2059	.76455	.01366	1.55109	.64471	28.82123	.03470
64.000	46.8426	71.5331	46.8276	71.8522	.75858	.01392	1.53440	.65172	28.28825	.03535
64.500	46.4795	70.2596	46.4646	70.5610	.75270	.01417	1.51860	.65850	27.77993	.03600
65.000	46.1219	69.0426	46.1072	69.3278	.74691	.01442	1.50362	.66506	27.29442	.03664
65.500	45.7698	67.8780	45.7552	68.1483	.74121	.01467	1.48941	.67141	26.83003	.03727
66.000	45.4231	66.7622	45.4086	67.0186	.73559	.01492	1.47590	.67755	26.38527	.03790
66.500	45.0816	65.6917	45.0672	65.9353	.73006	.01517	1.46304	.68351	25.95877	.03852
67.000	44.7451	64.6637	44.7308	64.8953	.72461	.01541	1.45079	.68928	25.54932	.03914
67.500	44.4137	63.6752	44.3995	63.8957	.71925	.01565	1.43911	.69487	25.15578	.03975
68.000	44.0871	62.7239	44.0730	62.9340	.71396	.01589	1.42795	.70031	24.77716	.04036
68.500	43.7653	61.8074	43.7513	62.0078	.70875	.01613	1.41728	.70558	24.41253	.04096
69.000	43.4482	60.9237	43.4343	61.1150	.70361	.01636	1.40707	.71070	24.06103	.04156
69.500	43.1356	60.0707	43.1218	60.2536	.69855	.01660	1.39729	.71567	23.72189	.04216
70.000	42.8275	59.2469	42.8138	59.4218	.69356	.01683	1.38791	.72051	23.39440	.04275
70.500	42.5238	58.4504	42.5102	58.6179	.68864	.01706	1.37891	.72521	23.07790	.04333
71.000	42.2243	57.6800	42.2108	57.8403	.68379	.01729	1.37027	.72978	22.77179	.04391
71.500	41.9290	56.9340	41.9156	57.0878	.67901	.01752	1.36197	.73423	22.47550	.04449
72.000	41.6378	56.2114	41.6245	56.3589	.67429	.01774	1.35398	.73856	22.18853	.04507
72.500	41.3507	55.5108	41.3375	55.6524	.66964	.01797	1.34629	.74278	21.91038	.04564
73.000	41.0675	54.8312	41.0543	54.9672	.66506	.01819	1.33889	.74689	21.64062	.04621
73.500	40.7881	54.1715	40.7750	54.3022	.66053	.01842	1.33175	.75089	21.37883	.04678
74.000	40.5125	53.5308	40.4995	53.6565	.65607	.01864	1.32487	.75479	21.12462	.04734
74.500	40.2406	52.9082	40.2277	53.0292	.65167	.01886	1.31823	.75860	20.87764	.04790
75.000	39.9723	52.3029	39.9595	52.4194	.64732	.01908	1.31181	.76231	20.63754	.04846
75.500	39.7076	51.7140	39.6949	51.8262	.64303	.01930	1.30561	.76592	20.40402	.04901
76.000	39.4464	51.1408	39.4338	51.2490	.63880	.01951	1.29962	.76945	20.17677	.04956
76.500	39.1886	50.5827	39.1760	50.6870	.63463	.01973	1.29383	.77290	19.95552	.05011
77.000	38.9341	50.0390	38.9216	50.1396	.63051	.01994	1.28822	.77626	19.74001	.05066
77.500	38.6829	49.5091	38.6705	49.6062	.62644	.02016	1.28279	.77955	19.53000	.05120
78.000	38.4349	48.9924	38.4226	49.0862	.62242	.02037	1.27753	.78276	19.32526	.05175
78.500	38.1901	48.4884	38.1779	48.5789	.61846	.02059	1.27244	.78589	19.12557	.05229
79.000	37.9484	47.9965	37.9363	48.0840	.61455	.02080	1.26749	.78896	18.93072	.05282
79.500	37.7097	47.5163	37.6977	47.6009	.61068	.02101	1.26270	.79195	18.74053	.05336
80.000	37.4741	47.0474	37.4621	47.1292	.60686	.02122	1.25805	.79488	18.55481	.05389
80.500	37.2413	46.5892	37.2294	46.6684	.60309	.02143	1.25354	.79774	18.37339	.05443
81.000	37.0114	46.1415	36.9996	46.2181	.59937	.02164	1.24915	.80054	18.19611	.05496
81.500	36.7844	45.7038	36.7726	45.7779	.59569	.02184	1.24489	.80328	18.02281	.05549
82.000	36.5601	45.2757	36.5484	45.3475	.59206	.02205	1.24075	.80596	17.85335	.05601
82.500	36.3385	44.8569	36.3269	44.9265	.58847	.02226	1.23673	.80858	17.68759	.05654
83.000	36.1196	44.4470	36.1080	44.5145	.58493	.02246	1.23281	.81115	17.52539	.05706
83.500	35.9033	44.0459	35.8918	44.1113	.58143	.02267	1.22901	.81367	17.36664	.05758
84.000	35.6896	43.6531	35.6782	43.7165	.57797	.02287	1.22530	.81613	17.21120	.05810
84.500	35.4784	43.2683	35.4671	43.3298	.57455	.02308	1.22169	.81854	17.05898	.05862
85.000	35.2697	42.8914	35.2584	42.9510	.57117	.02328	1.21818	.82090	16.90985	.05914
85.500	35.0635	42.5220	35.0522	42.5799	.56783	.02349	1.21475	.82321	16.76373	.05965
86.000	34.8596	42.1599	34.8484	42.2161	.56452	.02369	1.21142	.82548	16.62050	.06017
86.500	34.6581	41.8048	34.6470	41.8594	.56126	.02389	1.20817	.82770	16.48008	.06068
87.000	34.4589	41.4566	34.4479	41.5096	.55804	.02409	1.20500	.82988	16.34237	.06119
87.500	34.2620	41.1151	34.2510	41.1665	.55485	.02429	1.20191	.83201	16.20730	.06170
88.000	34.0673	40.7799	34.0564	40.8299	.55169	.02449	1.19889	.83410	16.07477	.06221
88.500	33.8749	40.4510	33.8640	40.4996	.54858	.02469	1.19595	.83616	15.94472	.06272
89.000	33.6846	40.1281	33.6738	40.1753	.54550	.02489	1.19307	.83817	15.81706	.06322
89.500	33.4964	39.8111	33.4857	39.8570	.54245	.02509	1.19027	.84015	15.69172	.06373
90.000	33.3103	39.4997	33.2996	39.5444	.53943	.02529	1.18753	.84208	15.56864	.06423

TABLE 34

IEC-R 900, IEC-P 900 Brit: WG-27, WG-27P Amer: WR-10

Outside dimensions: 0.180 X 0.130 ±0.002 inches
4.57 X 3.30 ±0.05 millimeters or
0.2953 - 0.0006, + 0.000 inch diameter
7.500 - 0.015, + 0.000 millimeter diameter

Inside dimensions: 0.1000 X 0.0500 ±0.0008 inches
2.540 X 1.270 ±0.020 millimeters
corner radius: 0.15 millimeters
a/b: 2.000

Cutoff: Rectangle in Vacuum / Waveguide in Air
Wavelength: 5.0800mm / 5.0496mm
Frequency: 59014.272 MHz / 59350.753 MHz

	THEORETICAL		PHYSICAL							
f (GHz)	λ (mm)	λ_g (mm)	λ (mm)	λ_g (mm)	λ/λ_c	$1/\lambda_g$ (1/mm)	λ_g/λ	λ/λ_g	λ_g (in/10)	$1/\lambda_g$ (10/in)
75.000	39.9723	64.7708	39.9595	65.3429	.79134	.01530	1.63523	.61154	25.72557	.03887
76.000	39.4464	62.6021	39.4338	63.1169	.78093	.01584	1.60058	.62477	24.84917	.04024
77.000	38.9341	60.6128	38.9216	61.0785	.77079	.01637	1.56927	.63724	24.04665	.04159
78.000	38.4349	58.7793	38.4226	59.2025	.76091	.01689	1.54082	.64900	23.30808	.04290
79.000	37.9484	57.0819	37.9363	57.4683	.75128	.01740	1.51486	.66013	22.62530	.04420
80.000	37.4741	55.5046	37.4621	55.8586	.74188	.01790	1.49107	.67066	21.99158	.04547
81.000	37.0114	54.0336	36.9996	54.3591	.73273	.01840	1.46918	.68065	21.40124	.04673
82.000	36.5601	52.6575	36.5484	52.9577	.72379	.01888	1.44898	.69014	20.84951	.04796
83.000	36.1196	51.3663	36.1080	51.6441	.71507	.01936	1.43027	.69917	20.33232	.04918
84.000	35.6896	50.1516	35.6782	50.4093	.70656	.01984	1.41289	.70777	19.84619	.05039
85.000	35.2697	49.0061	35.2584	49.2458	.69824	.02031	1.39671	.71597	19.38810	.05158
86.000	34.8596	47.9235	34.8484	48.1468	.69013	.02077	1.38161	.72380	18.95544	.05276
87.000	34.4589	46.8981	34.4479	47.1067	.68219	.02123	1.36748	.73127	18.54593	.05392
88.000	34.0673	45.9250	34.0564	46.1202	.67444	.02168	1.35423	.73843	18.15756	.05507
89.000	33.6846	44.9999	33.6738	45.1829	.66686	.02213	1.34178	.74528	17.78856	.05622
90.000	33.3103	44.1190	33.2996	44.2909	.65945	.02258	1.33007	.75184	17.43737	.05735
91.000	32.9442	43.2789	32.9337	43.4406	.65221	.02302	1.31903	.75813	17.10260	.05847
92.000	32.5861	42.4765	32.5757	42.6288	.64512	.02346	1.30861	.76417	16.78301	.05958
93.000	32.2358	41.7090	32.2254	41.8528	.63818	.02389	1.29875	.76997	16.47747	.06069
94.000	31.8928	40.9741	31.8826	41.1099	.63139	.02433	1.28941	.77555	16.19498	.06179
95.000	31.5571	40.2694	31.5470	40.3978	.62474	.02475	1.28056	.78091	15.90465	.06287
96.000	31.2284	39.5929	31.2184	39.7146	.61824	.02518	1.27215	.78607	15.63565	.06396
97.000	30.9064	38.9429	30.8966	39.0582	.61186	.02560	1.26416	.79104	15.37724	.06503
98.000	30.5911	38.3176	30.5813	38.4270	.60562	.02602	1.25655	.79583	15.12875	.06610
99.000	30.2821	37.7155	30.2724	37.8195	.59950	.02644	1.24931	.80044	14.88955	.06716
100.000	29.9792	37.1353	29.9697	37.2341	.59351	.02686	1.24239	.80490	14.65909	.06822
101.000	29.6824	36.5755	29.6729	36.6696	.58763	.02727	1.23579	.80920	14.43685	.06927
102.000	29.3914	36.0352	29.3820	36.1248	.58187	.02768	1.22949	.81335	14.22235	.07031
103.000	29.1061	35.5131	29.0968	35.5985	.57622	.02809	1.22345	.81736	14.01516	.07135
104.000	28.8262	35.0083	28.8170	35.0898	.57068	.02850	1.21768	.82124	13.81487	.07239
105.000	28.5517	34.5198	28.5425	34.5976	.56525	.02890	1.21214	.82498	13.62112	.07342
106.000	28.2823	34.0469	28.2733	34.1212	.55991	.02931	1.20684	.82861	13.43356	.07444
107.000	28.0180	33.5886	28.0090	33.6597	.55468	.02971	1.20175	.83212	13.25186	.07546
108.000	27.7586	33.1443	27.7497	33.2124	.54954	.03011	1.19686	.83552	13.07574	.07648
109.000	27.5039	32.7133	27.4951	32.7785	.54450	.03051	1.19216	.83882	12.90491	.07749
110.000	27.2539	32.2950	27.2451	32.3574	.53955	.03090	1.18764	.84201	12.73912	.07850

TABLE 35

IEC-R 1200, IEC-P 1200 Brit: WG-28, WG-28P Amer: WR-8, RG-138/U, RG-278/U

Outside dimensions: 0.160 X 0.120 ±0.002 inches
4.06 X 3.05 ±0.05 millimeters or
0.1575 - 0.0005, + 0.000 inch diameter
4.000 - 0.012, + 0.000 millimeter diameter

Inside dimensions: 0.0800 X 0.0400 ±0.002 inches
2.032 X 1.016 ±0.020 millimeters
corner radius: 0.15 millimeters
a/b: 2.000

Cutoff: Rectangle in Vacuum / Waveguide in Air
Wavelength: 4.0640mm / 4.0260mm
Frequency: 73767.840 MHz / 74440.661 MHz

	THEORETICAL		PHYSICAL							
f (GHz)	λ (mm)	λ_g (mm)	λ (mm)	λ_g (mm)	λ/λ_c	$1/\lambda_g$ (1/mm)	λ_g/λ	λ/λ_g	λ_g (in/10)	$1/\lambda_g$ (10/in)
90.000	33.3103	58.1458	33.2996	59.2286	.82712	.01688	1.77866	.56222	23.31834	.04288
91.000	32.9442	56.2619	32.9337	57.2399	.81803	.01747	1.73803	.57536	22.53539	.04437
92.000	32.5861	54.5320	32.5757	55.4200	.80914	.01804	1.70127	.58780	21.81889	.04583
93.000	32.2358	52.9359	32.2254	53.7460	.80044	.01861	1.66781	.59959	21.15985	.04726
94.000	31.8928	51.4571	31.8826	52.1993	.79192	.01916	1.63723	.61079	20.55090	.04866
95.000	31.5571	50.0817	31.5470	50.7643	.78359	.01970	1.60916	.62144	19.98593	.05004
96.000	31.2284	48.7980	31.2184	49.4280	.77542	.02023	1.58330	.63159	19.45983	.05139
97.000	30.9064	47.5963	30.8966	48.1795	.76743	.02076	1.55938	.64128	18.96831	.05272
98.000	30.5911	46.4680	30.5813	47.0095	.75960	.02127	1.53720	.65053	18.50768	.05403
99.000	30.2821	45.4059	30.2724	45.9100	.75193	.02178	1.51657	.65938	18.07482	.05533
100.000	29.9792	44.4037	29.9697	44.8742	.74441	.02228	1.49732	.66786	17.66701	.05660
101.000	29.6824	43.4559	29.6729	43.8961	.73704	.02278	1.47933	.67598	17.28191	.05786
102.000	29.3914	42.5578	29.3820	42.9704	.72981	.02327	1.46247	.68377	16.91746	.05911
103.000	29.1061	41.7051	29.0968	42.0926	.72272	.02376	1.44664	.69126	16.57187	.06034
104.000	28.8262	40.8940	28.8170	41.2586	.71578	.02424	1.43175	.69845	16.24355	.06156
105.000	28.5517	40.1213	28.5425	40.4650	.70896	.02471	1.41771	.70536	15.93109	.06277
106.000	28.2823	39.3840	28.2733	39.7085	.70227	.02518	1.40445	.71202	15.63325	.06397
107.000	28.0180	38.6795	28.0090	38.9863	.69571	.02565	1.39192	.71843	15.34892	.06515
108.000	27.7586	38.0054	27.7497	38.2958	.68927	.02611	1.38005	.72461	15.07710	.06633
109.000	27.5039	37.3595	27.4951	37.6349	.68294	.02657	1.36879	.73057	14.81688	.06749
110.000	27.2539	36.7400	27.2451	37.0014	.67673	.02703	1.35809	.73633	14.56747	.06865
111.000	27.0083	36.1450	26.9997	36.3935	.67064	.02748	1.34792	.74188	14.32814	.06979
112.000	26.7672	35.5730	26.7586	35.8094	.66465	.02793	1.33824	.74725	14.09821	.07093
113.000	26.5303	35.0226	26.5218	35.2478	.65877	.02837	1.32901	.75244	13.87708	.07206
114.000	26.2976	34.4924	26.2892	34.7071	.65299	.02881	1.32021	.75746	13.66421	.07318
115.000	26.0689	33.9812	26.0606	34.1861	.64731	.02925	1.31179	.76231	13.45910	.07430
116.000	25.8442	33.4879	25.8359	33.6836	.64173	.02969	1.30375	.76702	13.26128	.07541
117.000	25.6233	33.0115	25.6151	33.1986	.63624	.03012	1.29606	.77157	13.07032	.07651
118.000	25.4061	32.5510	25.3980	32.7301	.63085	.03055	1.28869	.77598	12.88585	.07760
119.000	25.1926	32.1055	25.1846	32.2771	.62555	.03098	1.28162	.78026	12.70750	.07869
120.000	24.9827	31.6744	24.9747	31.8388	.62034	.03141	1.27484	.78441	12.53494	.07978
121.000	24.7762	31.2567	24.7683	31.4144	.61521	.03183	1.26833	.78844	12.36787	.08085
122.000	24.5732	30.8519	24.5653	31.0032	.61017	.03225	1.26207	.79235	12.20600	.08193
123.000	24.3734	30.4593	24.3656	30.6046	.60521	.03267	1.25606	.79614	12.04906	.08299
124.000	24.1768	30.0782	24.1691	30.2179	.60033	.03309	1.25027	.79983	11.89682	.08406
125.000	23.9834	29.7082	23.9757	29.8426	.59553	.03351	1.24470	.80341	11.74904	.08511
126.000	23.7931	29.3487	23.7854	29.4780	.59080	.03392	1.23933	.80689	11.60551	.08617
127.000	23.6057	28.9992	23.5982	29.1237	.58615	.03434	1.23415	.81027	11.46603	.08721
128.000	23.4213	28.6593	23.4138	28.7793	.58157	.03475	1.22916	.81356	11.33042	.08826
129.000	23.2397	28.3286	23.2323	28.4442	.57706	.03516	1.22434	.81677	11.19850	.08930
130.000	23.0610	28.0066	23.0536	28.1181	.57262	.03556	1.21968	.81988	11.07011	.09033
131.000	22.8849	27.6930	22.8776	27.8005	.56825	.03597	1.21519	.82292	10.94510	.09137
132.000	22.7116	27.3874	22.7043	27.4912	.56394	.03638	1.21084	.82587	10.82331	.09239
133.000	22.5408	27.0895	22.5336	27.1897	.55970	.03678	1.20663	.82875	10.70462	.09342
134.000	22.3726	26.7989	22.3654	26.8958	.55553	.03718	1.20256	.83156	10.58890	.09444
135.000	22.2069	26.5155	22.1997	26.6091	.55141	.03758	1.19862	.83429	10.47603	.09546
136.000	22.0436	26.2388	22.0365	26.3294	.54736	.03798	1.19481	.83696	10.36589	.09647
137.000	21.8827	25.9687	21.8757	26.0563	.54336	.03838	1.19111	.83955	10.25838	.09748
138.000	21.7241	25.7048	21.7171	25.7896	.53943	.03878	1.18752	.84209	10.15339	.09849
139.000	21.5678	25.4470	21.5609	25.5291	.53554	.03917	1.18405	.84456	10.05083	.09949
140.000	21.4137	25.1950	21.4069	25.2746	.53172	.03957	1.18067	.84697	9.95061	.10050

TABLE 36

IEC-R 1400, IEC-P 1400 Brit: WG-28, WG-28P

Amer: WR-8, RG-138/U, RG-278/U

Outside dimensions: Rectangular dimensions not yet standardized
0.1575 - 0.0005, + 0.000 inch diameter
4.000 - 0.012, + 0.000 millimeter diameter

Inside dimensions: 0.0650 X 0.0325 ±0.0002 inches
1.651 X 0.826 ±0.003 millimeters
corner radius: 0.09 millimeters (j)

Cutoff: Rectangle in Vacuum Waveguide in Air

Wavelength: 3.3020mm 3.2852mm
Frequency: 90791.187 MHz 91227.280 MHz

f (GHz)	THEORETICAL λ (mm)	THEORETICAL λ_g (mm)	PHYSICAL λ (mm)	λ_g (mm)	λ/λ_c	$1/\lambda_g$ (1/mm)	λ_g/λ	λ/λ_g	λ_g (in/10)	$1/\lambda_g$ (10/in)
110.000	27.2539	48.2723	27.2451	48.7441	.82934	.02052	1.78909	.55894	19.19058	.05211
111.000	27.0083	46.9461	26.9997	47.3788	.82187	.02111	1.75479	.56987	18.65308	.05361
112.000	26.7672	45.7128	26.7586	46.1113	.81453	.02169	1.72323	.58031	18.15405	.05508
113.000	26.5303	44.5621	26.5218	44.9302	.80732	.02226	1.69409	.59029	17.68907	.05653
114.000	26.2976	43.4849	26.2892	43.8261	.80024	.02282	1.66708	.59985	17.25438	.05796
115.000	26.0689	42.4738	26.0606	42.7909	.79328	.02337	1.64198	.60902	16.84681	.05936
116.000	25.8442	41.5220	25.8359	41.8176	.78644	.02391	1.61858	.61782	16.46362	.06074
117.000	25.6233	40.6241	25.6151	40.9002	.77972	.02445	1.59672	.62628	16.10243	.06210
118.000	25.4061	39.7750	25.3980	40.0335	.77311	.02498	1.57624	.63442	15.76121	.06345
119.000	25.1926	38.9704	25.1846	39.2129	.76662	.02550	1.55702	.64225	15.43816	.06477
120.000	24.9827	38.2065	24.9747	38.4345	.76023	.02602	1.53894	.64980	15.13169	.06609
121.000	24.7762	37.4800	24.7683	37.6947	.75394	.02653	1.52189	.65708	14.84044	.06738
122.000	24.5732	36.7879	24.5653	36.9904	.74776	.02703	1.50580	.66410	14.56316	.06867
123.000	24.3734	36.1275	24.3656	36.3189	.74169	.02753	1.49058	.67088	14.29877	.06994
124.000	24.1768	35.4965	24.1691	35.6775	.73570	.02803	1.47616	.67743	14.04628	.07119
125.000	23.9834	34.8927	23.9757	35.0642	.72982	.02852	1.46249	.68377	13.80482	.07244
126.000	23.7931	34.3142	23.7854	34.4769	.72403	.02900	1.44950	.68989	13.57360	.07367
127.000	23.6057	33.7593	23.5982	33.9139	.71833	.02949	1.43714	.69583	13.35192	.07490
128.000	23.4213	33.2264	23.4138	33.3734	.71271	.02996	1.42537	.70157	13.13912	.07611
129.000	23.2397	32.7140	23.2323	32.8540	.70719	.03044	1.41415	.70714	12.93463	.07731
130.000	23.0610	32.2209	23.0536	32.3543	.70175	.03091	1.40344	.71254	12.73791	.07851
131.000	22.8849	31.7459	22.8776	31.8732	.69639	.03137	1.39320	.71777	12.54849	.07969
132.000	22.7116	31.2879	22.7043	31.4094	.69112	.03184	1.38341	.72285	12.36591	.08087
133.000	22.5408	30.8459	22.5336	30.9620	.68592	.03230	1.37404	.72778	12.18978	.08204
134.000	22.3726	30.4190	22.3654	30.5301	.68080	.03275	1.36506	.73257	12.01972	.08320
135.000	22.2069	30.0063	22.1997	30.1127	.67576	.03321	1.35644	.73722	11.85538	.08435
136.000	22.0436	29.6071	22.0365	29.7090	.67079	.03366	1.34817	.74175	11.69646	.08550
137.000	21.8827	29.2207	21.8757	29.3183	.66589	.03411	1.34023	.74614	11.54265	.08664
138.000	21.7241	28.8463	21.7171	28.9400	.66107	.03455	1.33259	.75042	11.39370	.08777
139.000	21.5678	28.4833	21.5609	28.5733	.65631	.03500	1.32524	.75458	11.24934	.08889
140.000	21.4137	28.1313	21.4069	28.2178	.65162	.03544	1.31816	.75863	11.10936	.09001
141.000	21.2619	27.7896	21.2551	27.8727	.64700	.03588	1.31134	.76258	10.97352	.09113
142.000	21.1121	27.4578	21.1054	27.5377	.64245	.03631	1.30477	.76642	10.84163	.09224
143.000	20.9645	27.1353	20.9578	27.2123	.63795	.03675	1.29843	.77016	10.71350	.09334
144.000	20.8189	26.8218	20.8123	26.8959	.63352	.03718	1.29231	.77381	10.58895	.09444
145.000	20.6753	26.5169	20.6687	26.5883	.62915	.03761	1.28640	.77736	10.46783	.09553
146.000	20.5337	26.2201	20.5272	26.2889	.62484	.03804	1.28069	.78083	10.34997	.09662
147.000	20.3940	25.9311	20.3875	25.9975	.62059	.03847	1.27517	.78421	10.23524	.09770
148.000	20.2562	25.6496	20.2498	25.7137	.61640	.03889	1.26983	.78751	10.12349	.09878
149.000	20.1203	25.3752	20.1139	25.4371	.61226	.03931	1.26465	.79073	10.01461	.09985
150.000	19.9862	25.1077	19.9798	25.1675	.60818	.03973	1.25965	.79387	9.90846	.10092
151.000	19.8538	24.8468	19.8475	24.9046	.60415	.04015	1.25480	.79694	9.80494	.10199
152.000	19.7232	24.5922	19.7169	24.6480	.60018	.04057	1.25010	.79994	9.70395	.10305
153.000	19.5943	24.3437	19.5880	24.3977	.59626	.04099	1.24554	.80286	9.60538	.10411
154.000	19.4670	24.1009	19.4608	24.1532	.59238	.04140	1.24112	.80572	9.50913	.10516
155.000	19.3415	23.8638	19.3353	23.9144	.58856	.04182	1.23683	.80852	9.41512	.10621
156.000	19.2175	23.6321	19.2113	23.6811	.58479	.04223	1.23266	.81125	9.32326	.10726
157.000	19.0951	23.4056	19.0890	23.4530	.58107	.04264	1.22862	.81392	9.23347	.10830
158.000	18.9742	23.1841	18.9681	23.2300	.57739	.04305	1.22469	.81654	9.14568	.10934
159.000	18.8549	22.9674	18.8488	23.0119	.57376	.04346	1.22087	.81909	9.05981	.11038
160.000	18.7370	22.7554	18.7310	22.7985	.57017	.04386	1.21715	.82159	8.97580	.11141
161.000	18.6207	22.5478	18.6147	22.5897	.56663	.04427	1.21354	.82404	8.89358	.11244
162.000	18.5057	22.3446	18.4998	22.3852	.56313	.04467	1.21003	.82643	8.81308	.11347
163.000	18.3922	22.1456	18.3863	22.1850	.55968	.04508	1.20661	.82877	8.73425	.11449
164.000	18.2800	21.9506	18.2742	21.9889	.55626	.04548	1.20327	.83107	8.65703	.11551
165.000	18.1692	21.7596	18.1634	21.7967	.55289	.04588	1.20003	.83331	8.58138	.11653
166.000	18.0598	21.5723	18.0540	21.6084	.54956	.04628	1.19687	.83551	8.50723	.11755
167.000	17.9516	21.3887	17.9459	21.4237	.54627	.04668	1.19379	.83767	8.43453	.11856
168.000	17.8448	21.2086	17.8391	21.2427	.54302	.04708	1.19079	.83978	8.36325	.11957
169.000	17.7392	21.0320	17.7335	21.0651	.53981	.04747	1.18787	.84184	8.29334	.12058
170.000	17.6349	20.8587	17.6292	20.8909	.53663	.04787	1.18501	.84387	8.22475	.12158

TABLE 37

IEC-R 1800, IEC-P 1800 Brit: WB-30, WG-30P

Amer: WR-5, RG-135/U, RG-275/U

Outside dimensions: Rectangular dimensions not yet standardized
0.1575 -0.0005, +0.000 inch diameter
4.000 -0.012, +0.000 millimeter diameter

Inside dimensions: 0.0510 X 0.0255 ±0.0001 inches
1.295 X 0.648 ±0.003 millimeters
corner radius: 0.08 millimeters (j)
a/b: 2.000

Cutoff: Rectangle in Vacuum Waveguide in Air

Wavelength: 2.5900mm 2.5730mm
Frequency: 115750.00 MHz 116475.52 MHz

f (GHz)	THEORETICAL λ (mm)	THEORETICAL λ_g (mm)	PHYSICAL λ (mm)	λ_g (mm)	λ/λ_c	$1/\lambda_g$ (1/mm)	λ_g/λ	λ/λ_g	λ_g (in/10)	$1/\lambda_g$ (10/in)
140.000	2.1414	3.8068	2.1407	3.8569	.83197	.25927	1.80173	.55502	1.51848	.65855
141.000	2.1262	3.7234	2.1255	3.7702	.82607	.26524	1.77379	.56376	1.48433	.67370
142.000	2.1112	3.6447	2.1105	3.6885	.82025	.27111	1.74766	.57219	1.45217	.68863
143.000	2.0965	3.5702	2.0958	3.6114	.81451	.27690	1.72317	.58033	1.42180	.70333
144.000	2.0819	3.4997	2.0812	3.5384	.80886	.28261	1.70015	.58818	1.39307	.71784
145.000	2.0675	3.4328	2.0669	3.4692	.80328	.28825	1.67848	.59578	1.36583	.73215
146.000	2.0534	3.3691	2.0527	3.4035	.79778	.29382	1.65804	.60312	1.33996	.74629
147.000	2.0394	3.3084	2.0388	3.3410	.79235	.29932	1.63872	.61023	1.31534	.76026
148.000	2.0256	3.2506	2.0250	3.2813	.78700	.30475	1.62044	.61712	1.29187	.77407
149.000	2.0120	3.1953	2.0114	3.2244	.78171	.31013	1.60310	.62379	1.26947	.78773
150.000	1.9986	3.1423	1.9980	3.1701	.77650	.31545	1.58663	.63027	1.24805	.80125
151.000	1.9854	3.0916	1.9847	3.1180	.77136	.32072	1.57098	.63655	1.22755	.81463
152.000	1.9723	3.0430	1.9717	3.0681	.76629	.32594	1.55607	.64265	1.20791	.82788
153.000	1.9594	2.9963	1.9588	3.0202	.76128	.33110	1.54186	.64857	1.18905	.84101
154.000	1.9467	2.9514	1.9461	2.9742	.75633	.33623	1.52829	.65432	1.17094	.85402
155.000	1.9341	2.9081	1.9335	2.9299	.75145	.34130	1.51533	.65992	1.15352	.86691
156.000	1.9217	2.8665	1.9211	2.8873	.74664	.34634	1.50294	.66536	1.13675	.87970
157.000	1.9095	2.8264	1.9089	2.8463	.74188	.35133	1.49107	.67066	1.12059	.89239
158.000	1.8974	2.7876	1.8968	2.8067	.73719	.35629	1.47969	.67582	1.10500	.90498
159.000	1.8855	2.7502	1.8849	2.7685	.73255	.36121	1.46878	.68084	1.08995	.91747
160.000	1.8737	2.7140	1.8731	2.7315	.72797	.36609	1.45830	.68573	1.07541	.92988
161.000	1.8621	2.6790	1.8615	2.6958	.72345	.37094	1.44823	.69050	1.06135	.94219
162.000	1.8506	2.6451	1.8500	2.6613	.71898	.37576	1.43855	.69514	1.04775	.95443
163.000	1.8392	2.6122	1.8386	2.6278	.71457	.38054	1.42923	.69968	1.03458	.96658

164.000	1.8280	2.5804	1.8274	2.5954	.71022	.38530	1.42026	.70410	1.02181	.97865
165.000	1.8169	2.5495	1.8163	2.5640	.70591	.39002	1.41161	.70841	1.00944	.99065
166.000	1.8060	2.5195	1.8054	2.5335	.70166	.39472	1.40327	.71262	.99743	1.00258
167.000	1.7952	2.4904	1.7946	2.5038	.69746	.39939	1.39522	.71673	.98577	1.01444
168.000	1.7845	2.4621	1.7839	2.4751	.69331	.40403	1.38744	.72075	.97444	1.02623
169.000	1.7739	2.4346	1.7734	2.4471	.68920	.40865	1.37993	.72467	.96343	1.03796
170.000	1.7635	2.4078	1.7629	2.4199	.68515	.41324	1.37267	.72850	.95272	1.04962
171.000	1.7532	2.3818	1.7526	2.3935	.68114	.41781	1.36565	.73225	.94231	1.06123
172.000	1.7430	2.3564	1.7424	2.3677	.67718	.42235	1.35885	.73591	.93216	1.07277
173.000	1.7329	2.3317	1.7324	2.3426	.67327	.42687	1.35227	.73950	.92229	1.08426
174.000	1.7229	2.3076	1.7224	2.3182	.66940	.43138	1.34590	.74300	.91266	1.09569
175.000	1.7131	2.2841	1.7126	2.2943	.66557	.43586	1.33972	.74643	.90328	1.10707
176.000	1.7034	2.2612	1.7028	2.2711	.66179	.44032	1.33372	.74978	.89413	1.11840
177.000	1.6937	2.2388	1.6932	2.2484	.65805	.44476	1.32791	.75306	.88520	1.12968
178.000	1.6842	2.2170	1.6837	2.2263	.65436	.44918	1.32227	.75628	.87649	1.14091
179.000	1.6748	2.1957	1.6743	2.2047	.65070	.45358	1.31679	.75942	.86798	1.15210
180.000	1.6655	2.1748	1.6650	2.1836	.64709	.45797	1.31147	.76250	.85967	1.16323
181.000	1.6563	2.1544	1.6558	2.1629	.64351	.46233	1.30630	.76552	.85155	1.17433
182.000	1.6472	2.1345	1.6467	2.1428	.63998	.46668	1.30127	.76848	.84361	1.18538
183.000	1.6382	2.1151	1.6377	2.1231	.63648	.47102	1.29638	.77138	.83585	1.19638
184.000	1.6293	2.0960	1.6288	2.1038	.63302	.47533	1.29162	.77422	.82826	1.20735
185.000	1.6205	2.0773	1.6200	2.0849	.62960	.47964	1.28700	.77700	.82083	1.21828
186.000	1.6118	2.0591	1.6113	2.0664	.62621	.48392	1.28249	.77973	.81356	1.22917
187.000	1.6032	2.0412	1.6027	2.0484	.62286	.48820	1.27810	.78241	.80644	1.24002
188.000	1.5946	2.0237	1.5941	2.0306	.61955	.49245	1.27383	.78503	.79947	1.25083
189.000	1.5862	2.0065	1.5857	2.0133	.61627	.49670	1.26966	.78761	.79264	1.26161
190.000	1.5779	1.9897	1.5774	1.9963	.61303	.50093	1.26560	.79014	.78595	1.27235
191.000	1.5696	1.9732	1.5691	1.9796	.60982	.50514	1.26165	.79262	.77939	1.28306
192.000	1.5614	1.9570	1.5609	1.9633	.60664	.50935	1.25779	.79505	.77295	1.29374
193.000	1.5533	1.9412	1.5528	1.9473	.60350	.51354	1.25402	.79744	.76665	1.30438
194.000	1.5453	1.9256	1.5448	1.9316	.60039	.51771	1.25034	.79978	.76046	1.31500
195.000	1.5374	1.9104	1.5369	1.9161	.59731	.52188	1.24676	.80208	.75439	1.32558
196.000	1.5296	1.8954	1.5291	1.9010	.59426	.52603	1.24325	.80434	.74843	1.33613
197.000	1.5218	1.8807	1.5213	1.8862	.59125	.53018	1.23983	.80656	.74258	1.34665
198.000	1.5141	1.8662	1.5136	1.8716	.58826	.53431	1.23649	.80874	.73684	1.35714
199.000	1.5065	1.8520	1.5060	1.8573	.58530	.53843	1.23323	.81088	.73120	1.36761
200.000	1.4990	1.8381	1.4985	1.8432	.58238	.54254	1.23003	.81299	.72566	1.37805
201.000	1.4915	1.8244	1.4910	1.8294	.57948	.54664	1.22692	.81505	.72022	1.38846
202.000	1.4841	1.8109	1.4836	1.8158	.57661	.55073	1.22387	.81708	.71488	1.39885
203.000	1.4768	1.7977	1.4763	1.8024	.57377	.55481	1.22088	.81908	.70962	1.40921
204.000	1.4696	1.7847	1.4691	1.7893	.57096	.55887	1.21796	.82104	.70445	1.41954
205.000	1.4624	1.7719	1.4619	1.7764	.56817	.56293	1.21511	.82297	.69937	1.42985
206.000	1.4553	1.7593	1.4548	1.7637	.56542	.56698	1.21231	.82487	.69438	1.44014
207.000	1.4483	1.7469	1.4478	1.7512	.56268	.57102	1.20958	.82673	.68946	1.45040
208.000	1.4413	1.7347	1.4408	1.7390	.55998	.57506	1.20690	.82857	.68463	1.46064
209.000	1.4344	1.7227	1.4340	1.7269	.55730	.57908	1.20428	.83037	.67988	1.47086
210.000	1.4276	1.7110	1.4271	1.7150	.55465	.58309	1.20171	.83215	.67520	1.48105
211.000	1.4208	1.6993	1.4204	1.7033	.55202	.58710	1.19920	.83389	.67059	1.49123
212.000	1.4141	1.6879	1.4137	1.6918	.54941	.59109	1.19673	.83561	.66605	1.50138
213.000	1.4075	1.6767	1.4070	1.6804	.54683	.59508	1.19432	.83730	.66159	1.51151
214.000	1.4009	1.6656	1.4005	1.6693	.54428	.59906	1.19195	.83896	.65719	1.52162
215.000	1.3944	1.6546	1.3939	1.6583	.54175	.60304	1.18963	.84060	.65286	1.53172
216.000	1.3879	1.6439	1.3875	1.6474	.53924	.60700	1.18735	.84221	.64860	1.54179
217.000	1.3815	1.6333	1.3811	1.6368	.53675	.61096	1.18512	.84379	.64439	1.55184
218.000	1.3752	1.6229	1.3748	1.6262	.53429	.61491	1.18294	.84535	.64025	1.56188
219.000	1.3689	1.6126	1.3685	1.6159	.53185	.61886	1.18079	.84689	.63617	1.57189
220.000	1.3627	1.6024	1.3623	1.6057	.52943	.62279	1.17868	.84840	.63215	1.58189

TABLE 38

IEC-R 2200, PEC-P 2200 Brit: WG-31, WG-31P

Amer: WR-4, RG-137/U, RG-277/U

Outside dimensions: Rectangular dimensions not yet standardized
0.1575 -0.0005, +0.000 inch diameter
4.000 -0.012, +0.000 millimeter diameter

Inside dimensions: 0.0430 X 0.0215 ±0.0001 inches
1.092 X 0.546 ±0.003 millimeters
corner radius: 0.06 millimeters (j)
a/b: 2.000

Cutoff: Rectangle in Vacuum Waveguide in Air

Wavelength: 2.1840mm 2.1727mm
Frequency: 137267.63 MHz 137938.66 MHz

	THEORETICAL					PHYSICAL				
f (GHz)	λ (mm)	λ_g (mm)	λ (mm)	λ_g (mm)	$\frac{\lambda}{\lambda_c}$	$1/\lambda_g$ (1/mm)	$\frac{\lambda_g}{\lambda}$	$\frac{\lambda}{\lambda_g}$	λ_g (in/10)	$1/\lambda_g$ (10/in)
170.000	1.7635	2.9893	1.7629	3.0153	.81140	.33165	1.71038	.58467	1.18711	.84238
171.500	1.7481	2.9160	1.7475	2.9400	.80431	.34014	1.68240	.59439	1.15748	.86394
173.000	1.7329	2.8472	1.7324	2.8695	.79733	.34849	1.65643	.60371	1.12973	.88517
174.500	1.7180	2.7826	1.7175	2.8033	.79048	.35672	1.63225	.61265	1.10367	.90607
176.000	1.7034	2.7216	1.7028	2.7410	.78374	.36483	1.60967	.62124	1.07913	.92667
177.500	1.6890	2.6640	1.6884	2.6821	.77712	.37284	1.58855	.62951	1.05596	.94700
179.000	1.6748	2.6095	1.6743	2.6265	.77061	.38074	1.56873	.63746	1.03405	.96707
180.500	1.6609	2.5578	1.6604	2.5737	.76420	.38854	1.55010	.64512	1.01328	.98689
182.000	1.6472	2.5086	1.6467	2.5236	.75790	.39625	1.53255	.65251	.99356	1.00649
183.500	1.6337	2.4618	1.6332	2.4760	.75171	.40388	1.51600	.65963	.97479	1.02586
185.000	1.6205	2.4172	1.6200	2.4305	.74561	.41143	1.50035	.66651	.95691	1.04504
186.500	1.6075	2.3745	1.6070	2.3872	.73962	.41890	1.48554	.67316	.93984	1.06401
188.000	1.5946	2.3338	1.5941	2.3457	.73372	.42630	1.47149	.67958	.92352	1.08281
189.500	1.5820	2.2947	1.5815	2.3061	.72791	.43363	1.45816	.68580	.90791	1.10143
191.000	1.5696	2.2573	1.5691	2.2681	.72219	.44090	1.44548	.69181	.89295	1.11989
192.500	1.5574	2.2214	1.5569	2.2316	.71656	.44810	1.43341	.69764	.87859	1.13819
194.000	1.5453	2.1868	1.5448	2.1966	.71102	.45525	1.42190	.70328	.86480	1.15633
195.500	1.5335	2.1536	1.5330	2.1629	.70557	.46234	1.41093	.70875	.85154	1.17434
197.000	1.5218	2.1216	1.5213	2.1305	.70020	.46937	1.40044	.71406	.83878	1.19221
198.500	1.5103	2.0908	1.5098	2.0993	.69491	.47636	1.39042	.71921	.82648	1.20995
200.000	1.4990	2.0610	1.4985	2.0691	.68969	.48329	1.38082	.72421	.81462	1.22756
201.500	1.4878	2.0323	1.4873	2.0401	.68456	.49018	1.37163	.72906	.80317	1.24506
203.000	1.4768	2.0046	1.4763	2.0120	.67950	.49702	1.36281	.73378	.79212	1.26244
204.500	1.4660	1.9777	1.4655	1.9848	.67452	.50382	1.35436	.73836	.78143	1.27971
206.000	1.4553	1.9517	1.4548	1.9585	.66961	.51058	1.34623	.74281	.77108	1.29688
207.500	1.4448	1.9266	1.4443	1.9331	.66476	.51730	1.33842	.74715	.76107	1.31394
209.000	1.4344	1.9022	1.4340	1.9085	.65999	.52398	1.33091	.75136	.75137	1.33091
210.500	1.4242	1.8786	1.4237	1.8846	.65529	.53062	1.32368	.75547	.74196	1.34778
212.000	1.4141	1.8556	1.4137	1.8614	.65065	.53723	1.31672	.75946	.73283	1.36457
213.500	1.4042	1.8333	1.4037	1.8389	.64608	.54380	1.31001	.76335	.72398	1.38126
215.000	1.3944	1.8117	1.3939	1.8170	.64158	.55034	1.30353	.76715	.71537	1.39788
216.500	1.3847	1.7906	1.3843	1.7958	.63713	.55685	1.29729	.77084	.70701	1.41441
218.000	1.3752	1.7702	1.3748	1.7752	.63275	.56333	1.29125	.77444	.69888	1.43086
219.500	1.3658	1.7503	1.3654	1.7551	.62842	.56978	1.28542	.77795	.69097	1.44724
221.000	1.3565	1.7309	1.3561	1.7355	.62416	.57620	1.27979	.78138	.68327	1.46354
222.500	1.3474	1.7120	1.3470	1.7165	.61995	.58259	1.27434	.78472	.67578	1.47978
224.000	1.3384	1.6936	1.3379	1.6979	.61580	.58896	1.26907	.78798	.66847	1.49595
225.500	1.3295	1.6757	1.3290	1.6798	.61170	.59529	1.26396	.79116	.66136	1.51205
227.000	1.3207	1.6582	1.3202	1.6622	.60766	.60161	1.25901	.79427	.65441	1.52808
228.500	1.3120	1.6411	1.3116	1.6450	.60367	.60790	1.25422	.79731	.64764	1.54406
230.000	1.3034	1.6245	1.3030	1.6282	.59973	.61416	1.24958	.80027	.64104	1.55997
231.500	1.2950	1.6082	1.2946	1.6118	.59585	.62041	1.24507	.80317	.63459	1.57583
233.000	1.2867	1.5923	1.2863	1.5958	.59201	.62663	1.24070	.80600	.62829	1.59163
234.500	1.2784	1.5768	1.2780	1.5802	.58822	.63283	1.23645	.80877	.62213	1.60738
236.000	1.2703	1.5616	1.2699	1.5649	.58449	.63900	1.23233	.81147	.61612	1.62307

f (GHz)	Theoretical λ (mm)	Theoretical λg (mm)	Physical λ (mm)	λg (mm)	λ/λc	1/λg (1/mm)	λg/λ	λ/λg	λg (in/10)	1/λg (10/in)
237.500	1.2623	1.5468	1.2619	1.5500	.58079	.64516	1.22833	.81412	.61024	1.63871
239.000	1.2544	1.5323	1.2540	1.5354	.57715	.65130	1.22443	.81670	.60449	1.65430
240.500	1.2465	1.5181	1.2461	1.5211	.57355	.65742	1.22065	.81924	.59886	1.66984
242.000	1.2388	1.5042	1.2384	1.5071	.56999	.66352	1.21697	.82171	.59335	1.68534
243.500	1.2312	1.4906	1.2308	1.4934	.56648	.66960	1.21339	.82414	.58796	1.70079
245.000	1.2236	1.4773	1.2233	1.4800	.56301	.67566	1.20991	.82651	.58269	1.71619
246.500	1.2162	1.4642	1.2158	1.4669	.55959	.68171	1.20652	.82883	.57752	1.73155
248.000	1.2088	1.4515	1.2085	1.4540	.55620	.68774	1.20322	.83111	.57245	1.74687
249.500	1.2016	1.4389	1.2012	1.4414	.55286	.69376	1.20000	.83333	.56749	1.76214
251.000	1.1944	1.4266	1.1940	1.4291	.54956	.69975	1.19687	.83551	.56263	1.77738
252.500	1.1873	1.4146	1.1869	1.4170	.54629	.70574	1.19381	.83765	.55786	1.79257
254.000	1.1803	1.4028	1.1799	1.4051	.54307	.71171	1.19084	.83975	.55318	1.80773
255.500	1.1734	1.3912	1.1730	1.3934	.53988	.71766	1.18793	.84180	.54859	1.82285
257.000	1.1665	1.3798	1.1661	1.3820	.53673	.72360	1.18510	.84381	.54409	1.83794
258.500	1.1597	1.3686	1.1594	1.3708	.53361	.72952	1.18234	.84578	.53967	1.85298
260.000	1.1530	1.3577	1.1527	1.3597	.53053	.73543	1.17964	.84772	.53533	1.86800

TABLE 39

IEC-R 2600, IEC-P 2600 Brit: WG-32, WG-32P

Amer: WR-3, RG-139/U

Outside dimensions: Rectangular dimensions not yet standardized
0.1575 -0.005, +0.000 inch diameter
4.000 -0.012, +0.000 millimeter diameter

Inside dimensions: 0.0340 X 0.0170 ±0.0001 inches
0.864 X 0.432 ±0.003 millimeters
corner radius: 0.05 millimeters (j)
a/b: 2.000

Cutoff: Rectangle in Vacuum — Waveguide in Air

Wavelength: 1.7280mm — 1.7181mm
Frequency: 173491.03 MHz — 174438.49 MHz

f (GHz)	THEORETICAL λ (mm)	THEORETICAL λ_g (mm)	PHYSICAL λ (mm)	λ_g (mm)	λ/λ_c	$1/\lambda_g$ (1/mm)	λ_g/λ	λ/λ_g	λ_g (in/10)	$1/\lambda_g$ (10/in)
220.000	1.3627	2.2161	1.3623	2.2350	.79290	.44743	1.64065	.60951	.87992	1.13647
221.500	1.3535	2.1770	1.3530	2.1949	.78753	.45559	1.62223	.61643	.86415	1.15721
223.000	1.3444	2.1397	1.3439	2.1567	.78224	.46367	1.60478	.62314	.84910	1.17772
224.500	1.3354	2.1041	1.3350	2.1202	.77701	.47166	1.58820	.62964	.83471	1.19802
226.000	1.3265	2.0699	1.3261	2.0852	.77185	.47957	1.57244	.63595	.82095	1.21811
227.500	1.3178	2.0371	1.3173	2.0517	.76676	.48740	1.55745	.64208	.80775	1.23800
229.000	1.3091	2.0057	1.3087	2.0195	.76174	.49516	1.54315	.64803	.79510	1.25771
230.500	1.3006	1.9754	1.3002	1.9887	.75678	.50285	1.52951	.65381	.78294	1.27724
232.000	1.2922	1.9463	1.2918	1.9590	.75189	.51047	1.51647	.65943	.77125	1.29660
233.500	1.2839	1.9183	1.2835	1.9304	.74706	.51803	1.50401	.66489	.76000	1.31580
235.000	1.2757	1.8913	1.2753	1.9028	.74229	.52553	1.49207	.67021	.74915	1.33484
236.500	1.2676	1.8652	1.2672	1.8763	.73758	.53297	1.48064	.67538	.73870	1.35374
238.000	1.2596	1.8401	1.2592	1.8507	.73293	.54035	1.46967	.68043	.72860	1.37249
239.500	1.2517	1.8157	1.2513	1.8259	.72834	.54768	1.45914	.68534	.71885	1.39111
241.000	1.2440	1.7922	1.2436	1.8019	.72381	.55496	1.44902	.69012	.70943	1.40959
242.500	1.2363	1.7694	1.2359	1.7788	.71933	.56219	1.43930	.69478	.70030	1.42795
244.000	1.2287	1.7473	1.2283	1.7563	.71491	.56937	1.42994	.69933	.69147	1.44619
245.500	1.2212	1.7259	1.2208	1.7346	.71054	.57650	1.42092	.70377	.68292	1.46431
247.000	1.2137	1.7052	1.2133	1.7135	.70623	.58359	1.41224	.70810	.67462	1.48232
248.500	1.2064	1.6850	1.2060	1.6931	.70197	.59064	1.40386	.71232	.66657	1.50022
250.000	1.1992	1.6655	1.1988	1.6732	.69775	.59764	1.39578	.71645	.65876	1.51801
251.500	1.1920	1.6465	1.1916	1.6540	.69359	.60461	1.38797	.72047	.65117	1.53571
253.000	1.1850	1.6280	1.1846	1.6352	.68948	.61154	1.38043	.72441	.64379	1.55330
254.500	1.1780	1.6100	1.1776	1.6170	.68542	.61843	1.37315	.72825	.63662	1.57081
256.000	1.1711	1.5926	1.1707	1.5993	.68140	.62528	1.36610	.73201	.62964	1.58822
257.500	1.1642	1.5755	1.1639	1.5820	.67743	.63210	1.35928	.73569	.62284	1.60554
259.000	1.1575	1.5589	1.1571	1.5652	.67351	.63889	1.35267	.73928	.61623	1.62278
260.500	1.1508	1.5428	1.1505	1.5488	.66963	.64564	1.34627	.74279	.60978	1.63994
262.000	1.1442	1.5270	1.1439	1.5329	.66580	.65237	1.34007	.74623	.60350	1.65701
263.500	1.1377	1.5116	1.1374	1.5173	.66201	.65906	1.33406	.74959	.59737	1.67401
265.000	1.1313	1.4966	1.1309	1.5021	.65826	.66572	1.32823	.75288	.59139	1.69093
266.500	1.1249	1.4820	1.1246	1.4873	.65455	.67235	1.32257	.75611	.58556	1.70778
268.000	1.1186	1.4677	1.1183	1.4728	.65089	.67896	1.31707	.75926	.57986	1.72456
269.500	1.1124	1.4537	1.1120	1.4587	.64727	.68554	1.31173	.76235	.57429	1.74127
271.000	1.1062	1.4400	1.1059	1.4449	.64368	.69209	1.30654	.76538	.56886	1.75791
272.500	1.1002	1.4267	1.0998	1.4314	.64014	.69862	1.30150	.76834	.56354	1.77449
274.000	1.0941	1.4136	1.0938	1.4182	.63664	.70512	1.29660	.77125	.55835	1.79100
275.500	1.0882	1.4008	1.0878	1.4053	.63317	.71160	1.29183	.77410	.55326	1.80746
277.000	1.0823	1.3883	1.0819	1.3927	.62974	.71805	1.28719	.77689	.54829	1.82385
278.500	1.0765	1.3761	1.0761	1.3803	.62635	.72448	1.28267	.77962	.54342	1.84018
280.000	1.0707	1.3641	1.0703	1.3682	.62299	.73089	1.27827	.78231	.53866	1.85646
281.500	1.0650	1.3524	1.0646	1.3563	.61967	.73728	1.27399	.78494	.53399	1.87269
283.000	1.0593	1.3408	1.0590	1.3447	.61639	.74364	1.26981	.78752	.52942	1.88886
284.500	1.0538	1.3296	1.0534	1.3334	.61314	.74999	1.26574	.79005	.52494	1.90497
286.000	1.0482	1.3185	1.0479	1.3222	.60992	.75631	1.26177	.79253	.52055	1.92104
287.500	1.0428	1.3077	1.0424	1.3113	.60674	.76262	1.25791	.79497	.51625	1.93705
289.000	1.0373	1.2971	1.0370	1.3005	.60359	.76891	1.25413	.79737	.51203	1.95302
290.500	1.0320	1.2866	1.0317	1.2900	.60048	.77517	1.25045	.79971	.50789	1.96894
292.000	1.0267	1.2764	1.0264	1.2797	.59739	.78142	1.24685	.80202	.50383	1.98482
293.500	1.0214	1.2664	1.0211	1.2696	.59434	.78766	1.24334	.80428	.49984	2.00064
295.000	1.0162	1.2565	1.0159	1.2597	.59132	.79387	1.23991	.80651	.49593	2.01643
296.500	1.0111	1.2468	1.0108	1.2499	.58833	.80007	1.23656	.80869	.49208	2.03217
298.000	1.0060	1.2373	1.0057	1.2403	.58536	.80625	1.23329	.81084	.48831	2.04787
299.500	1.0010	1.2280	1.0007	1.2309	.58243	.81241	1.23009	.81295	.48461	2.06353
301.000	.9960	1.2188	.9957	1.2217	.57953	.81856	1.22697	.81502	.48097	2.07915
302.500	.9910	1.2098	.9907	1.2126	.57666	.82469	1.22391	.81705	.47739	2.09472
304.000	.9862	1.2009	.9858	1.2036	.57381	.83081	1.22092	.81905	.47387	2.11027
305.500	.9813	1.1922	.9810	1.1949	.57099	.83692	1.21800	.82102	.47042	2.12577
307.000	.9765	1.1836	.9762	1.1862	.56820	.84301	1.21514	.82295	.46702	2.14123
308.500	.9718	1.1752	.9715	1.1777	.56544	.84908	1.21234	.82485	.46368	2.15666
310.000	.9671	1.1669	.9668	1.1694	.56270	.85514	1.20960	.82672	.46039	2.17206
311.500	.9624	1.1588	.9621	1.1612	.56000	.86119	1.20692	.82856	.45716	2.18742
313.000	.9578	1.1508	.9575	1.1531	.55731	.86722	1.20429	.83036	.45398	2.20275
314.500	.9532	1.1429	.9529	1.1452	.55465	.87324	1.20172	.83214	.45085	2.21804
316.000	.9487	1.1351	.9484	1.1373	.55202	.87925	1.19920	.83389	.44777	2.23330
317.500	.9442	1.1274	.9439	1.1296	.54941	.88525	1.19673	.83561	.44473	2.24853
319.000	.9398	1.1199	.9395	1.1220	.54683	.89123	1.19431	.83730	.44175	2.26373
320.500	.9354	1.1125	.9351	1.1146	.54427	.89720	1.19194	.83897	.43881	2.27890
322.000	.9310	1.1052	.9307	1.1072	.54173	.90316	1.18962	.84061	.43591	2.29403
323.500	.9267	1.0980	.9264	1.1000	.53922	.90911	1.18734	.84222	.43306	2.30914
325.000	.9224	1.0909	.9221	1.0928	.53673	.91505	1.18511	.84381	.43025	2.32422

COMMONLY USED WAVEGUIDE CALCULATIONS

The following table gives the values computed for several commonly used waveguide calculations for the ratio of fo/fc from 1.00 to 2.00. The eight columns below are respectively:

1. $1/\mu = fo/fc = \lambda c/\lambda o$ (for rectangular waveguide $\lambda c = 2a$, a is the wide inner dimension of the waveguide.)
2. $\mu = fc/fo = \lambda o/\lambda c$
3. μ^2
4. $1 - \mu^2$
5. $\sqrt{1-\mu^2} = \lambda o/\lambda g$
6. $1/\sqrt{1-\mu^2} = \lambda g/\lambda o$
7. $\sqrt{1-\mu^2}/\mu = \lambda c/\lambda g$
8. $\mu/\sqrt{1-\mu^2} = \lambda g/\lambda c$

$1/\mu$	μ	μ^2	$1-\mu^2$	$\sqrt{1-\mu^2}$	$\frac{1}{\sqrt{1-\mu^2}}$	$\frac{\sqrt{1-\mu^2}}{\mu}$	$\frac{\mu}{\sqrt{1-\mu^2}}$
1.00	1.00 000	1.00 000	0.00 000	0.00 000	∞	0.00 000	∞
1.01	0.99 010	0.98 030	.01 970	.14 037	7.12 399	.14 177	7.05 345
1.02	.98 039	.96 117	.03 883	.19 706	5.07 469	.20 100	4.97 519
1.03	.97 087	.94 260	.05 740	.23 959	4.17 377	.24 678	4.05 221
1.04	.96 154	.92 456	.07 544	.27 467	3.64 073	.28 566	3.50 070
1.05	0.95 238	0.90 703	0.09 297	0.30 491	3.27 965	0.32 016	3.12 348
1.06	.94 340	.89 000	.11 000	.33 167	3.01 506	.35 157	2.84 440
1.07	.93 458	.87 344	.12 656	.35 575	2.81 093	.38 066	2.62 703
1.08	.92 593	.85 734	.14 266	.37 771	2.64 757	.40 792	2.45 145
1.09	.91 743	.84 168	.15 832	.39 789	2.51 323	.43 371	2.30 571
1.10	0.90 909	0.82 645	0.17 355	0.41 660	2.40 040	0.45 826	2.18 218
1.11	.90 090	.81 162	.18 838	.43 402	2.30 402	.48 177	2.07 569
1.12	.89 286	.79 719	.20 281	.45 034	2.22 054	.50 438	1.98 263
1.13	.88 496	.78 315	.21 685	.46 568	2.14 742	.52 621	1.90 037
1.14	.87 719	.76 947	.23 053	.48 014	2.08 273	.54 736	1.82 696
1.15	0.86 957	0.75 614	0.24 386	0.49 382	2.02 504	0.56 789	1.76 090
1.16	.86 207	.74 316	.25 684	.50 679	1.97 320	.58 788	1.70 103
1.17	.85 470	.73 051	.26 949	.51 912	1.92 633	.60 737	1.64 644
1.18	.84 746	.71 818	.28 182	.53 086	1.88 372	.62 642	1.59 638
1.19	.84 034	.70 616	.29 384	.54 207	1.84 479	.64 506	1.55 025
1.20	0.83 333	0.69 444	0.30 556	0.55 277	1.80 907	0.66 332	1.50 756
1.21	.82 645	.68 301	.31 699	.56 302	1.77 615	.68 125	1.46 789
1.22	.81 967	.67 186	.32 814	.57 283	1.74 571	.69 886	1.43 091
1.23	.81 301	.66 098	.33 902	.58 225	1.71 747	.71 617	1.39 632
1.24	.80 645	.65 036	.34 964	.59 130	1.69 119	.73 321	1.36 386
1.25	0.80 000	0.64 000	0.36 000	0.60 000	1.66 667	0.75 000	1.33 333
1.26	.79 365	.62 988	.37 012	.60 837	1.64 373	.76 655	1.30 455
1.27	.78 740	.62 000	.38 000	.61 644	1.62 222	.78 288	1.27 734
1.28	.78 125	.61 035	.38 965	.62 422	1.60 200	.79 900	1.25 157
1.29	.77 519	.60 093	.39 907	.63 172	1.58 297	.81 492	1.22 711
1.30	0.76 923	0.59 172	0.40 828	0.63 897	1.56 502	0.83 066	1.20 386
1.31	.76 336	.58 272	.41 728	.64 597	1.54 805	.84 623	1.18 172
1.32	.75 758	.57 392	.42 608	.65 275	1.53 199	.86 163	1.16 060
1.33	.75 188	.56 532	.43 468	.65 930	1.51 676	.87 687	1.14 042
1.34	.74 627	.55 692	.44 308	.66 564	1.50 230	.89 196	1.12 112
1.35	0.74 074	0.54 870	0.45 130	0.67 179	1.48 856	0.90 692	1.10 264
1.36	.73 529	.54 066	.45 934	.67 775	1.47 547	.92 174	1.08 491
1.37	.72 993	.53 279	.46 721	.68 353	1.46 300	.93 643	1.06 789
1.38	.72 464	.52 510	.47 490	.68 913	1.45 110	.95 100	1.05 153
1.39	.71 942	.51 757	.48 243	.69 457	1.43 974	.96 545	1.03 578
1.40	0.71 429	0.51 020	0.48 980	0.69 985	1.42 887	0.97 980	1.02 062
1.41	.70 922	.50 299	.49 701	.70 499	1.41 847	.99 403	1.00 600
1.42	.70 423	.49 593	.50 407	.70 998	1.40 850	1.00 817	0.99 190
1.43	.69 930	.48 902	.51 098	.71 483	1.39 894	1.02 220	.97 828
1.44	.69 444	.48 225	.51 775	.71 955	1.38 976	1.03 615	.96 511
1.45	0.68 966	0.47 562	0.52 438	0.72 414	1.38 095	1.05 000	0.95 238
1.46	.68 493	.46 913	.53 087	.72 861	1.37 248	1.06 377	.94 006
1.47	.68 027	.46 277	.53 723	.73 296	1.36 433	1.07 745	.92 812
1.48	.67 568	.45 654	.54 346	.73 720	1.35 649	1.09 105	.91 654
1.49	.67 114	.45 043	.54 957	.74 133	1.34 893	1.10 458	.90 532
1.50	0.66 667	0.44 444	0.55 556	0.74 536	1.34 164	1.11 803	0.89 443
1.51	.66 225	.43 858	.56 142	.74 928	1.33 461	1.13 141	.88 385
1.52	.65 789	.43 283	.56 717	.75 311	1.32 783	1.14 473	.87 357
1.53	.65 359	.42 719	.57 281	.75 684	1.32 128	1.15 797	.86 358
1.54	.64 935	.42 166	.57 834	.76 049	1.31 494	1.17 115	.85 386
1.55	0.64 516	0.41 623	0.58 377	0.76 405	1.30 882	1.18 427	0.84 440
1.56	.64 103	.41 091	.58 909	.76 752	1.30 290	1.19 733	.83 519
1.57	.63 694	.40 570	.59 430	.77 091	1.29 717	1.21 033	.82 622
1.58	.63 291	.40 058	.59 942	.77 422	1.29 162	1.22 327	.81 748
1.59	.62 893	.39 555	.60 445	.77 746	1.28 624	1.23 616	.80 895
1.60	0.62 500	0.39 062	0.60 938	0.78 062	1.28 103	1.24 900	0.80 064
1.61	.62 112	.38 579	.61 421	.78 372	1.27 597	1.26 178	.79 253
1.62	.61 728	.38 104	.61 896	.78 674	1.27 107	1.27 452	.78 461
1.63	.61 350	.37 638	.62 362	.78 970	1.26 631	1.28 721	.77 688
1.64	.60 976	.37 180	.62 820	.79 259	1.26 169	1.29 985	.76 932
1.65	0.60 606	0.36 731	0.63 269	0.79 542	1.25 720	1.31 244	0.76 194
1.66	.60 241	.36 290	.63 710	.79 819	1.25 284	1.32 499	.75 472
1.67	.59 880	.35 856	.64 144	.80 090	1.24 860	1.33 750	.74 766
1.68	.59 524	.35 431	.64 569	.80 355	1.24 448	1.34 996	.74 076
1.69	.59 172	.35 013	.64 987	.80 615	1.24 047	1.36 239	.73 401
1.70	0.58 824	0.34 602	0.65 398	0.80 869	1.23 657	1.37 477	0.72 739
1.71	.58 480	.34 199	.65 801	.81 118	1.23 277	1.38 712	.72 092
1.72	.58 140	.33 802	.66 198	.81 362	1.22 907	1.39 943	.71 458
1.73	.57 803	.33 412	.66 588	.81 601	1.22 547	1.41 170	.70 837
1.74	.57 471	.33 029	.66 971	.81 836	1.22 196	1.42 394	.70 228
1.75	0.57 143	0.32 653	0.67 347	0.82 065	1.21 854	1.43 614	0.69 631
1.76	.56 818	.32 283	.67 717	.82 290	1.21 521	1.44 831	.69 046
1.77	.56 497	.31 919	.68 081	.82 511	1.21 196	1.46 044	.68 472
1.78	.56 180	.31 562	.68 438	.82 727	1.20 879	1.47 255	.67 909
1.79	.55 866	.31 210	.68 790	.82 940	1.20 569	1.48 462	.67 357
1.80	0.55 556	0.30 864	0.69 136	0.83 148	1.20 268	1.49 666	0.66 815
1.81	.55 249	.30 524	.69 476	.83 352	1.19 973	1.50 867	.66 283
1.82	.54 945	.30 190	.69 810	.83 553	1.19 685	1.52 066	.65 761
1.83	.54 645	.29 861	.70 139	.83 749	1.19 404	1.53 261	.65 248
1.84	.54 348	.29 537	.70 463	.83 942	1.19 129	1.54 454	.64 744
1.85	0.54 054	0.29 218	0.70 782	0.84 132	1.18 861	1.55 644	0.64 249
1.86	.53 763	.28 905	.71 095	.84 318	1.18 599	1.56 831	.63 763
1.87	.53 476	.28 597	.71 403	.84 500	1.18 343	1.58 016	.63 285
1.88	.53 191	.28 293	.71 707	.84 680	1.18 092	1.59 198	.62 815
1.89	.52 910	.27 995	.72 005	.84 856	1.17 847	1.60 378	.62 353
1.90	0.52 632	0.27 701	0.72 299	0.85 029	1.17 607	1.61 555	0.61 898
1.91	.52 356	.27 412	.72 588	.85 199	1.17 372	1.62 730	.61 452
1.92	.52 083	.27 127	.72 873	.85 366	1.17 143	1.63 902	.61 012
1.93	.51 813	.26 846	.73 154	.85 530	1.16 918	1.65 073	.60 579
1.94	.51 546	.26 570	.73 430	.85 691	1.16 698	1.66 241	.60 154
1.95	0.51 282	0.26 298	0.73 702	0.85 850	1.16 483	1.67 407	0.59 735
1.96	.51 020	.26 031	.73 969	.86 005	1.16 272	1.68 570	.59 322
1.97	.50 761	.25 767	.74 233	.86 158	1.16 065	1.69 732	.58 916
1.98	.50 505	.25 508	.74 492	.86 309	1.15 863	1.70 892	.58 517
1.99	.50 251	.25 252	.74 748	.86 457	1.15 664	1.72 049	.58 123
2.00	0.50 000	0.25 000	0.75 000	0.86 603	1.15 470	1.73 205	0.57 735

Courtesy of DeMornay-Bonardi

RADIAL LINE CHOKE DESIGN CHART

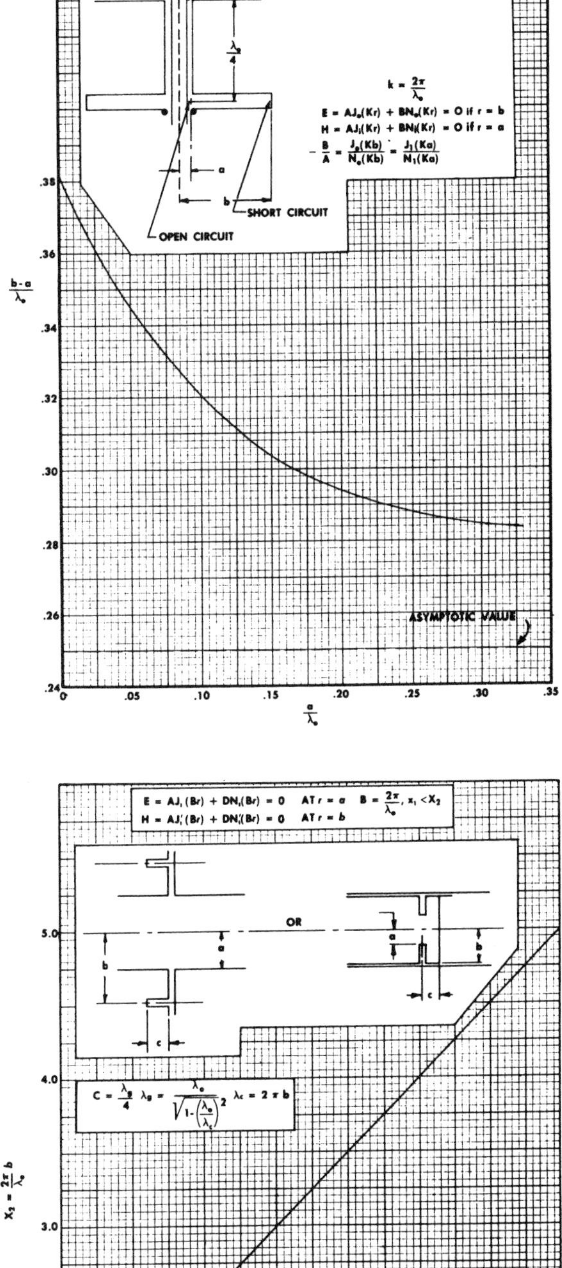

DESIGN CURVE FOR RADIAL CHOKE EXCITED BY TE_{11} MODE

Prepared by John Reed and other members of the staff, Surface Radar and Navigation Operation, Raytheon Co.

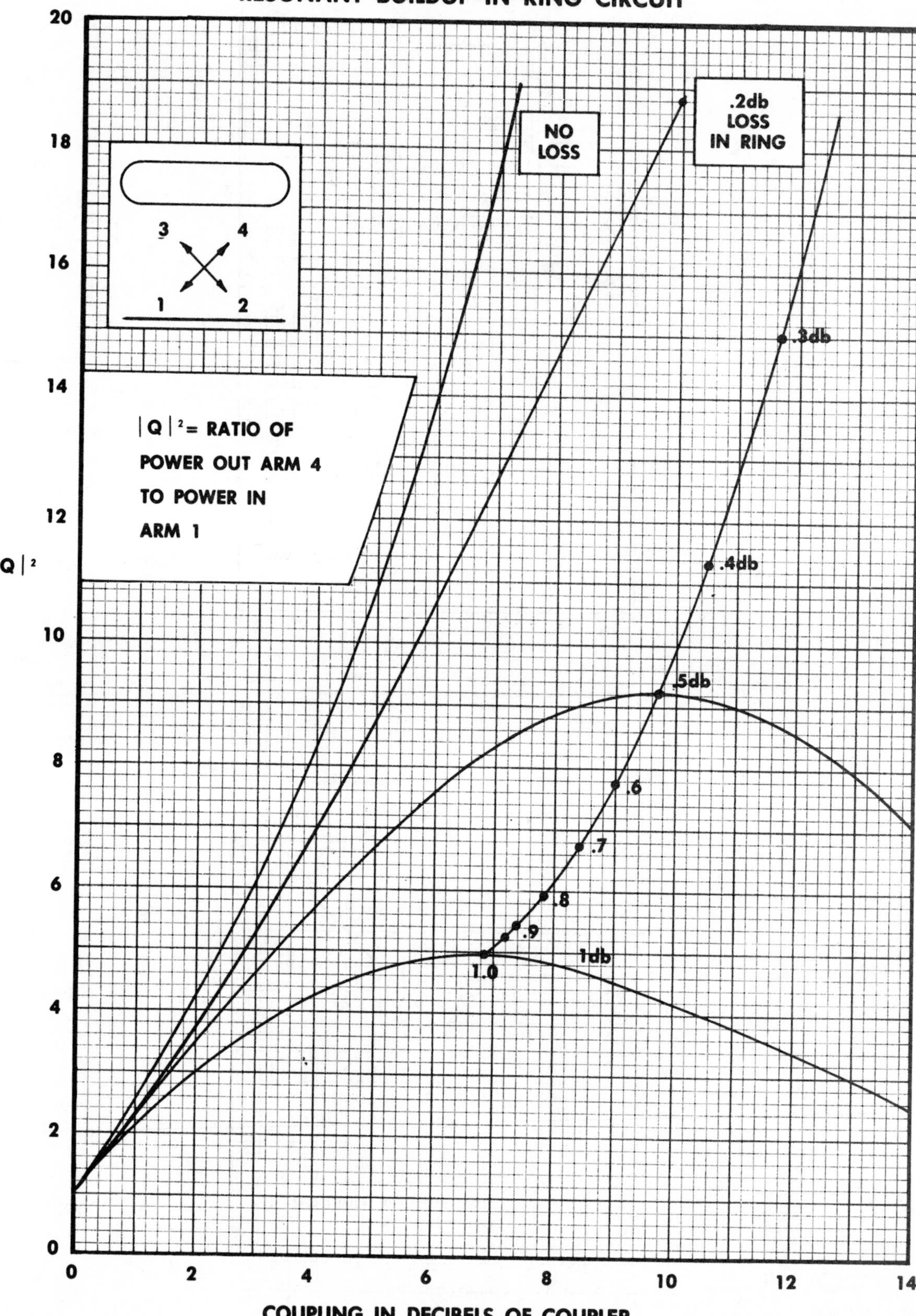

Prepared by John Reed and other members of the staff, Surface Radar and Navigation Operation, Raytheon Co.

IMPEDANCE OF CAPACITIVE SCREW IN RG 52/U WAVEGUIDE

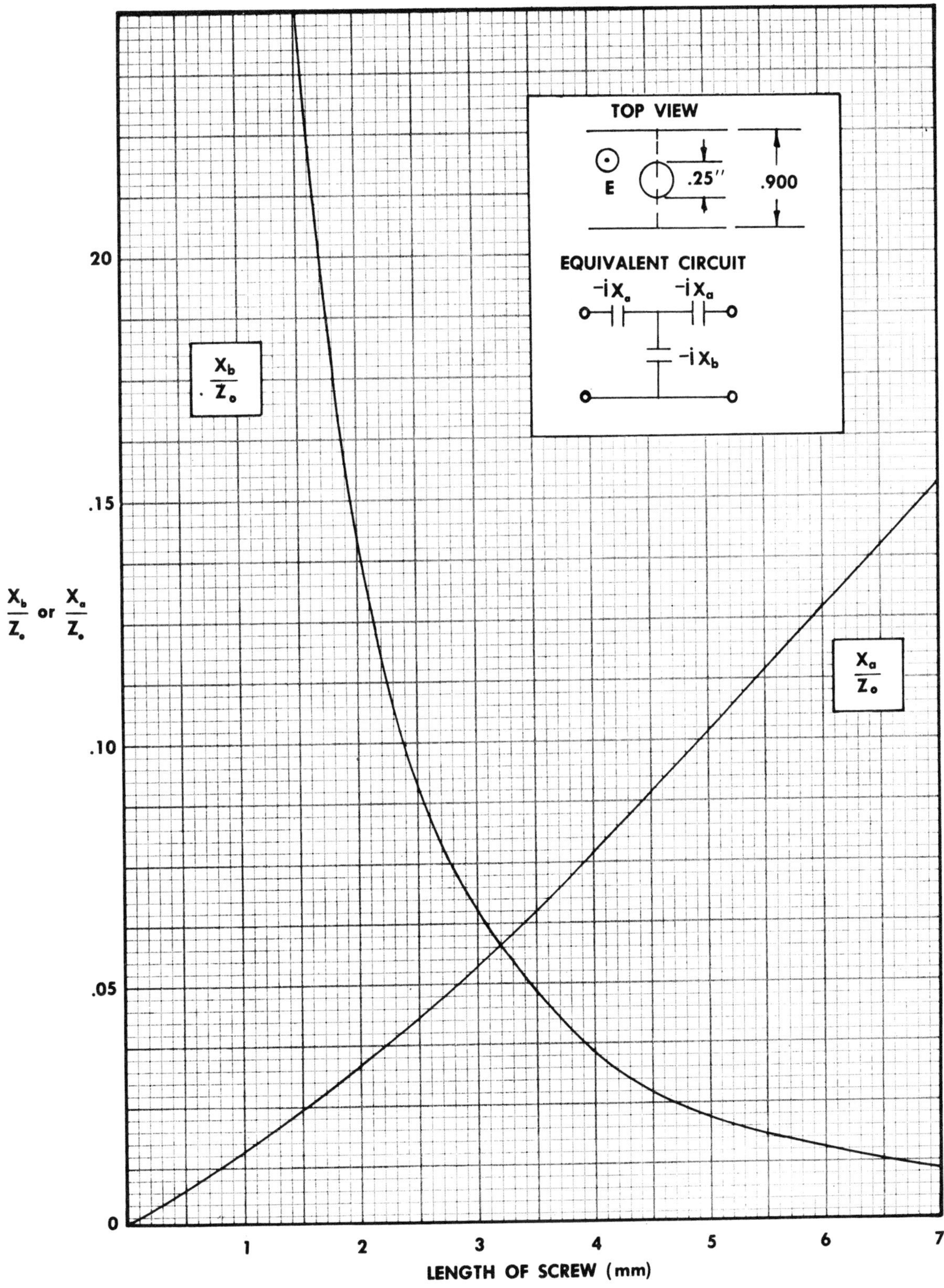

Reprinted from Massachusetts Institute of Technology Radiation Laboratory Report No. 43, Feb. 1944. Prepared under contract with the Office of Scientific Research and Development.

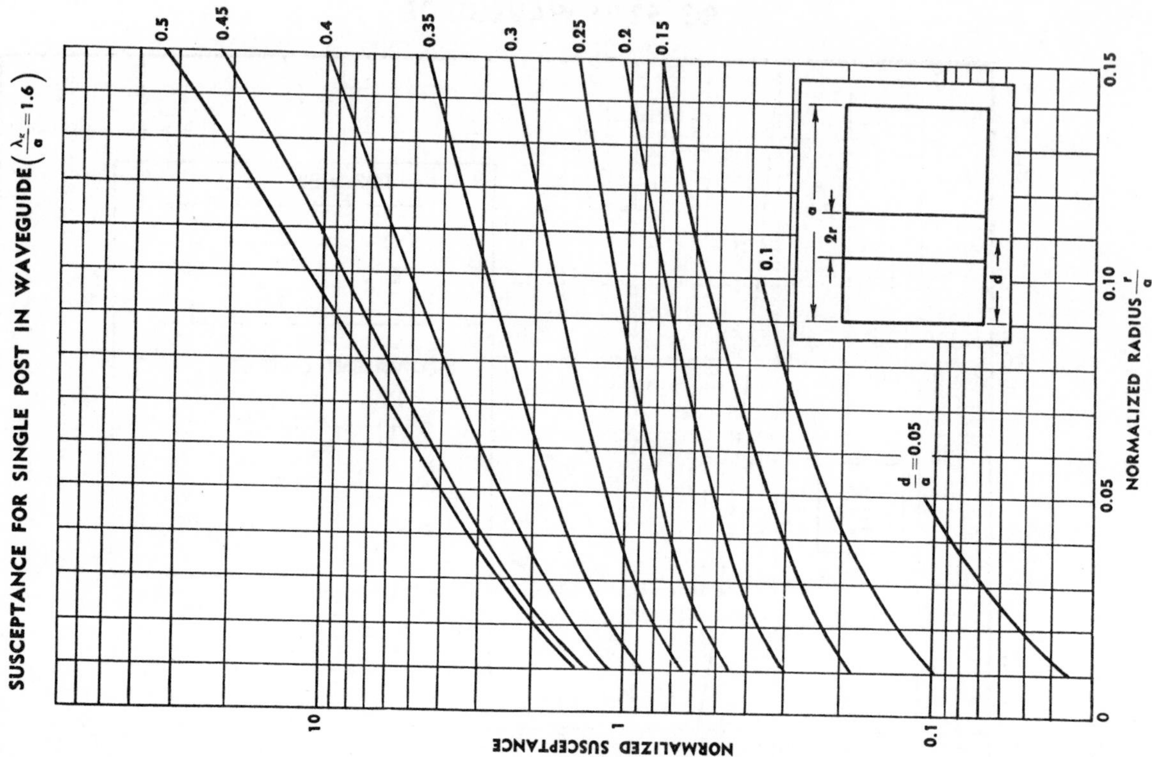

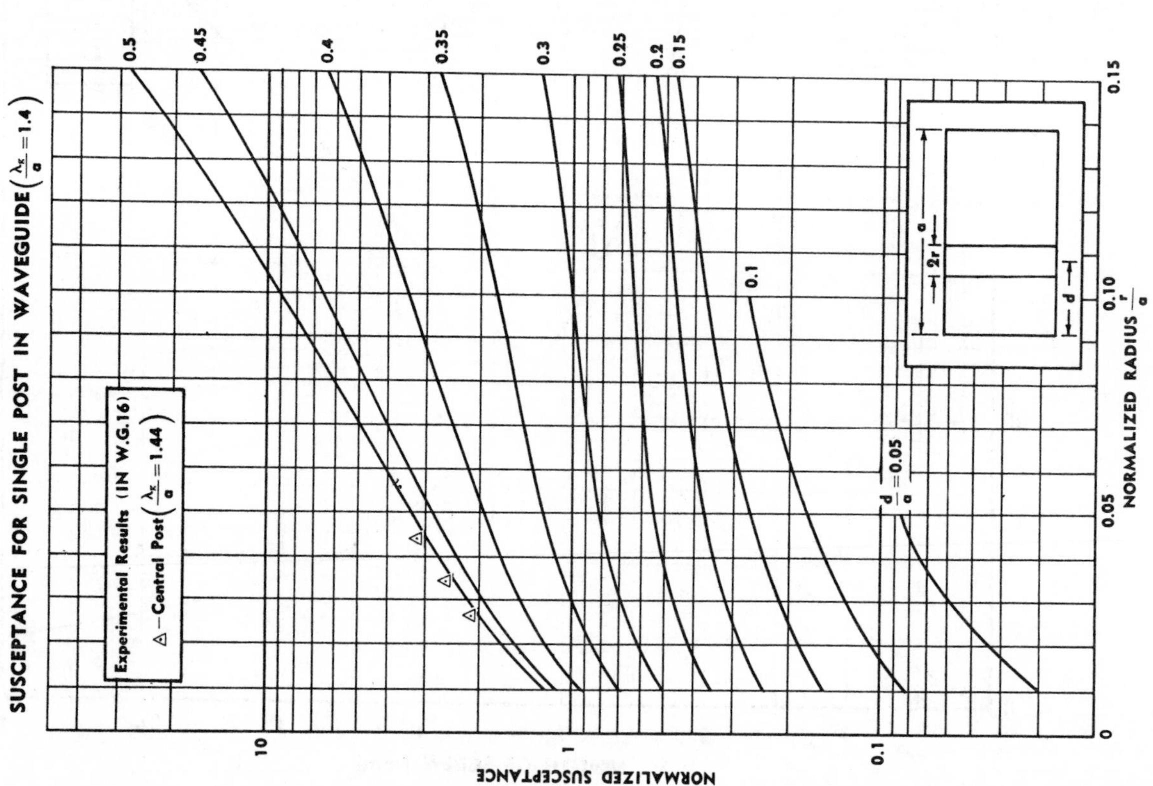

Prepared by K. B. Whiting. Courtesy of Chief Scientist, Department of Supply, Australia.

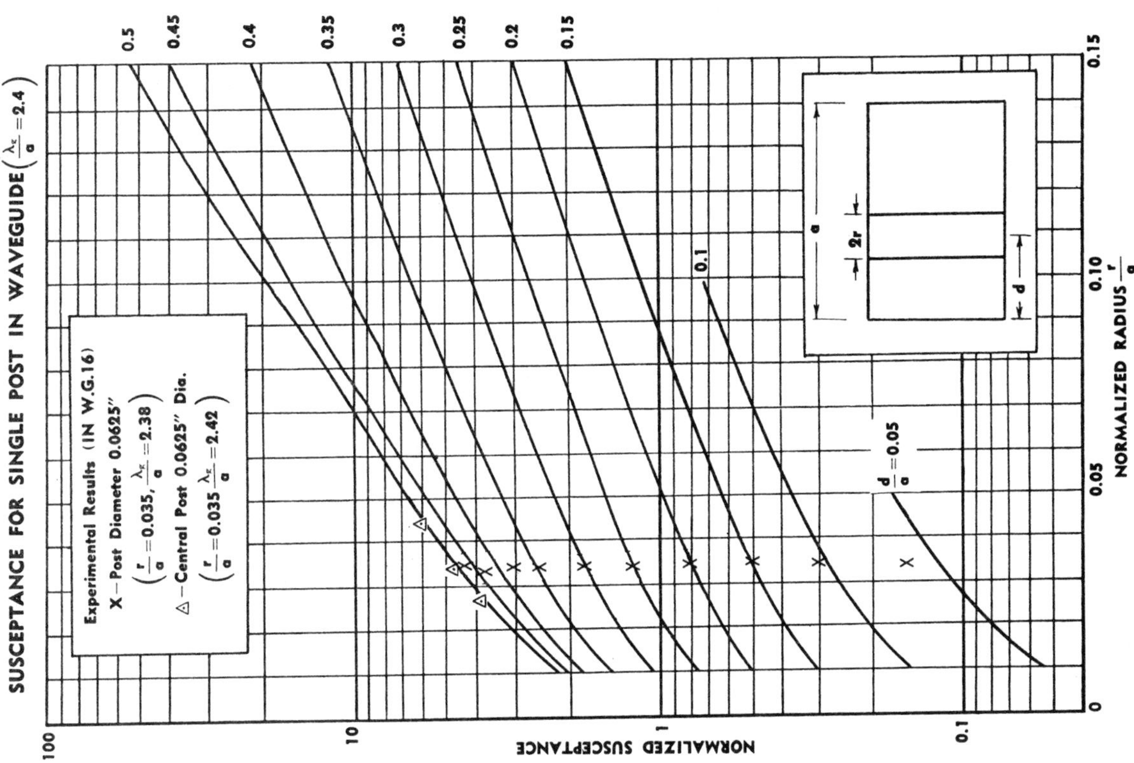

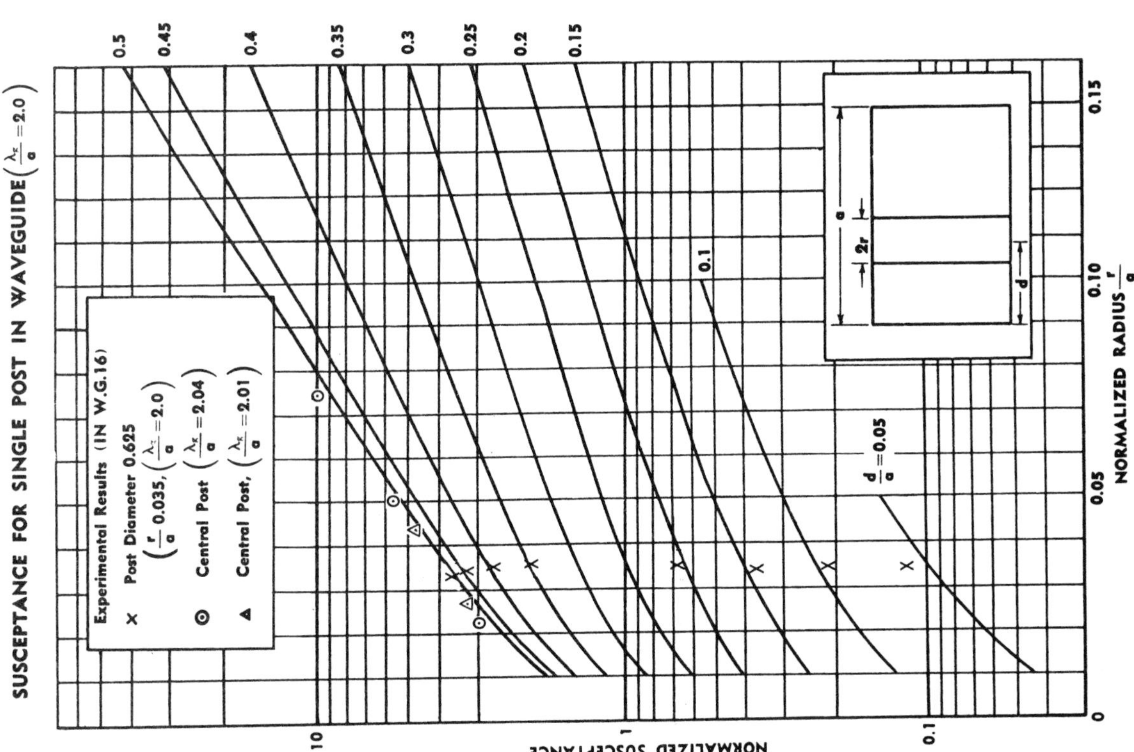

Prepared by K. B. Whiting. Courtesy of Chief Scientist, Department of Supply, Australia.

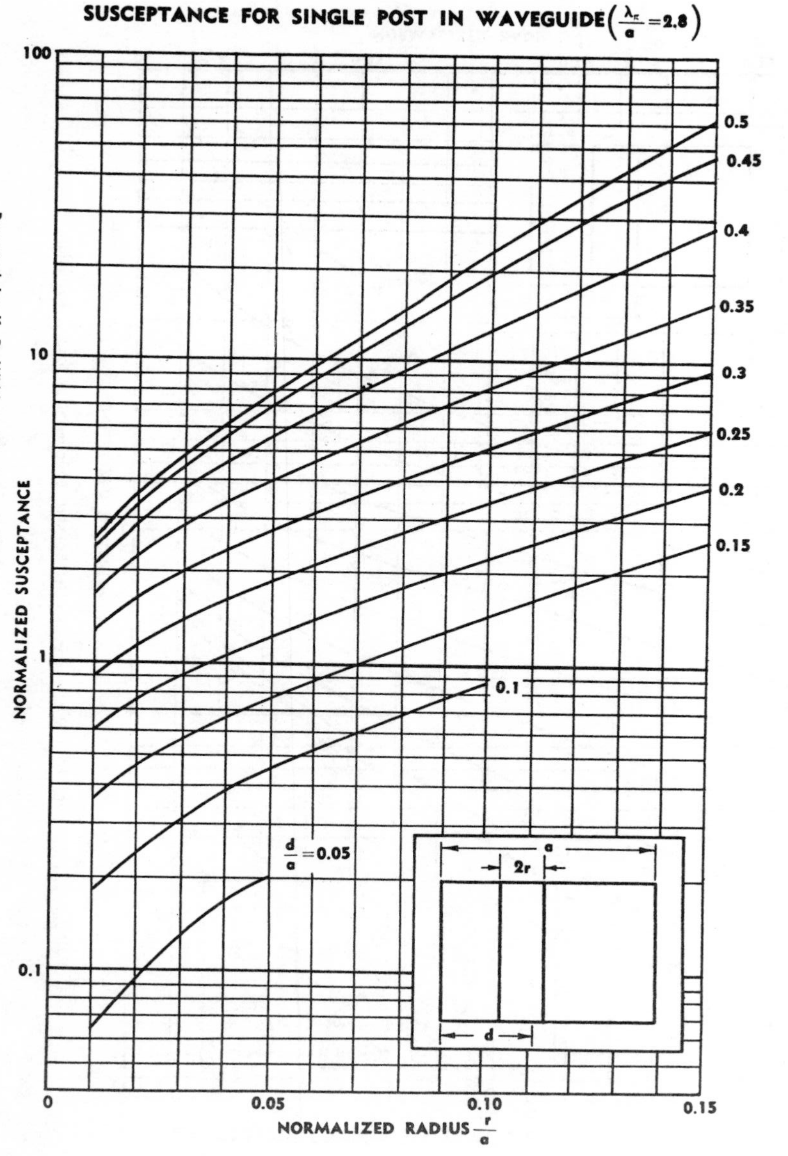

Prepared by K. B. Whiting. Courtesy of Chief Scientist, Department of Supply, Australia.

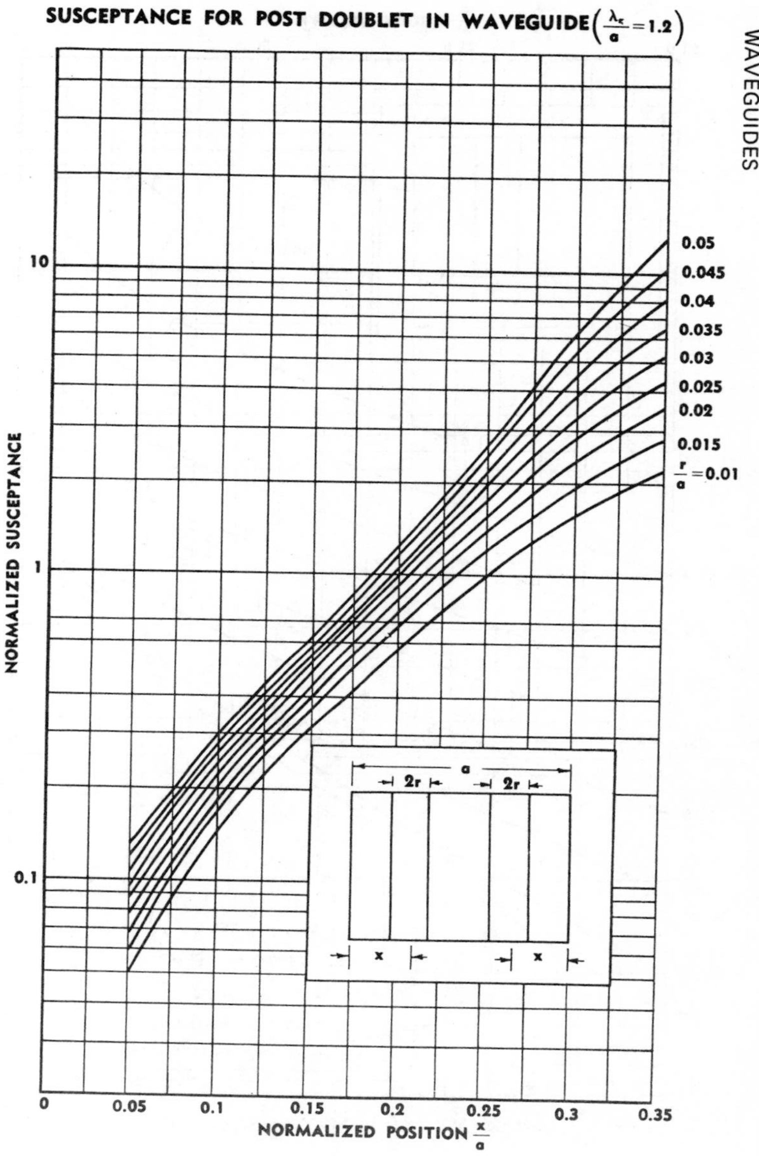

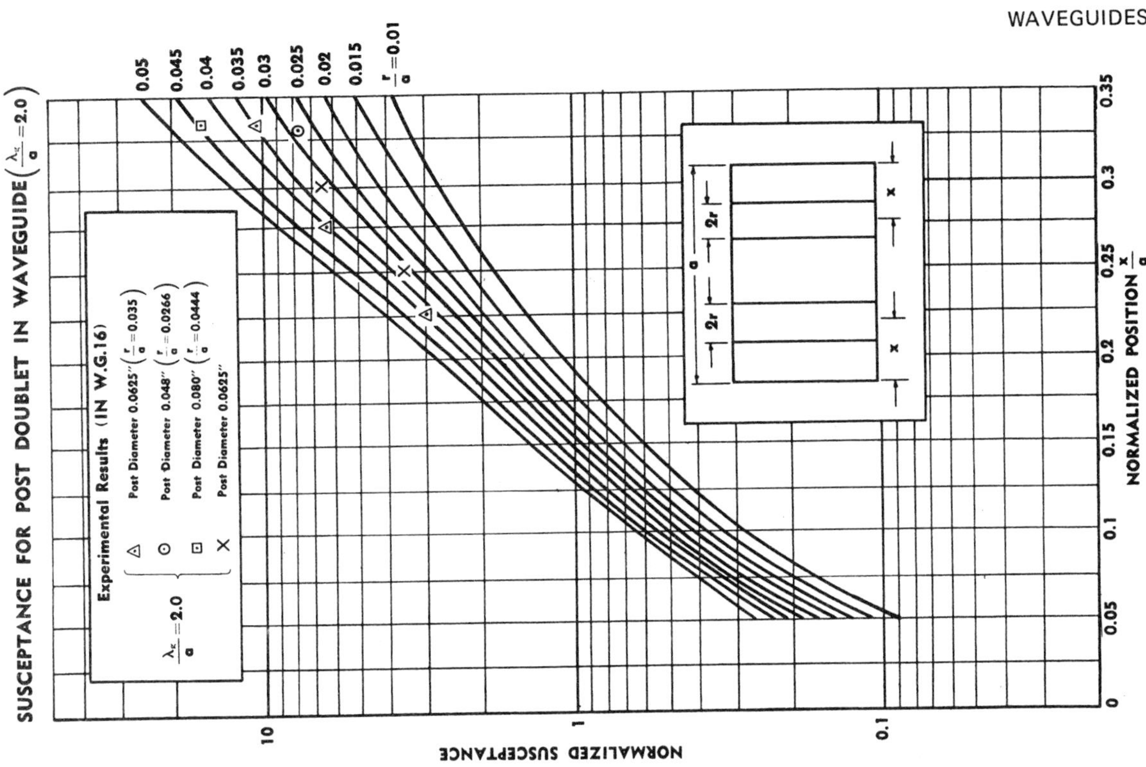

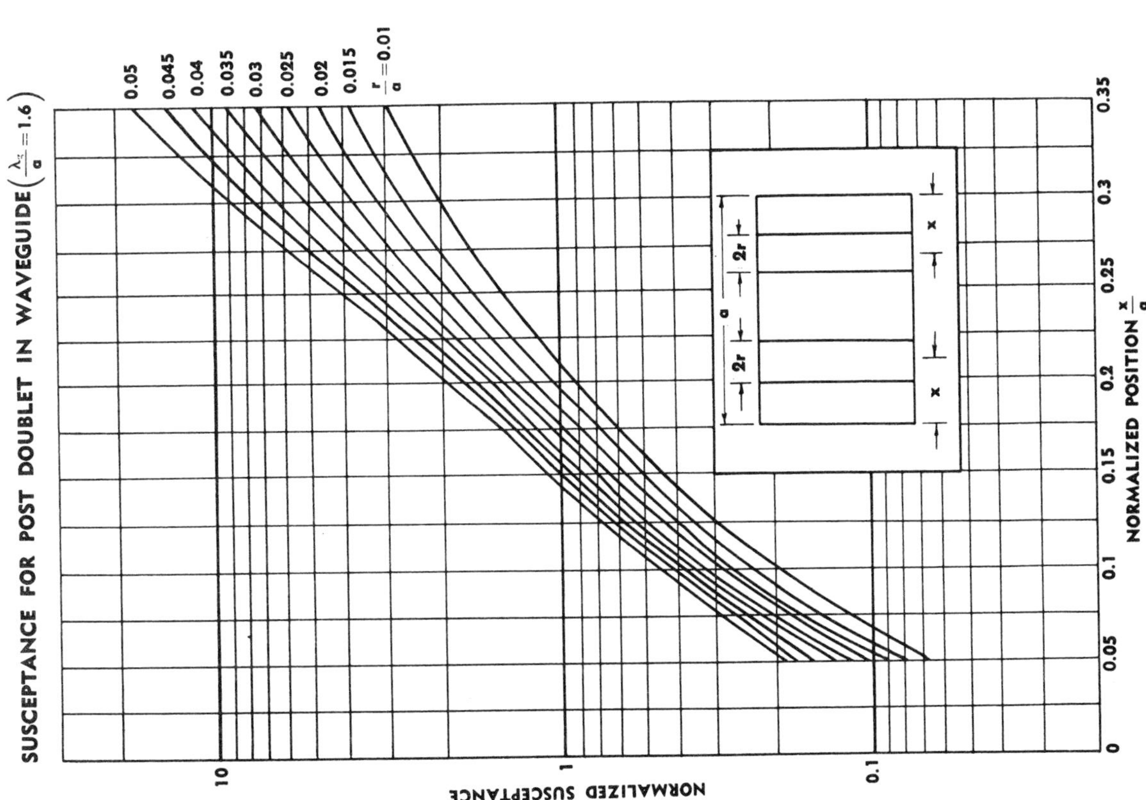

Prepared by K. B. Whiting. Courtesy of Chief Scientist, Department of Supply, Australia.

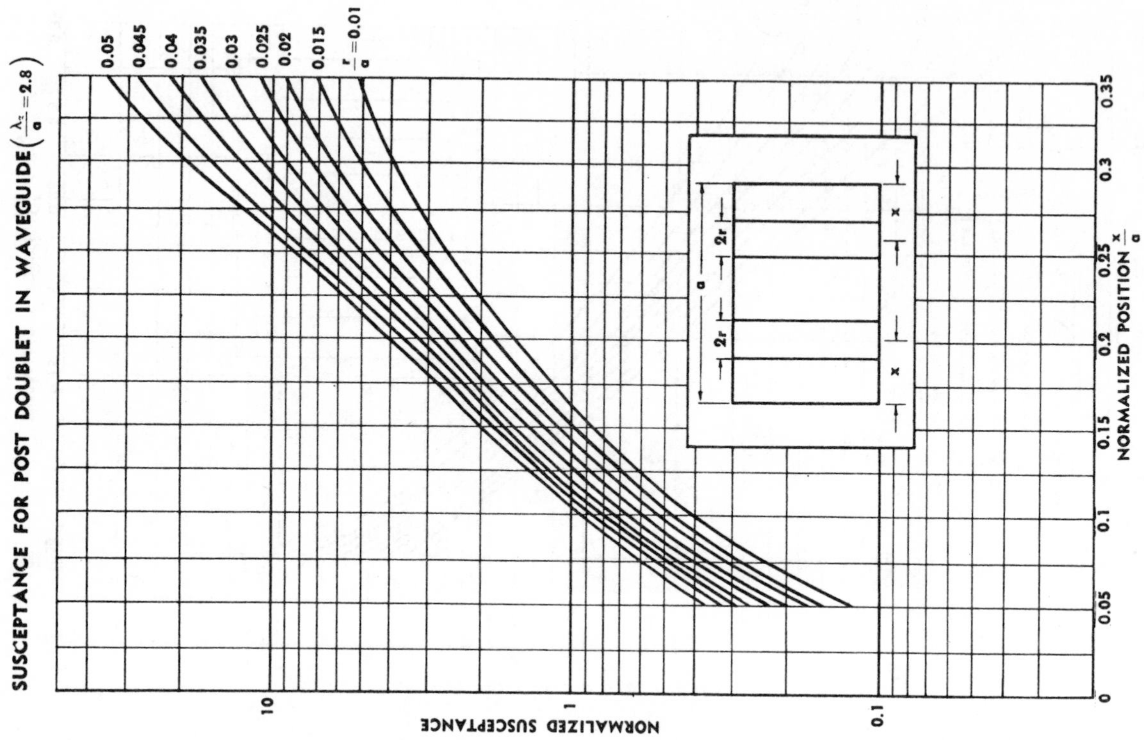

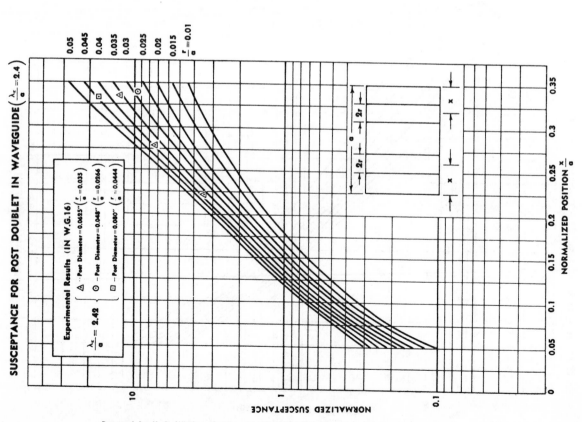

SUSCEPTANCE FOR POST DOUBLET IN WAVEGUIDE $\left(\frac{\lambda_c}{a} = 2.4\right)$

Experimental Results (IN W.G.16)

$\frac{\lambda_c}{a} = 2.42$ — △ – Post Diameter = 0.0625″ $\left(\frac{r}{a} = 0.035\right)$; ⊙ – Post Diameter = 0.048″ $\left(\frac{r}{a} = 0.0266\right)$; ⊡ – Post Diameter = 0.080″ $\left(\frac{r}{a} = 0.0444\right)$

0.05, 0.045, 0.04, 0.035, 0.03, 0.025, 0.02, 0.015, $\frac{r}{a} = 0.01$

NORMALIZED SUSCEPTANCE: 10, 1, 0.1

NORMALIZED POSITION $\frac{x}{a}$: 0, 0.05, 0.1, 0.15, 0.2, 0.25, 0.3, 0.35

Prepared by K. B. Whiting. Courtesy of Chief Scientist, Department of Supply, Australia.

SUSCEPTANCE OF ASYMMETRICAL IRIS IN WAVEGUIDE

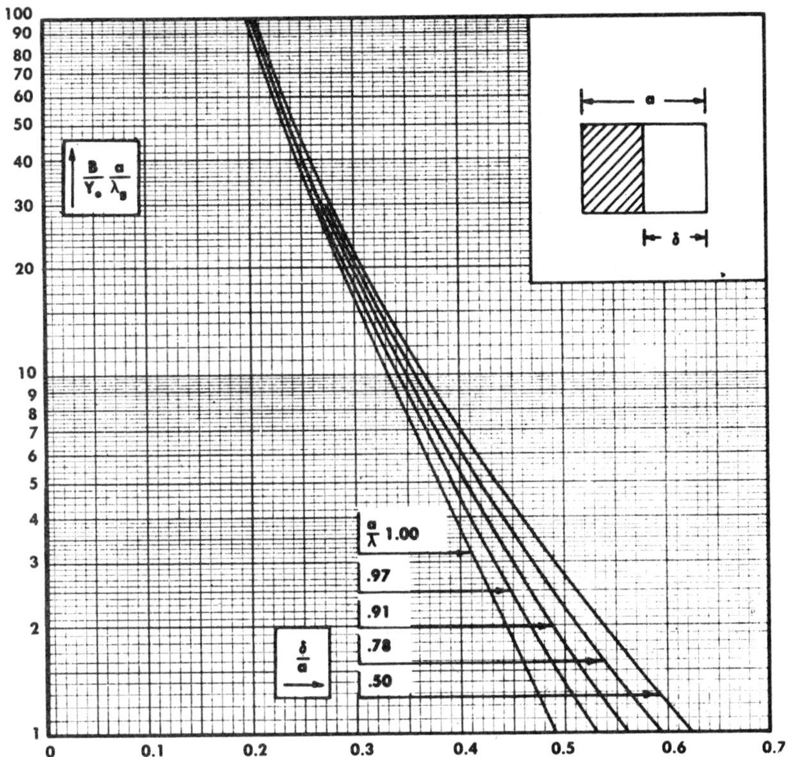

SUSCEPTANCE OF ASYMMETRICAL IRIS IN WAVEGUIDE

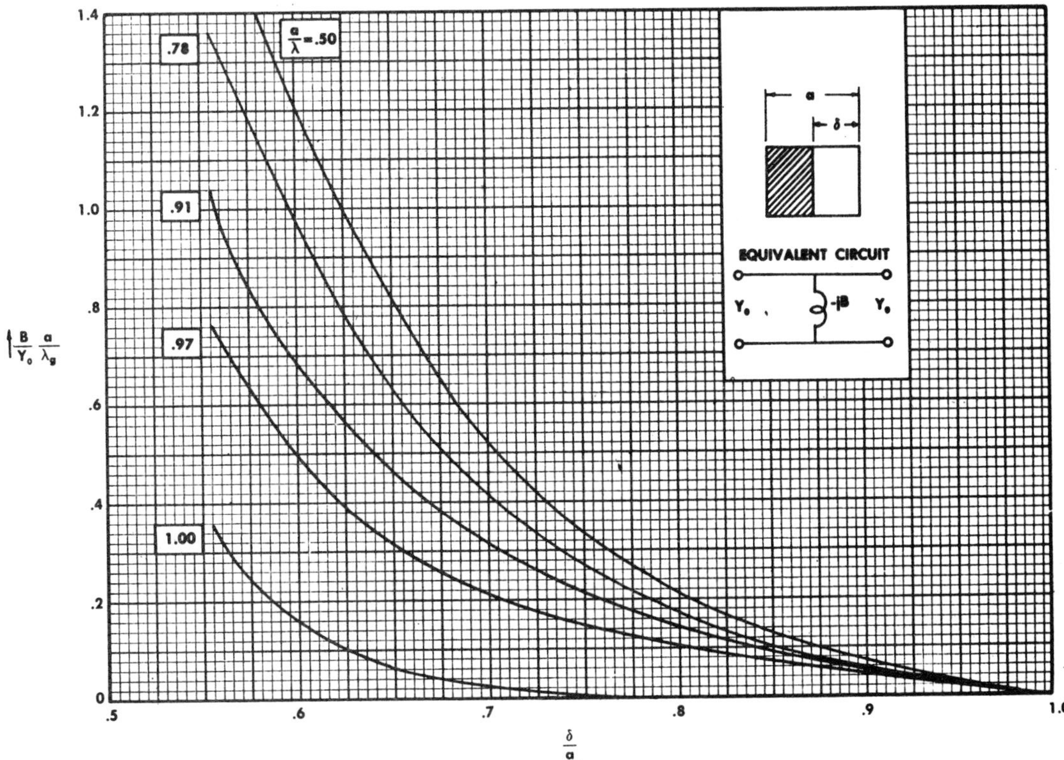

Reprinted from Massachusetts Institute of Technology Radiation Laboratory Report No. 43, Feb. 1944. Prepared under contract with the Office of Scientific Research and Development.

SUSCEPTANCE OF TWO SYMMETRICAL IRISES IN WAVEGUIDE

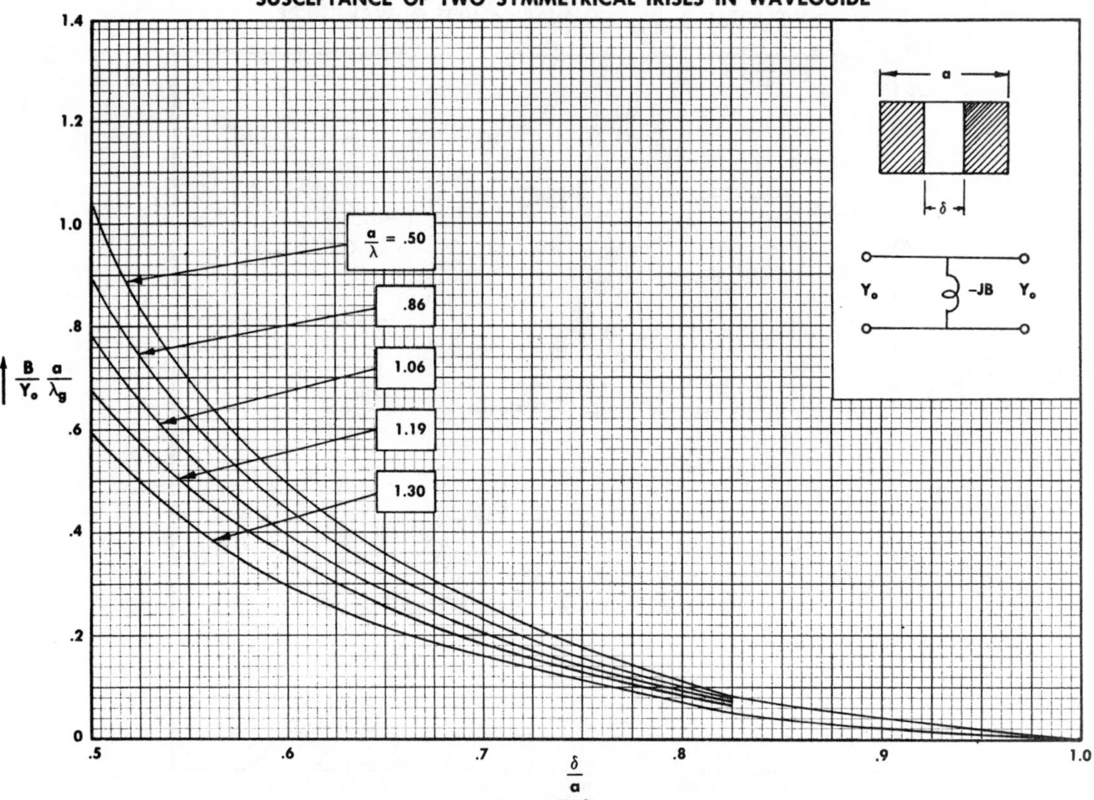

SUSCEPTANCE OF SYMMETRICAL IRISES IN WAVEGUIDE

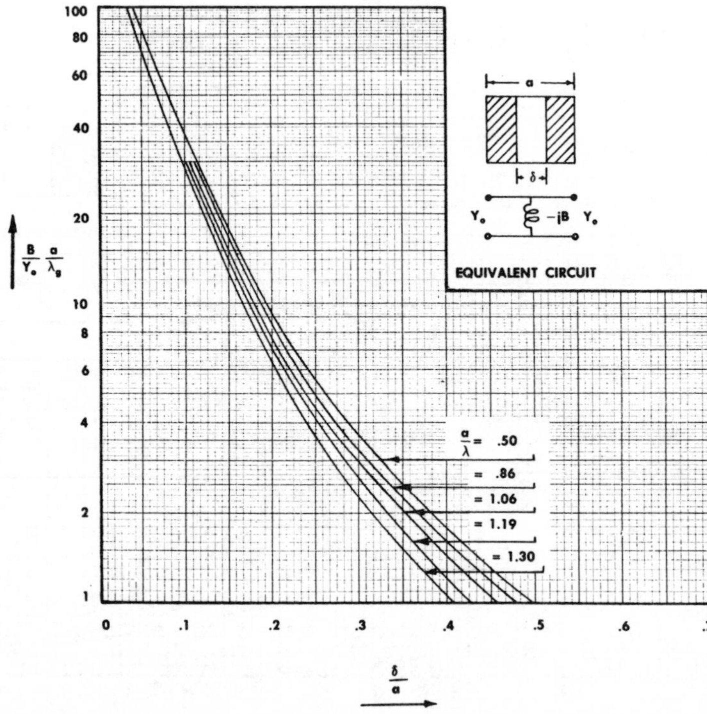

Reprinted from Massachusetts Institute of Technology Radiation Laboratory Report No. 43, Feb. 1944. Prepared under contract with the Office of Scientific Research and Development.

SUSCEPTANCE OF HOLE IN IRIS IN WAVEGUIDE

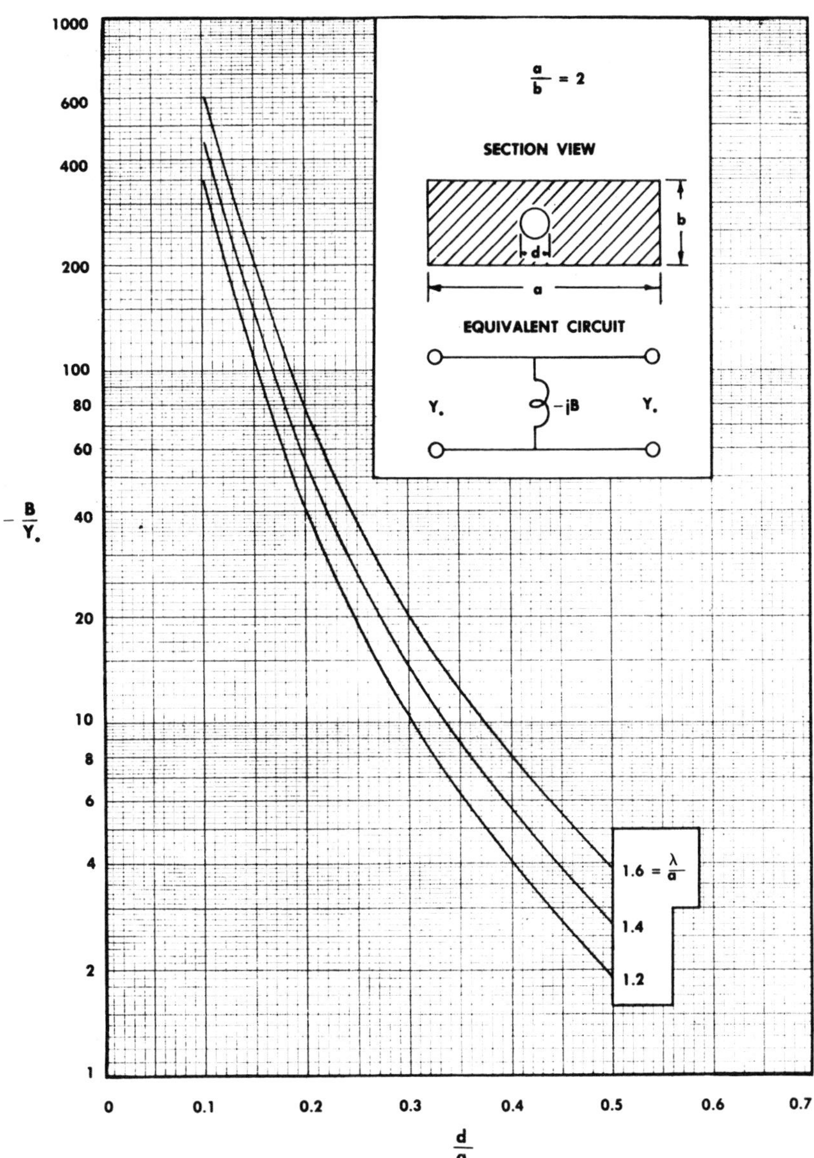

83

Reprinted from Massachusetts Institute of Technology Radiation Laboratory Report No. 43, Feb. 1944. Prepared under contract with the Office of Scientific Research and Development.

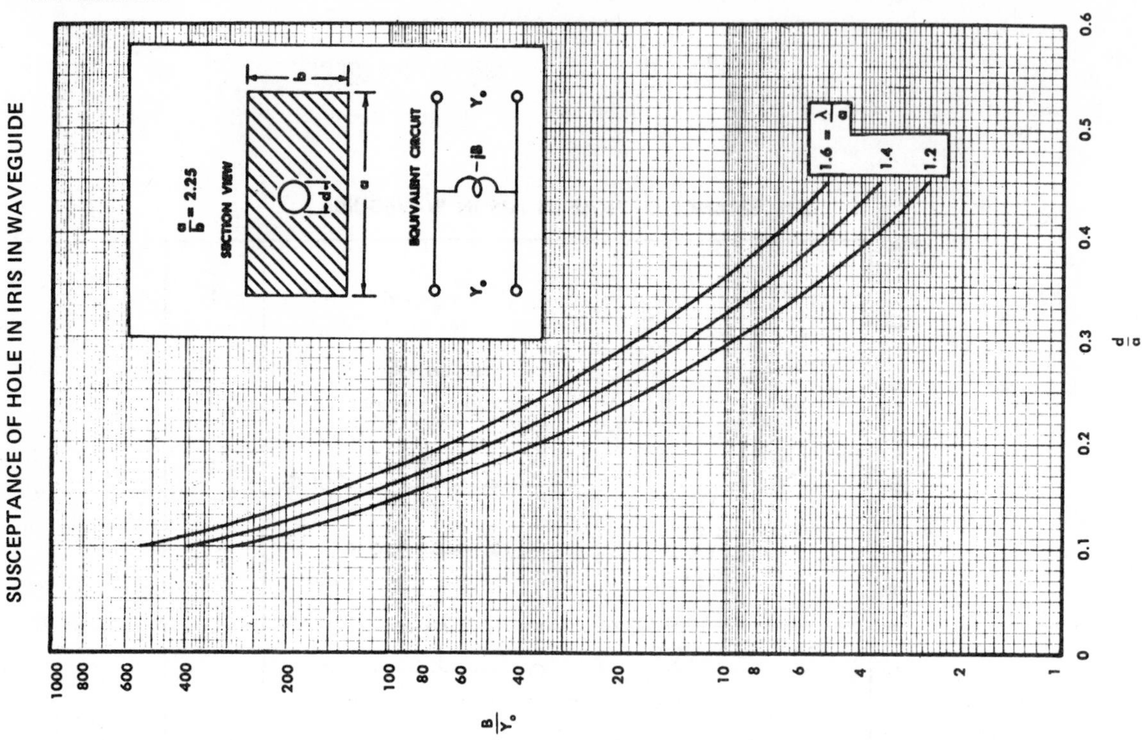

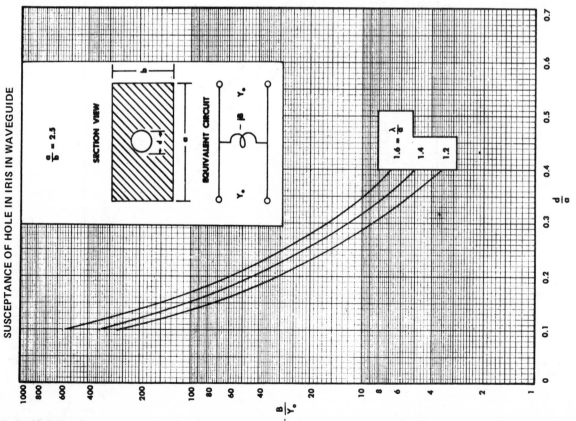

SUSCEPTANCE OF HOLE IN IRIS IN WAVEGUIDE

a/b = 2.5

SECTION VIEW

EQUIVALENT CIRCUIT

Y_o $-jB$ Y_o

$1.6 = \frac{\lambda}{a}$ 1.4 1.2

$-\frac{B}{Y_o}$

$\frac{d}{a}$

Reprinted from Massachusetts Institute of Technology Radiation Laboratory Report No. 43, Feb. 1944. Prepared under contract with the Office of Scientific Research and Development.

SUSCEPTANCE OF CAPACITIVE IRISES IN WAVEGUIDE

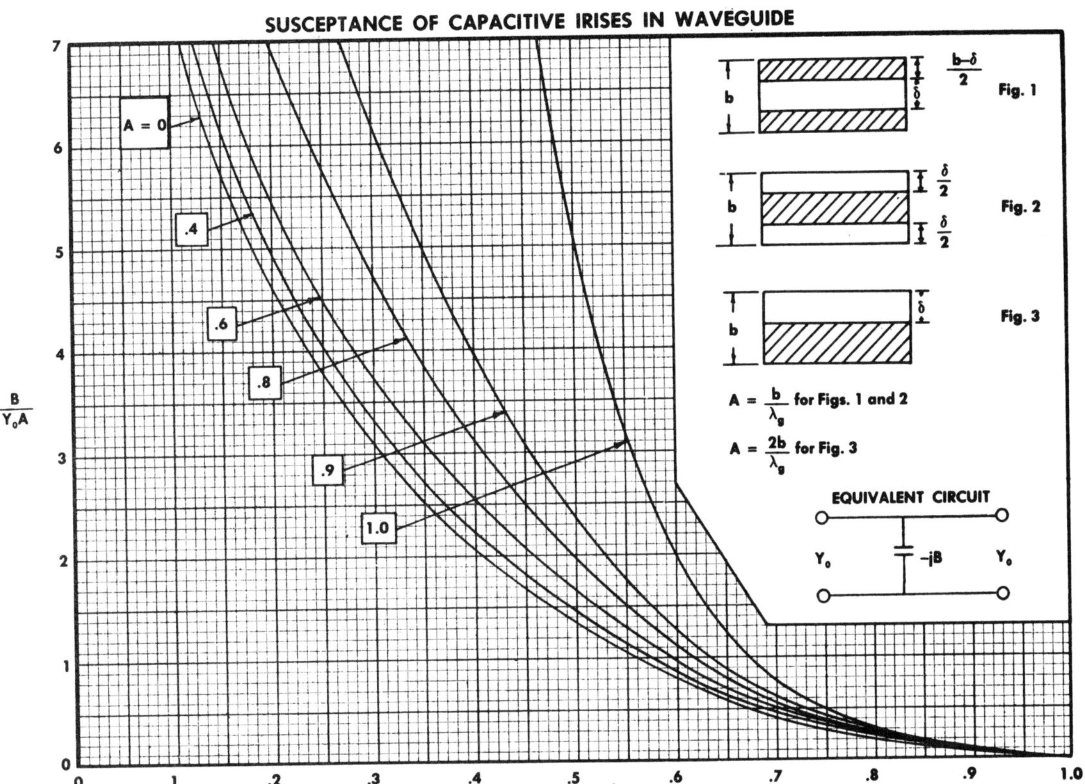

SUSCEPTANCE OF CENTERED THIN VANE IN WAVEGUIDE

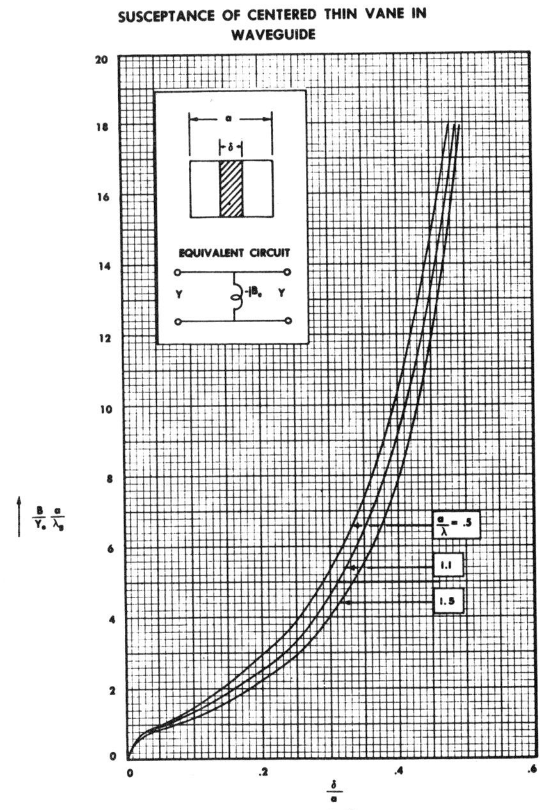

Reprinted from Massachusetts Institute of Technology Radiation Laboratory Report No. 43, Feb. 1944. Prepared under contract with the Office of Scientific Research and Development.

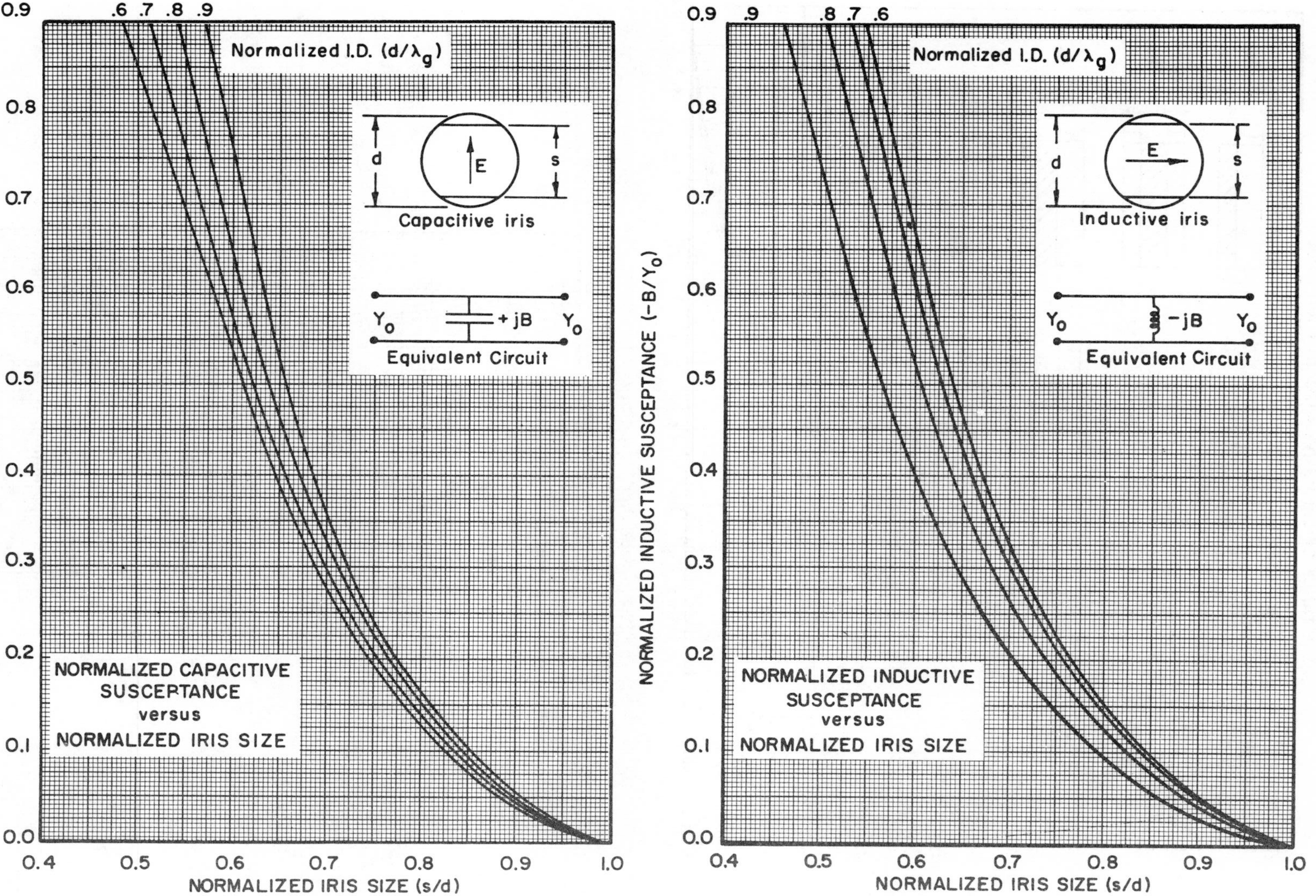

Courtesy of H. Yates and C. A. Lovejoy

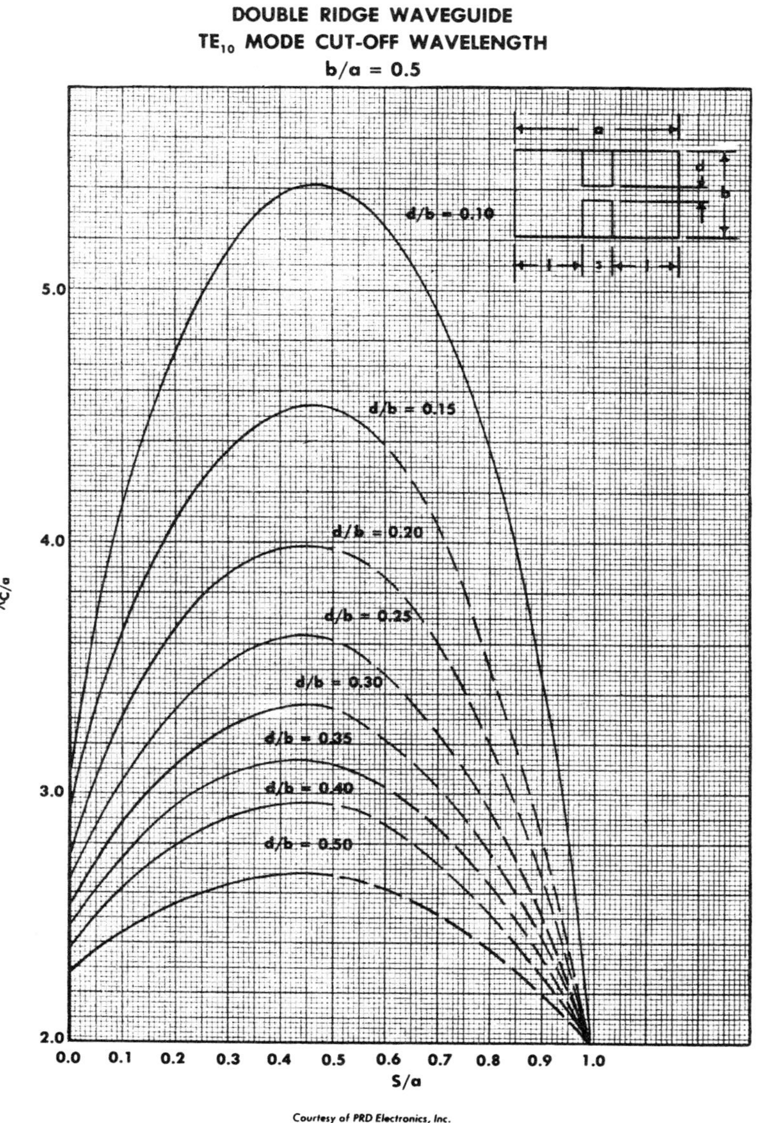
DOUBLE RIDGE WAVEGUIDE
TE_{10} MODE CUT-OFF WAVELENGTH
b/a = 0.5
d/b = 0.10
d/b = 0.15
d/b = 0.20
d/b = 0.25
d/b = 0.30
d/b = 0.35
d/b = 0.40
d/b = 0.50
a
b
d
l
s
λ_c/a
S/a
Courtesy of PRD Electronics, Inc.

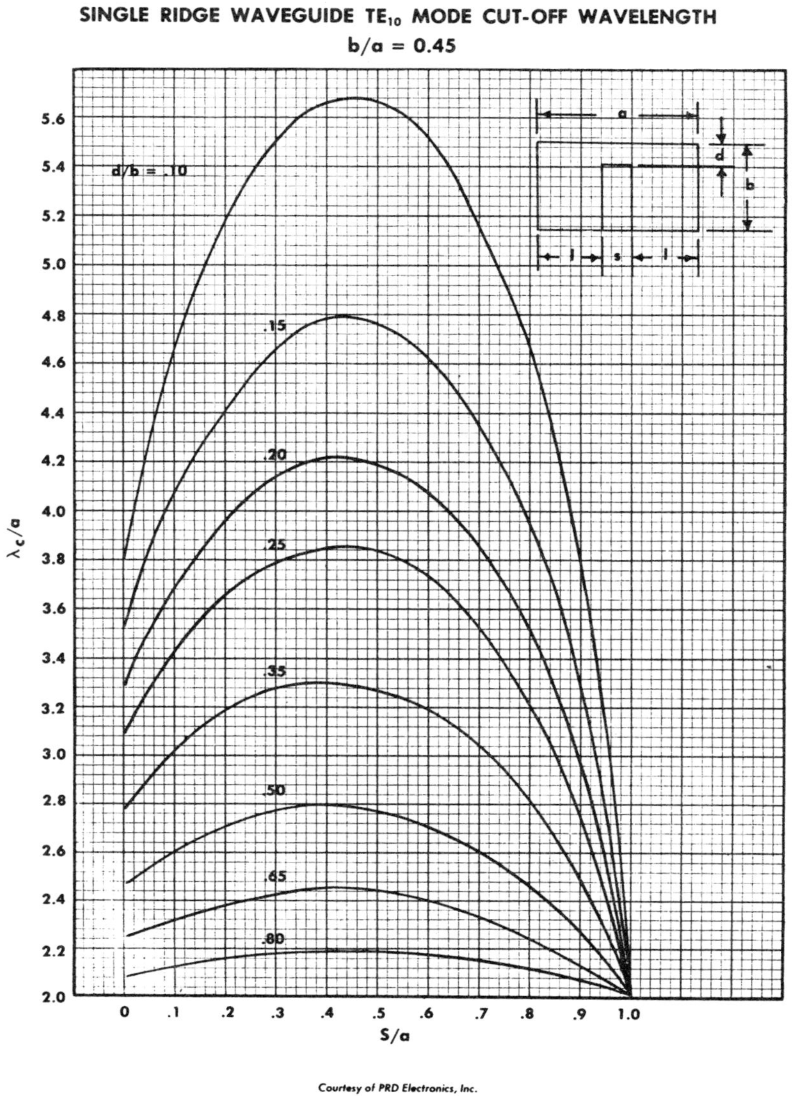
SINGLE RIDGE WAVEGUIDE TE_{10} MODE CUT-OFF WAVELENGTH
b/a = 0.45
d/b = .10
.15
.20
.25
.35
.50
.65
.80
a
b
d
l
s
λ_c/a
S/a
Courtesy of PRD Electronics, Inc.

SINGLE RIDGE WAVEGUIDE BANDWIDTH CURVES

b/a = 0.45

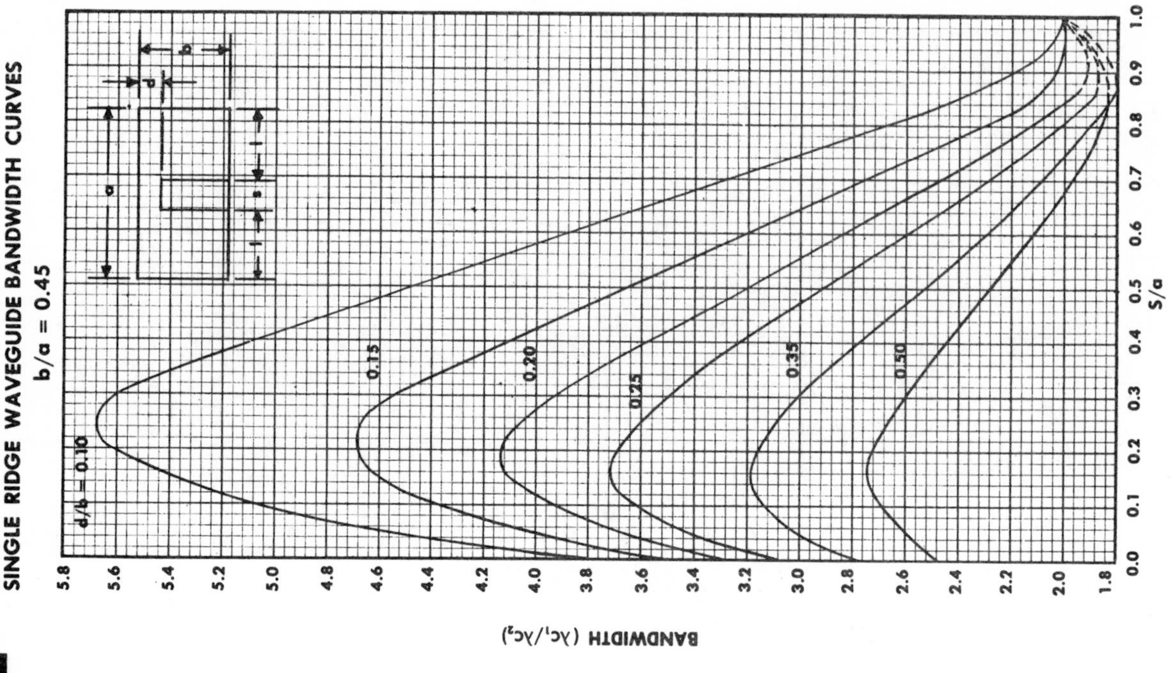

Courtesy of PRD Electronics, Inc.

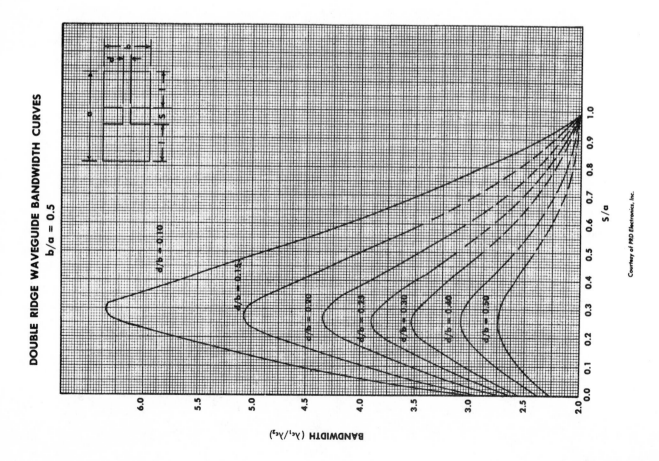

DOUBLE RIDGE WAVEGUIDE BANDWIDTH CURVES

b/a = 0.5

Courtesy of PRD Electronics, Inc.

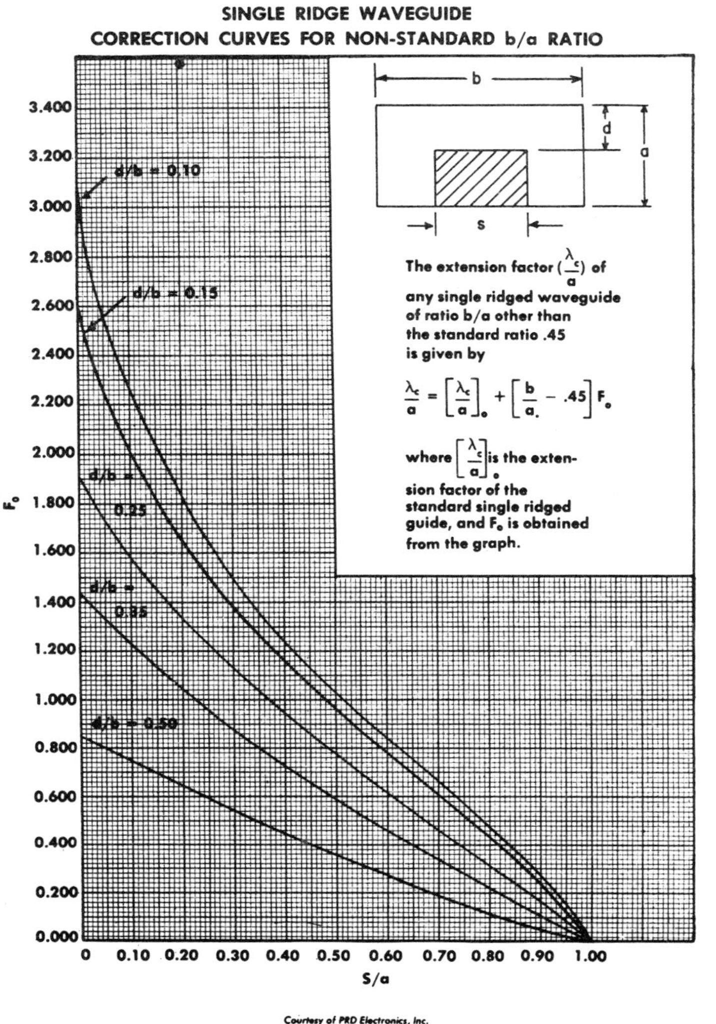
SINGLE RIDGE WAVEGUIDE
CORRECTION CURVES FOR NON-STANDARD b/a RATIO
b
d
a
s
The extension factor $\left(\frac{\lambda_c}{a}\right)$ of any single ridged waveguide of ratio b/a other than the standard ratio .45 is given by
$\frac{\lambda_c}{a} = \left[\frac{\lambda_c}{a}\right]_o + \left[\frac{b}{a_o} - .45\right] F_o$
where $\left[\frac{\lambda_c}{a}\right]_o$ is the extension factor of the standard single ridged guide, and F_o is obtained from the graph.
d/b = 0.10
d/b = 0.15
d/b = 0.25
d/b = 0.35
d/b = 0.50
F_o
S/a
Courtesy of PRD Electronics, Inc.

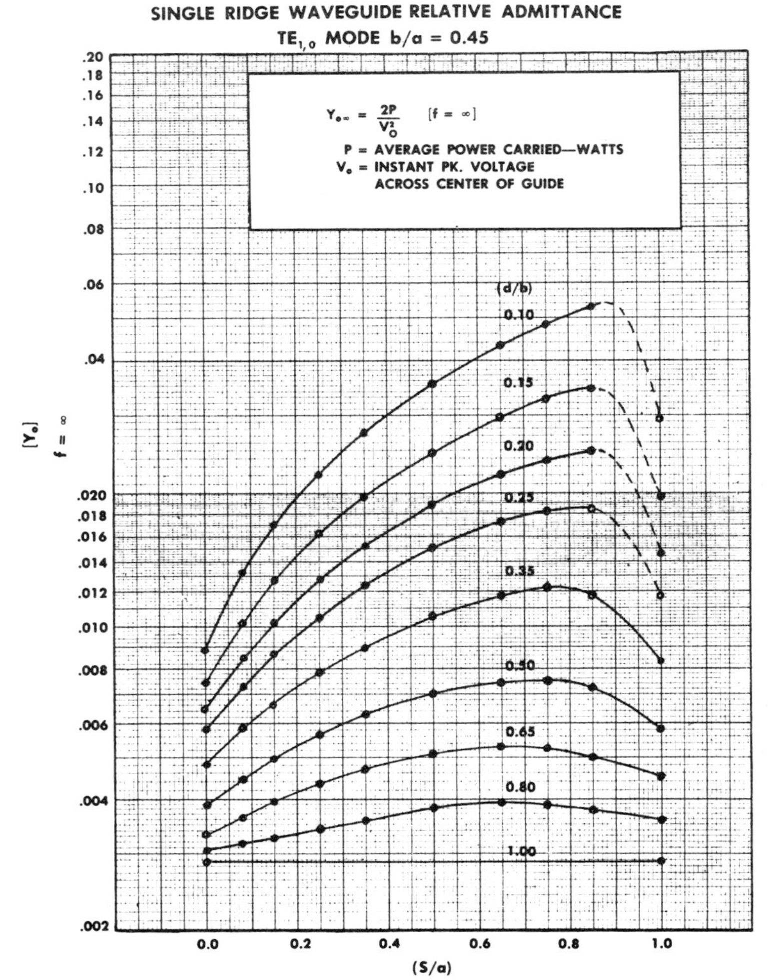
SINGLE RIDGE WAVEGUIDE RELATIVE ADMITTANCE
$TE_{1,0}$ MODE b/a = 0.45
$Y_{o\infty} = \frac{2P}{V_O^2}$ [f = ∞]
P = AVERAGE POWER CARRIED—WATTS
V_o = INSTANT PK. VOLTAGE ACROSS CENTER OF GUIDE
(d/b)
0.10
0.15
0.20
0.25
0.35
0.50
0.65
0.80
1.00
$[Y_o]$
f = ∞
(S/a)
Courtesy of PRD Electronics, Inc.

89

CROSS – SECTIONS OF RIDGE GUIDES

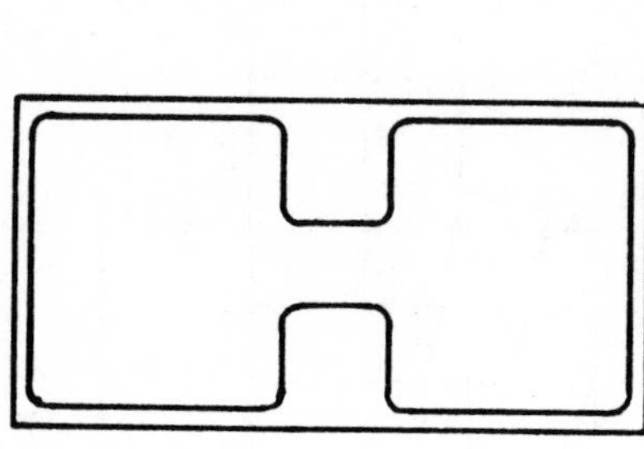

FIGURE A

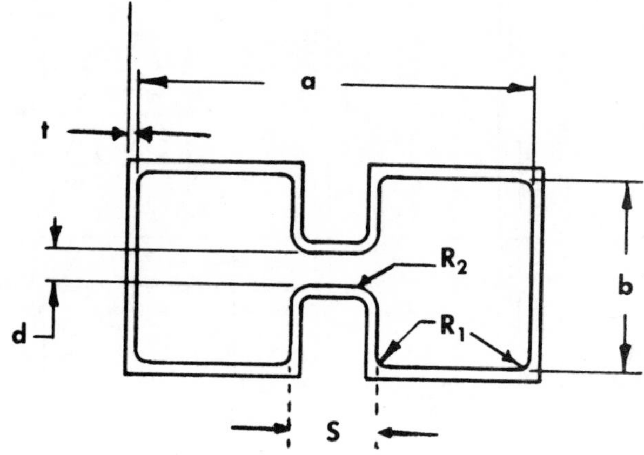

FIGURE B

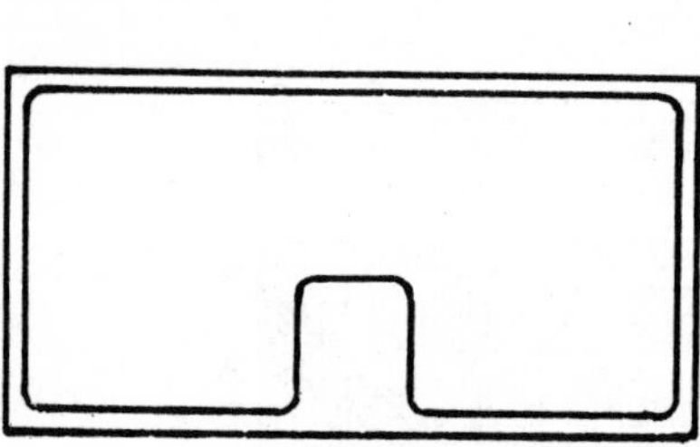

FIGURE C

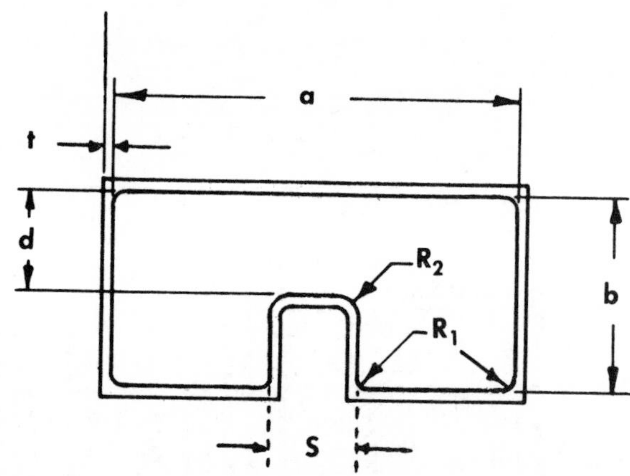

FIGURE D

Courtesy of David Andrews.

E. I. A. PROPOSED STANDARD DOUBLE RIDGED WAVEGUIDE 3.6:1 BANDWIDTH

Cross-section Fig.	Freq. range KMC	fc 10 KMC	fc 20 KMC	Dimensions in inches a	b	d	s	t	R_1	R_2	Att. DB/FT.
B	0.108–0.39	0.092	0.401	34.638	14.894	2.904	8.660			0.581	0.0014
B	0.27–0.97	0.229	0.999	13.916	5.984	1.167	3.479			0.233	0.0055
B	0.39–1.4	0.331	1.444	9.628	4.140	0.807	2.407	0.125	0.050	0.161	0.0097
B	0.97–3.5	0.822	3.587	3.877	1.667	0.325	0.969	0.080	0.050	0.065	0.038
B	1.4–5.0	1.186	5.176	2.687	1.155	0.225	0.672	0.080	0.050	0.045	0.066
B	3.5–12.4	2.966	12.944	1.074	0.462	0.090	0.269	0.050	0.030	0.018	0.26
B	5.0–18.0	4.237	18.490	0.752	0.323	0.063	0.188	0.050	0.020	0.013	0.44
A	12.4–40.0	10.508	45.857	0.303	0.130	0.025	0.076	0.040	0.015	0.005	1.73

$$\frac{f\,min}{fc\,10} = 1.18 \qquad \frac{f\,max}{fc\,20} = 0.98$$

$$\frac{s}{a} = 0.25$$

$$\frac{d}{b} = 0.195 \qquad \lambda c\,10 = 3.706a$$

$$\frac{b}{a} = 0.43 \qquad \lambda c\,20 = 0.8493a$$

$$R_2 = 0.2d$$

E. I. A. PROPOSED STANDARD SINGLE RIDGED WAVEGUIDE 3.6:1 BANDWIDTH

Cross-section Fig.	Freq. range KMC	fc 10 KMC	fc 20 KMC	Dimensions in inches a	b	d	s	t	R_1	R_2	Att. DB/FT.
D	0.108–0.39	0.092	0.440	31.218	14.048	1.798	5.307			0.360	0.0023
D	0.27–0.97	0.229	1.096	12.542	5.644	0.722	2.132			0.144	0.0092
D	0.39–1.4	0.331	1.584	8.677	3.905	0.500	1.475	0.125	0.047	0.100	0.016
D	0.97–3.5	0.822	3.932	3.494	1.572	0.201	0.594	0.080	0.047	0.040	0.062
D	1.4–5.0	1.186	5.674	2.422	1.090	0.140	0.412	0.080	0.047	0.028	0.11
D	3.5–12.4	2.966	14.189	0.968	0.436	0.056	0.165	0.050	0.031	0.011	0.43
C	5.0–18.0	4.237	20.270	0.678	0.305	0.039	0.115	0.050	0.015	0.008	0.73
C	12.4–40.0	10.508	50.270	0.273	0.123	0.016	0.046	0.040	0.015	0.003	2.85

$$\frac{f\,min}{fc\,10} = 1.18 \qquad \frac{f\,max}{fc\,20} = 0.98$$

$$\frac{s}{a} = 0.170$$

$$\frac{d}{b} = 0.128 \qquad \lambda c\,10 = 4.112a$$

$$\frac{b}{a} = 0.45 \qquad \lambda c\,20 = 0.8595\,a$$

$$R_2 = 0.2d$$

Courtesy of David Andrews.

E. I. A. PROPOSED STANDARD DOUBLE RIDGED WAVEGUIDE 2.4:1 BANDWIDTH

Cross-section Fig.	Freq. range KMC	fc 10 KMC	fc 20 KMC	a	b	d	s	t	R_1	R_2	Att. DB/FT.
				Dimensions in inches							
B	0.175–0.42	0.148	0.435	29.667	13.795	5.863	7.417			1.173	0.00023
B	0.267–0.64	0.226	0.664	19.428	9.034	3.839	4.857			0.768	0.00043
B	0.42–1.0	0.356	1.047	12.333	5.735	2.437	3.083	0.125	0.050	0.487	0.00085
B	0.64–1.53	0.542	1.593	8.100	3.767	1.601	2.025	0.125	0.050	0.320	0.0016
B	0.84–2.0	0.712	2.093	6.167	2.868	1.219	1.542	0.125	0.050	0.244	0.0024
B	1.5–3.6	1.271	3.736	3.455	1.607	0.683	0.864	0.080	0.050	0.137	0.0058
B	2.0–4.8	1.695	4.984	2.590	1.205	0.512	0.648	0.080	0.050	0.102	0.0089
B	3.5–8.2	2.966	8.722	1.480	0.688	0.292	0.370	0.064	0.030	0.058	0.020
B	4.75–11.0	4.025	11.842	1.090	0.506	0.215	0.272	0.050	0.030	0.043	0.032
B	7.5–18.0	6.356	18.680	0.691	0.321	0.136	0.173	0.050	0.020	0.027	0.064
A	11.0–26.5	9.322	27.406	0.471	0.219	0.093	0.118	0.040	0.015	0.019	0.11
A	18.0–40.0	15.254	44.820	0.288	0.134	0.057	0.072	0.040	0.015	0.011	0.24

$\frac{f\ min}{fc\ 10} = 1.18$ $\frac{f\ max}{fc\ 20} = 0.97$ $\lambda c\ 10 = 2.69a$

$\frac{s}{a} = 0.25$ $\frac{d}{b} = 0.425$ $\lambda c\ 20 = 0.915a$

$\frac{b}{a} = 0.465$ $R_2 = 0.2d$

E. I. A. PROPOSED STANDARD SINGLE RIDGED WAVEGUIDE 2.4:1 BANDWIDTH

Cross-section Fig.	Freq. range KMC	fc 10 KMC	fc 20 KMC	a	b	d	s	t	R_1	R_2	Att. DB/FT.
				Dimensions in inches							
D	0.175–0.42	0.148	0.431	28.129	12.658	5.278	4.360			1.056	0.00024
D	0.267–0.64	0.226	0.658	18.421	8.289	3.457	2.855			0.691	0.00045
D	0.42–1.0	0.356	1.036	11.695	5.263	2.195	1.813	0.125	0.047	0.439	0.00087
D	0.64–1.53	0.542	1.577	7.682	3.457	1.442	1.191	0.125	0.047	0.288	0.0016
D	0.84–2.0	0.712	2.072	5.847	2.631	1.097	0.906	0.080	0.047	0.219	0.0025
D	1.5–3.6	1.271	3.699	3.276	1.474	0.615	0.508	0.080	0.047	0.123	0.0059
D	2.0–4.8	1.695	4.933	2.456	1.105	0.461	0.381	0.080	0.047	0.092	0.0091
D	3.5–8.2	2.966	8.632	1.404	0.632	0.264	0.218	0.064	0.031	0.053	0.021
D	4.75–11.0	4.025	11.714	1.034	0.465	0.194	0.160	0.050	0.031	0.039	0.033
C	7.5–18.0	6.356	18.498	0.655	0.295	0.123	0.1015	0.050	0.015	0.025	0.066
C	11.0–26.5	9.322	27.130	0.4466	0.2010	0.0838	0.0692	0.040	0.015	0.017	0.12
C	18.0–40.0	15.254	44.393	0.2729	0.1228	0.0512	0.0423	0.040	0.015	0.010	0.25

$\frac{f\ min}{fc\ 10} = 1.18$ $\frac{f\ max}{fc\ 20} = 0.98$ $\lambda c\ 10 = 2.837a$

$\frac{s}{a} = 0.155$ $\frac{d}{b} = 0.417$ $\lambda c\ 20 = 0.9748a$

$\frac{b}{a} = 0.45$ $R_2 = 0.2d$

Courtesy of David Andrews.

COAXIAL LINES

Characteristic Impedance of Coaxial Lines

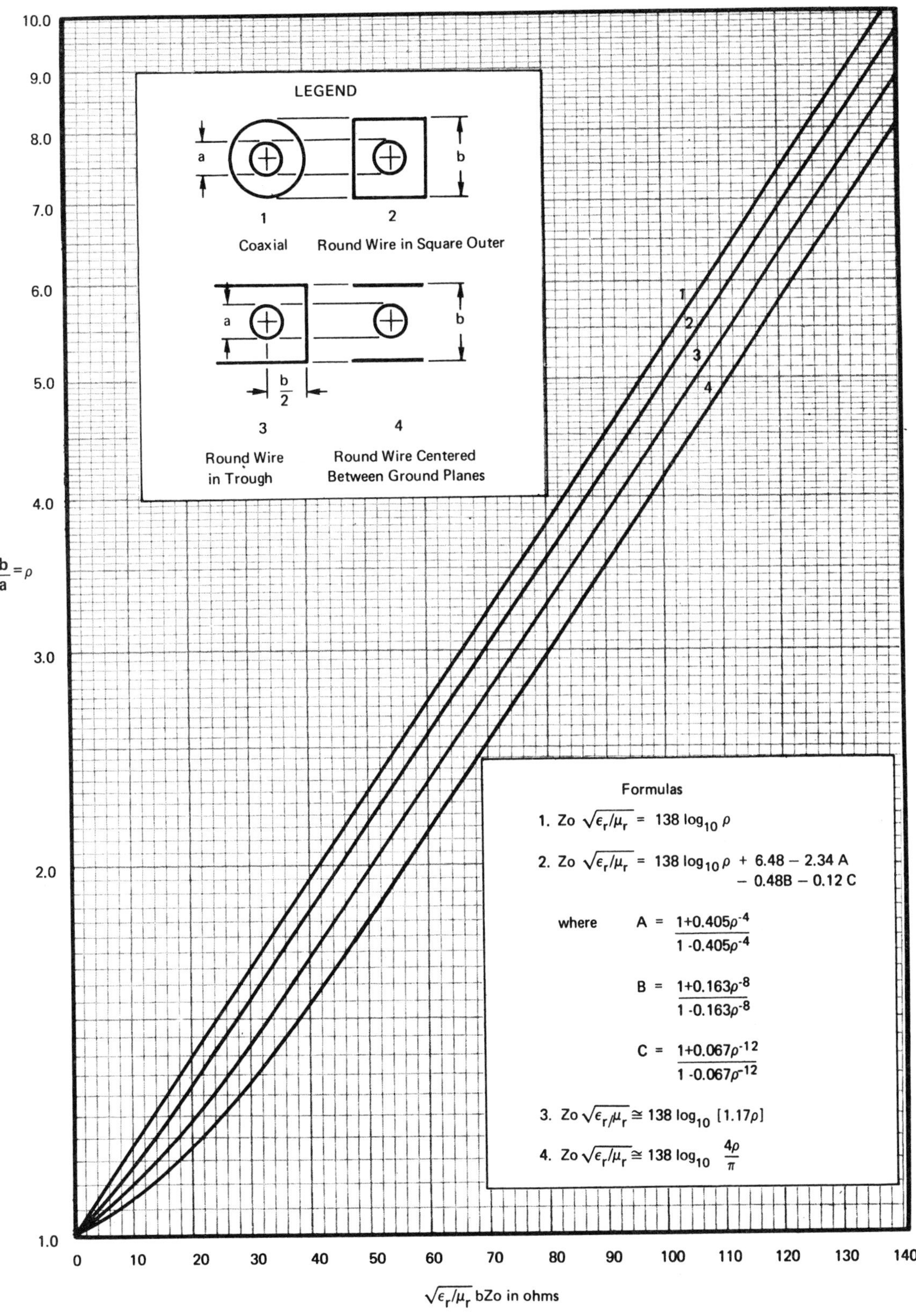

1. $Zo\sqrt{\epsilon_r/\mu_r} = 138 \log_{10} \rho$

2. $Zo\sqrt{\epsilon_r/\mu_r} = 138 \log_{10} \rho + 6.48 - 2.34\,A - 0.48B - 0.12\,C$

where $A = \dfrac{1+0.405\rho^{-4}}{1-0.405\rho^{-4}}$

$B = \dfrac{1+0.163\rho^{-8}}{1-0.163\rho^{-8}}$

$C = \dfrac{1+0.067\rho^{-12}}{1-0.067\rho^{-12}}$

3. $Zo\sqrt{\epsilon_r/\mu_r} \cong 138 \log_{10} [1.17\rho]$

4. $Zo\sqrt{\epsilon_r/\mu_r} \cong 138 \log_{10} \dfrac{4\rho}{\pi}$

Courtesy of W.A.Edson, Electromagnetic Technology Corporation, Mountain View, California.

Inductance and Capacitance of Coaxial Lines

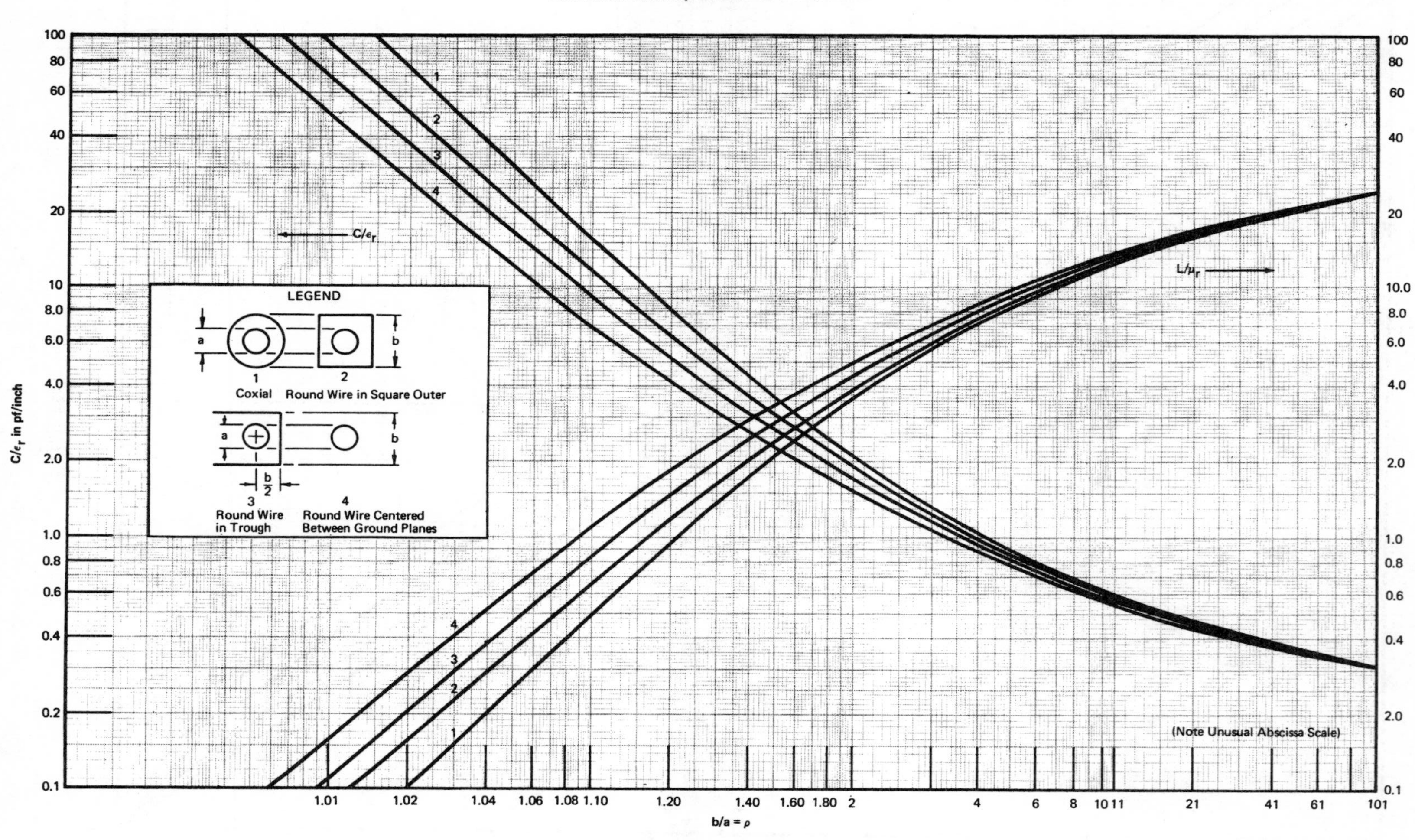

Courtesy of W.A.Edson, Electromagnetic Technology Corporation, Mountain View, California

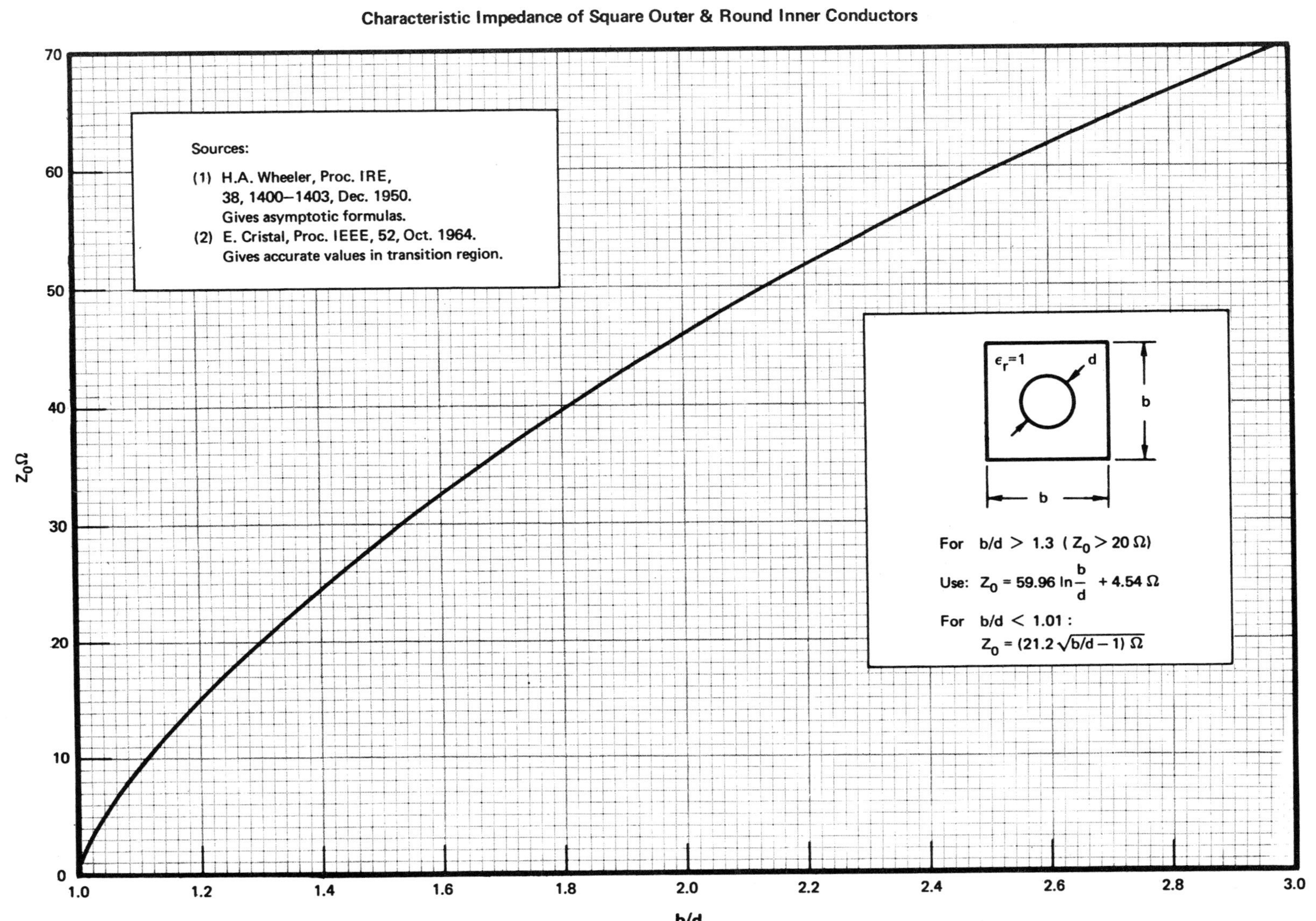

Courtesy of S. B. Cohn, S. B. Cohn Associates, Tarzana, California

CHARACTERISTIC IMPEDANCE (Zo) OF ROUND WIRE IN SQUARE OUTER CONDUCTOR

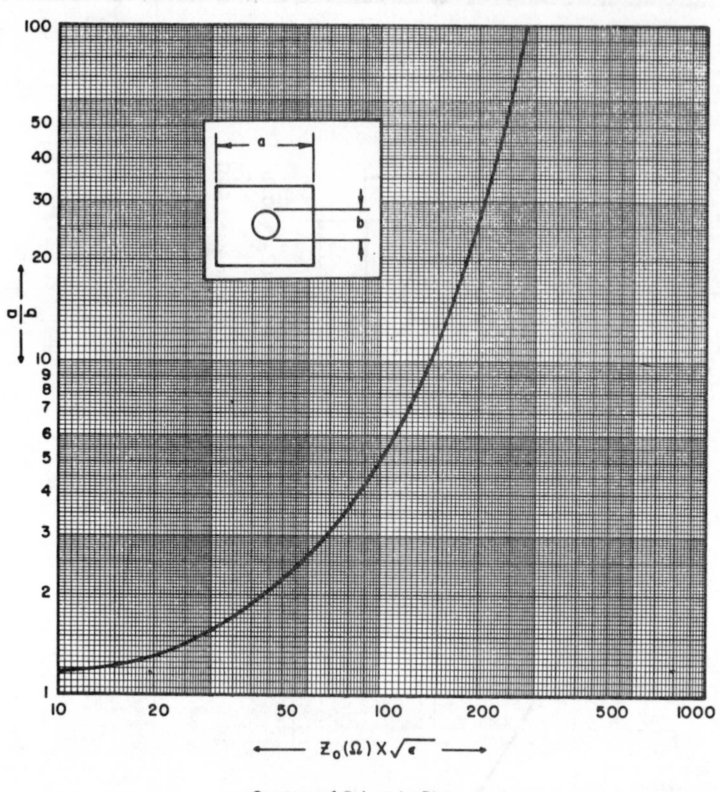

Courtesy of Robert Le Blanc

CHARACTERISTIC IMPEDANCE OF RECTANGULAR COAXIAL TRANSMISSION LINES

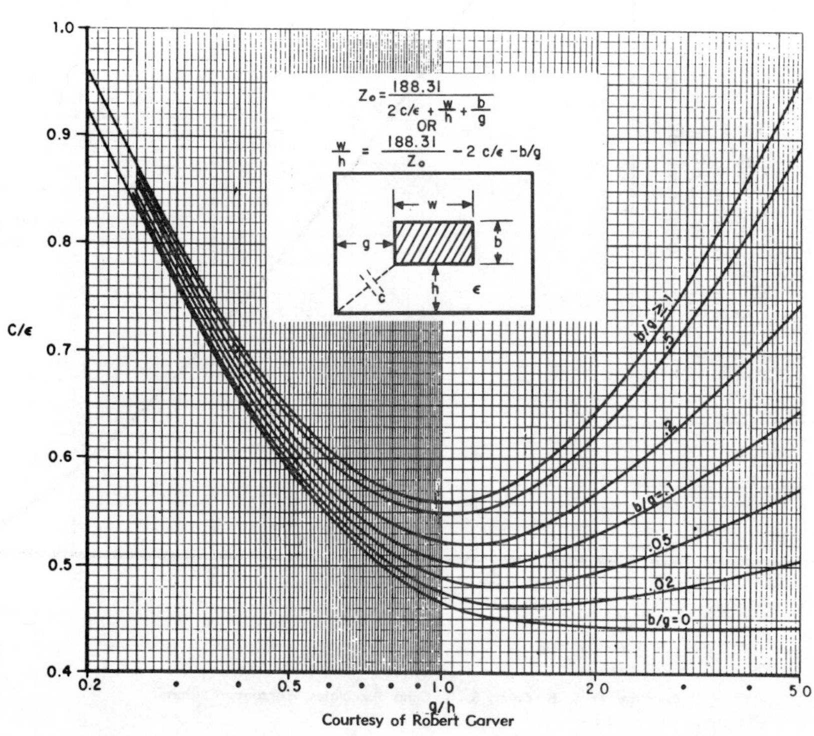

Courtesy of Robert Garver

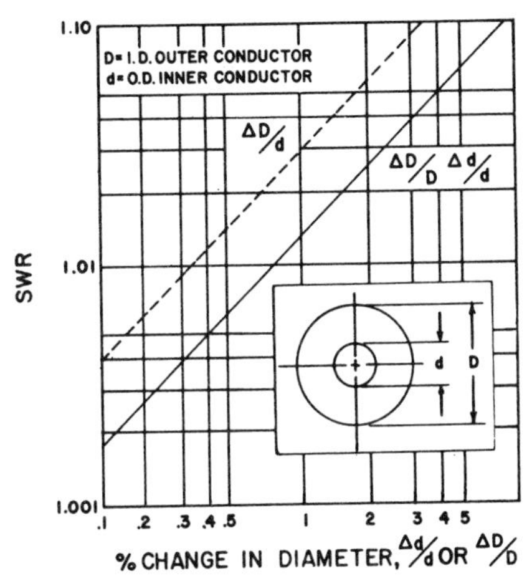

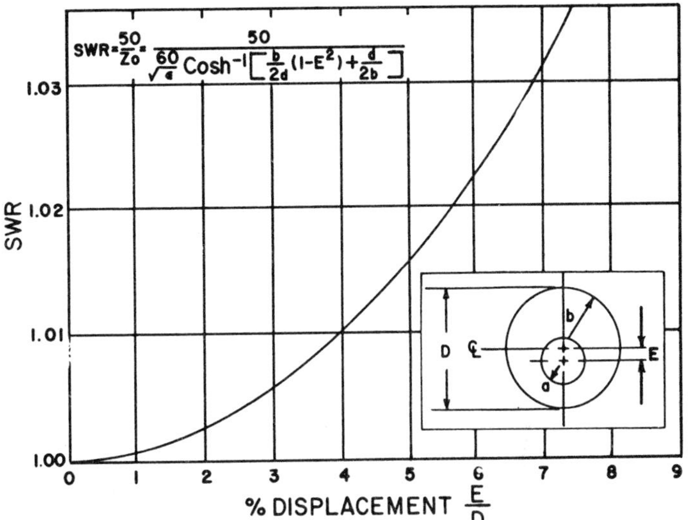

$$SWR = \frac{50}{Z_0} = \frac{50}{\frac{60}{\sqrt{\epsilon}} \cosh^{-1}\left[\frac{b}{2d}(1-E^2) + \frac{d}{2b}\right]}$$

Courtesy of Tore N. Anderson — Amphenol RF Division

FREQUENCY IN MEGACYCLES

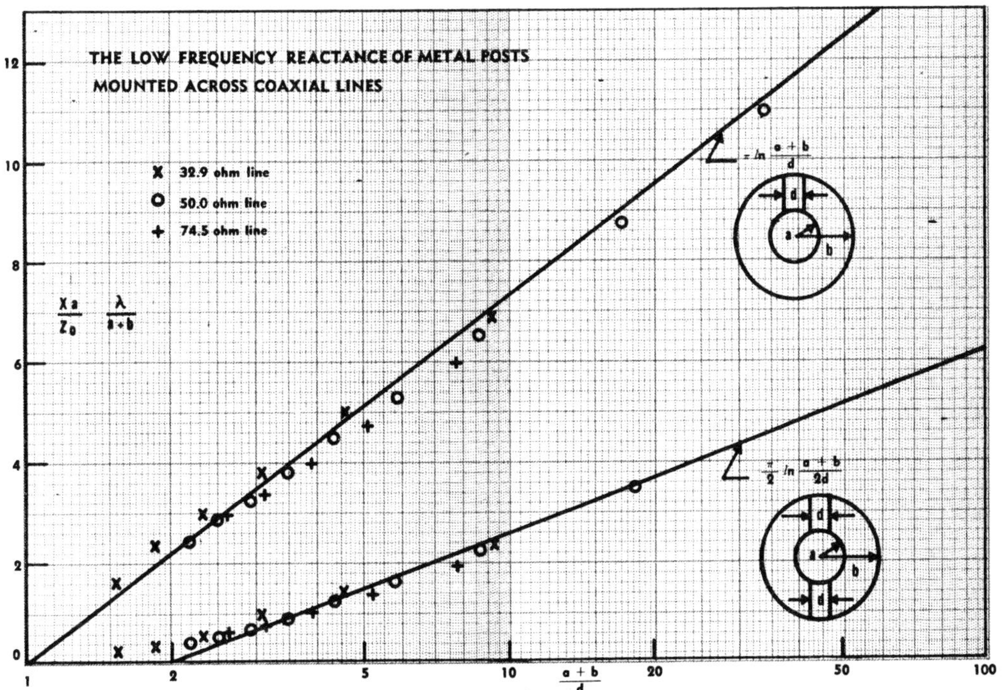

Courtesy of Charles E. Muehe, MIT Lincoln Laboratory, Lexington, Mass.

CHARACTERISTIC IMPEDANCE, CAPACITANCE, AND INDUCTANCE OF COAXIAL LINES

FORMULAS:

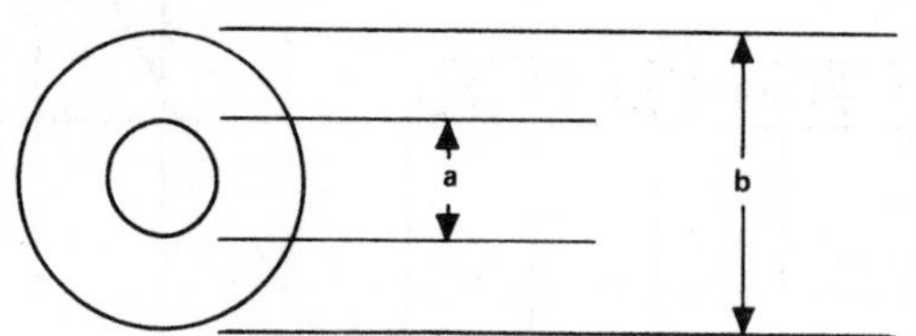

$$C = 1.41306\ \epsilon_r / l_\mu\ b/a \text{ pf/inch}$$

$$L = 0.0050799\ \mu_r\ l_\mu\ b/a\ \mu\text{h/inch}$$

$$Z_o = \sqrt{\frac{L\ (\text{ph})}{C\ (\text{pf})}} \text{ ohms}$$

where: ϵ_r = Relative Dielectric Constant

μ_r = Relative Permeability Constant

b/a	$\sqrt{\epsilon_r/\mu_r}\,Z_o$ (ohms)	C/ϵ_r (pf/inch)	L/μ_r (μh/inch)	b/a	$\sqrt{\epsilon_r/\mu_r}\,Z_o$ (ohms)	C/ϵ_r (pf/inch)	L/μ_r (μh/inch)
1.00	0.00000	1.41306	0.000000	1.45	22.2784	3.80302	0.001887
1.01	0.59661	142.012	0.000050	1.46	22.6905	3.73395	0.001922
1.02	1.18734	71.3574	0.000101	1.47	23.0997	3.66780	0.001957
1.03	1.77230	47.8052	0.000150	1.48	23.5062	3.60437	0.001991
1.04	2.35161	36.0285	0.000199	1.49	23.9100	3.54350	0.002026
1.05	2.92538	28.9621	0.000248	1.50	24.3111	3.48505	0.002060
1.06	3.49372	24.2507	0.000296	1.51	24.7095	3.42885	0.002093
1.07	4.05671	20.8852	0.000344	1.52	25.1052	3.37480	0.002127
1.08	4.61447	18.3608	0.000391	1.53	25.4984	3.32276	0.002160
1.09	5.16708	16.3971	0.000438	1.54	25.8890	3.27263	0.002193
1.10	5.71466	14.8259	0.000484	1.55	26.2771	3.22430	0.002226
1.11	6.25727	13.5403	0.000530	1.56	26.6627	3.17767	0.002259
1.12	6.79502	12.4687	0.000576	1.57	27.0458	3.13265	0.002291
1.13	7.32799	11.5619	0.000621	1.58	27.4265	3.08917	0.002324
1.14	7.85626	10.7844	0.000666	1.59	27.8048	3.04714	0.002356
1.15	8.37992	10.1105	0.000710	1.60	28.1807	3.00650	0.002388
1.16	8.89904	9.52071	0.000754	1.61	28.5543	2.96716	0.002419
1.17	9.41371	9.00019	0.000797	1.62	28.9255	2.92908	0.002451
1.18	9.92400	8.53741	0.000841	1.63	29.2945	2.89219	0.002482
1.19	10.4300	8.12324	0.000884	1.64	29.6612	2.85643	0.002513
1.20	10.9317	7.75040	0.000926	1.65	30.0257	2.82175	0.002544
1.21	11.4293	7.41298	0.000968	1.66	30.3880	2.78811	0.002575
1.22	11.9228	7.10615	0.001010	1.67	30.7481	2.75546	0.002605
1.23	12.4123	6.82593	0.001052	1.68	31.1061	2.72375	0.002635
1.24	12.8977	6.56899	0.001093	1.69	31.4619	2.69294	0.002666
1.25	13.3793	6.33253	0.001133	1.70	31.8157	2.66300	0.002695
1.26	13.8571	6.11420	0.001174	1.71	32.1673	2.63389	0.002725
1.27	14.3311	5.91198	0.001214	1.72	32.5169	2.60557	0.002755
1.28	14.8014	5.72415	0.001254	1.73	32.8645	2.57801	0.002784
1.29	15.2680	5.54921	0.001293	1.74	33.2101	2.55119	0.002814
1.30	15.7310	5.38589	0.001333	1.75	33.5537	2.52506	0.002843
1.31	16.1904	5.23305	0.001372	1.76	33.8954	2.49961	0.002872
1.32	16.6464	5.08971	0.001410	1.77	34.2351	2.47481	0.002900
1.33	17.0989	4.95501	0.001449	1.78	34.5729	2.45063	0.002929
1.34	17.5480	4.82819	0.001487	1.79	34.9088	2.42705	0.002958
1.35	17.9938	4.70857	0.001524	1.80	35.2428	2.40404	0.002986
1.36	18.4363	4.59556	0.001562	1.81	35.5750	2.38159	0.003014
1.37	18.8756	4.48862	0.001599	1.82	35.9053	2.35968	0.003042
1.38	19.3116	4.38726	0.001636	1.83	36.2339	2.33829	0.003070
1.39	19.7445	4.29107	0.001673	1.84	36.5606	2.31739	0.003098
1.40	20.1744	4.19965	0.001709	1.85	36.8856	2.29697	0.003125
1.41	20.6011	4.11265	0.001745	1.86	37.2088	2.27702	0.003152
1.42	21.0249	4.02976	0.001781	1.87	37.5303	2.25751	0.003180
1.43	21.4456	3.95070	0.001817	1.88	37.8501	2.23844	0.003207
1.44	21.8634	3.87520	0.001852	1.89	38.1682	2.21979	0.003234

Courtesy of M. Miller

b/a	$\sqrt{\epsilon_r/\mu_r}\, Z_o$ (ohms)	C/ϵ_r (pf/inch)	L/μ_r (μh/inch)	b/a	$\sqrt{\epsilon_r/\mu_r}\, Z_o$ (ohms)	C/ϵ_r (pf/inch)	L/μ_r (μh/inch)
1.90	38.4846	2.20154	0.003261	2.58	56.8280	1.49091	0.004815
1.91	38.7993	2.18368	0.003287	2.59	57.0600	1.48484	0.004834
1.92	39.1124	2.16620	0.003314	2.60	57.2910	1.47886	0.004854
1.93	39.4239	2.14908	0.003340	2.61	57.5212	1.47294	0.004873
1.94	39.7338	2.13232	0.003366	2.62	57.7505	1.46709	0.004893
1.95	40.0420	2.11591	0.003392	2.63	57.9789	1.46131	0.004912
1.96	40.3487	2.09982	0.003418	2.64	58.2064	1.45560	0.004931
1.97	40.6539	2.08406	0.003444	2.65	58.4331	1.44995	0.004951
1.98	40.9575	2.06861	0.003470	2.66	58.6590	1.44437	0.004970
1.99	41.2595	2.05347	0.003496	2.67	58.8839	1.43885	0.004989
2.00	41.5601	2.03862	0.003521	2.68	59.1081	1.43339	0.005008
2.01	41.8591	2.02406	0.003546	2.69	59.3314	1.42800	0.005027
2.02	42.1567	2.00977	0.003572	2.70	59.5539	1.42266	0.005046
2.03	42.4528	1.99575	0.003597	2.71	59.7755	1.41739	0.005064
2.04	42.7474	1.98200	0.003622	2.72	59.9964	1.41217	0.005083
2.05	43.0406	1.96850	0.003647	2.73	60.2164	1.40701	0.005102
2.06	43.3324	1.95524	0.003671	2.74	60.4556	1.40191	0.005120
2.07	43.6227	1.94223	0.003696	2.75	60.6541	1.39686	0.005139
2.08	43.9117	1.92945	0.003720	2.76	60.8717	1.39186	0.005157
2.09	44.1992	1.91689	0.003745	2.77	61.0885	1.38692	0.005176
2.10	44.4854	1.90456	0.003769	2.78	61.3046	1.38204	0.005194
2.11	44.7703	1.89244	0.003793	2.79	61.5199	1.37720	0.005212
2.12	45.0538	1.88053	0.003817	2.80	61.7344	1.37241	0.005230
2.13	45.3359	1.86883	0.003841	2.81	61.9482	1.36768	0.005248
2.14	45.6168	1.85733	0.003865	2.82	62.1612	1.36299	0.005267
2.15	45.8963	1.84601	0.003888	2.83	62.3734	1.35835	0.005285
2.16	46.1745	1.83489	0.003912	2.84	62.5849	1.35376	0.005302
2.17	46.4515	1.82395	0.003936	2.85	62.7957	1.34922	0.005320
2.18	46.7271	1.81319	0.003959	2.86	63.0057	1.34472	0.005338
2.19	47.0015	1.80260	0.003982	2.87	63.2150	1.34027	0.005356
2.20	47.2747	1.79219	0.004005	2.88	63.4235	1.33586	0.005373
2.21	47.5466	1.78194	0.004028	2.89	63.6313	1.33150	0.005391
2.22	47.8173	1.77185	0.004051	2.90	63.8384	1.32718	0.005409
2.23	48.0868	1.76192	0.004074	2.91	64.0448	1.32290	0.005426
2.24	48.3551	1.75215	0.004097	2.92	64.2505	1.31867	0.005444
2.25	48.6221	1.74252	0.004119	2.93	64.4555	1.31448	0.005461
2.26	48.8880	1.73305	0.004142	2.94	64.6598	1.31032	0.005478
2.27	49.1528	1.72371	0.004164	2.95	64.8634	1.30621	0.005495
2.28	49.4163	1.71452	0.004187	2.96	65.0663	1.30214	0.005513
2.29	49.6787	1.70546	0.004209	2.97	65.2685	1.29810	0.005530
2.30	49.9400	1.69654	0.004231	2.98	65.4701	1.29411	0.005547
2.31	50.2001	1.68775	0.004253	2.99	65.6709	1.29015	0.005564
2.32	50.4591	1.67909	0.004275	3.00	65.8711	1.28623	0.005581
2.33	50.7170	1.67055	0.004297	3.10	67.8372	1.24895	0.005747
2.34	50.9738	1.66213	0.004319	3.20	69.7408	1.21486	0.005909
2.35	51.2294	1.65384	0.004340	3.30	71.5858	1.18355	0.006065
2.36	51.4841	1.64566	0.004362	3.40	73.3757	1.15468	0.006217
2.37	51.7376	1.63759	0.004383	3.50	75.1138	1.12796	0.006364
2.38	51.9900	1.62964	0.004405	3.60	76.8029	1.10315	0.006507
2.39	52.2414	1.62180	0.004426	3.70	78.4457	1.08005	0.006646
2.40	52.4918	1.61407	0.004447	3.80	80.0447	1.05847	0.006782
2.41	52.7411	1.60644	0.004468	3.90	81.6021	1.03827	0.006914
2.42	52.9894	1.59891	0.004489	4.00	83.1201	1.01931	0.007042
2.43	53.2366	1.59148	0.004510	4.10	84.6007	1.00147	0.007168
2.44	53.4829	1.58416	0.004531	4.20	86.0455	0.984656	0.007290
2.45	53.7281	1.57693	0.004552	4.30	87.4564	0.968771	0.007410
2.46	53.9723	1.56979	0.004573	4.40	88.8348	0.953739	0.007526
2.47	54.2156	1.56275	0.004593	4.50	90.1822	0.939489	0.007641
2.48	54.4578	1.55579	0.004614	4.60	91.5000	0.925958	0.007752
2.49	54.6991	1.54893	0.004634	4.70	92.7895	0.913090	0.007862
2.50	54.9394	1.54216	0.004655	4.80	94.0518	0.900835	0.007968
2.51	55.1788	1.53547	0.004675	4.90	95.2881	0.889147	0.008073
2.52	55.4172	1.52886	0.004695	5.00	96.4995	0.877986	0.008176
2.53	55.6546	1.52234	0.004715	5.10	97.6868	0.867315	0.008276
2.54	55.8911	1.51590	0.004735	5.20	98.8511	0.857099	0.008375
2.55	56.1267	1.50953	0.004755	5.30	99.9932	0.847310	0.008472
2.56	56.3614	1.50325	0.004775	5.40	101.114	0.837918	0.008567
2.57	56.5952	1.49704	0.004795	5.50	102.214	0.828899	0.008660

Courtesy of M. Miller

b/a	$\sqrt{\epsilon_r/\mu_r}\, Z_o$ (ohms)	C/ϵ_r (pf/inch)	L/μ_r (μh/inch)	b/a	$\sqrt{\epsilon_r/\mu_r}\, Z_o$ (ohms)	C/ϵ_r (pf /inch)	L/μ_r (μh/inch)
5.60	103.294	0.820230	0.008752	34.00	211.435	0.400715	0.017914
5.70	104.356	0.811888	0.008841	35.00	213.173	0.397448	0.018061
5.80	105.398	0.803856	0.008930	36.00	214.862	0.394323	0.018204
5.90	106.423	0.796114	0.009017	37.00	216.505	0.391331	0.018343
6.00	107.431	0.788646	0.009102	38.00	218.104	0.388462	0.018479
6.10	108.422	0.781437	0.009186	39.00	219.662	0.385708	0.018611
6.20	109.397	0.774473	0.009269	40.00	221.180	0.383061	0.018739
6.30	110.356	0.767740	0.009350	41.00	222.660	0.380514	0.018865
6.40	111.301	0.761227	0.009430	42.00	224.105	0.378060	0.018987
6.50	112.230	0.754922	0.009509	43.00	225.516	0.375695	0.019107
6.60	113.146	0.748814	0.009586	44.00	226.894	0.373413	0.019224
6.70	114.047	0.742894	0.009663	45.00	228.242	0.371208	0.019338
6.80	114.936	0.737153	0.009738	46.00	229.560	0.369077	0.019449
6.90	115.811	0.731581	0.009812	47.00	230.849	0.367016	0.019559
7.00	116.674	0.726171	0.009885	48.00	232.111	0.365020	0.019666
7.10	117.524	0.720916	0.009957	49.00	233.348	0.363086	0.019770
7.20	118.363	0.715809	0.010028	50.00	234.559	0.361211	0.019873
7.30	119.190	0.710842	0.010098	51.00	235.746	0.359391	0.019974
7,40	120.006	0.706010	0.010167	52.00	236.911	0.357625	0.020072
7.50	120.810	0.701306	0.010236	53.00	238.053	0.355909	0.020169
7.60	121.605	0.696726	0.010303	54.00	239.173	0.354242	0.020264
7.70	122.388	0.692265	0.010369	55.00	240.274	0.352620	0.020357
7.80	123.162	0.687916	0.010435	56.00	241.354	0.351041	0.020449
7.90	123.926	0.683676	0.010500	57.00	242.415	0.349504	0.020539
8.00	124.680	0.679540	0.010563	58.00	243.458	0.348007	0.020627
8.10	125.425	0.675505	0.010627	59.00	244.483	0.346548	0.020714
8.20	126.161	0.671566	0.010689	60.00	245.491	0.345126	0.020799
8.30	126.887	0.667719	0.010750	61.00	246.482	0.343738	0.020883
8.40	127.605	0.663962	0.010811	62.00	247.457	0.342384	0.020966
8.50	128.315	0.660290	0.010871	63.00	248.416	0.341062	0.021047
8.60	129.016	0.656701	0.010931	64.00	249.360	0.339770	0.021127
8.70	129.710	0.653192	0.010990	65.00	250.290	0.338508	0.021206
8.80	130.395	0.649759	0.011048	66.00	251.205	0.337275	0.021283
8.90	131.072	0.646400	0.011105	67.00	252.107	0.336068	0.021360
9.00	131.742	0.643113	0.011162	68.00	252.995	0.334888	0.021435
9.10	132.405	0.639895	0.011218	69.00	253.871	0.333734	0.021509
9.20	133.060	0.636744	0.011273	70.00	254.733	0.332604	0.021582
9.30	133.708	0.633657	0.011328	71.00	255.584	0.331497	0.021654
9.40	134.349	0.630633	0.011383	72.00	256.422	0.330413	0.021725
9.50	134.984	0.627668	0.011436	73.00	257.249	0.329350	0.021795
9.60	135.612	0.624762	0.011490	74.00	258.065	0.328309	0.021865
9.70	136.233	0.621913	0.011542	75.00	258.870	0.327289	0.021933
9.80	136.848	0.619118	0.011594	76.00	259.664	0.326288	0.022000
9.90	137.457	0.616376	0.011646	77.00	260.488	0.325306	0.022066
10.00	138.059	0.613686	0.011697	78.00	261.222	0.324342	0.022132
11.00	143.774	0.589294	0.012181	79.00	261.985	0.323397	0.022197
12.00	148.991	0.568659	0.012623	80.00	262.740	0.322468	0.022261
13.00	153.790	0.550913	0.013030	81.00	263.484	0.321557	0.022324
14.00	158.234	0.535443	0.013406	82.00	264.220	0.320661	0.022386
15.00	162.371	0.521801	0.013757	83.00	264.947	0.319782	0.022448
16.00	166.240	0.509655	0.014085	84.00	265.665	0.318917	0.022508
17.00	169.875	0.498750	0.014393	85.00	266.375	0.318068	0.022569
18.00	173.302	0.488887	0.014683	86.00	267.076	0.317233	0.022628
19.00	176.544	0.479910	0.014958	87.00	267.769	0.316411	0.022687
20.00	179.620	0.471692	0.015218	88.00	268.454	0.315604	0.022745
21.00	182.545	0.464133	0.015466	89.00	269.132	0.314809	0.022802
22.00	185.334	0.457148	0.015702	90.00	269.802	0.314028	0.022859
23.00	187.999	0.450667	0.015928	91.00	270.464	0.313258	0.022915
24.00	190.551	0.444632	0.016144	92.00	271.120	0.312501	0.022971
25.00	192.999	0.438993	0.016352	93.00	271.768	0.311756	0.023025
26.00	195.350	0.433709	0.016551	94.00	272.409	0.311022	0.023080
27.00	197.613	0.428742	0.016743	95.00	273.044	0.310299	0.023134
28.00	199.794	0.424063	0.016927	96.00	273.671	0.309587	0.023187
29.00	201.898	0.419644	0.017106	97.00	274.293	0.308886	0.023239
30.00	203.931	0.415461	0.017278	98.00	274.908	0.308195	0.023292
31.00	205.897	0.411494	0.017445	99.00	275.516	0.307514	0.023343
32.00	207.800	0.407724	0.017606	100.00	276.119	0.306843	0.023394
33.00	209.645	0.404136	0.017762				

Courtesy of M. Miller

ATTENUATION AND POWER RATING OF STANDARD RIGID TRANSMISSION LINES

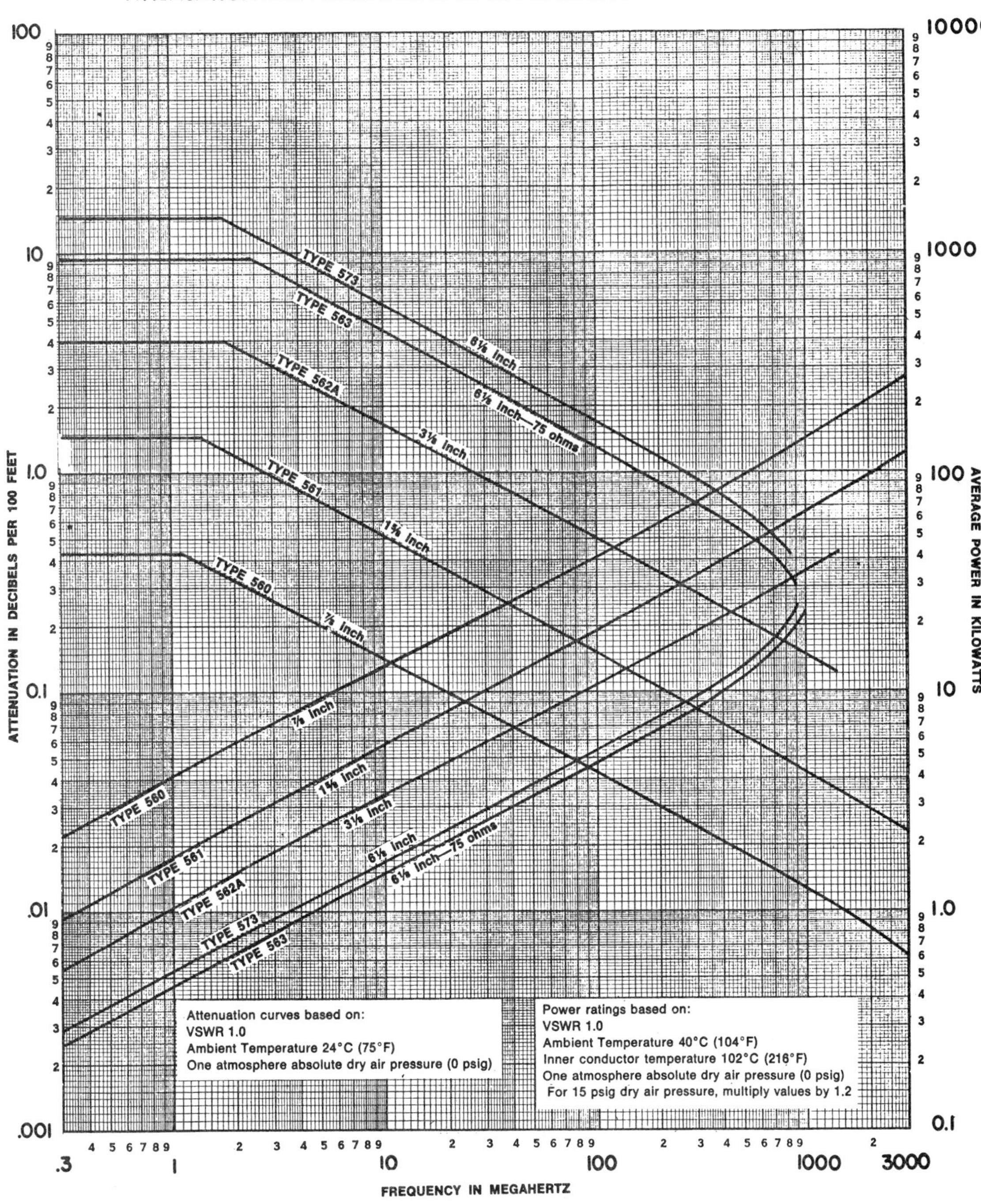

Courtesy of the Andrew Corp.

POWER AND ATTENUATION OF FLEXIBLE 50 OHM RF COAXIAL POLYETHYLENE CABLES

USASI C83.2 CABLE GROUP	1	2	3	4	5	6	7	8	9	10	11
APPROX SIZE O.D. INCHES	.080	.110	.160	.200	—	.330	.415	.415	.550	.725	.870
RG-( )/U CABLE DESIGNATION	178,A,B 196,A (TEFLON)	174 188,A	122	55,A,B 58,A,C 142A,B 223	75 ohm CABLES	5,A,B 21A,B 143,A 212 222 304	115,A	8,A 9,A,B 213 214 225	14,A 217	TEFLON CABLES	17,A 218

FOR TEFLON CABLES SAME SIZE, POWER RATING IS APPROXIMATELY FIVE TIMES VALUES SHOWN.

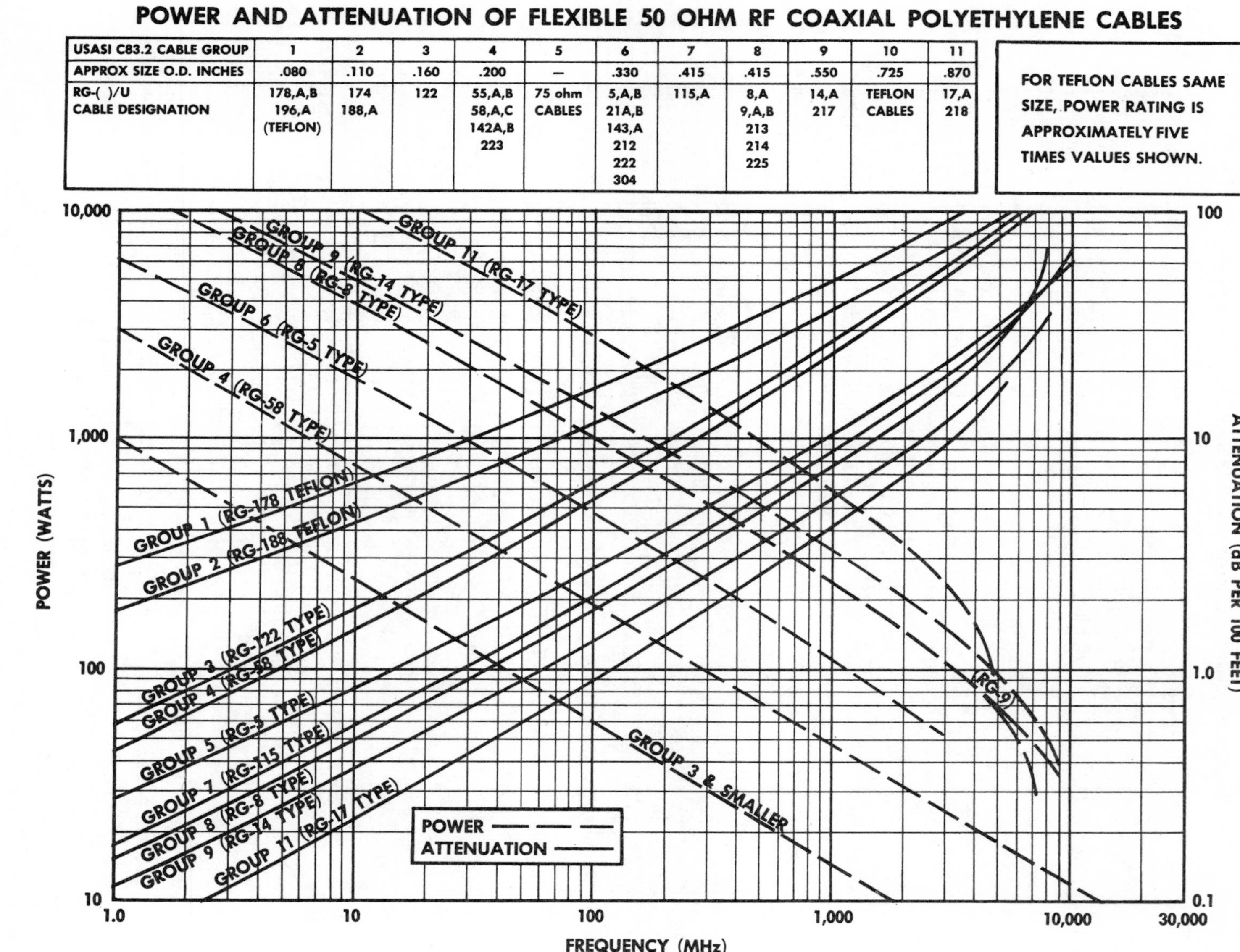

Courtesy of Tore Anderson

Attenuation and Power Rating of HELIAX® Coaxial Cables

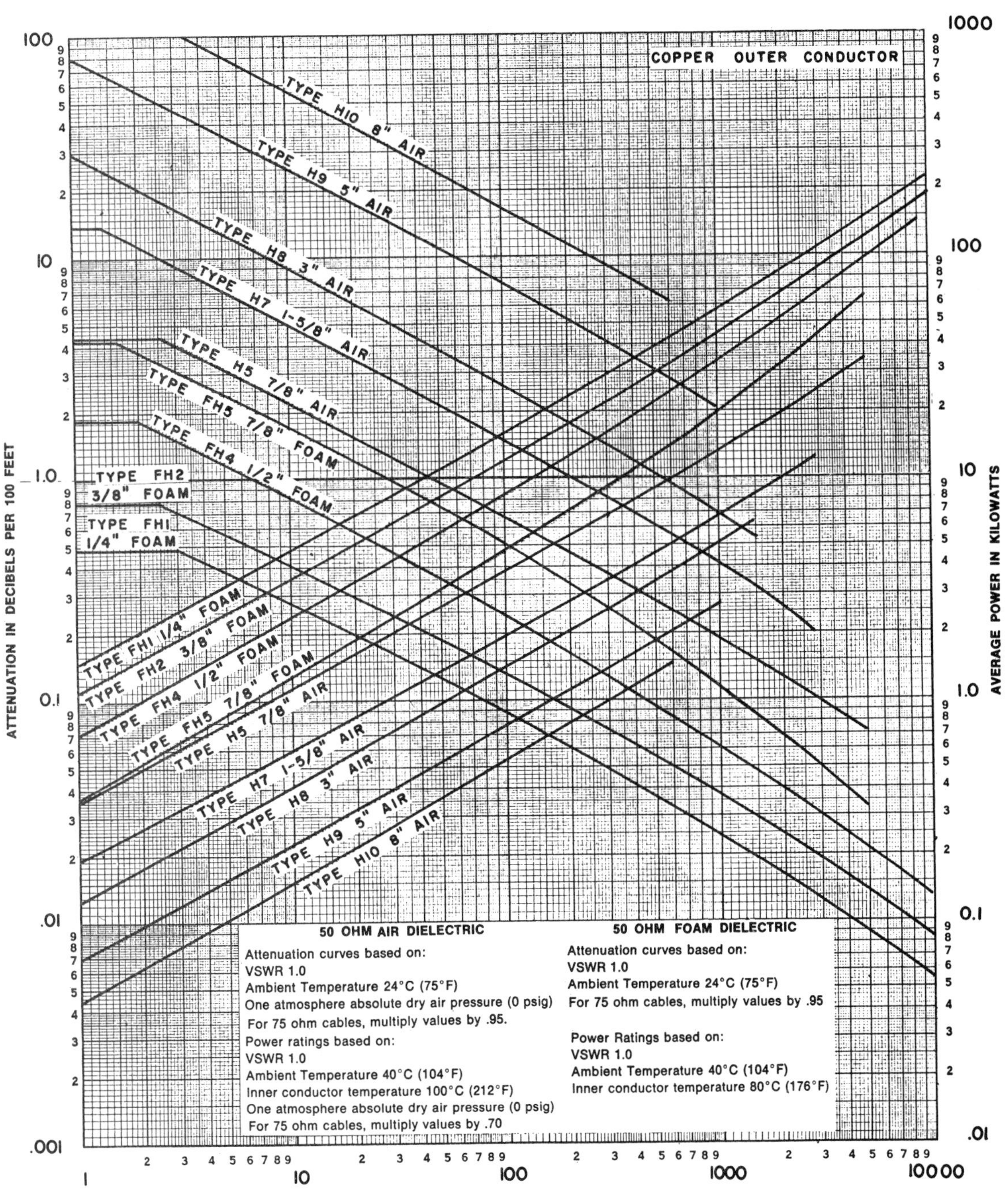

Courtesy of the Andrew Corp.

50 OHM STYROFLEX®CABLE ATTENUATION VERSUS FREQUENCY

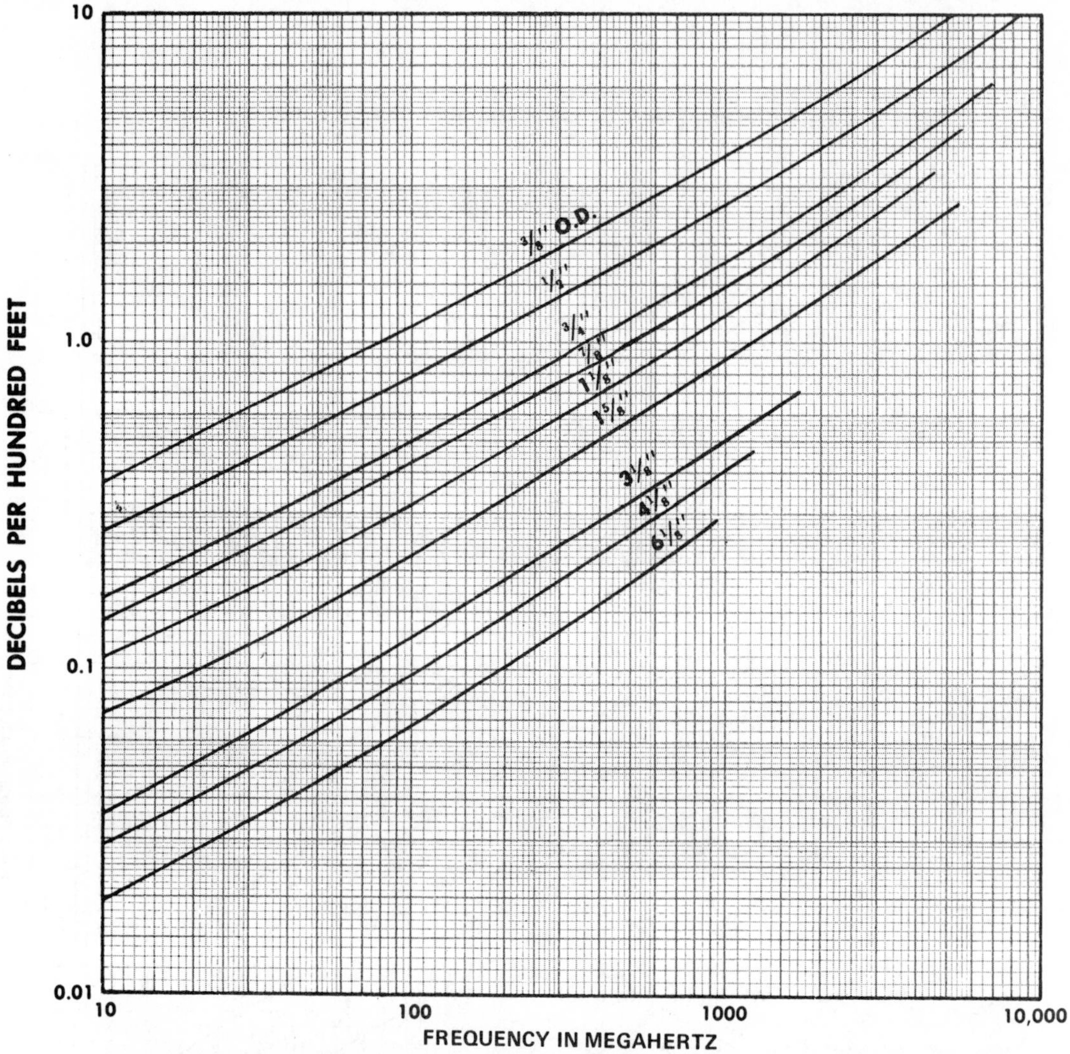

10
1.0
0.1
0.01
DECIBELS PER HUNDRED FEET
3/8" O.D.
1/2"
3/4"
7/8"
1 1/8"
1 5/8"
3 1/8"
4 1/8"
6 1/8"
10
100
1000
10,000
FREQUENCY IN MEGAHERTZ

TEMPERATURE-CORRECTION FACTOR ATTENUATION OF STYROFLEX®CABLE

The use of appropriate attenuation curves (based on 20°C) with a correction factor of 1% for each 5°C will enable accurate computation of the temperature-correction factor for a given cable.

1.20
1.10
1.00
0.90
0.80
0
CORRECTION FACTOR
–40 –30 –20 –10 0 10 20 30 40 50 60 70 80 90
TEMPERATURE DEGREES CENTIGRADE

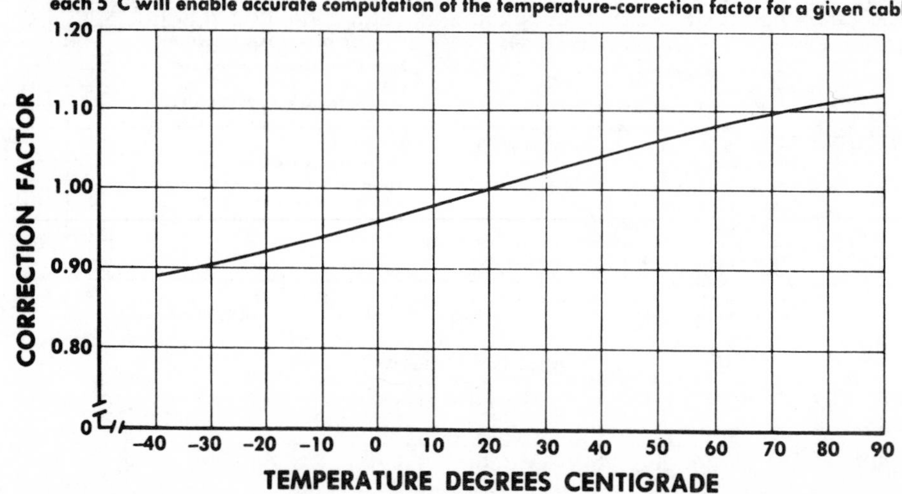

Courtesy of Phelps Dodge Electronic Products Corp.

50 OHM STYROFLEX® CABLE
AVERAGE POWER RATING IN AIR AT 40°C

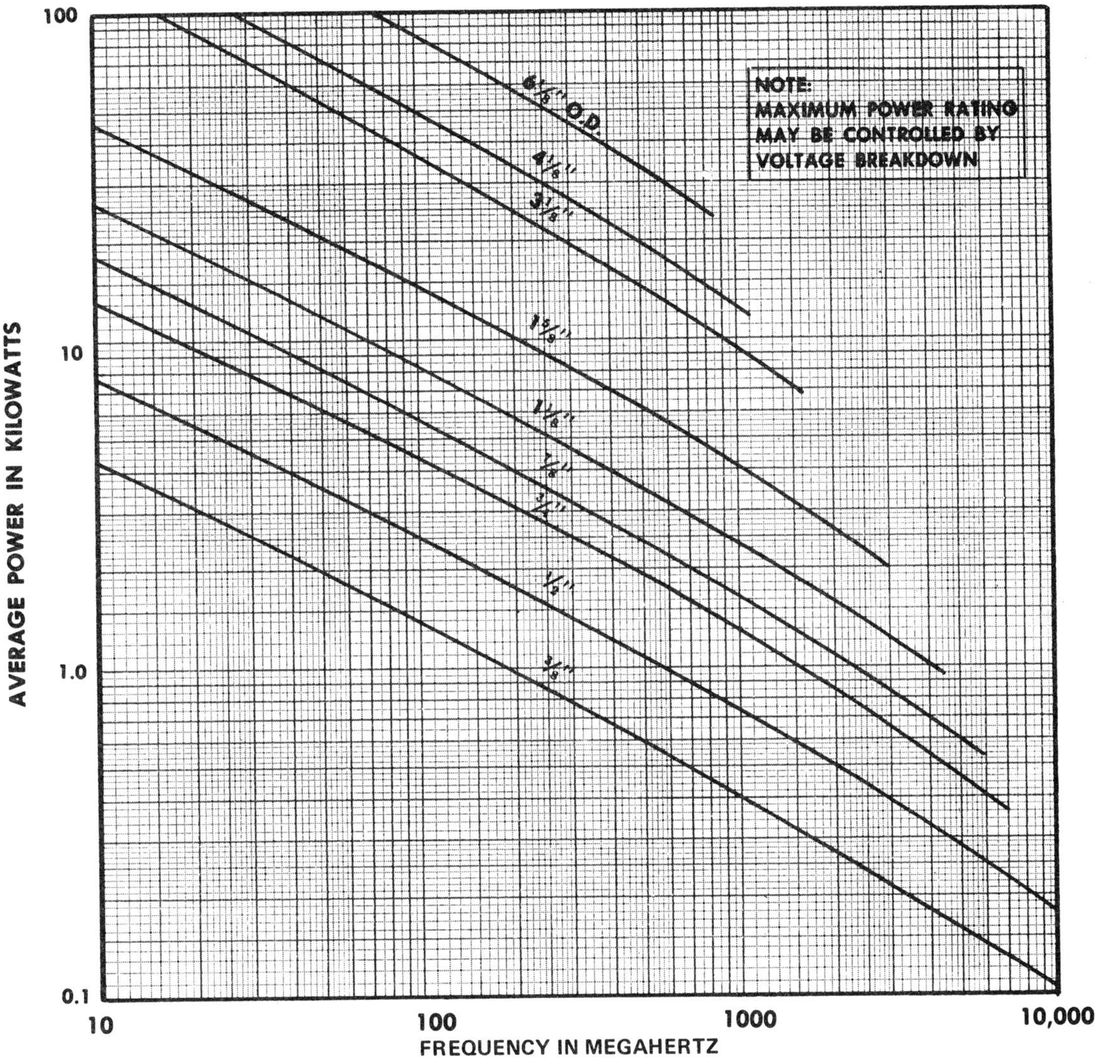

NOTE:
MAXIMUM POWER RATING
MAY BE CONTROLLED BY
VOLTAGE BREAKDOWN

6 1/8" O.D.
4 1/8"
3 1/8"
1 5/8"
1 1/8"
7/8"
3/4"
1/2"
3/8"

AVERAGE POWER IN KILOWATTS

100
10
1.0
0.1

10
100
1000
10,000

FREQUENCY IN MEGAHERTZ

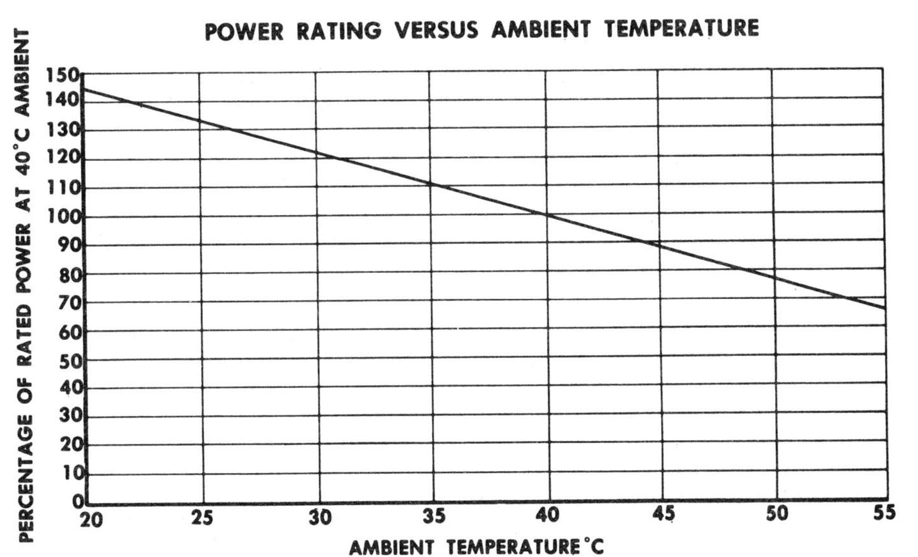

Courtesy of Phelps Dodge Electronic Products Corp.

RF Voltage Breakdown in 50 Ohm Air Filled Coaxial Line

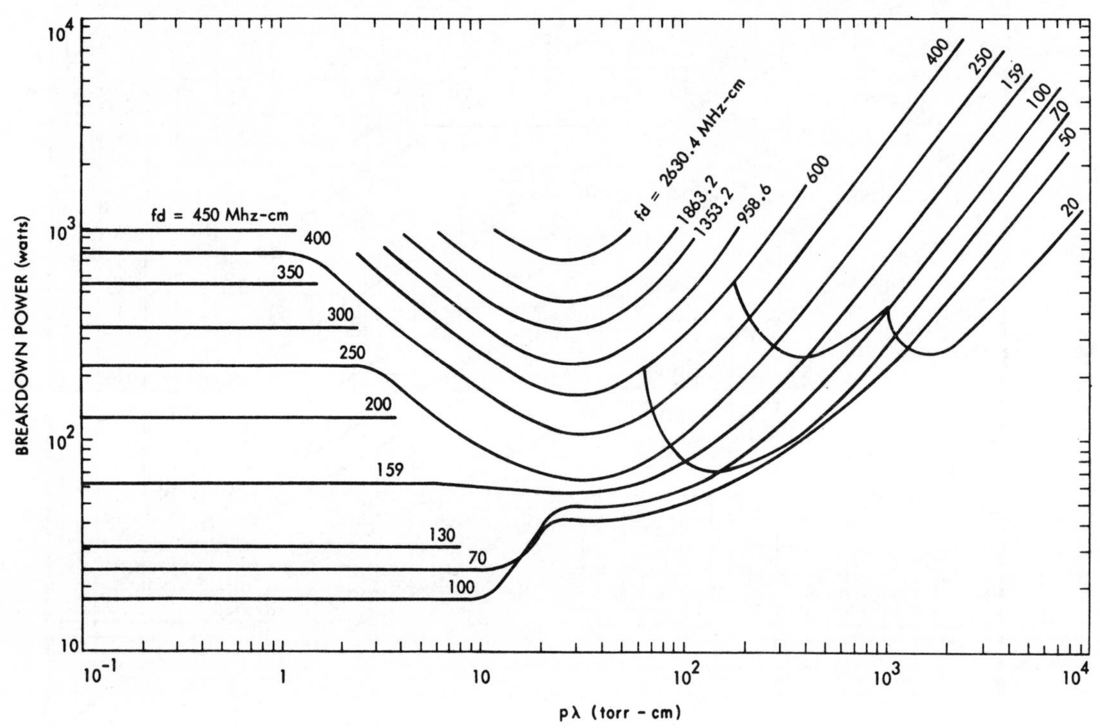

This plot shows the maximum power which can be transmitted in a 50-ohm air-filled coaxial transmission line for a very wide range of frequencies, dimensions, and pressures.

The somewhat unconventional notation used is as follows:

- d = distance in centimeters between inner and outer conductors.
- f = frequency in Megahertz
- λ = free-space wavelength corresponding to f.
- p = pressure in torr (One torr - one mm of mercury)

Additional details are given in the article by Richard Woo, "RF Voltage Breakdown in Coaxial Transmission Lines", Proc. IEEE (Letters), vol. 57, pp. 254-256, February 1969.

Courtesy of Richard Woo, Jet Propulsion Laboratory, Communications Research Elements Section.
Reference: "RF Voltage Breakdown in Coaxial Transmission Lines," Prsc. IEEE, Vol.57, pp. 254 - 256, February 1969.

Interface Dimensions of Type N Connectors

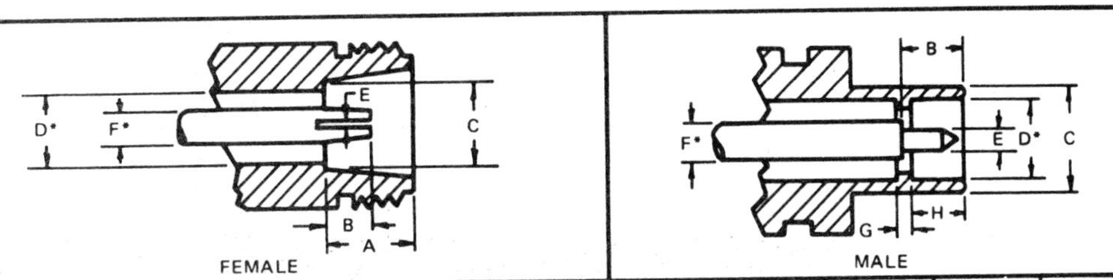

D* F* E C B A FEMALE

B F* E D* C G H MALE

Mfr. or Type	FEMALE				MALE				
	A	B	C	E	B	C	E	G	H
Narda Microwave fixed atten. (prior to 9-67)	0.359 ±0.002	0.194 ±0.007	0.323 ±0.001	0.068 ±0.001	0.223 ±0.009	0.323 ±0.001	0.067 ±0.001	0.026 ±0.002	0.179 ±0.006
Hewlett-Packard 806B slotted section	–	0.197 ±0.003	0.326 ±0.001	0.065 ±0.001	0.210 ±0.003	0.320 ±0.001	0.071 ±0.001	NA	NA
MIL-C-71 (prior to 1964)	0.359 ±0.003	0.197 ±0.016	0.318 ±0.001	0.071 ±0.001	0.223 ±0.009	0.328 ±0.002	0.065 +0.001 −0.002	0.026	0.197 ±0.002
Weinschel Engr. 1020-N prec. slotted line	–	0.207 +0.000 −0.003	0.318 ±0.001	0.065 ±0.001	0.207 +0.003 −0.000	0.315 ±0.001	0.065 ±0.001	NA	NA
Amphenol APC-N 131-10003, 4	0.359	0.207 +0.000 −0.003	0.316 min	0.071 min	0.207 +0.003 −0.000	0.316 max	0.066 max	NA	NA
MIL-C-39012 Class II	0.359 ±0.003	0.207 max	0.318 ±0.002	0.063 to 0.066	0.210 min	0.330 max	0.065 +0.001 −0.002	Optional	Optional
MIL-C-71 (after 1964)	0.359 ±0.003	0.197 ±0.010	0.318 ±0.002	0.071 ±0.001	0.223 ±0.010	0.328 ±0.002	0.065 +0.001 −0.002	0.026	0.197 ±0.002
Narda Microwave Precision	0.359 ±0.003	0.207 +0.000 −0.003	0.318 +0.002 −0.001	0.067 ±0.001	0.207 +0.003 −0.000	0.315 ±0.001	0.065 ±0.001	NA	NA
PRD 215 slotted line	0.359 ±0.002	0.197 ±0.005	0.316 +0.004 −0.000	0.067	0.2225 ±0.0025	0.328 ±0.002	0.065 +0.000 −0.002	0.026 ±0.003	0.197 ±0.002
General Radio 900-QNP, QNJ	0.359	0.206 +0.000 −0.003	0.318 ±0.001	0.065	0.208 +0.004 −0.000	0.318	0.065 ±0.0005	NA	NA
Alford Mfg. Co. Type NB/P	0.359 ±0.002	0.207 +0.000 −0.002	0.318 ±0.002	0.0650 ±0.0005	0.2075 +0.0020 −0.0000	0.328 ±0.002	0.0650 ±0.0005	NA	NA
Alford Mfg. Co. Type NR	0.359 ±0.002	0.213 +0.002 −0.000	0.318 ±0.001	0.0650 ±0.0005	0.206 +0.000 −0.002	0.3280 ±0.0005	0.0650 ±0.0005	0.026 ±0.002	0.197 ±0.005
Alford Mfg. Co. Type NS	0.359 ±0.002	0.206 +0.000 −0.002	0.318 ±0.002	0.0650 ±0.0005	0.215 +0.002 −0.000	0.328 ±0.002	0.0650 ±0.0005	0.026 ±0.002	0.197 ±0.005
Alford Mfg. Co. Type NB/L	0.359 ±0.002	0.2068 +0.0000 −0.0010	0.318 ±0.002	0.0650 ±0.0005	0.2071 +0.0010 −0.0000	0.318 ±0.001	0.0650 ±0.0005	NA	NA
Alford Mfg. Co. Type NB/L	–	0.207 max	0.318 ±0.002	0.065 +0.001 −0.002	0.207 min	0.315 ±0.001	0.065 ±0.001	NA	NA

All dimensions in inches
NA = not applicable
*D&F are 0.276, 0.120 nominal (tolerances differ by mfr.)

Courtesy of Salvatore Ammirati, Narda Microwave Corporation, Plainview, N.Y.
Reference: Electronic Design 6, March 14, 1968, pp.

109

Interface Compatibility of Type N Connectors

Female \ Male	Narda fixed atten. (prior to 1967)	HP 806B slotted section	MIL-C-71 (prior to 1964)	Weinschel 1020-N slotted line	Amphenol APC-N 131-10003	MIL-C-39012 Class II	MIL-C-71 (after 1964)	Narda precision	PRD 215 slotted line	General Radio 900-QNP	Alford NB/P	Alford NR	Alford NS	Alford NB/L	HP 816A slotted section
Narda fixed atten. (prior to 9-67)															
HP 806B slotted section		■													
MIL-C-71 (prior to 1964)				■	■	■		■		■	■	■			
Weinschel 1020-N slotted line											■	■			
Amphenol APC-N 131-10004											■	■			
MIL-C-29012 Class II		■									■	■			
MIL-C-71 (after 1964)											■	■			
Narda precision											■	■			
PRD 215 slotted line															
General Radio 900-QNJ												■			
Alford NB/P												■			
Alford NR	■	■	■	■	■	■	■	■		■	■	■	■	■	■
Alford NS												■			
Alford NB/L												■			■
HP 816A slotted section															

Mechanically possible: blank

Destructive interference possible: ■

Courtesy of Salvatore Ammirati, Narda Microwave Corporation, Plainview, N.Y.
Reference: Electronic Design 6, March 14, 1968, pp.

COAXIAL DISCONTINUITY CAPACITY STEP ON INNER CONDUCTOR

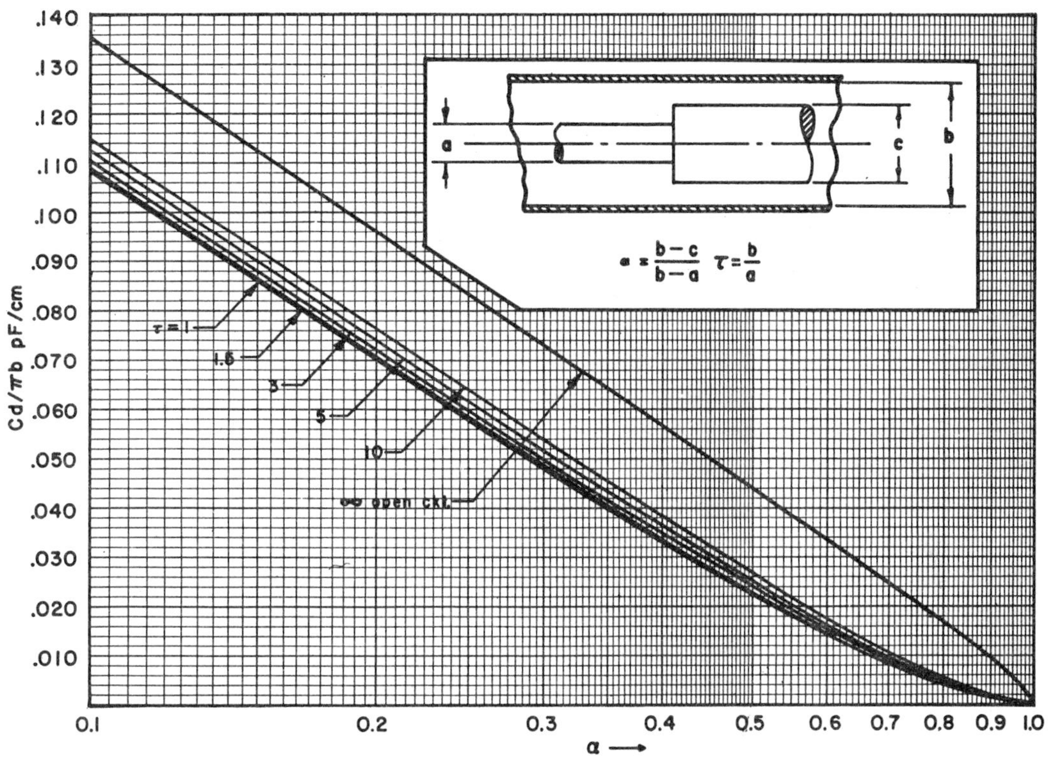

COAXIAL DISCONTINUITY CAPACITY STEP ON OUTER CONDUCTOR

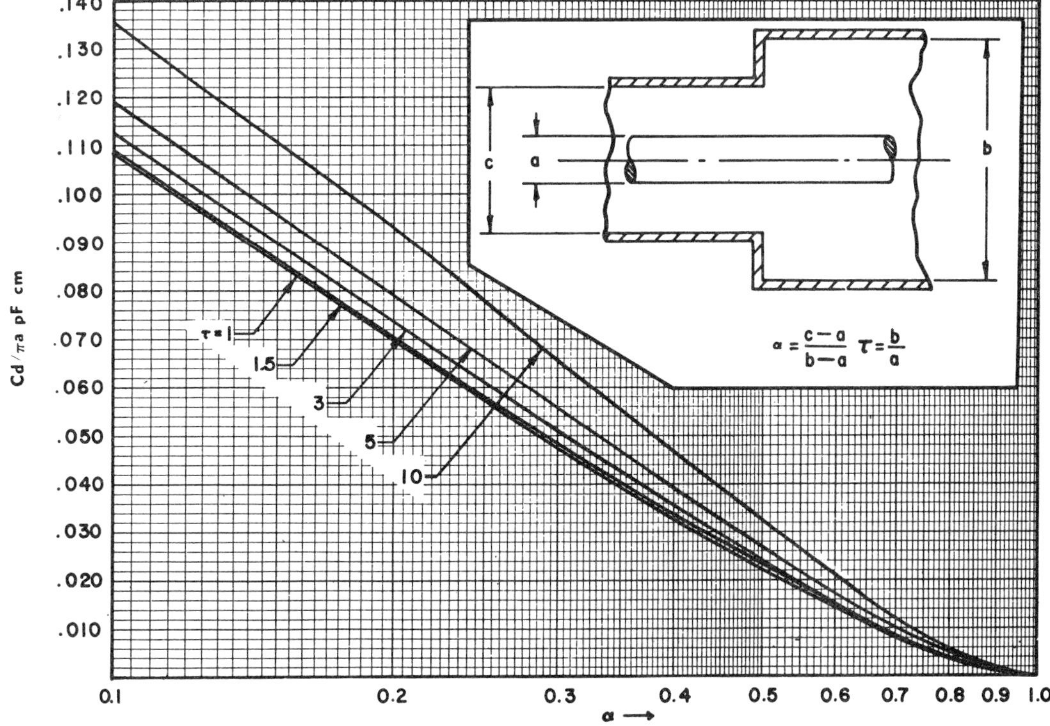

Courtesy of P. I. Somlo

DIAPHRAGM DISCONTINUITIES IN COAXIAL LINES

$C_{d_1}'(a, r)$ given by COAXIAL DISCONTINUITY CAPACITY I. $C_{d_2}'(a, r)$ given by COAXIAL DISCONTINUITY CAPACITY II.

Z_{OB} — C_d — Z_{OB}

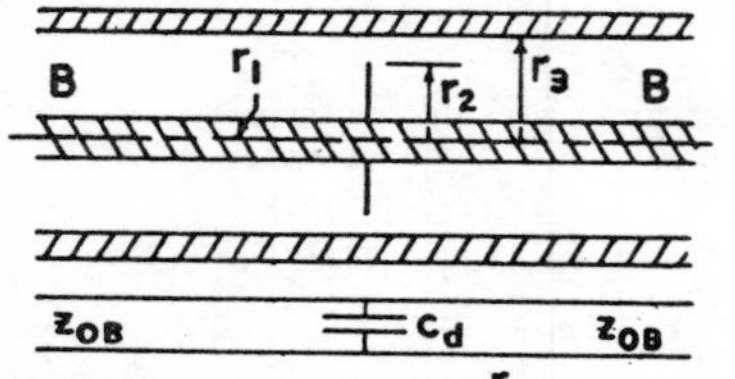

$C_d \cong 4\pi r_3 C'_{d1}(a/b, r_3/r_1)$
$a = r_3 - r_2$; $b = r_3 - r_1$

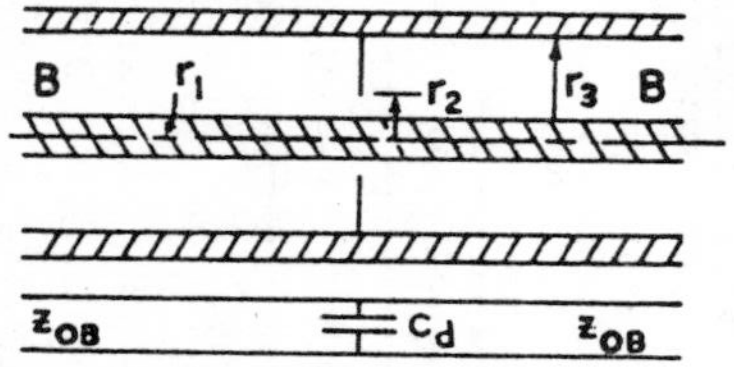

Z_{OB} — C_d — Z_{OB}

$C_d \cong 4\pi r_1 C'_{d2}(a/b, r_3/r_1)$
$a = r_2 - r_1$; $b = r_3 - r_1$

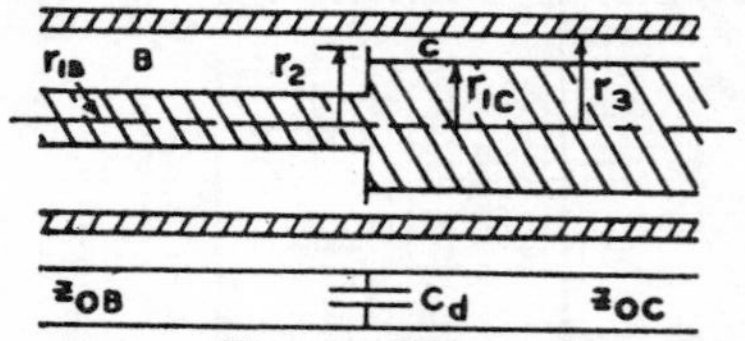

Z_{OB} — C_d — Z_{OC}

$C_d \cong 2\pi r_3 \left[C'_{d1}(a/b, r_3/r_{1B}) + C'_{d1}(a/c, r_3/r_{1C})\right]$
$a = r_3 - r_2$; $b = r_3 - r_{1B}$; $c = r_3 - r_{1C}$

Z_{OB} — C_d — Z_{OC}

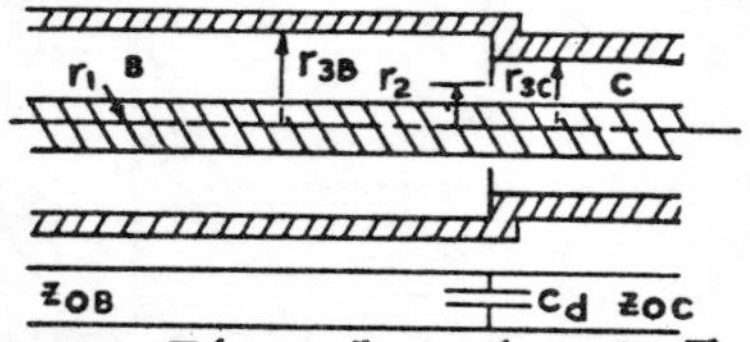

$C_d \cong 2\pi r_1 \left[C'_{d2}(a/b, r_{3B}/r_1) + C'_{d2}(a/c, r_{3C}/r_1)\right]$
$a = r_2 - r_1$; $b = r_{3B} - r_1$; $c = r_{3C} - r_1$

Z_{OB} — C_{dB} — Z_{OA} — C_{dC} — Z_{OC}

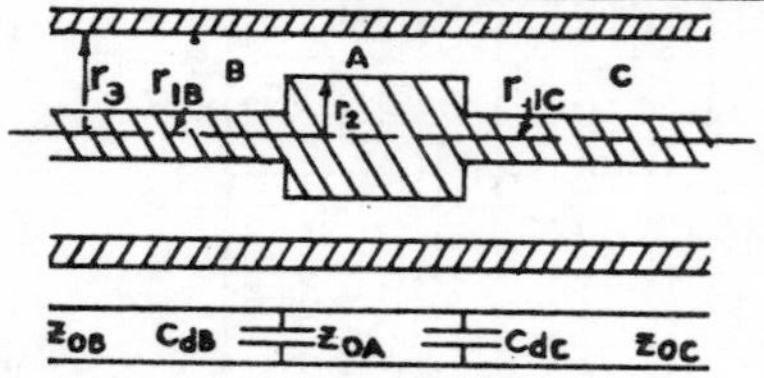

$C_{dB} \cong 2\pi r_3 \; C'_{d1}(a/b, r_3/r_{1B})$
$C_{dC} \cong 2\pi r_3 \; C'_{d1}(a/c, r_3/r_{1C})$
$a = r_3 - r_2$; $b = r_3 - r_{1B}$; $c = r_3 - r_{1C}$

Z_{OB} — C_{dB} — Z_{OA} — C_{dC} — Z_{OC}

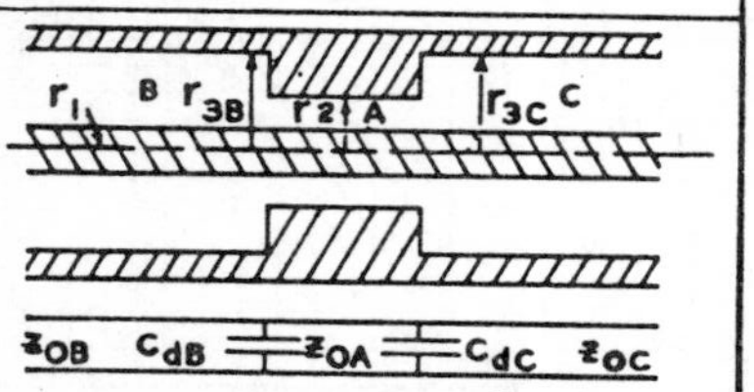

$C_{dB} \cong 2\pi r_1 \; C'_{d2}(a/b, r_{3B}/r_1)$
$C_{dC} \cong 2\pi r_1 \; C'_{d2}(a/c, r_{3C}/r_1)$
$a = r_2 - r_1$; $b = r_{3B} - r_1$; $c = r_{3C} - r_1$

DIELECTRIC DISCONTINUITIES IN COAXIAL LINES

$C_{d_1}'(a, r)$ given by COAXIAL DISCONTINUITY CAPACITY I. $C_{d_2}'(a, r)$ given by COAXIAL DISCONTINUITY CAPACITY II.

Z_{OA} — C_d — Z_{OB}

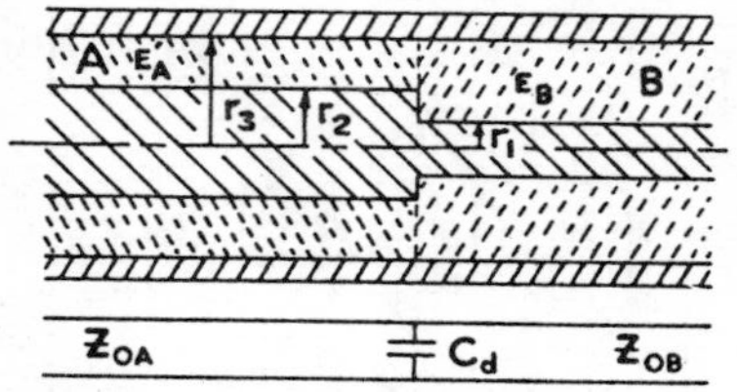

$C_d \cong 2\pi r_3 \epsilon'_B C'_{d1}(a/b, r_3/r_1)$
$a = r_3 - r_2$; $b = r_3 - r_1$

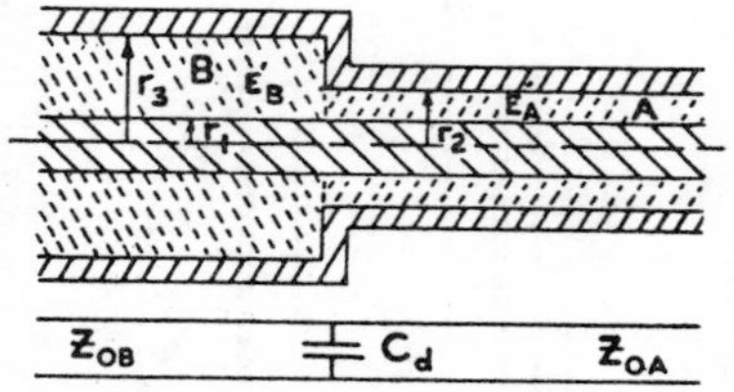

Z_{OB} — C_d — Z_{OA}

$C_d \cong 2\pi r_1 \epsilon'_B C'_{d2}(a/b, r_3/r_1)$
$a = r_2 - r_1$; $b = r_3 - r_1$

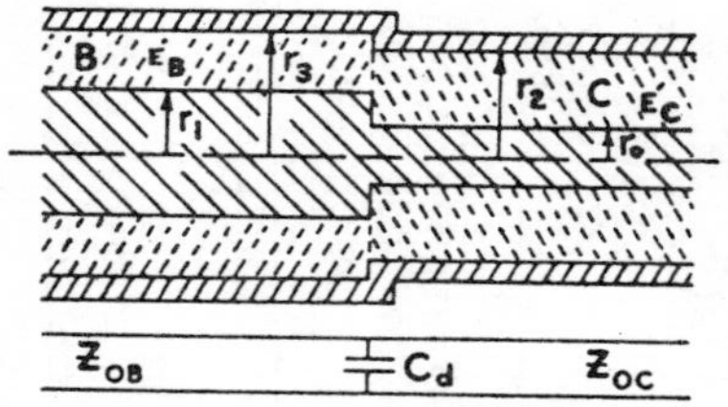

Z_{OB} — C_d — Z_{OC}

$C_d \cong 2\pi r_1 \epsilon'_B C'_{d2}(a/b, r_3/r_1) + 2\pi r_2 \epsilon'_C C'_{d1}(a/c, r_2/r_0)$
$a = r_2 - r_1$; $b = r_3 - r_1$; $c = r_2 - r_0$

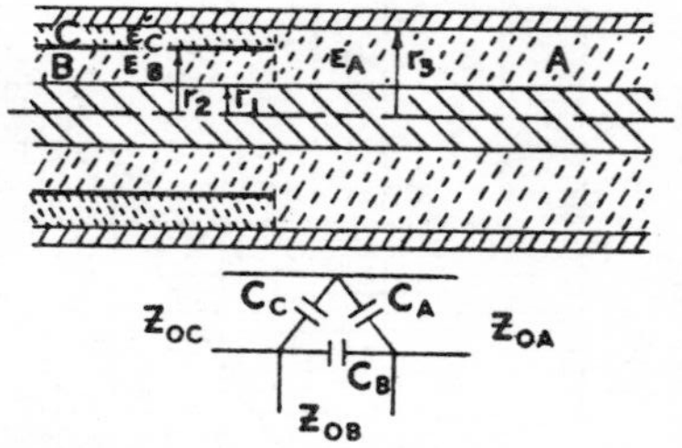

Z_{OC} — C_C, C_A, C_B — Z_{OA}, Z_{OB}

VALUES OF C_A, C_B, C_C APPROXIMATELY ϵ'_A TIMES VALUES FROM FIG. 12

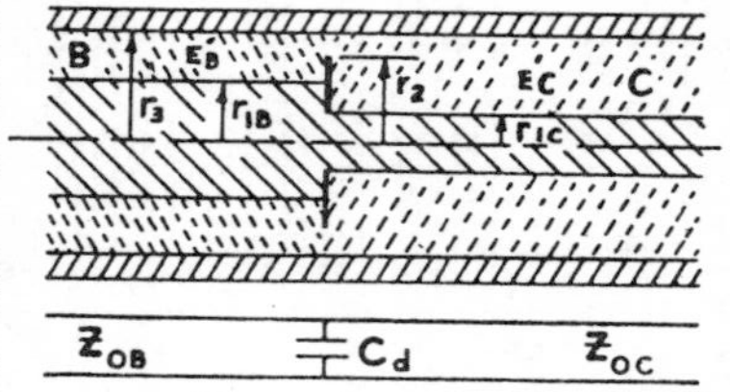

Z_{OB} — C_d — Z_{OC}

$C_d \cong 2\pi r_3 \left[\epsilon'_B C'_{d1}(a/b, r_3/r_{1B}) + \epsilon'_C C'_{d1}(a/c, r_3/r_{1C})\right]$
$a = r_3 - r_2$; $b = r_3 - r_{1B}$; $c = r_3 - r_{1C}$

Z_{OB} — C_d — Z_{OC}

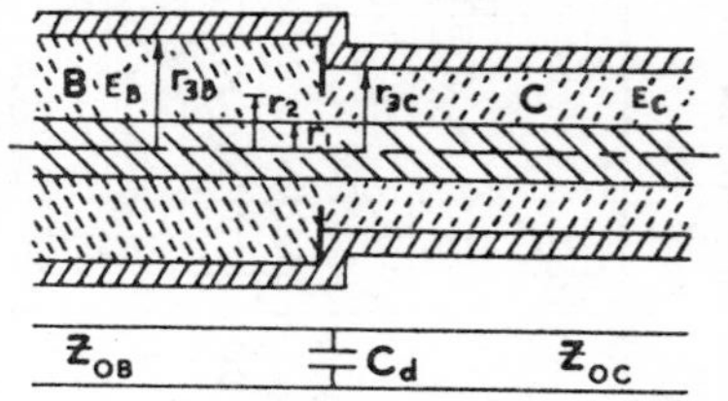

$C_d \cong 2\pi r_1 \left[\epsilon'_B C'_{d2}(a/b, r_{3B}/r_1) + \epsilon'_C C'_{d2}(a/c, r_{3C}/r_1)\right]$
$a = r_2 - r_1$; $b = r_{3B} - r_1$; $c = r_{3C} - r_1$

DESIGN CHART FOR QUARTER-WAVE STUBS IN COAXIAL LINE

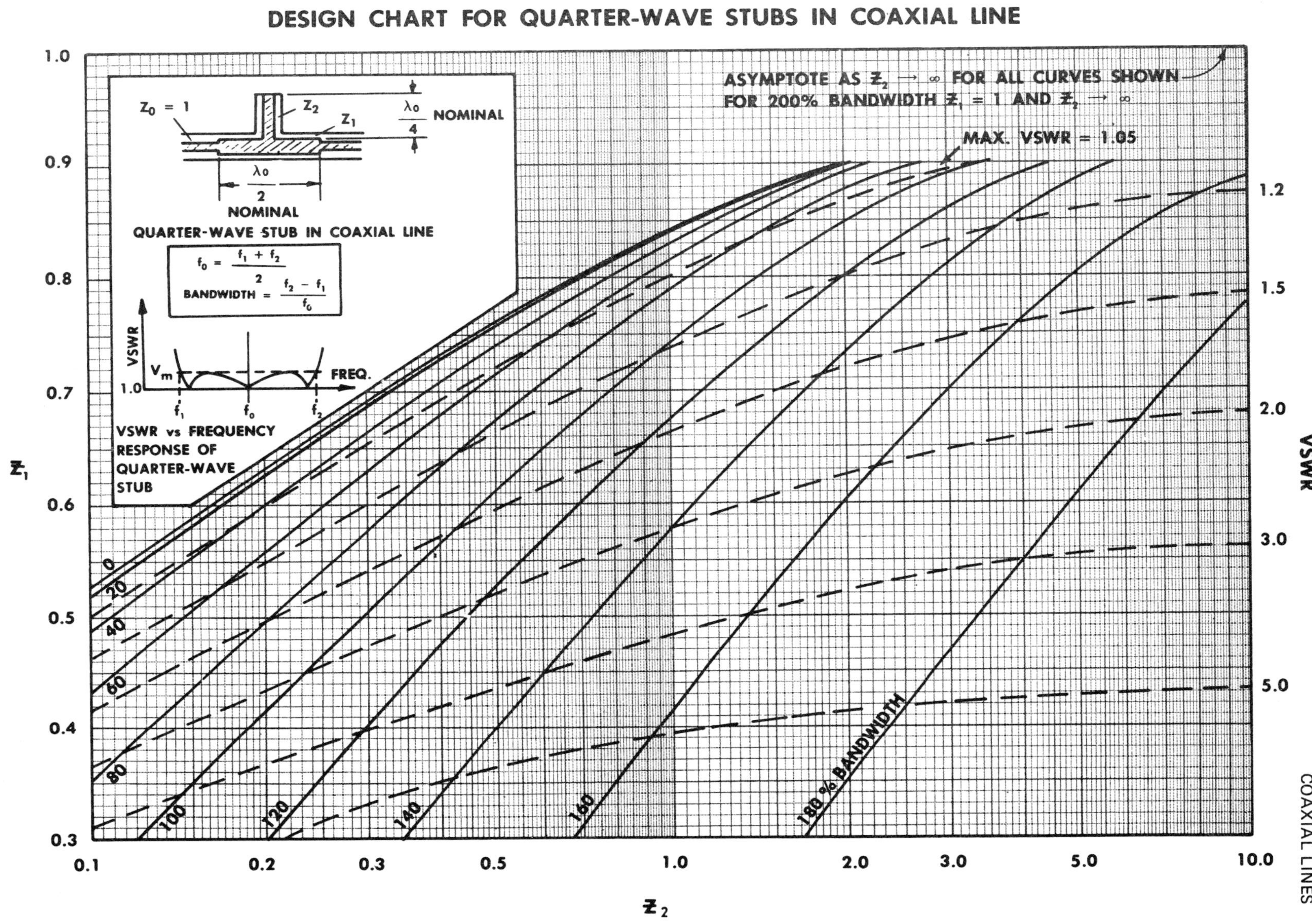

Courtesy of Leo Young, Stanford Research Institute, Menlo Park, Cal. Work supported by the U. S. Army Signal Research and Development Laboratory, Fort Monmouth, N. J. under Contract DA36-039 sc-87398.

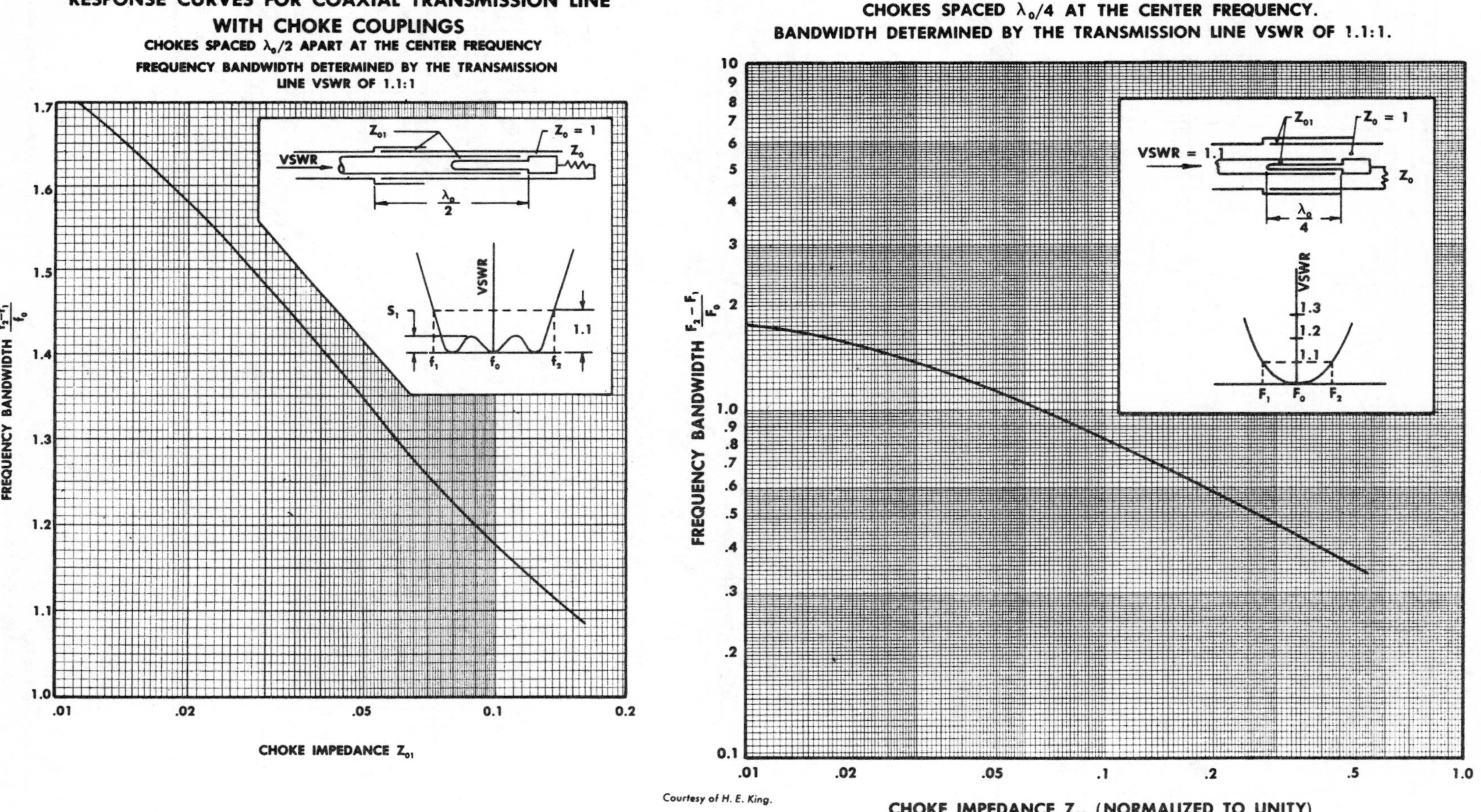
RESPONSE CURVES FOR COAXIAL TRANSMISSION LINE
WITH CHOKE COUPLINGS
CHOKES SPACED λ0/2 APART AT THE CENTER FREQUENCY
FREQUENCY BANDWIDTH DETERMINED BY THE TRANSMISSION
LINE VSWR OF 1.1:1
VSWR
Z01
Z0 = 1
Z0
λ0/2
S1
f1
f0
f2
1.1
FREQUENCY BANDWIDTH (f2−f1)/f0
CHOKE IMPEDANCE Z01
FREQUENCY BANDWIDTH CURVE OF COAXIAL TRANSMISSION LINE
WITH CHOKE COUPLINGS
CHOKES SPACED λ0/4 AT THE CENTER FREQUENCY.
BANDWIDTH DETERMINED BY THE TRANSMISSION LINE VSWR OF 1.1:1.
VSWR = 1.1
Z01
Z0 = 1
Z0
λ0/4
VSWR
1.3
1.2
1.1
F1
F0
F2
FREQUENCY BANDWIDTH (F2 − F1)/F0
CHOKE IMPEDANCE Z01 (NORMALIZED TO UNITY)
Courtesy of H. E. King.

STRIP TRANSMISSION LINES

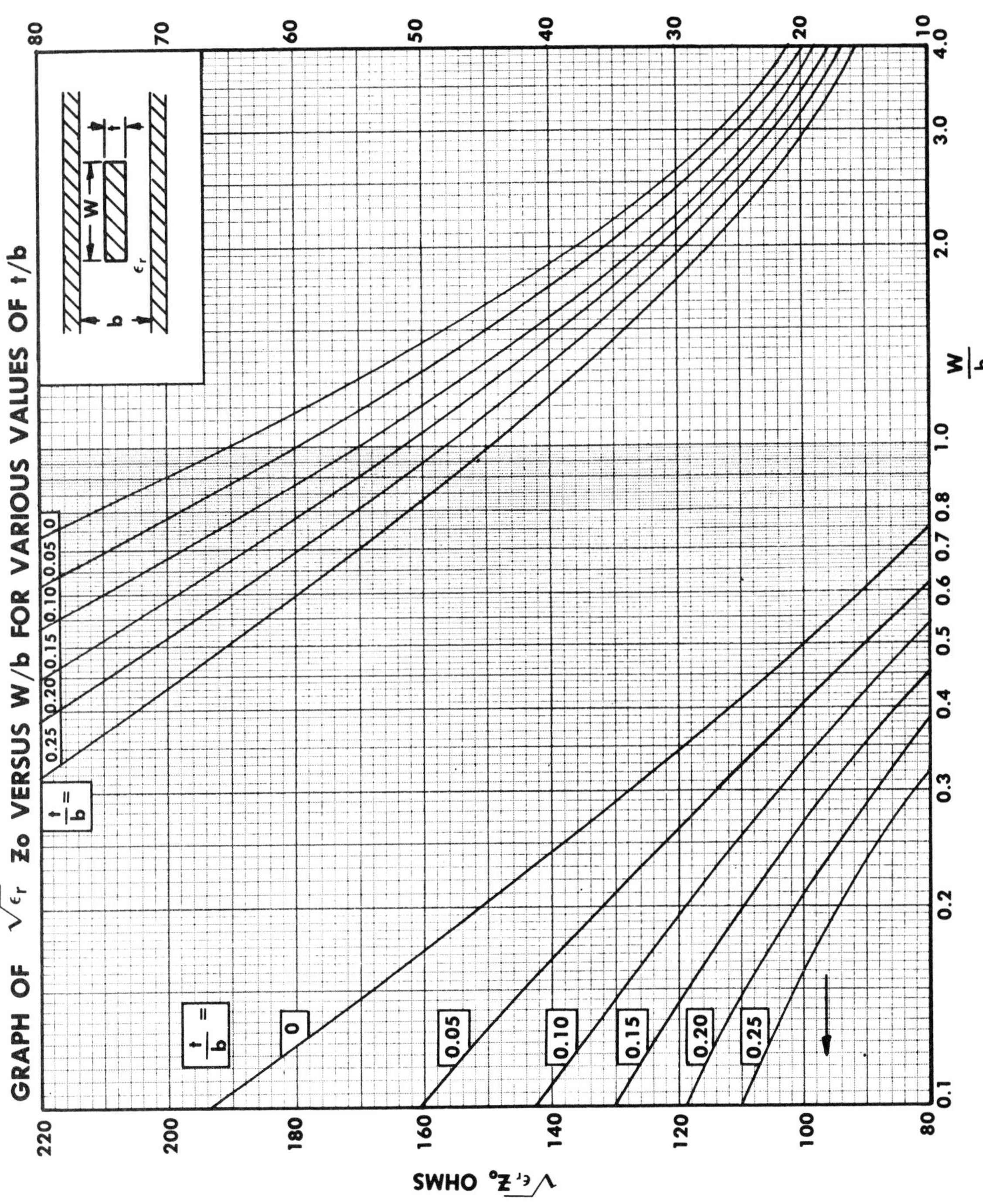

Courtesy of U. S. Army Electronics Research and Development Laboratory, Final Report on U. S. Army Contract DA36-039 sc-63232, Strip Transmission Lines and Components, Feb. 1957, Stanford Research Institute.

t/b VS W/b WITH $\sqrt{\epsilon_r}Z_o\Omega$ AS A PARAMETER

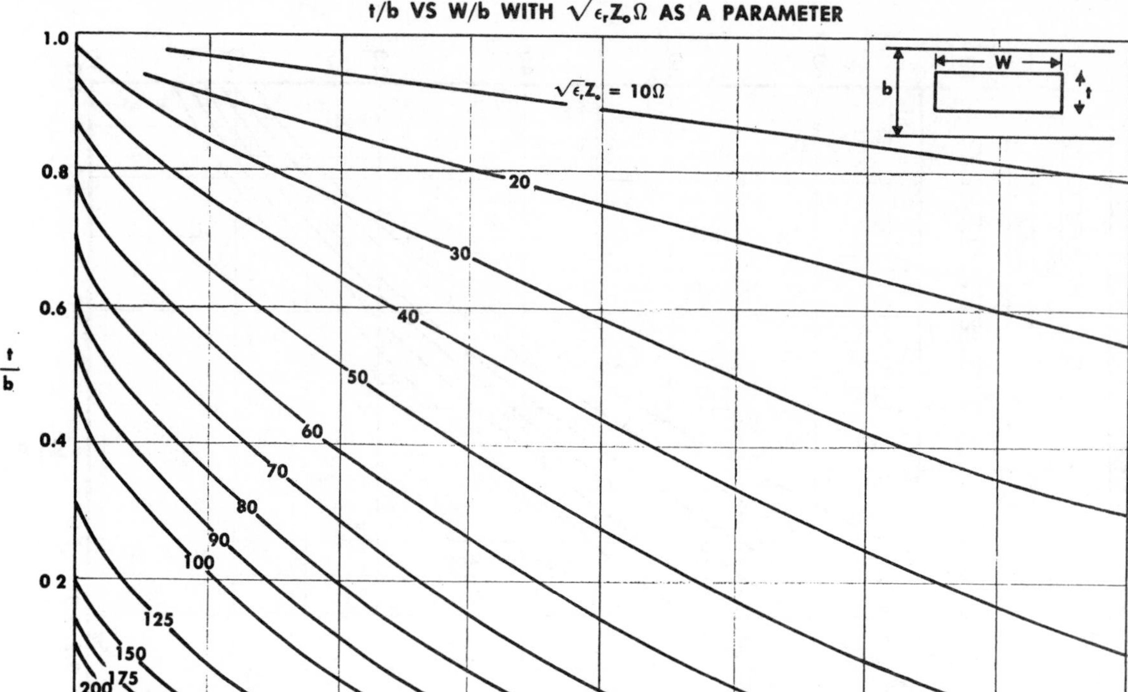

THEORETICAL Q OF COPPER-SHIELDED STRIP-LINE IN A DIELECTRIC MEDIUM

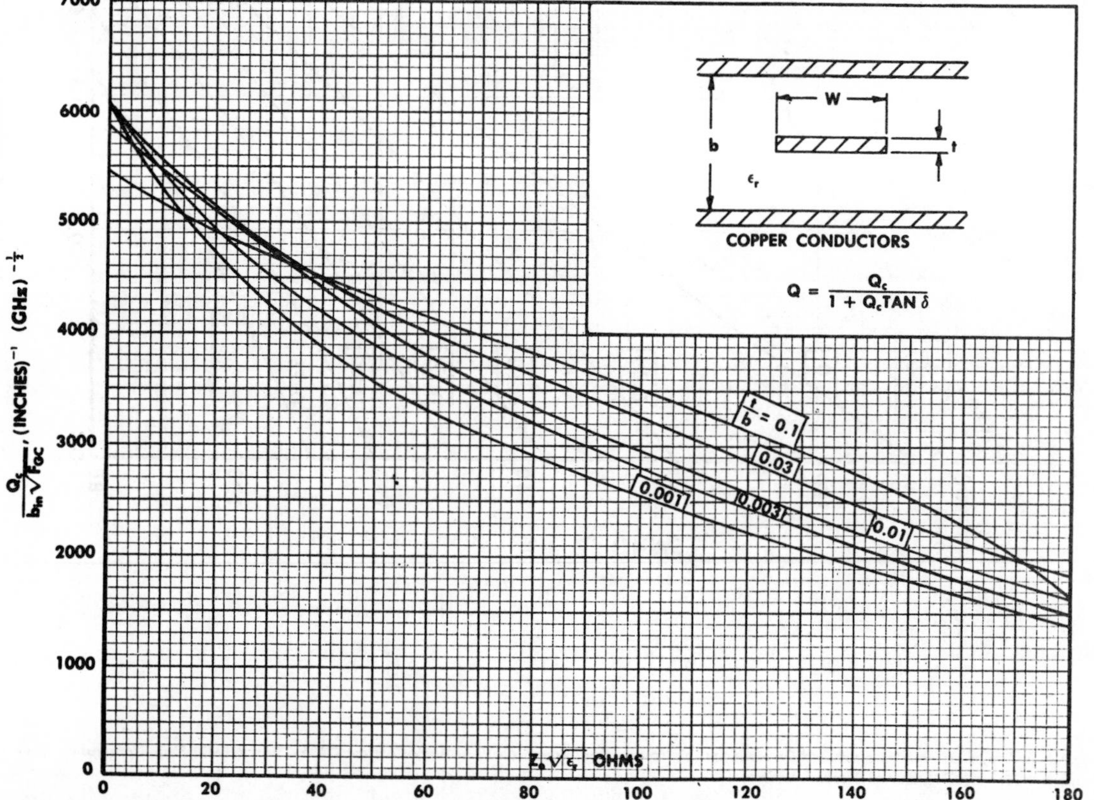

Top: R.H.T. Bates, from "The Characteristic Impedance of the Shielded Slab Line," PGMTT Transactions, January 1956.
Bottom: Courtesy of U. S. Army Electronics Research and Development Laboratory, Final Report on U. S. Army Contract DA36-039 sc-63232, Strip Transmission Lines and Components, Feb. 1957, Stanford Research Institute.

EQUIVALENCE BETWEEN CONDUCTORS OF RECTANGULAR AND CIRCULAR CROSS SECTIONS

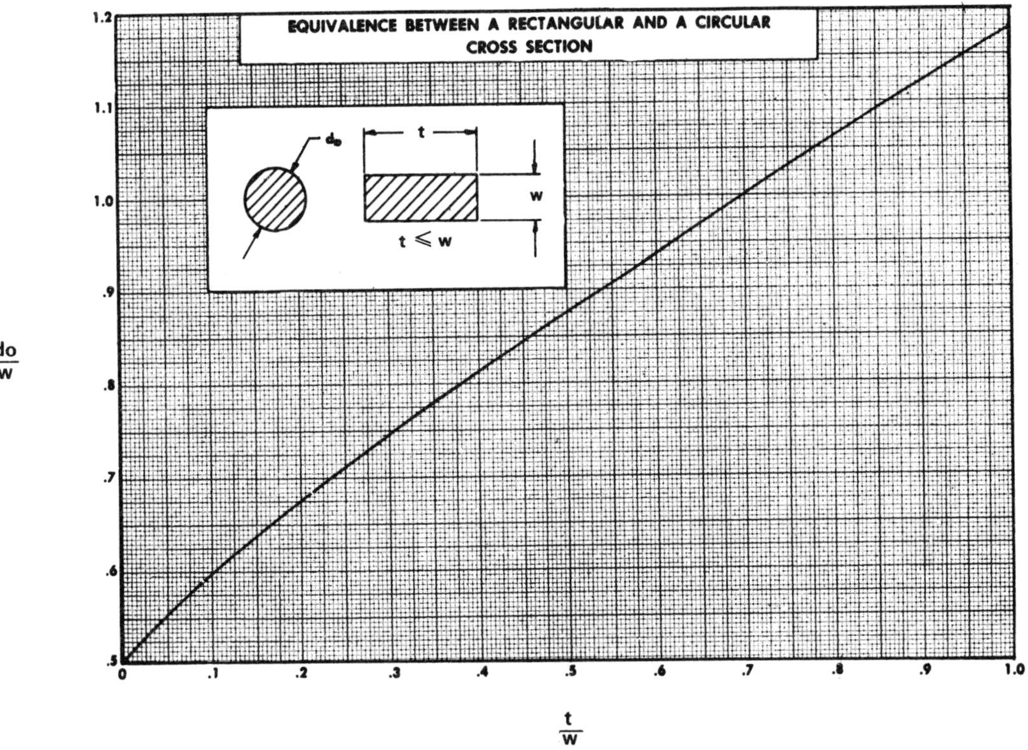

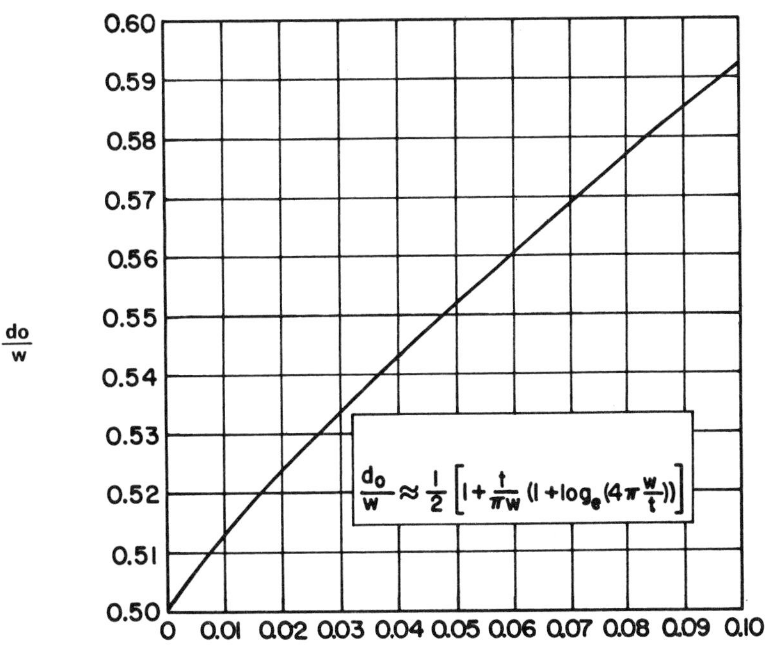

Courtesy of U. S. Army Electronics Research and Development Laboratory, Final Report on U. S. Army Contract DA-36-039 SC-63232, **Strip Transmission Lines and Components**, February 1967, Stanford Research Institute.

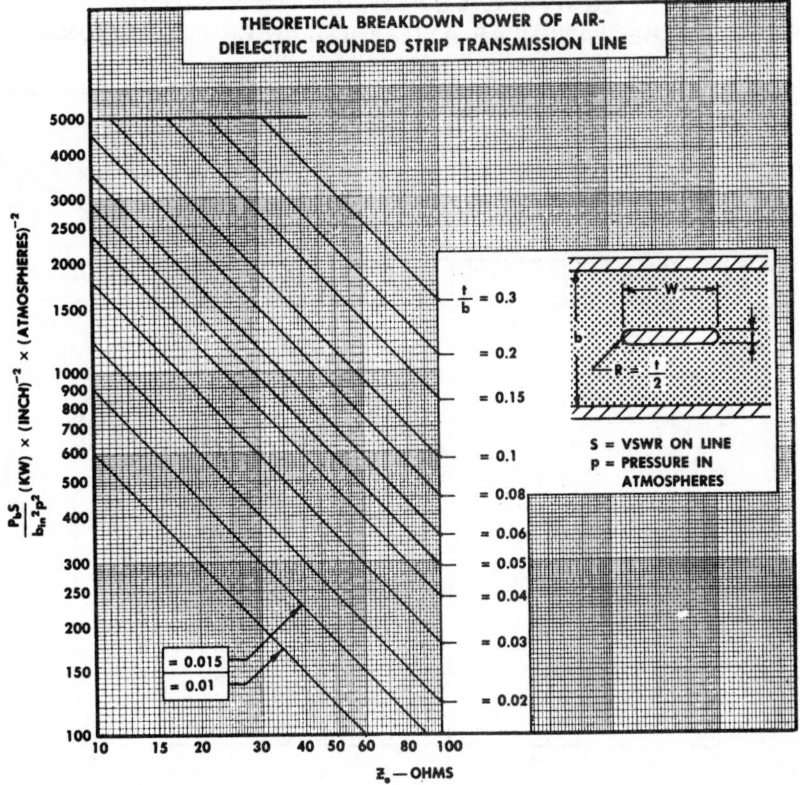

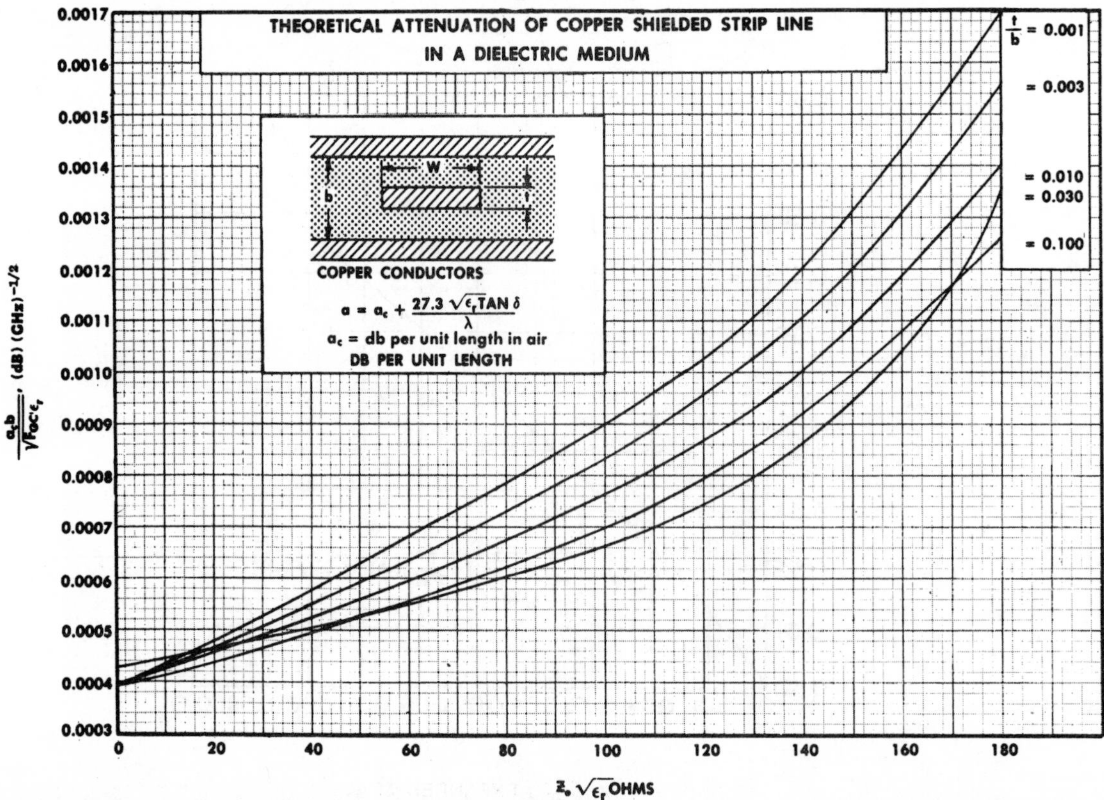

Courtesy of U. S. Army Electronics Research and Development Laboratory, Final Report on U. S. Army Contract DA 36-039 sc-63232, Strip Transmission Lines and Components, Feb. 1957, Stanford Research Institute.

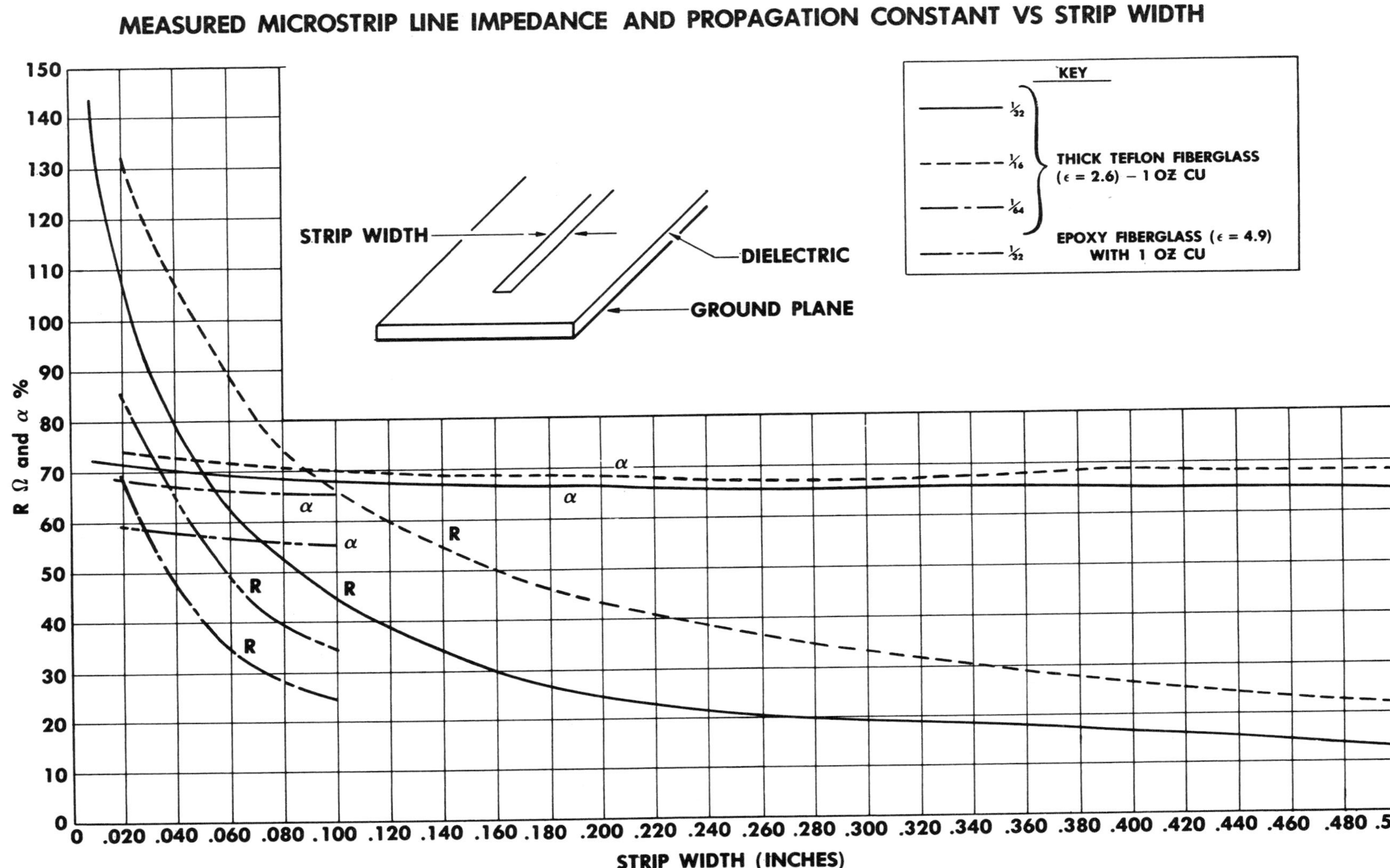

Courtesy of J. A. Kaiser, Diamond Ordnance Fuze Laboratories, Washington, D. C.

Microwave Printed Circuits MPC

Microwave printed circuit (strip) transmission line acts very much like the coaxial transmission line, having most of the same properties. The common conventional parameters are the equivalent electrical parameters of impedance, velocity and attention. The MPC transmission line shown in crossection below is formed by the printed conductor between two ground planes. It is assumed that the ground planes are flat, parallel to each other, and extend to infinity. However, mode suppression screws are usually located to limit the frequency range without higher order modes. The high density cross-linked polyethylene sheets are copper clad with 2-oz. copper and the material thickness is measured over the copper. Standard dimensions for 50 ohm transmission lines are given in table form with the recommended screw spacings and frequency limits. The maximum operating frequency completely free of higher order mode effects is a function of the size of the strip (z_0) and the distance to the mode suppression screws (d_2) as given in curve form for several different thickness MPC lines. The MPC Standard designation* MPC-125-2 means that the material is .125 thick with 2 oz. copper cladding.

*adopted at Bell Telephone Labs., Whippany, N. J.

MPC Limits for Standard 50-OHM Transmission Lines

Standard Designation	Material Thickness[1] (inches)	Copper Weight[2] (ounces)	Strip Width (inches)	Screw Spacing (inches) Long[3]	Screw Spacing (inches) Lat.[4]	Upper Frequency Limit[5] (GHz)
MPC-062-2	0.062	2	0.083 ± 0.0015	0.375	0.200	7.5
MPC-125-2	0.125	2	0.182 ± 0.003	0.375	0.300	5.0
MPC-187-2	0.187	2	0.280 ± 0.004	0.375	0.400	3.6
MPC-250-2	0.250	2	0.380 ± 0.005	0.375	0.500	2.8

[1] Material thickness measured over copper cladding.

[2] Copper thickness: 1 ounce, 0.0014 inch; 2 ounces, 0.0028 inch.

[3] Type 4-40 screws recommended.

[4] Lateral screw spacing measured from edge of strip to center of screw.

[5] Recommended for this lateral spacing from circuits. For higher frequency limits, the specified spacing should be reduced.

Courtesy of Bell Telephone Laboratories, Whippany, New Jersey

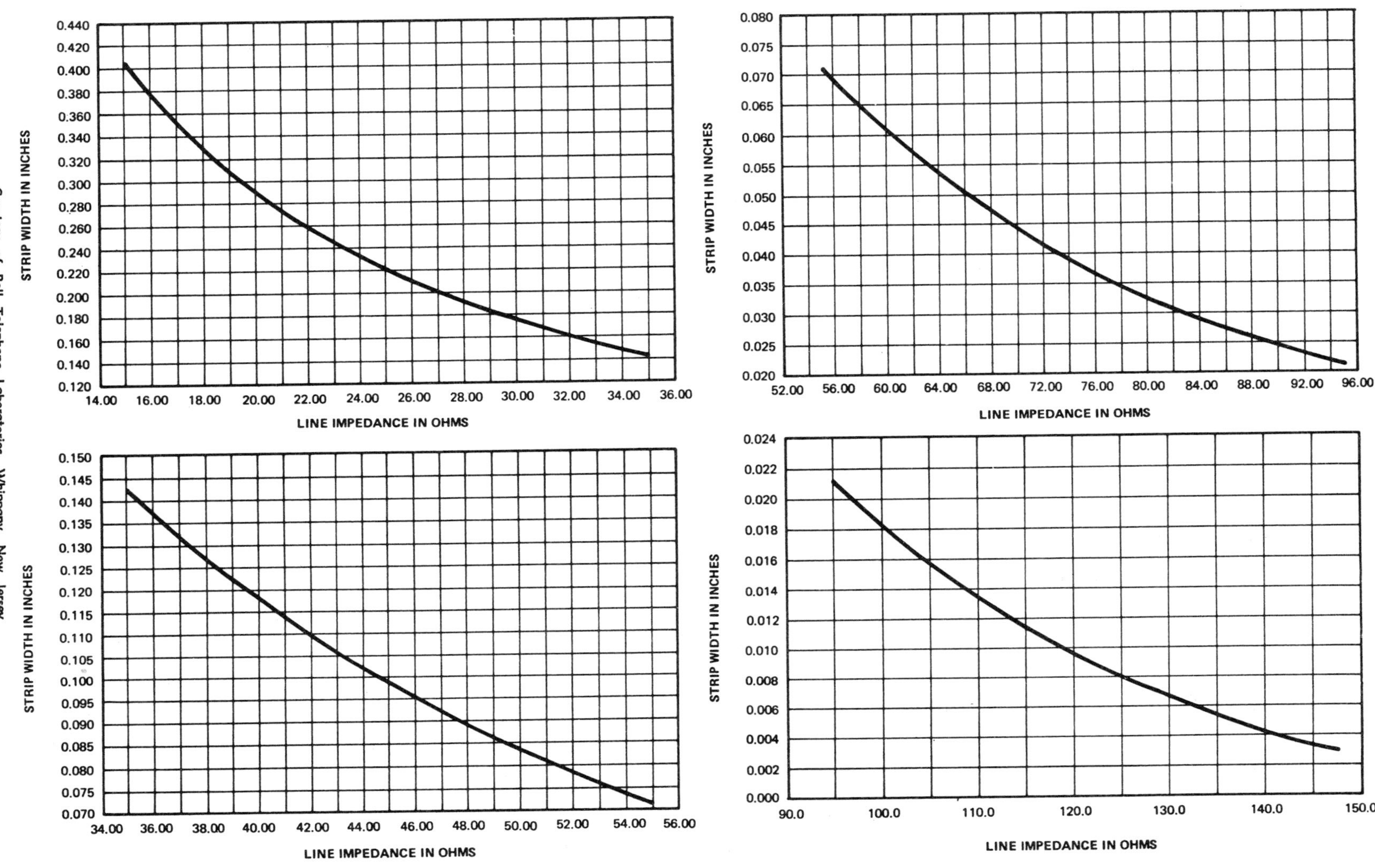

Courtesy of Bell Telephone Laboratories, Whippany, New Jersey

Strip Width vs Line Impedance for MPC - 125 - 2

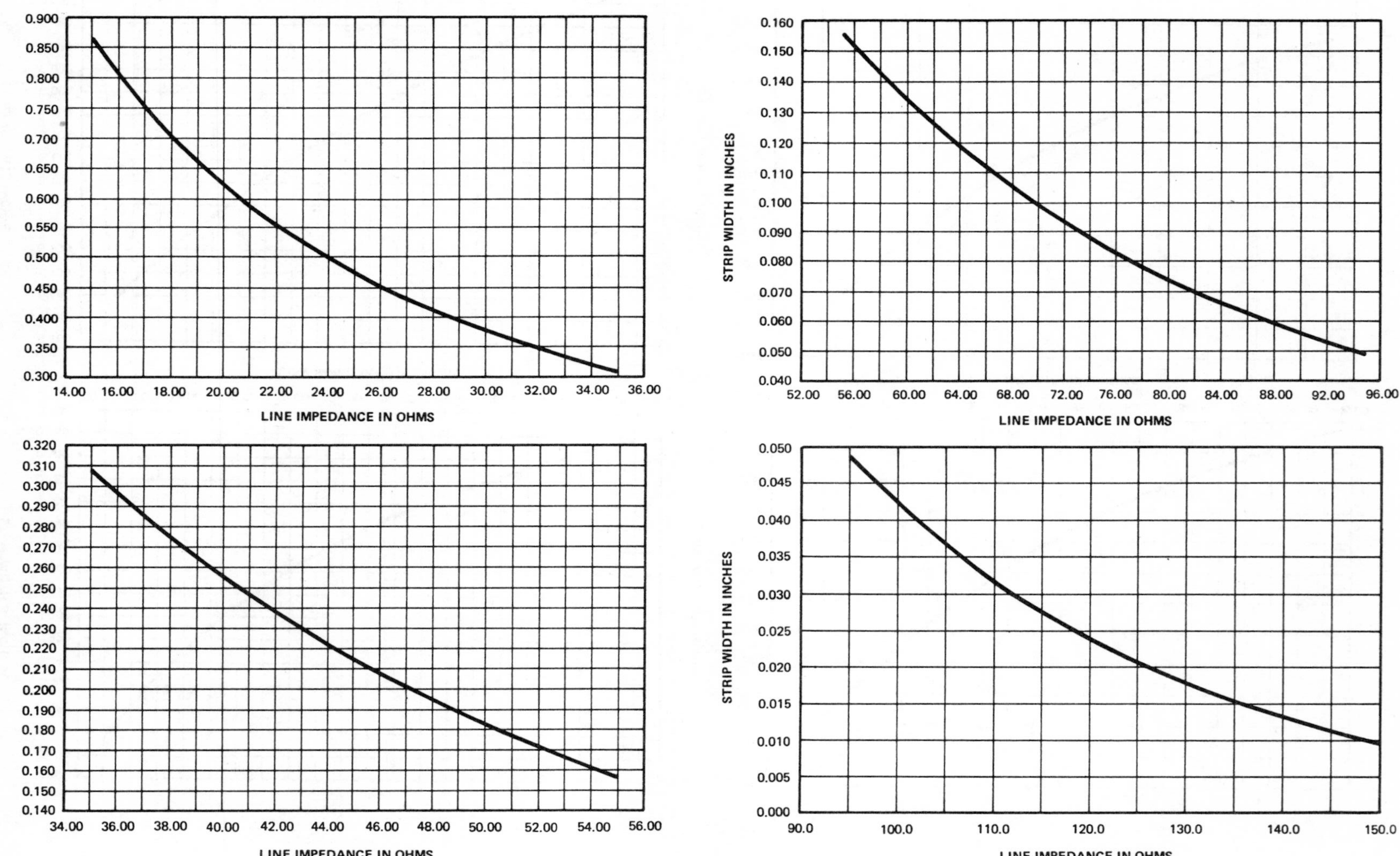

Courtesy of Bell Telephone Laboratories, Whippany, New Jersey

Strip Width vs Line Impedance for MPC - 187 - 2

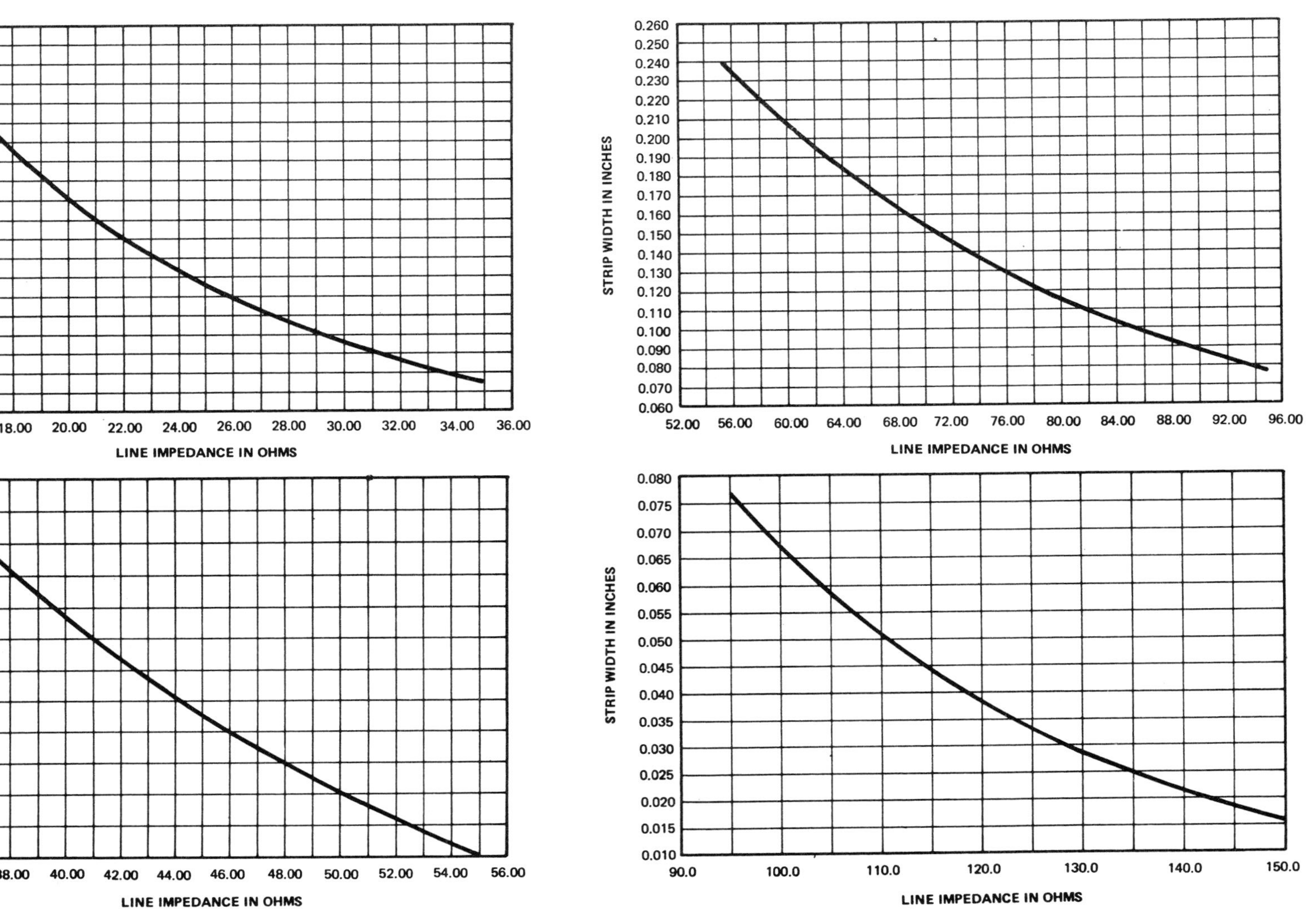

Courtesy of Bell Telephone Laboratories, Whippany, New Jersey

Strip Width vs Line Impedance for MPC - 250 - 2

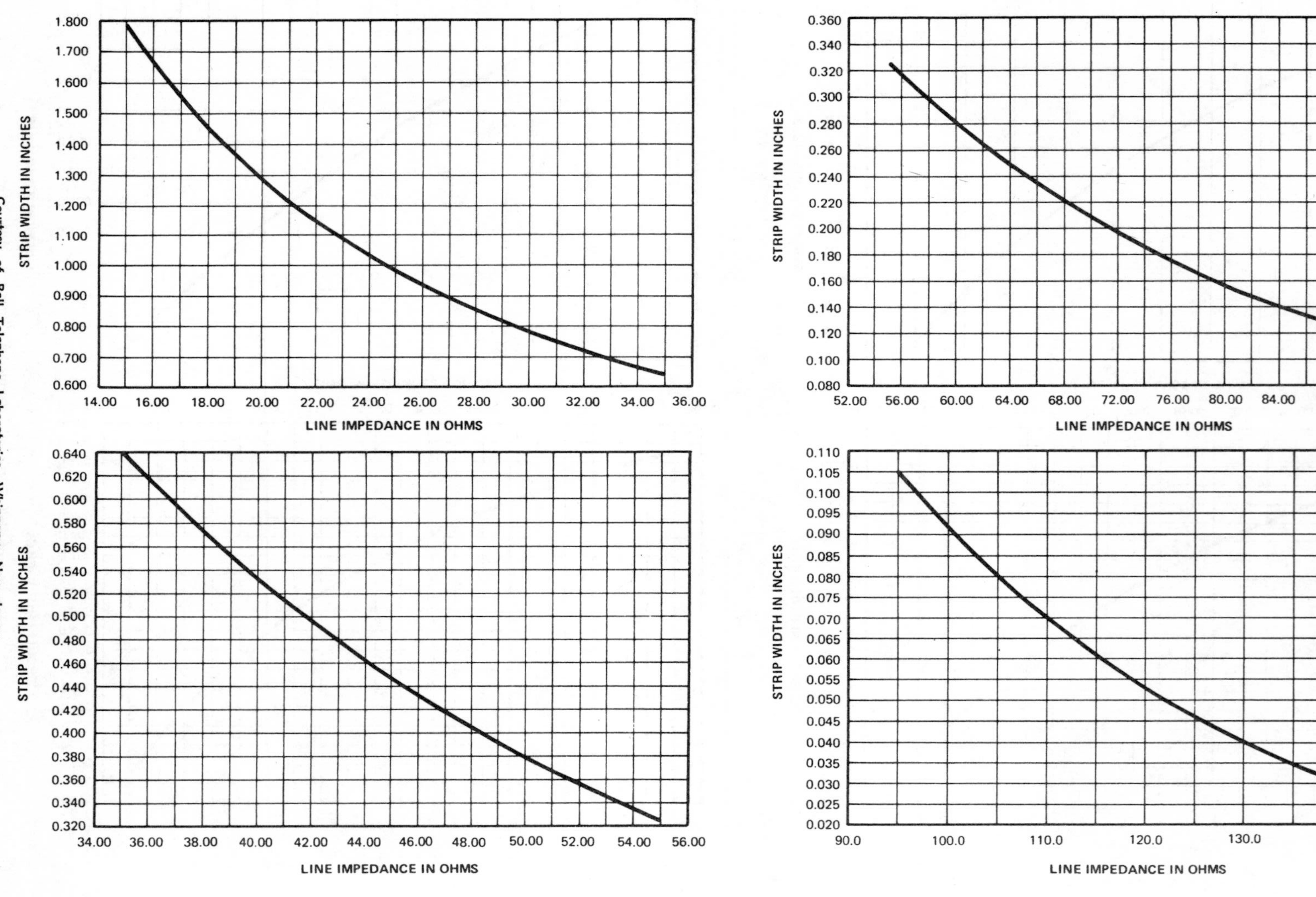

Courtesy of Bell Telephone Laboratories, Whippany, New Jersey

Loss vs Impedance for MPC

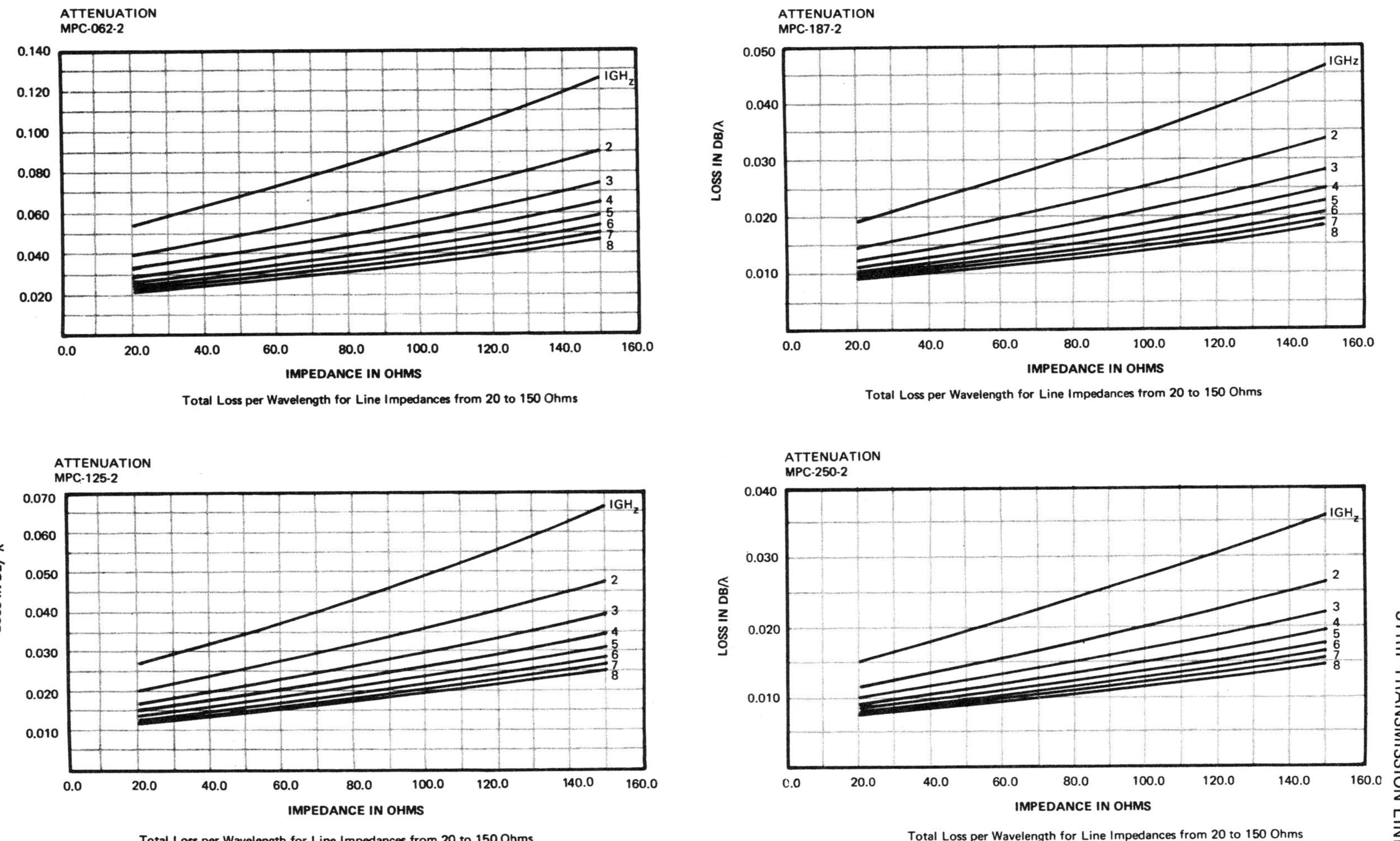

Courtesy of Bell Telephone Laboratories, Whippany, New Jersey

Copper Loss vs Frequency

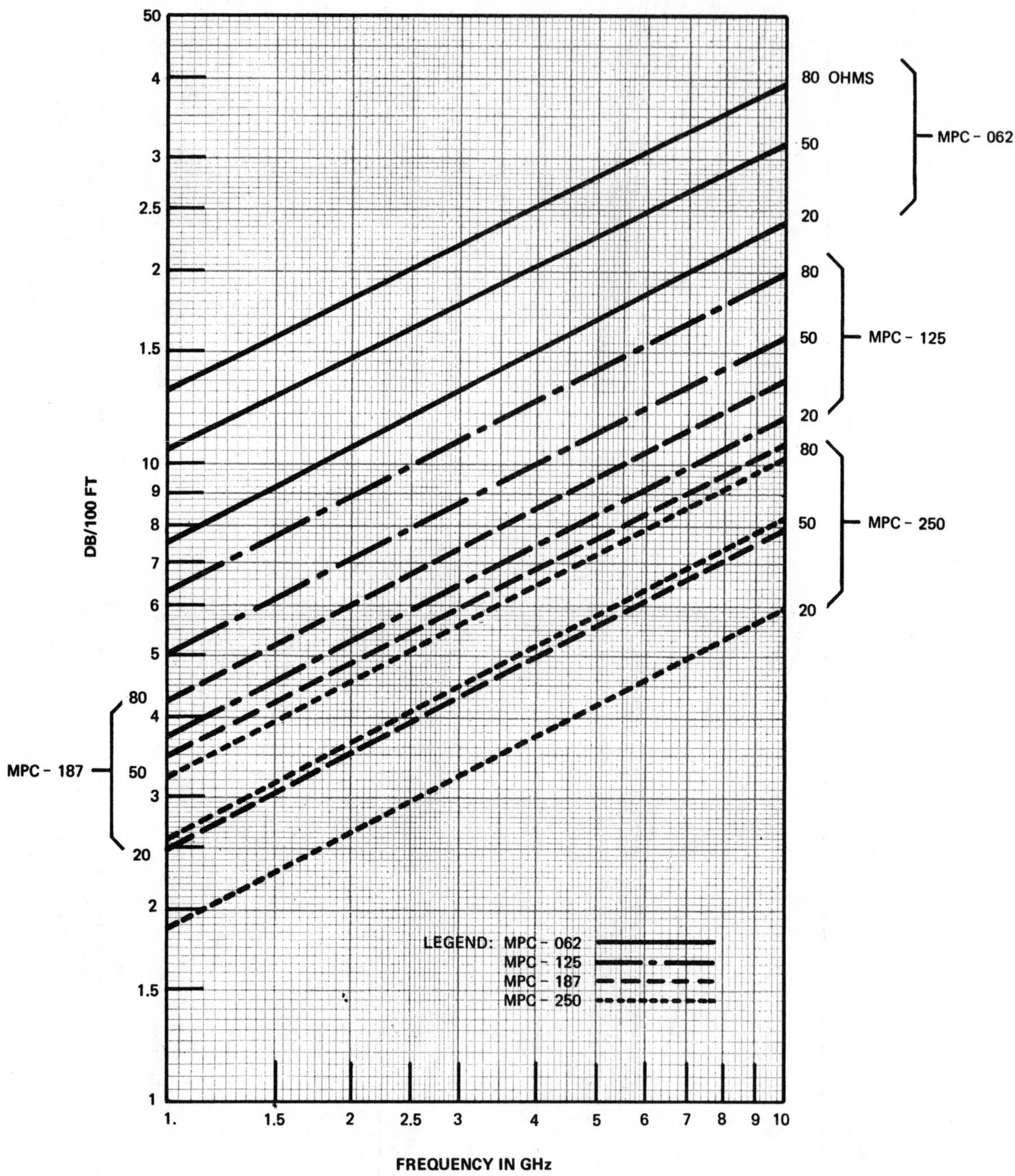

Courtesy of Harold Stinehelfer, Microwave Associates, Burlington, Mass.

Coupling as a Function of Gap Spacing for Lines with Characteristic Impedance of 50 OHMS

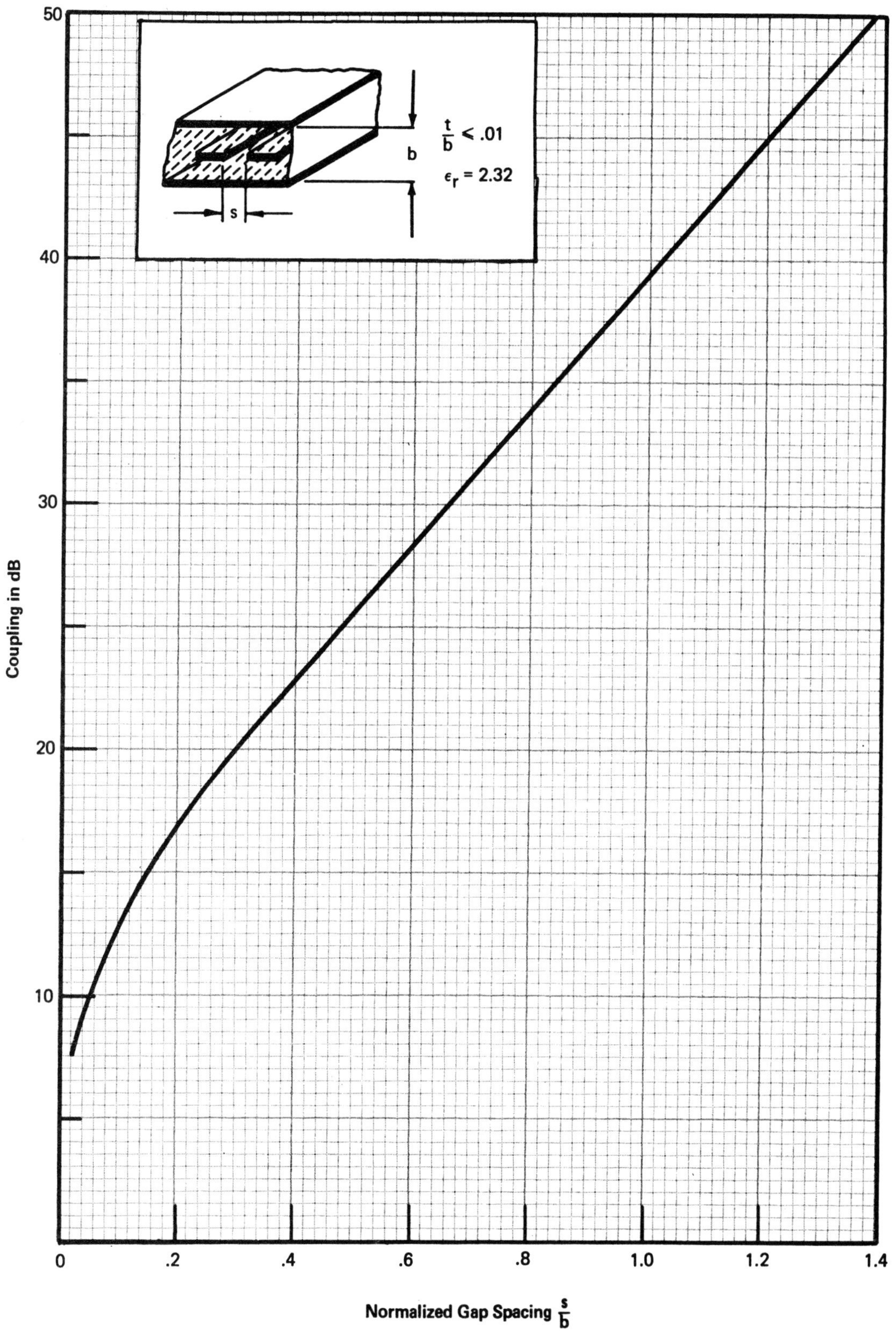

Courtesy of Harold Stinehelfer, Microwave Associates, Burlington, Mass.

Coupling Coefficient for a Directional Coupler

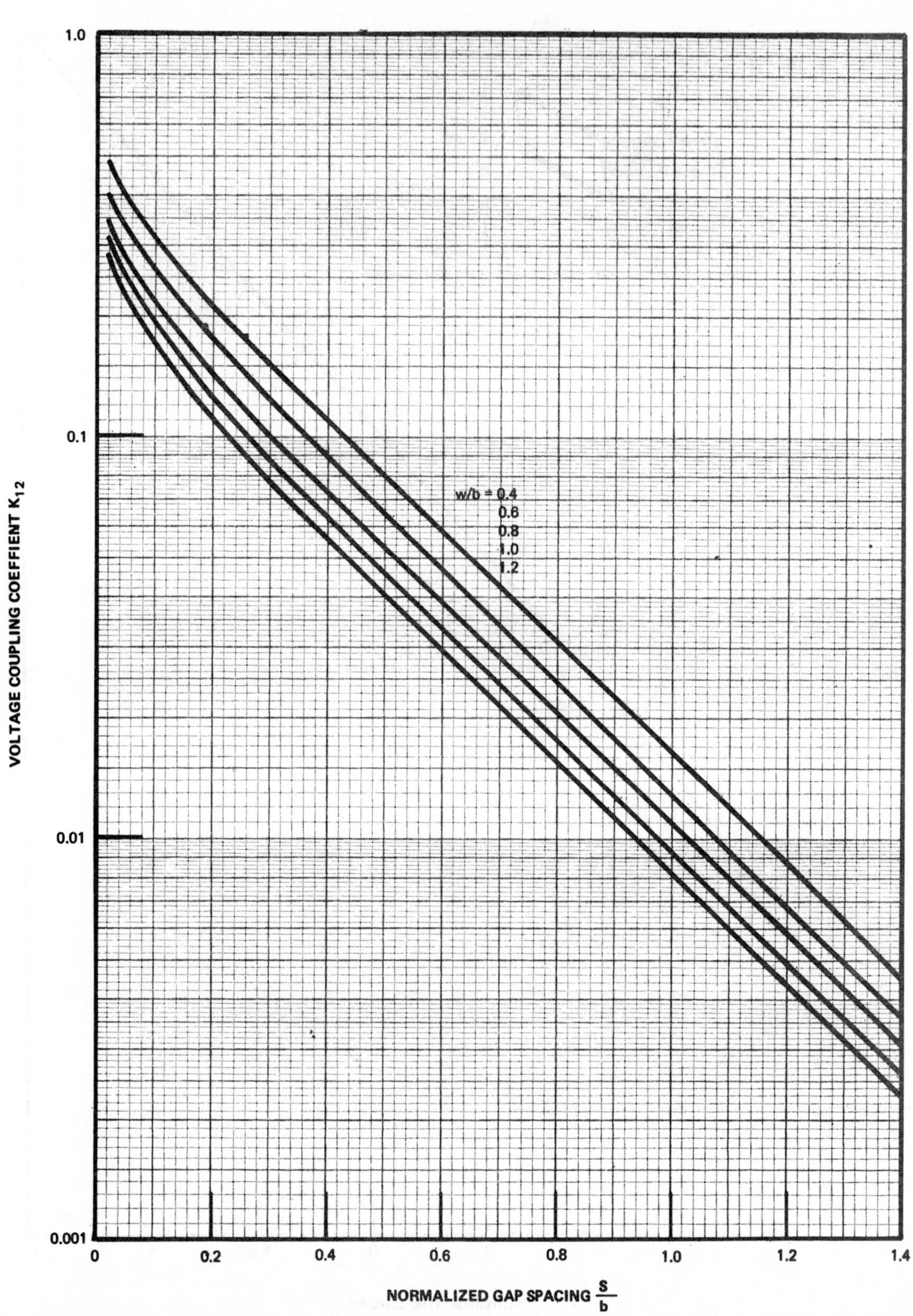

Courtesy of Harold Stinehelfer, Microwave Associates, Burlington, Mass.

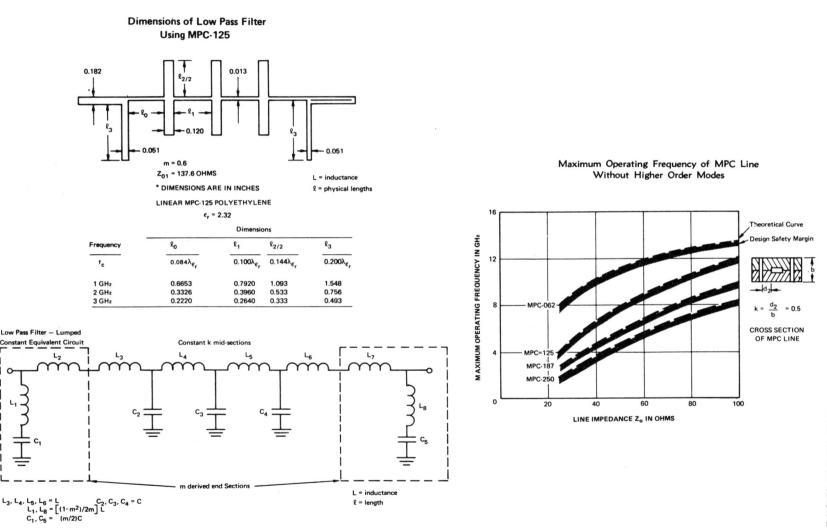

Dimensions of Low Pass Filter Using MPC-125

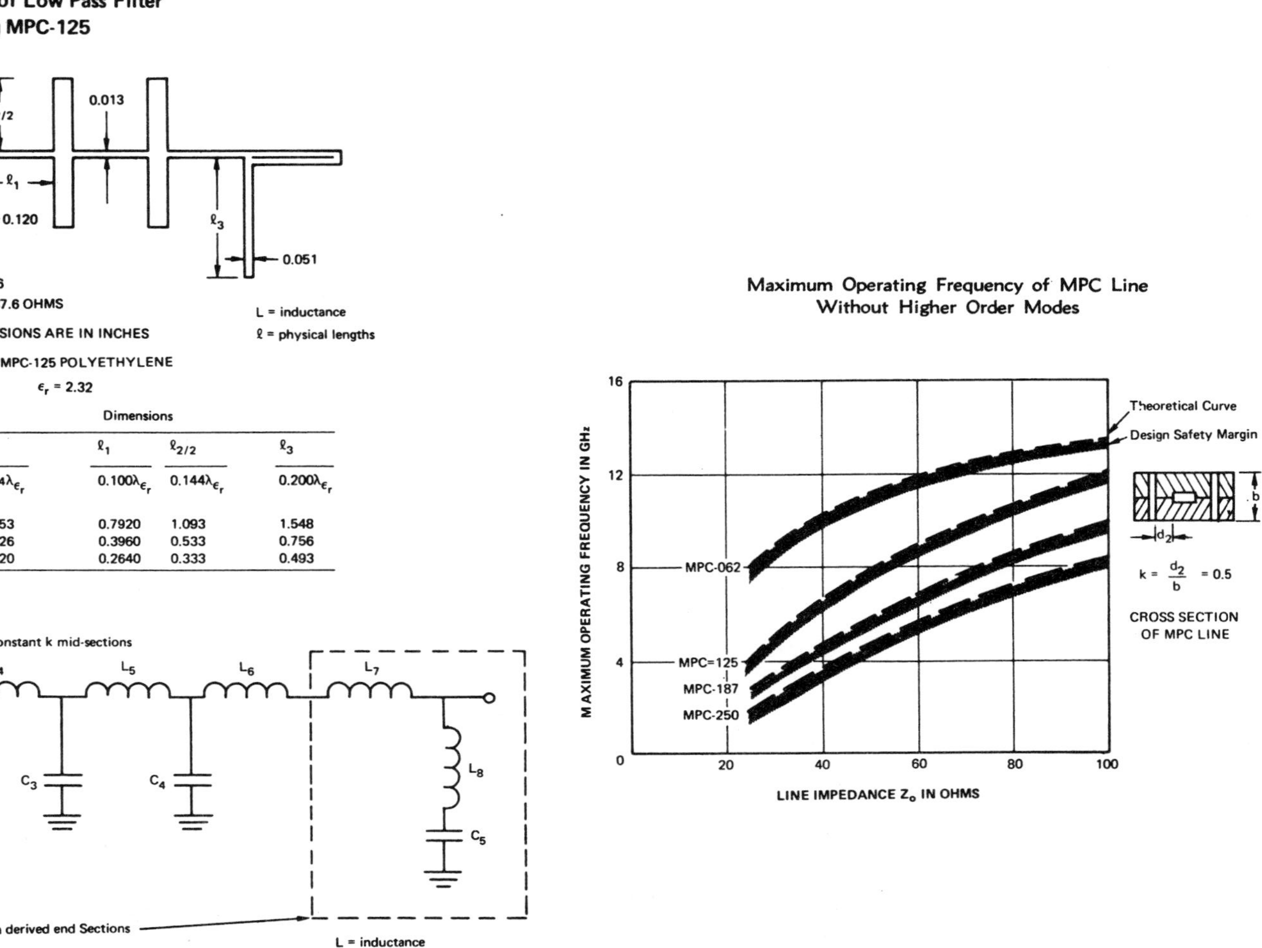

m = 0.6

Z_{01} = 137.6 OHMS

* DIMENSIONS ARE IN INCHES

LINEAR MPC-125 POLYETHYLENE

$\epsilon_r = 2.32$

L = inductance

ℓ = physical lengths

Frequency	Dimensions			
	ℓ_0	ℓ_1	$\ell_{2/2}$	ℓ_3
f_c	$0.084\lambda_{\epsilon_r}$	$0.100\lambda_{\epsilon_r}$	$0.144\lambda_{\epsilon_r}$	$0.200\lambda_{\epsilon_r}$
1 GHz	0.6653	0.7920	1.093	1.548
2 GHz	0.3326	0.3960	0.533	0.756
3 GHz	0.2220	0.2640	0.333	0.493

Low Pass Filter — Lumped Constant Equivalent Circuit

Constant k mid-sections

L_1 L_2 L_3 L_4 L_5 L_6 L_7 L_8

C_1 C_2 C_3 C_4 C_5

m derived end Sections

$L_3, L_4, L_5, L_6 = L$ $\quad C_2, C_3, C_4 = C$

$L_1, L_8 = \left[(1-m^2)/2m\right] L$

$C_1, C_5 = (m/2)C$

L = inductance

ℓ = length

Courtesy of Bell Telephone Laboratories, Whippany, New Jersey

Even and Odd Mode Characteristic Impedance for Coupled Microstrip

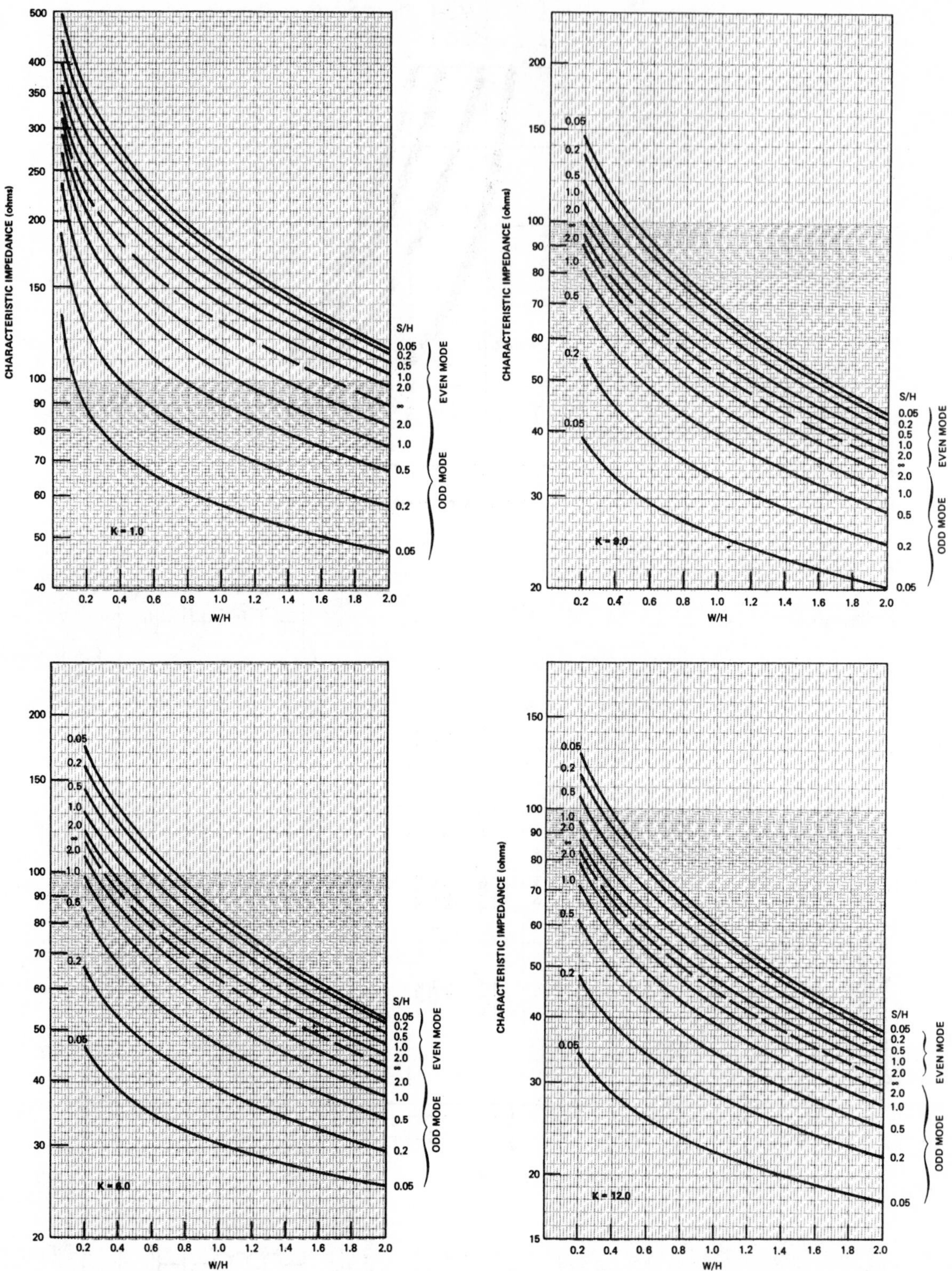

Courtesy of J.A.Weiss and T.G.Bryant, MIT Lincoln Laboratory, Lexington, Mass. This work was sponsored by the Department of the Army.

Even and Odd Mode Characteristic Impedance for Coupled Microstrip

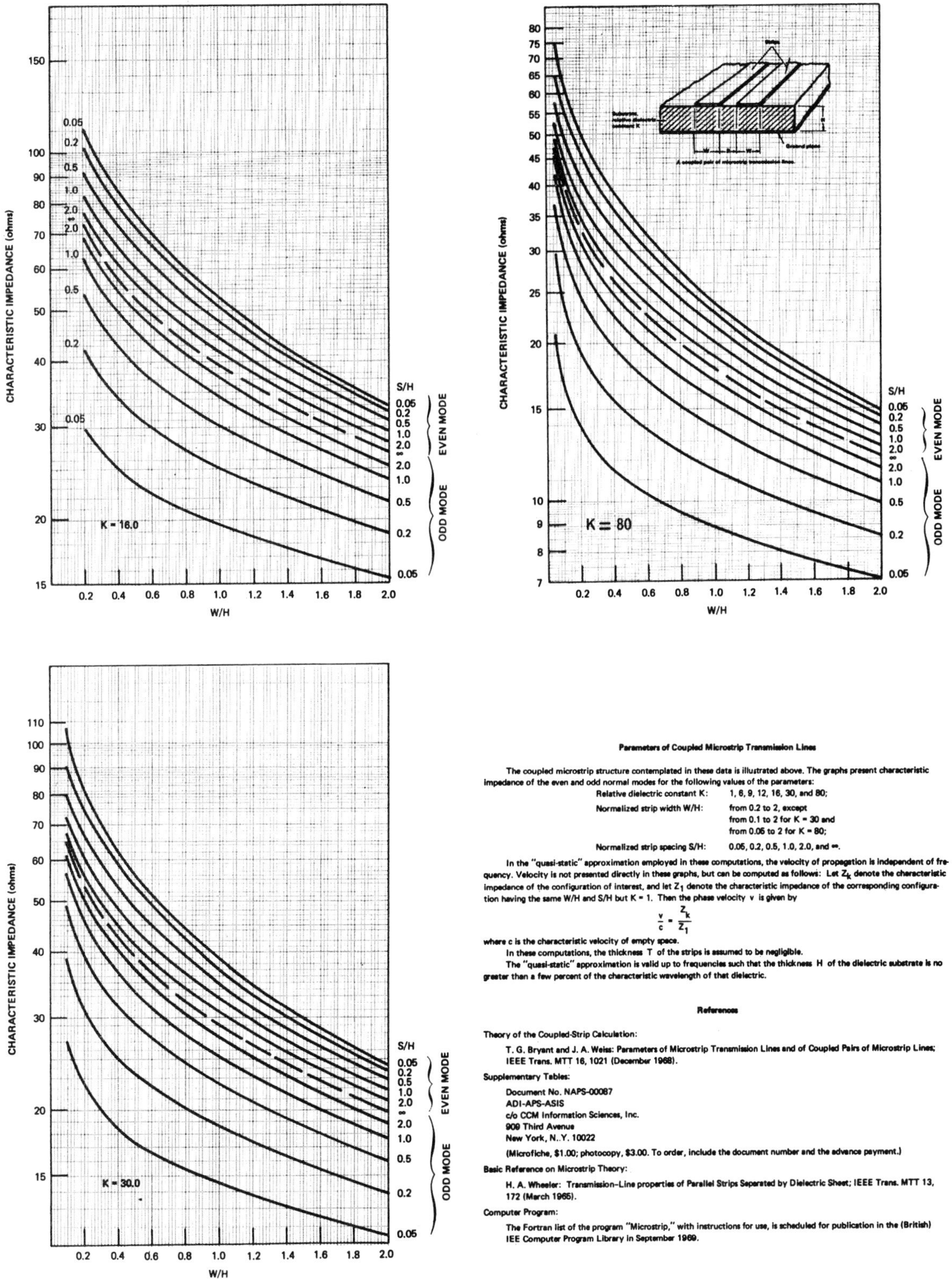

Parameters of Coupled Microstrip Transmission Lines

The coupled microstrip structure contemplated in these data is illustrated above. The graphs present characteristic impedance of the even and odd normal modes for the following values of the parameters:

Relative dielectric constant K:	1, 6, 9, 12, 16, 30, and 80;
Normalized strip width W/H:	from 0.2 to 2, except from 0.1 to 2 for K = 30 and from 0.05 to 2 for K = 80;
Normalized strip spacing S/H:	0.05, 0.2, 0.5, 1.0, 2.0, and ∞.

In the "quasi-static" approximation employed in these computations, the velocity of propagation is independent of frequency. Velocity is not presented directly in these graphs, but can be computed as follows: Let Z_k denote the characteristic impedance of the configuration of interest, and let Z_1 denote the characteristic impedance of the corresponding configuration having the same W/H and S/H but K = 1. Then the phase velocity v is given by

$$\frac{v}{c} = \frac{Z_k}{Z_1}$$

where c is the characteristic velocity of empty space.

In these computations, the thickness T of the strips is assumed to be negligible.

The "quasi-static" approximation is valid up to frequencies such that the thickness H of the dielectric substrate is no greater than a few percent of the characteristic wavelength of that dielectric.

References

Theory of the Coupled-Strip Calculation:

T. G. Bryant and J. A. Weiss: Parameters of Microstrip Transmission Lines and of Coupled Pairs of Microstrip Lines; IEEE Trans. MTT 16, 1021 (December 1968).

Supplementary Tables:

Document No. NAPS-00087
ADI-APS-ASIS
c/o CCM Information Sciences, Inc.
909 Third Avenue
New York, N..Y. 10022

(Microfiche, $1.00; photocopy, $3.00. To order, include the document number and the advance payment.)

Basic Reference on Microstrip Theory:

H. A. Wheeler: Transmission-Line properties of Parallel Strips Seperated by Dielectric Sheet; IEEE Trans. MTT 13, 172 (March 1965).

Computer Program:

The Fortran list of the program "Microstrip," with instructions for use, is scheduled for publication in the (British) IEE Computer Program Library in September 1969.

Courtesy of J.A.Weiss and T.G.Bryant, MIT Lincoln Laboratory, Lexington, Mass. This work was sponsored by the Department of the Army.

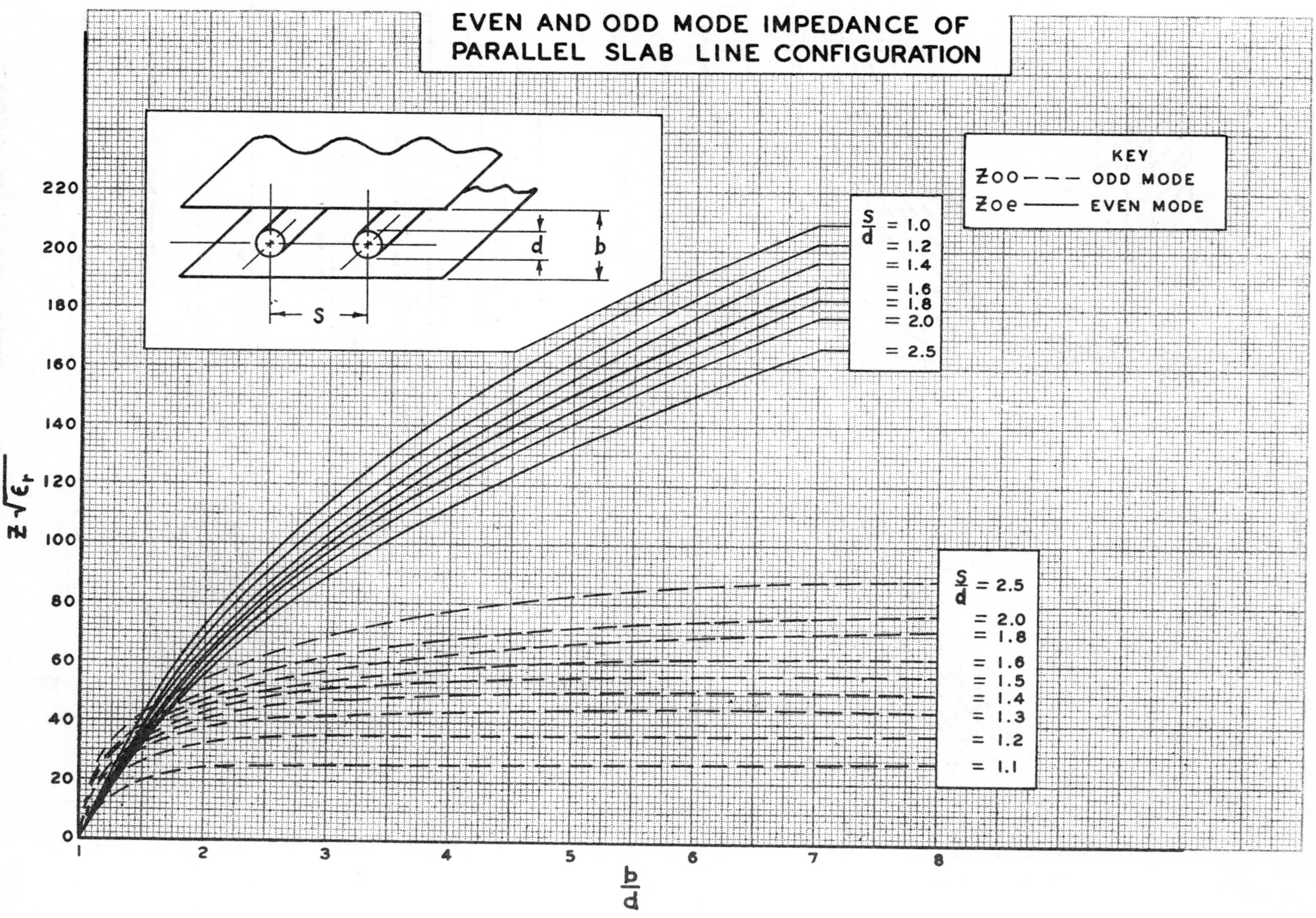

Courtesy of Leonard I. Parad, Sylvania Electric Products, Waltham, Mass.

LINE-WIDTH CORRECTION FOR FINITE-THICKNESS CENTER CONDUCTORS

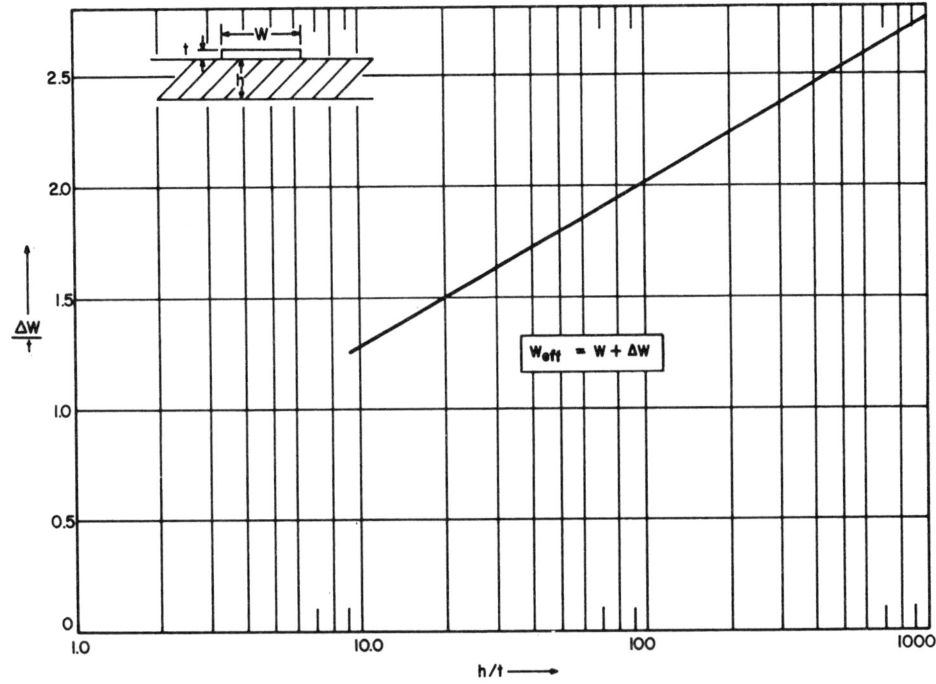

NORMALIZED CONDUCTOR LOSS AS FUNCTION OF GEOMETRY w/h and ε/r (MKS units)

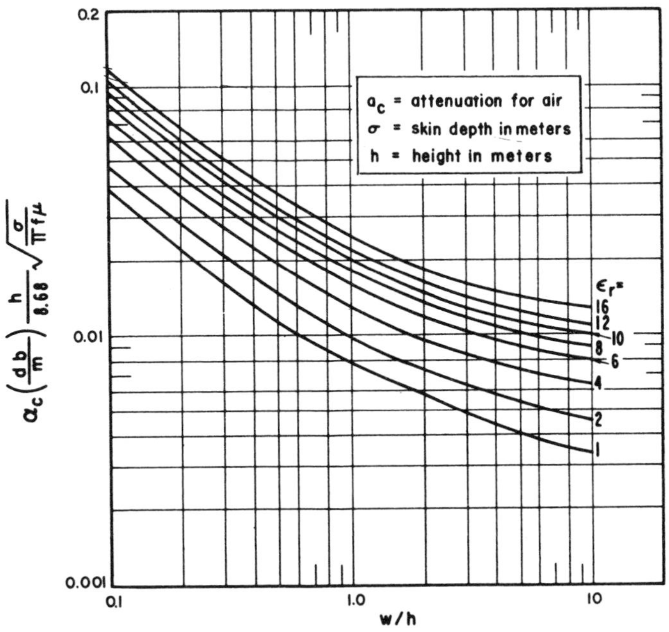

Reprinted from RCA Review, Sept. 1966. Courtesy of M. Caulton, J. J. Hughes, and H. Sobol

RATIO OF FREE SPACE WAVELENGTH (λ_o) TO MICROSTRIP WAVELENGTH (λ_m) CALCULATED FROM WORK OF WHEELER

WIDE STRIP APPROXIMATION (W/H > .1)

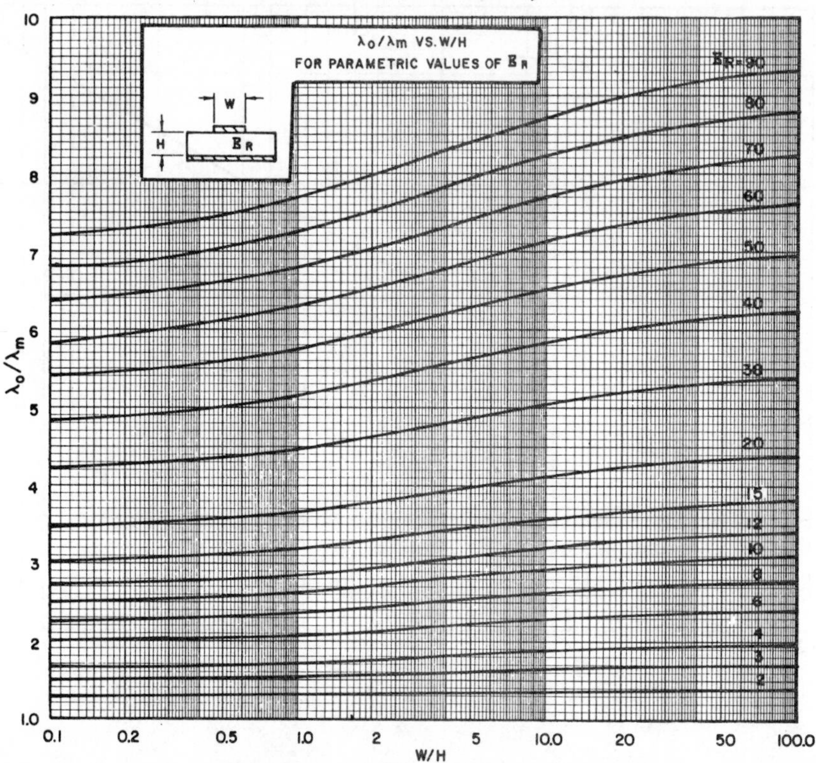

NARROW STRIP APPROXIMATION (W/H < 1.0)

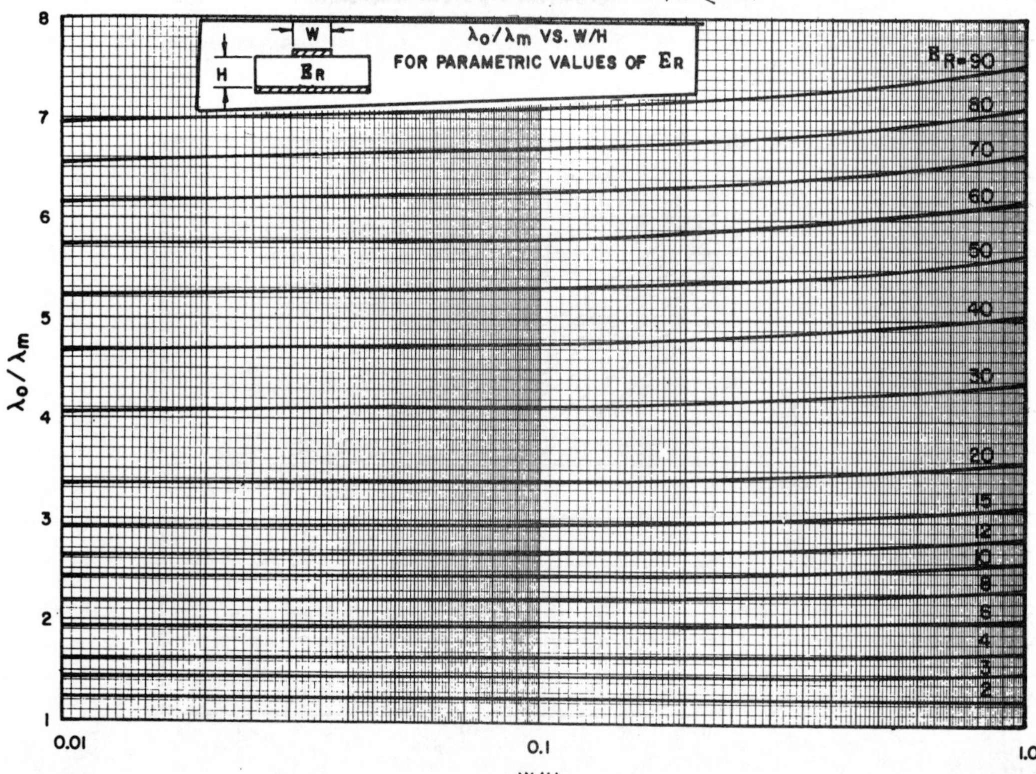

Courtesy of Burke, Gelnovatch and Chase after Wheeler

MICROSTRIP CHARACTERISTIC IMPEDANCE CALCULATED FROM WORK OF WHEELER

WIDE STRIP APPROXIMATION (W/H > .1)

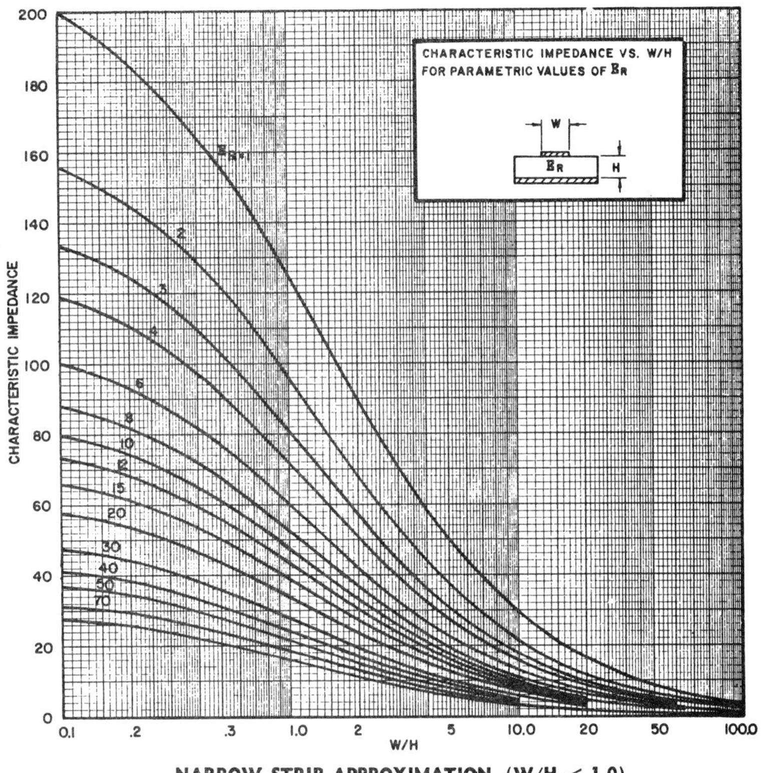

NARROW STRIP APPROXIMATION (W/H < 1.0)

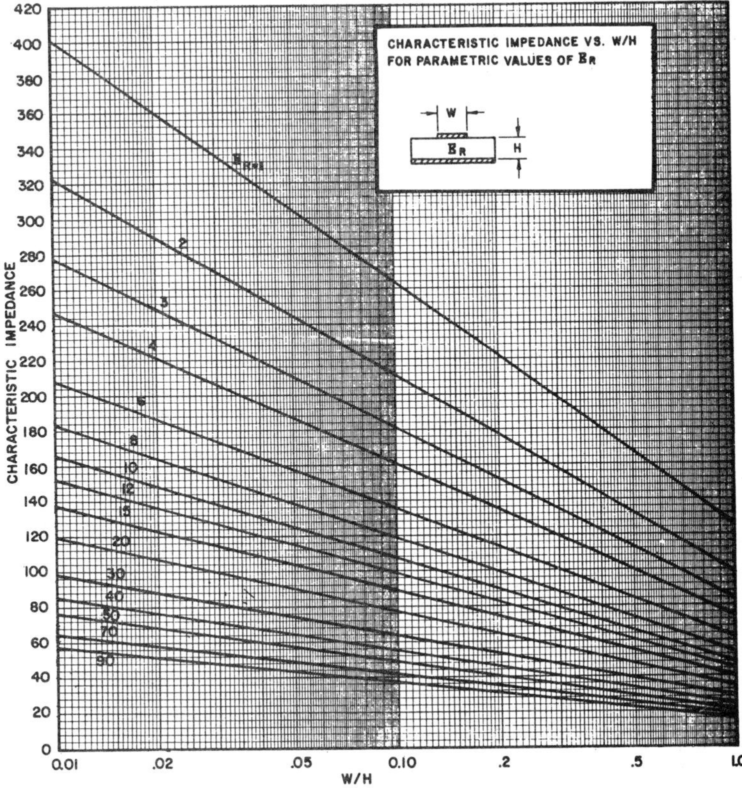

Courtesy of Burke, Gelnovatch and Chase after Wheeler

GAP IN STRIP LINE
50 OHM LINE
CENTERLINE REPRESENTATION

Circuit Parameters:

$$\frac{B_s}{Y_o} = -\frac{2b}{\lambda}\text{Ln}\cosh\frac{\pi s}{2b} \qquad \frac{B_a}{Y_o} = \frac{b}{\lambda}\text{Ln}\coth\frac{\pi s}{2b}$$

Arthur A. Oliner, reprinted from IRE Trans. on Microwave Theory and Techniques, published by the Professional Group on Microwave Theory and Techniques, March 1955.

GAP IN STRIP LINE
50 OHM LINE
EDGE REPRESENTATION

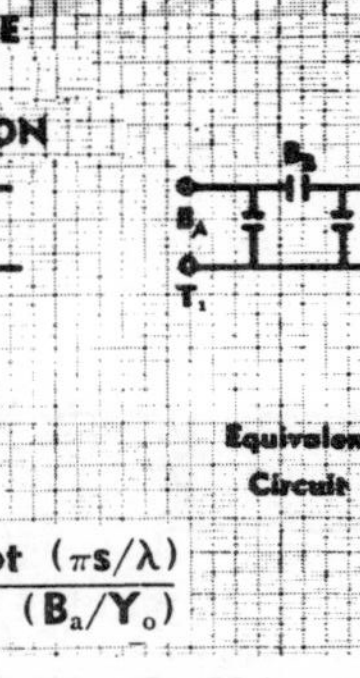

Circuit Parameters:

$$\frac{B_A}{Y_o} = \frac{1 + (B_a/Y_o)\cot(\pi s/\lambda)}{\cot(\pi s/\lambda) - (B_a/Y_o)}$$

$$\frac{B_B}{Y_o} = \frac{1}{2}\left[\frac{1 + (2B_b/Y_o + B_a/Y_o)\cot(\pi s/\lambda)}{\cot(\pi s/\lambda) - (2B_b/Y_o + B_a/Y_o)}\right] - \frac{1}{2}\frac{B_A}{Y_o}$$

For $s >> w$: $B_A/Y_o \sim \tan\left(\frac{2b}{\lambda}\text{Ln } 2\right)$

$\frac{B_A}{Y_o}$ and $\frac{B_B}{Y_o}$ vs. s/w

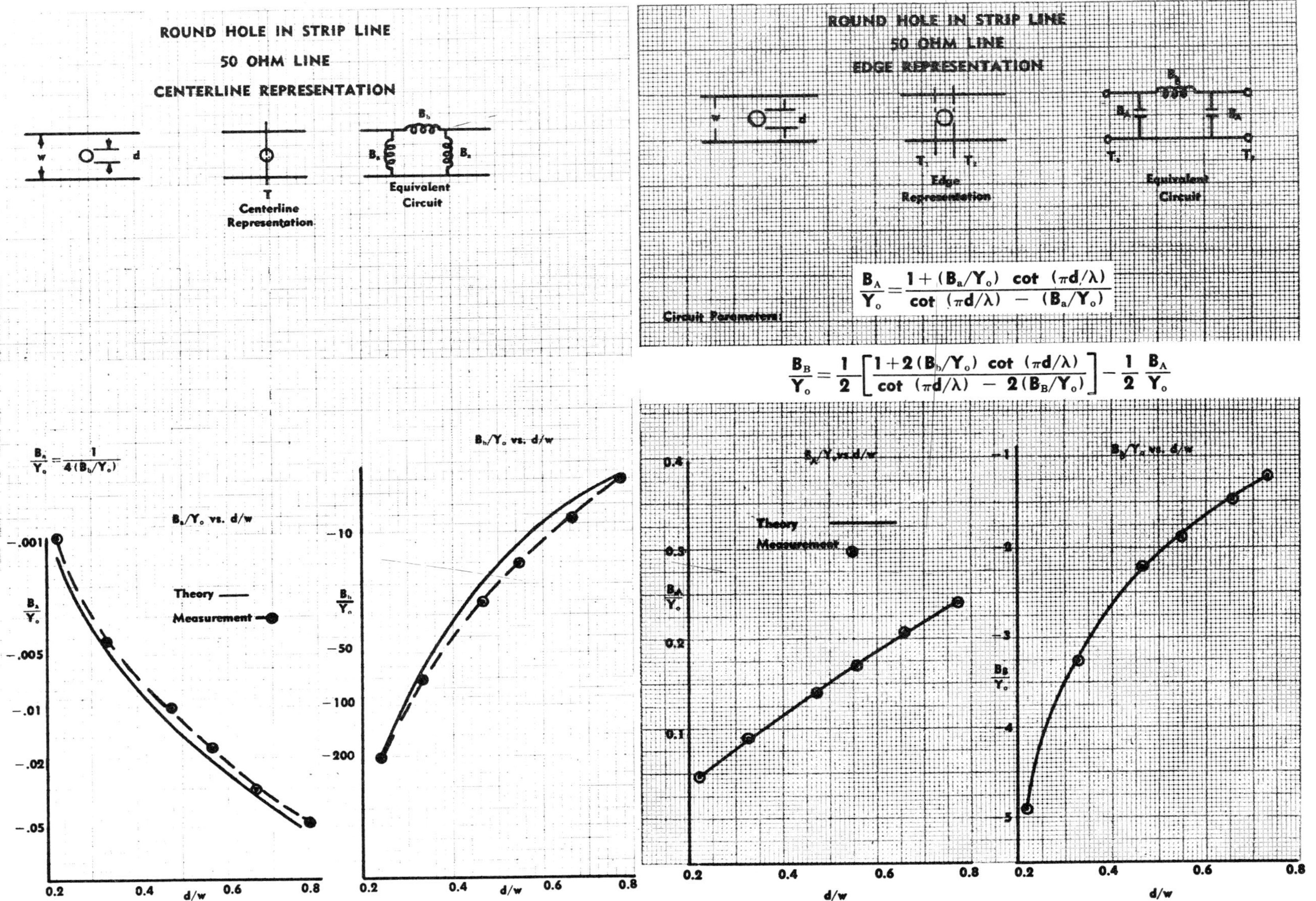

Arthur A. Oliner, reprinted from IRE Trans. on Microwave Theory and Techniques, published by the Professional Group on Microwave Theory and Techniques, March 1955.

MICROSTRIP IMPEDANCE VS. LINE WIDTH

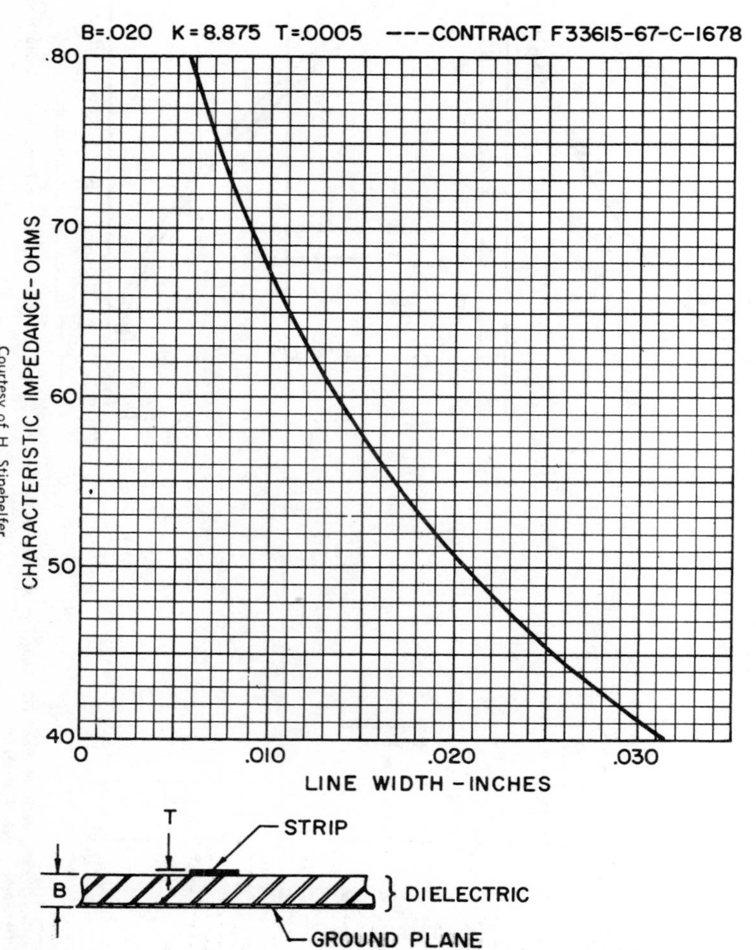

Courtesy of H. Stinehelfer

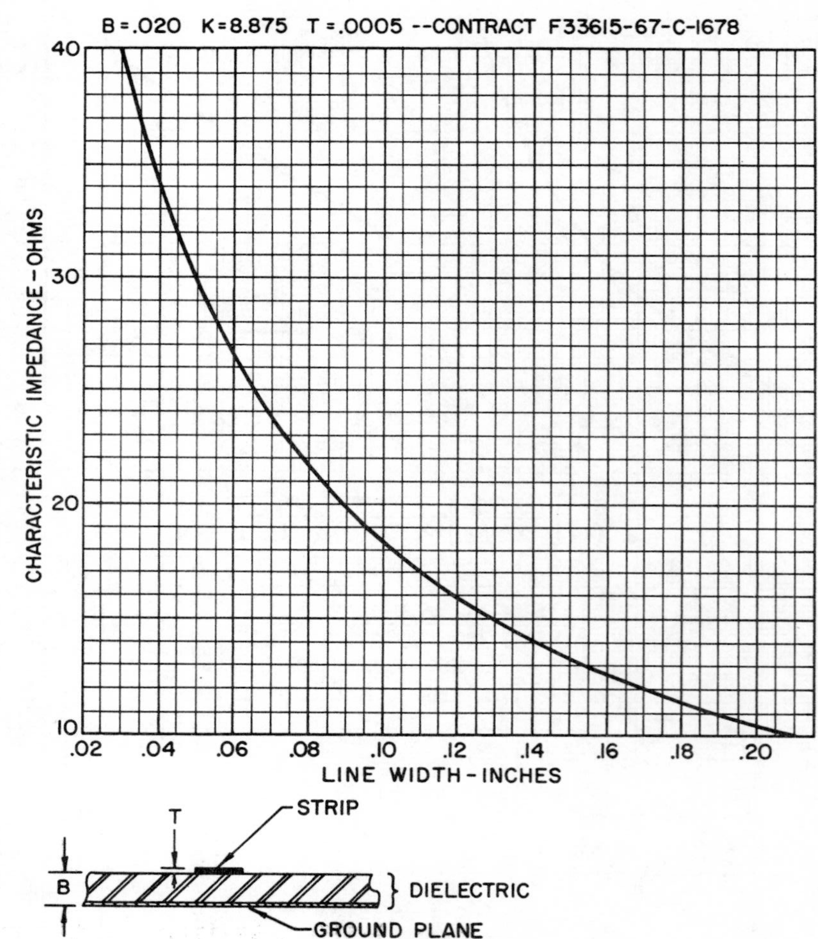

MICROSTRIP IMPEDANCE VS. LINE WIDTH

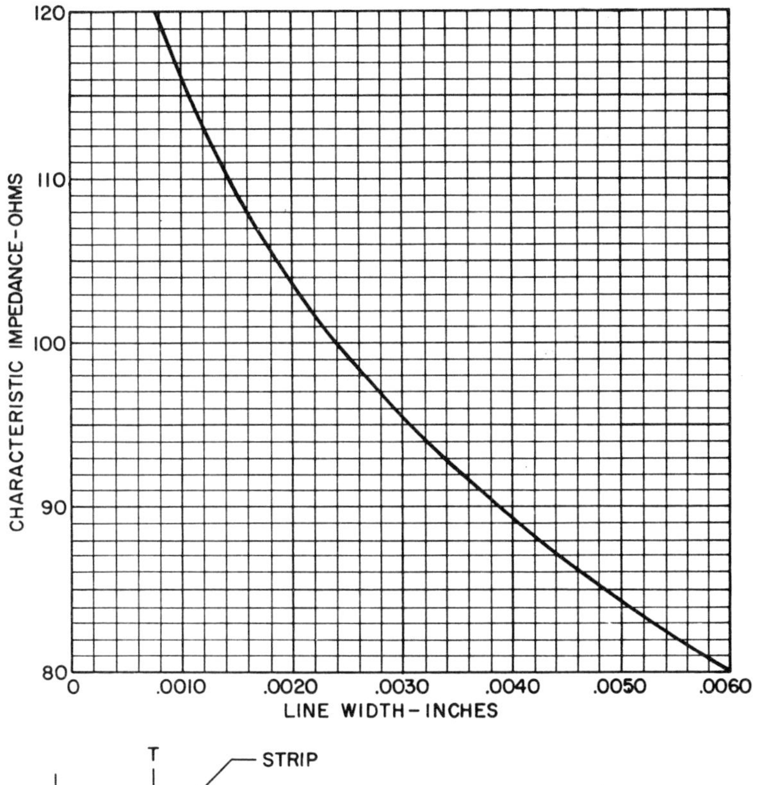

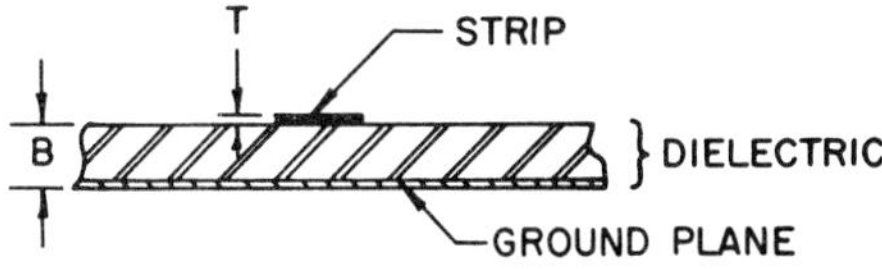

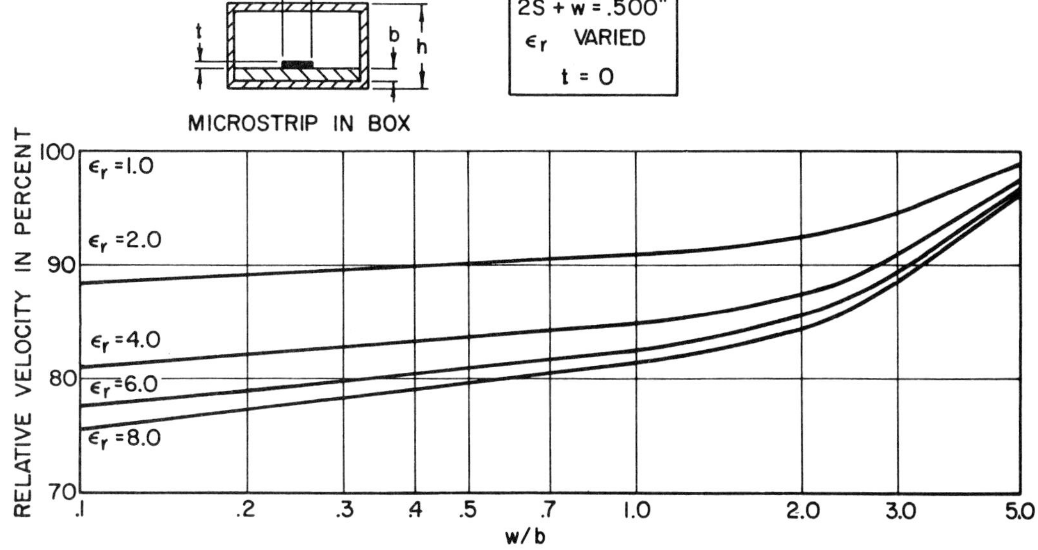

Courtesy of H. Stinehelfer

IMPEDANCE OF MICROSTRIP (Ω)

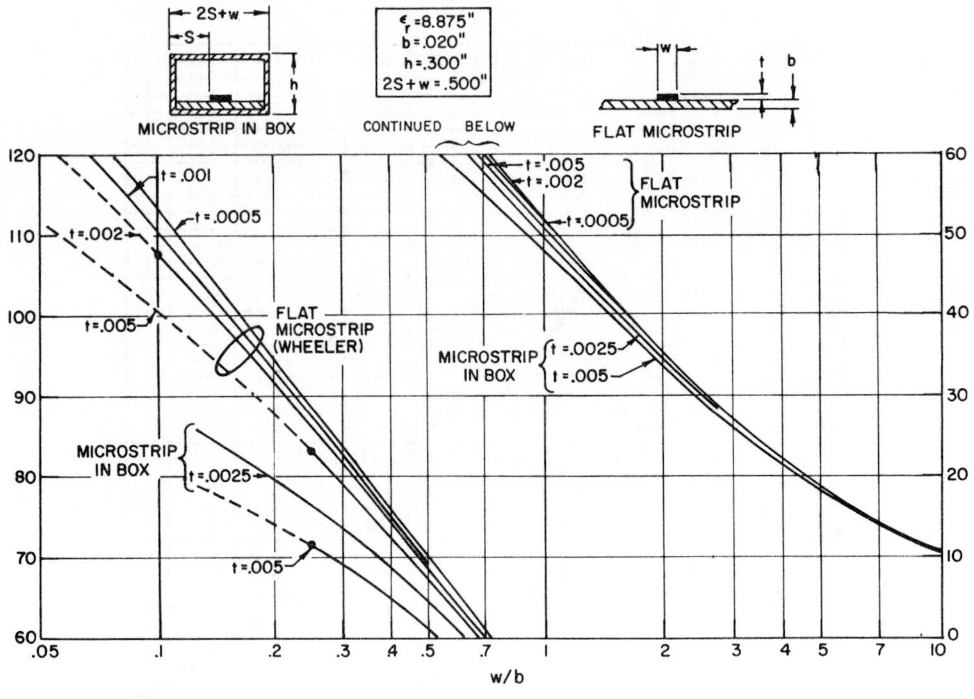

RELATIVE VELOCITY β/β_o VS w/b (PROPAGATION CONSTANT)

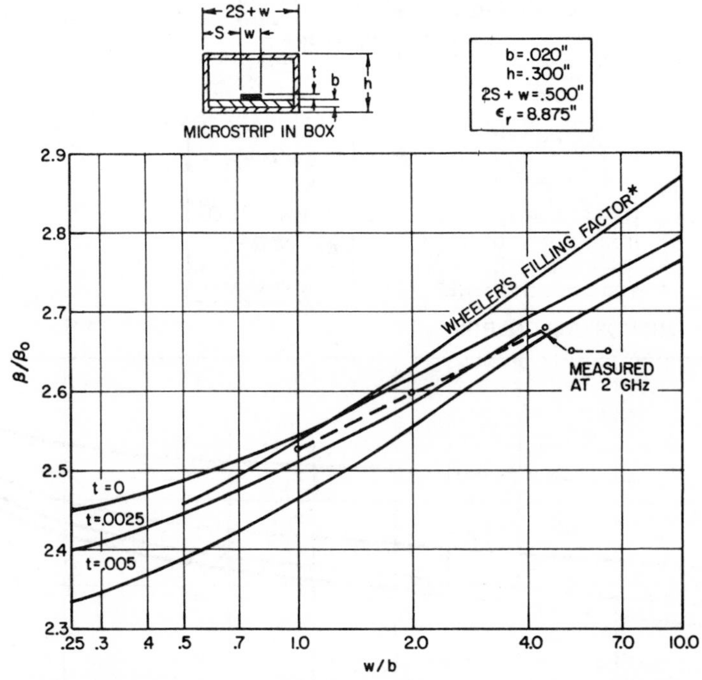

*"Transmission Line Properties of Parallel Strip Separated by a Dielectric Strip," Vol. MTT-13, Pp. 172–185 March 1965.

LOSS VS. w/b RATIO

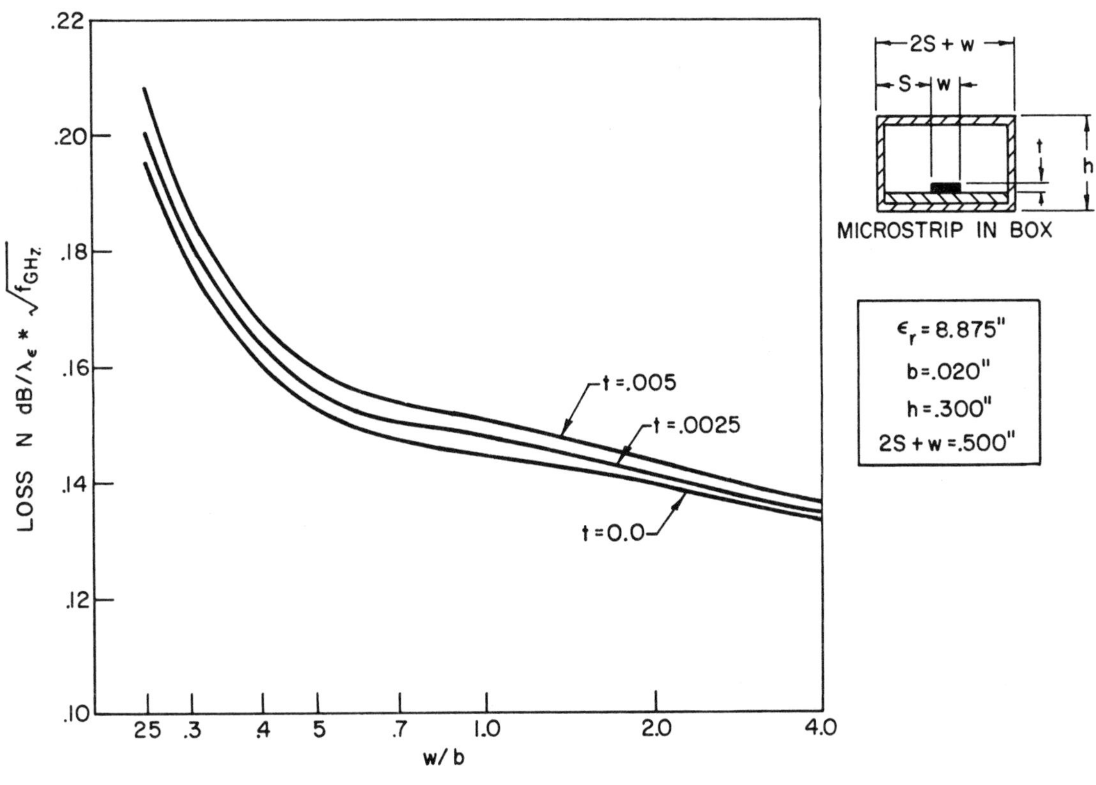

REFERENCE PLAN LOCATION FOR "T" AND "+" JUNCTION

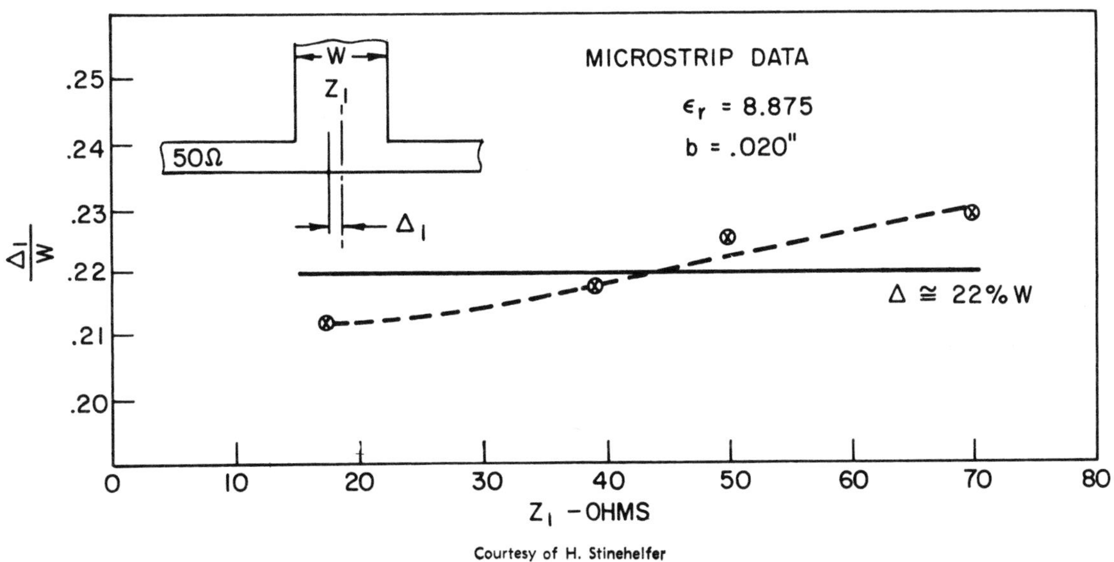

Courtesy of H. Stinehelfer

GAP CAPACITANCE VS. GAP SPACING

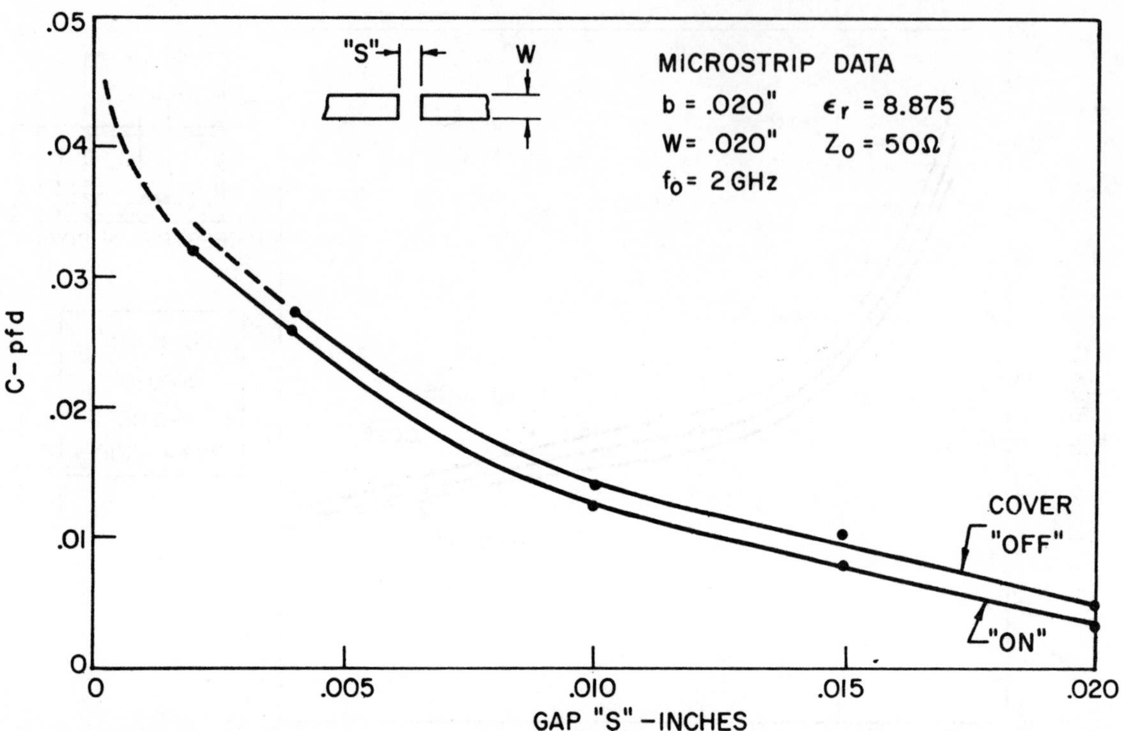

JUNCTION EFFECT AT "T" AND "X"

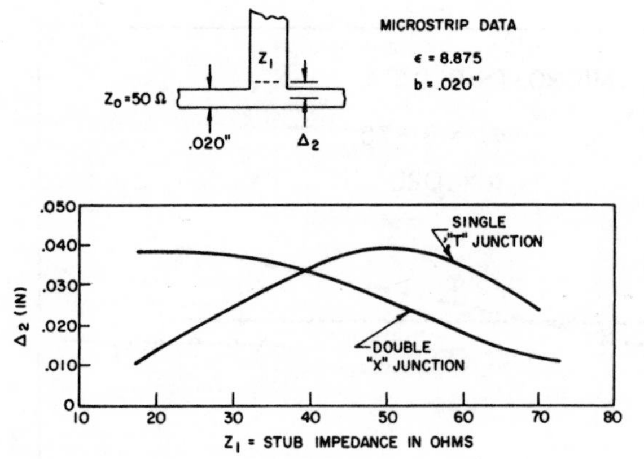

END EFFECT FOR MICROSTRIP LINE

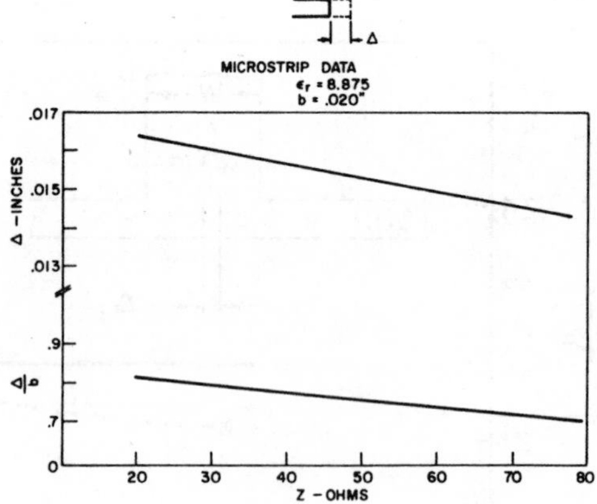

Courtesy of H. Stinehelfer

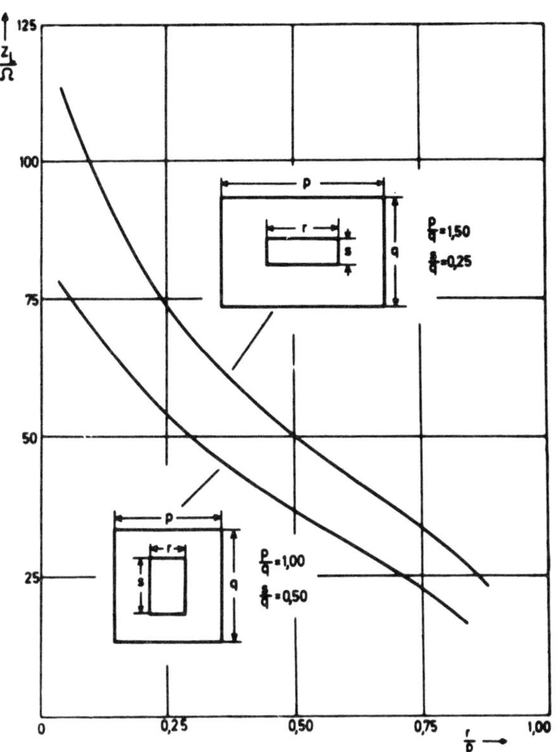

CHARACTERISTIC IMPEDANCE OF STRIP-LINES.

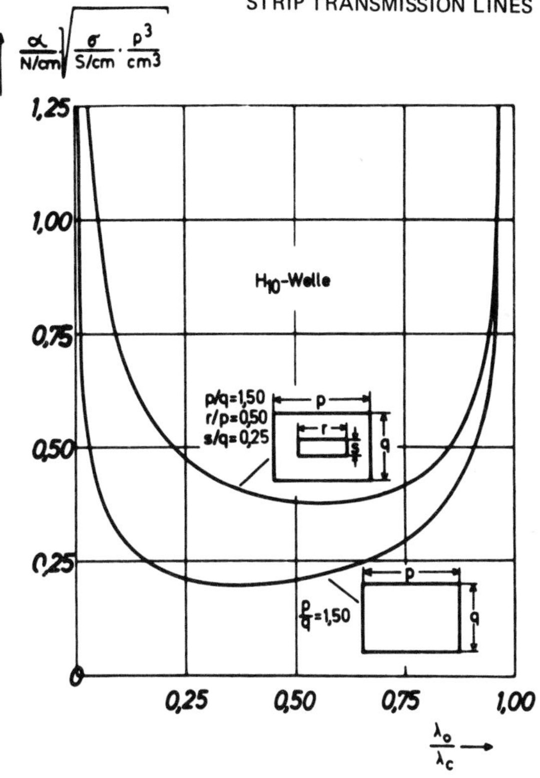

ATTENUATION CONSTANT OF THE FUNDAMENTAL TE-MODE (σ = WALL CONDUCTIVITY IN Mho/cm, λ_o = WAVELENGTH IN FREE SPACE) IN STRIPLINE WITH RECTANGULAR OUTER CONDUCTOR

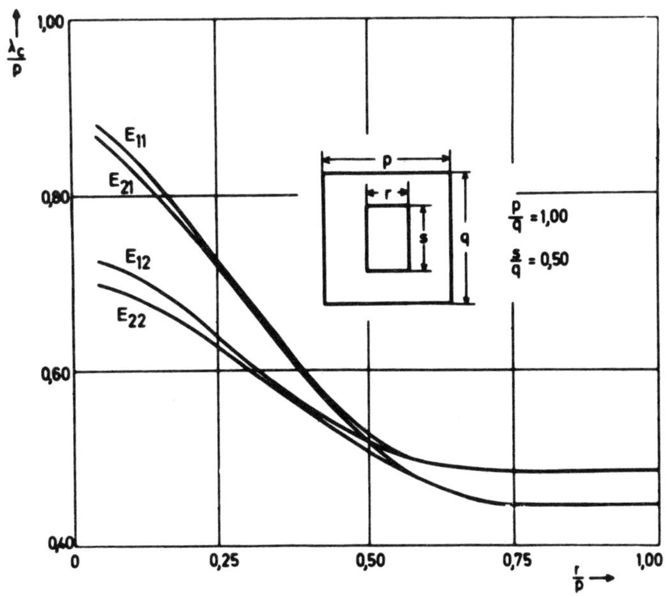

CRITICAL WAVELENGTHS OF E-MODES (TM-MODES) IN STRIP-LINES WITH SQUARE OUTER CONDUCTOR.

"First Published in Archiv Dev Elektrischen Ubertragung, *Vol. 22 (1968), No. 4, Pp. 179–185."*
Courtesy of H. H. Meinke and W. Baier

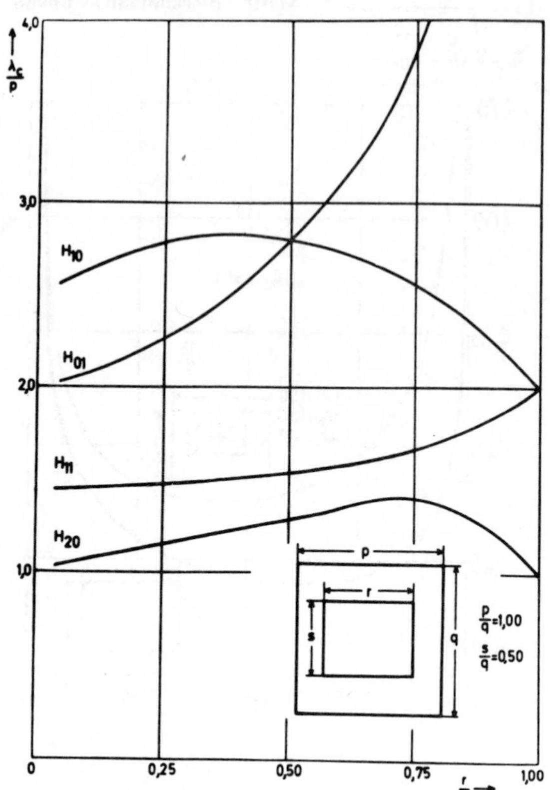

CRITICAL WAVELENGTHS OF H-MODES (TE-MODES) IN STRIP-LINES WITH SQUARE OUTER CONDUCTOR.

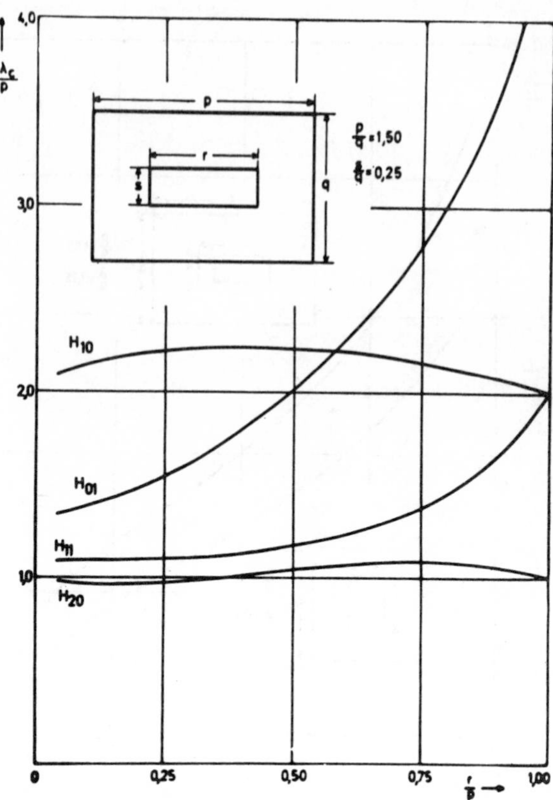

CRITICAL WAVELENGTHS OF H-MODES (TE-MODES) IN STRIP-LINES WITH RECTANGULAR OUTER CONDUCTOR.

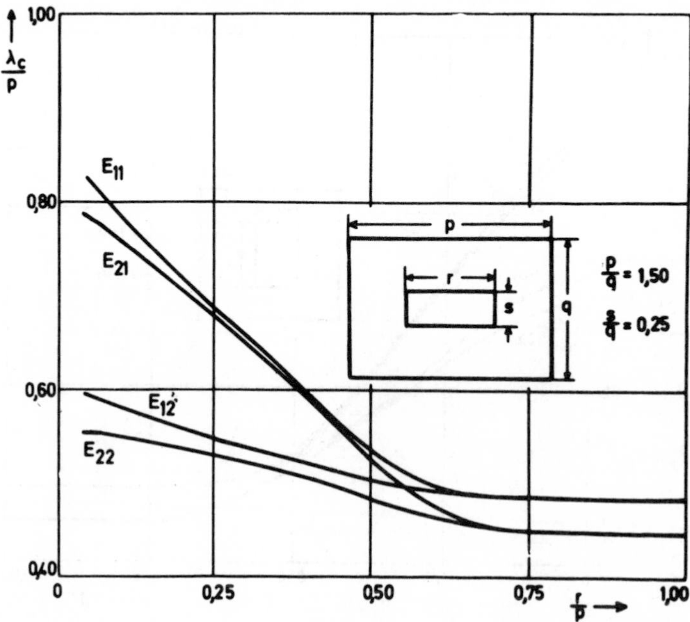

CRITICAL WAVELENGTHS OF E-MODES (TM-MODES) IN STRIP-LINES WITH RECTANGULAR OUTER CONDUCTOR.

"First Published in Archiv Dev Elektrischen Ubertragung, *Vol. 22 (1968), No. 4, Pp. 179–185."*
Courtesy of H. H. Meinke and W. Baier

STRIP TRANSMISSION LINE MODE CHARTS

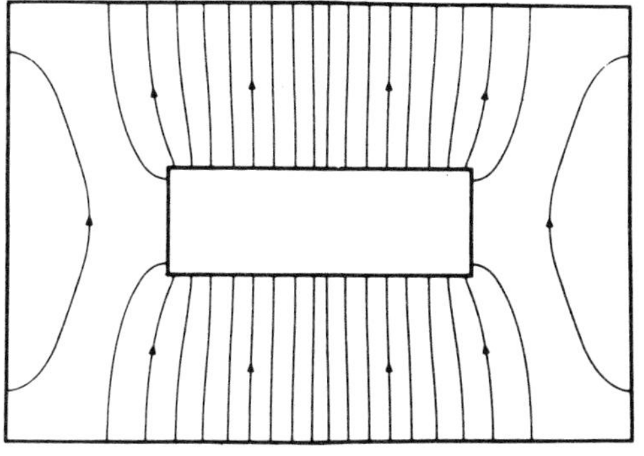

ELECTRICAL FIELD LINES OF THE TE_{10}-MODE.

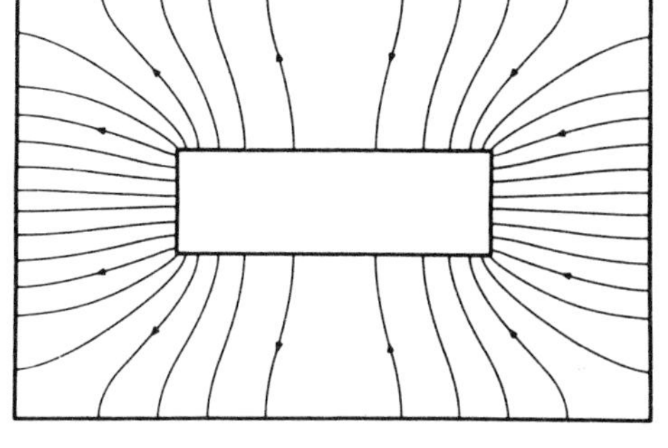

ELECTRICAL FIELD LINES OF THE TE_{01}-MODE

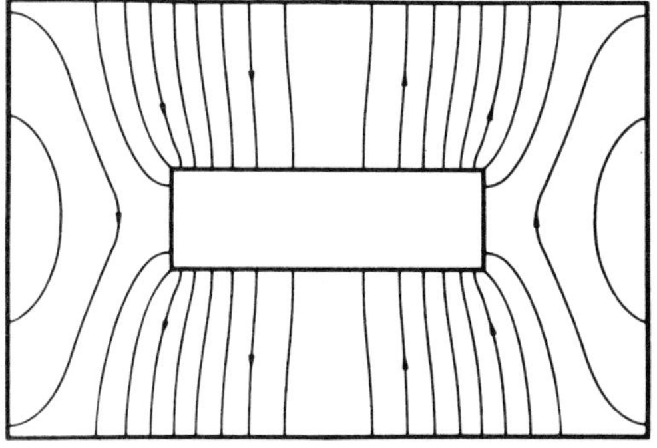

ELECTRICAL FIELD LINES OF THE TE_{20}-MODE.

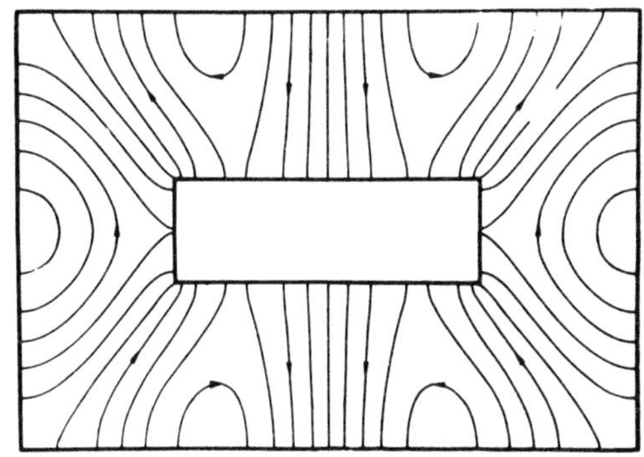

ELECTRICAL FIELD LINES OF THE TE_{30}-MODE.

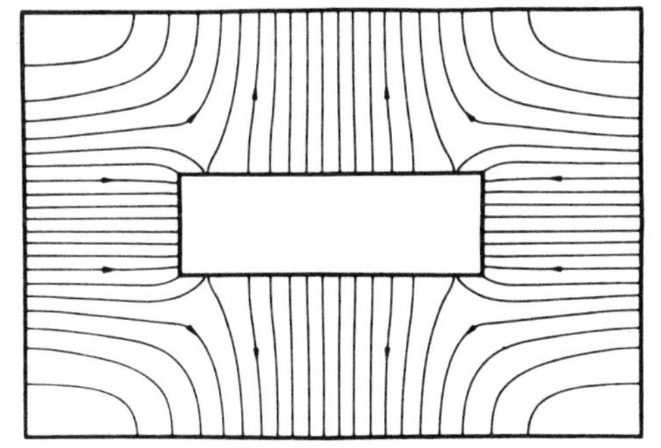

ELECTRICAL FIELD LINES OF THE TE_{11}-MODE.

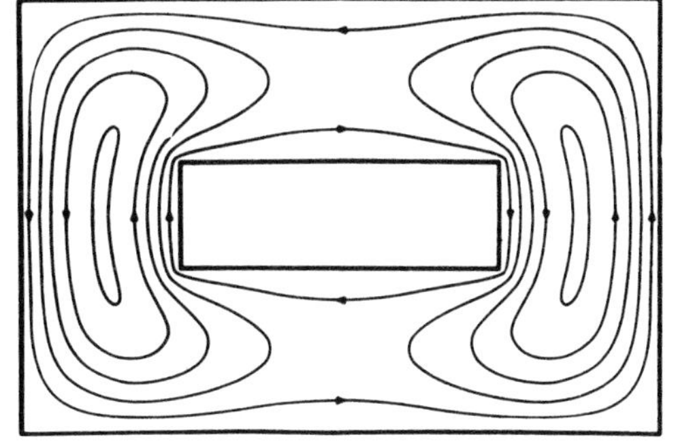

MAGNETIC FIELD LINES OF THE TM_{11}-MODE.

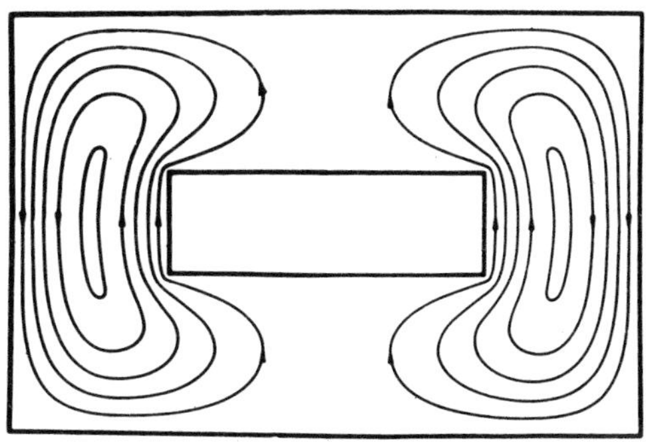

MAGNETIC FIELD LINES OF THE TM_{21}-MODE.

"First Published in Archiv Dev Elektrischen Ubertragung, *Vol. 22 (1968), No. 4, Pp. 179–185."*

Courtesy of H. H. Meinke and W. Baier

ODD AND EVEN IMPEDANCE OF COUPLED TRANSMISSION LINES

CHARACTERISTIC IMPEDANCE 50 Ω			CHARACTERISTIC IMPEDANCE 1.0 Ω	
ZOO OHMS	ZOE OHMS	–DB– COUPLING	ZOO OHMS	ZOE OHMS
11.9897	208.512	1	.239794	4.17025
16.928	147.684	2	.338561	2.95368
20.6759	120.914	3	.413518	2.31827
23.7841	105.112	4	.475682	2.10224
26.4637	94.4692	5	.529273	1.88938
28.8218	86.7398	6	.576437	1.7348
30.9222	80.8481	7	.618444	1.61696
32.8065	76.2045	8	.656129	1.52409
34.5043	72.4548	9	.690086	1.4491
36.038	69.3713	10	.720759	1.38743
37.4252	66.7998	11	.748505	1.336
38.6807	64.6317	12	.773615	1.29263
39.817	62.7872	13	.79634	1.23374
40.845	61.207	14	.8169	1.22414
41.7744	59.8452	15	.835488	1.1969
42.6142	58.666	16	.852283	1.17332
43.3722	57.6406	17	.867444	1.15281
44.0559	56.7461	18	.881118	1.13492
44.672	55.9635	19	.89344	1.11927
45.2267	55.2771	20	.904534	1.10554
45.7257	54.6738	21	.914514	1.09348
46.1743	54.1427	22	.923485	1.08285
46.5771	53.6744	23	.931543	1.07349
46.9387	53.2609	24	.938775	1.06522
47.2631	52.8954	25	.945262	1.05791
47.5538	42.572	26	.951077	1.05144
47.8143	52.2856	27	.956286	1.04571
48.0476	52.0218	28	.960951	1.04064
48.2563	51.8067	29	.965126	1.02613
48.4431	51.607	30	.968862	1.03214
48.6101	51.4296	31	.972202	1.02859
48.7594	51.2721	32	.975189	1.02544
48.8929	51.1322	33	.977858	1.02264
49.0121	51.0078	34	.980242	1.02016
49.1186	50.8972	35	.982373	1.01794
49.2137	50.7988	36	.984275	1.01598
49.2987	50.7113	37	.985973	1.01423
49.3745	50.6335	38	.987489	1.01267
49.4421	50.5642	39	.988842	1.01128
49.5025	50.5025	40	.990049	1.01005
49.5563	50.4476	41	.991127	1.00895
49.6044	50.3988	42	.992088	1.00798
49.6473	50.3552	43	.992946	1.0071
49.6855	50.3165	44	.99371	1.00633
49.7196	50.282	45	.994392	1.00564
49.75	50.2512	46	.995001	1.00502
49.7772	50.2239	47	.995543	1.00448
49.8013	50.1994	48	.996027	1.00399
49.8229	50.1777	49	.996458	1.00355
49.8421	50.1584	50	.996843	1.00317

Courtesy of H. Stinehelfer

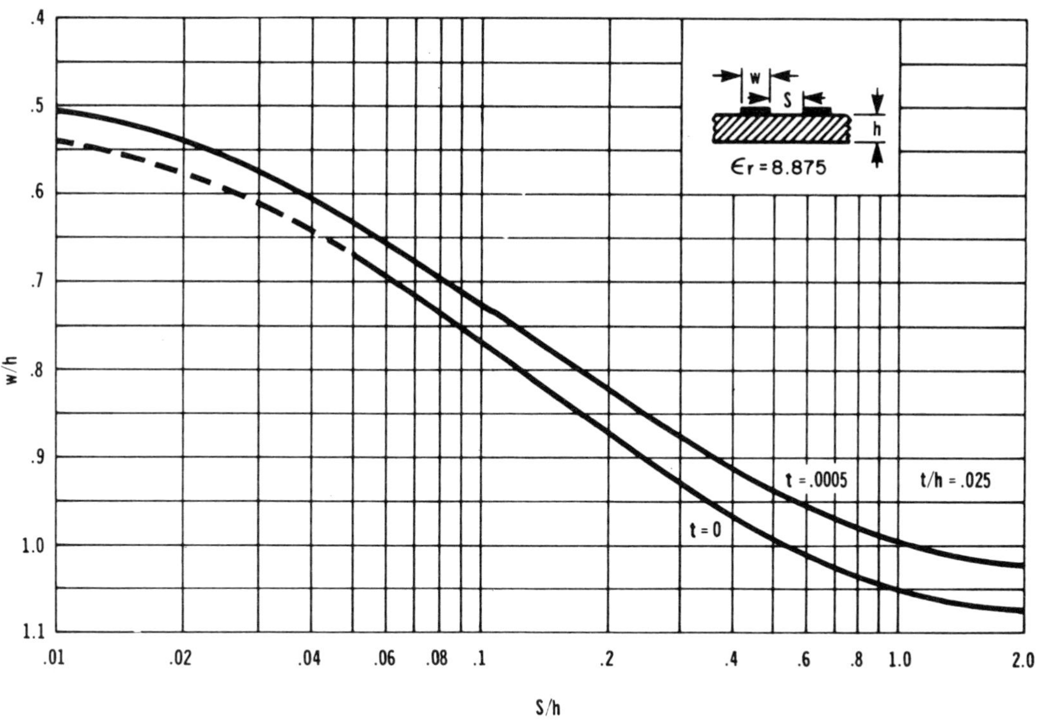

FIGURE 1 MICROSTRIP COUPLER

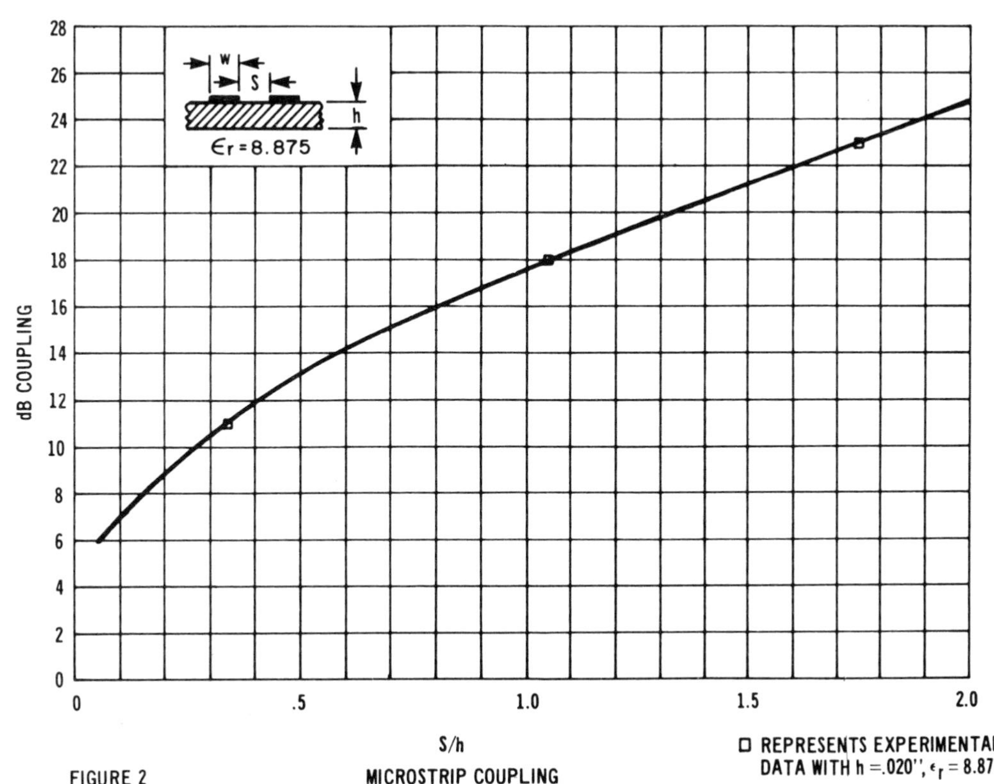

FIGURE 2 MICROSTRIP COUPLING

Courtesy of H. Stinehelfer

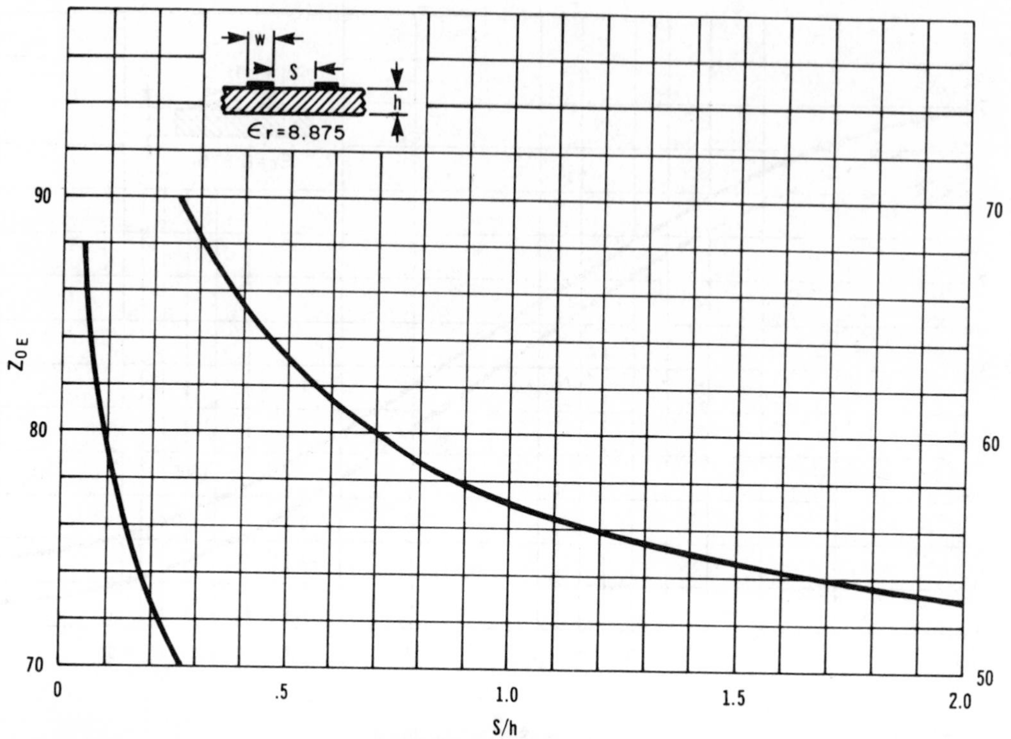

FIGURE 3 MICROSTRIP EVEN IMPEDANCE

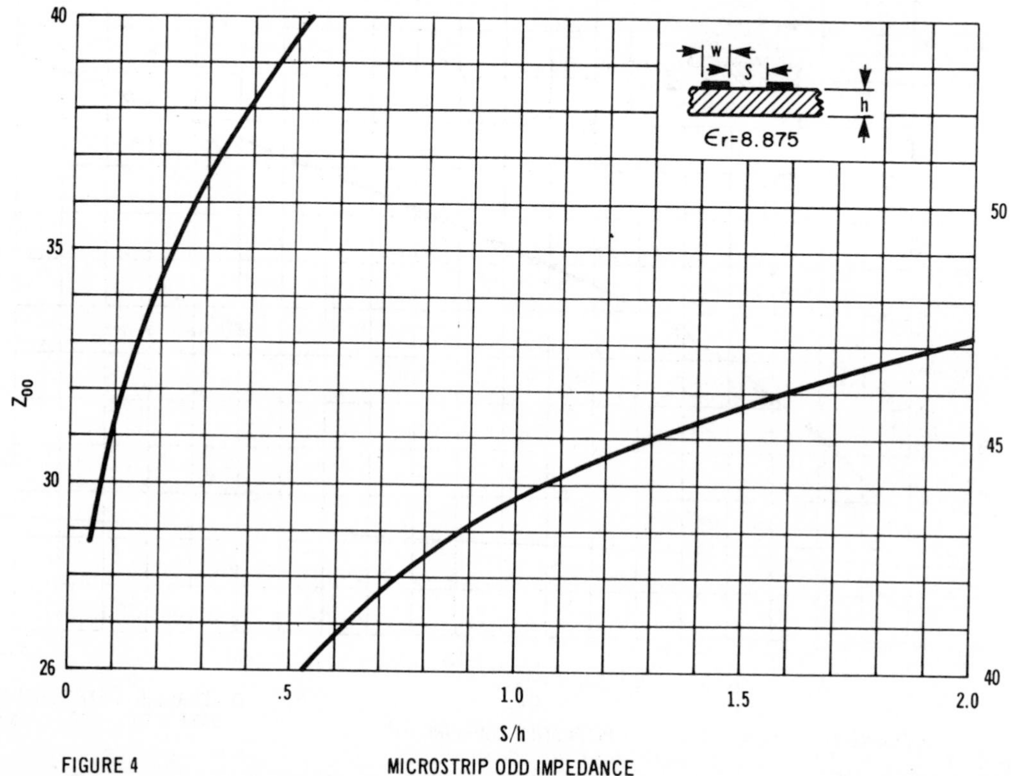

FIGURE 4 MICROSTRIP ODD IMPEDANCE

Courtesy of H. Stinehelfer

CHARACTERISTIC IMPEDANCE OF DIELECTRIC SUPPORTED STRIP TRANSMISSION LINE

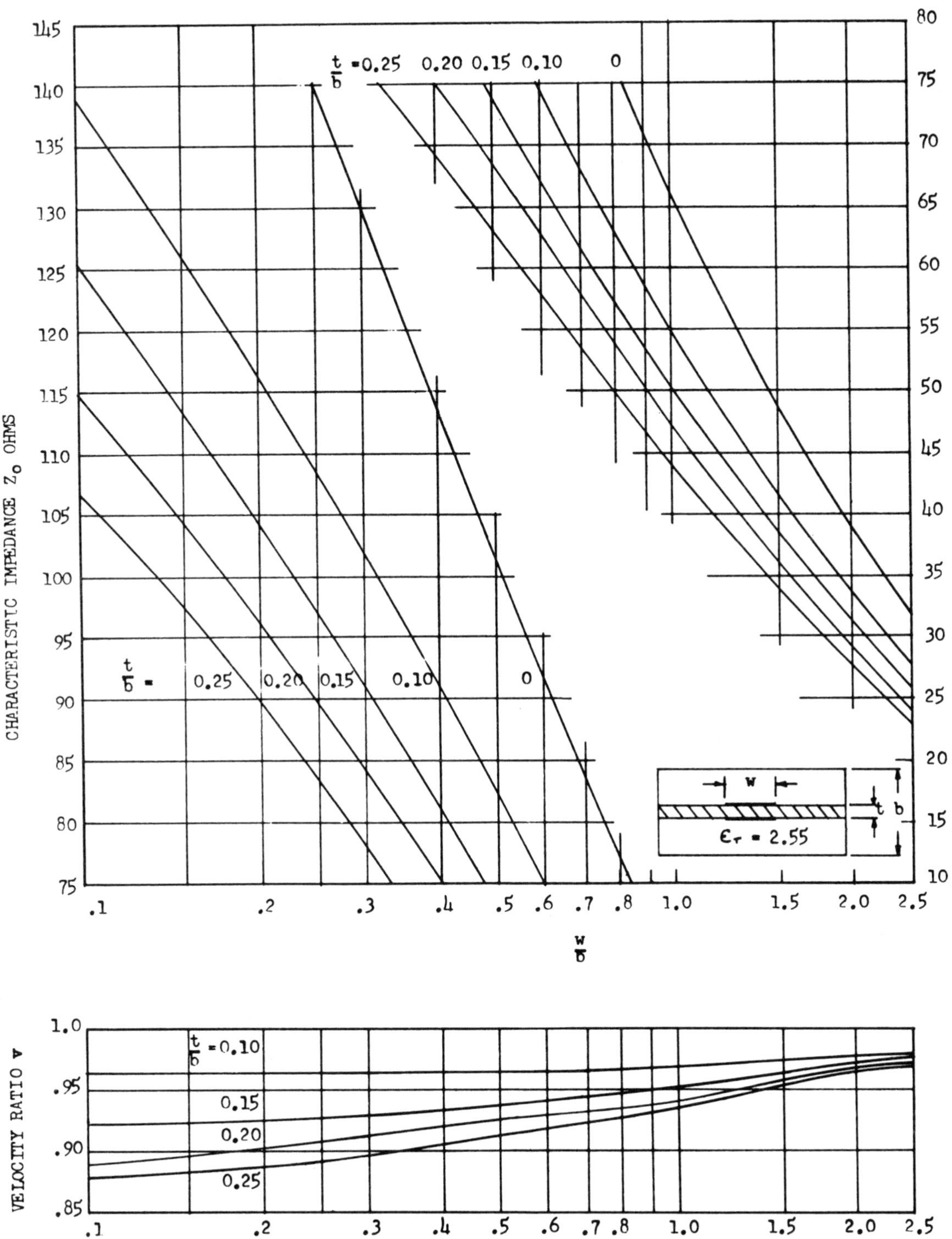

Courtesy of H. Stinehelfer

FILTERS AND CAVITIES

MICROWAVE FILTERS

(In describing the applications of microwave filters, the terms narrowband, moderate band, and wideband are taken to signify percentage bandwidth in the approximate ranges of 0-20%, 10-50%, 40% and up, respectively.)

I. COMMENSURATE LINELENGTH TEM FILTERS

Commensurate linelength filters exhibit periodic passbands and stopbands, with passbands (or stopbands) occurring at odd multiples (f_o, $3f_o$, $5f_o$, etc.) of the frequency for which the linelengths are one quarter wave. They are normally utilized as highpass and lowpass filters or as bandpass and bandstop filters by neglecting higher frequency repeating responses. Exact design and synthesis procedures applicable for arbitrary bandwidth are presently known for most commensurate linelength filter types. In many cases, element value tables are available. The following section summarizes the characteristics of several commonly used commensurate linelength filter forms and indicates where detailed design information, both approximate and exact, can be found.

LOWPASS FILTERS | HIGHPASS-BANDPASS

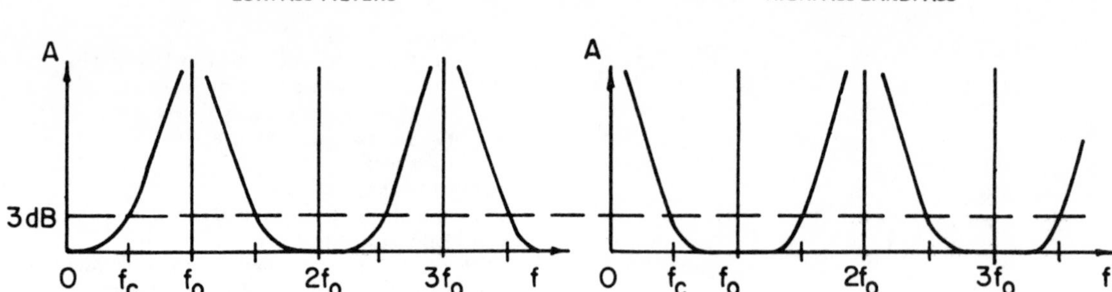

MAXIMALLY FLAT

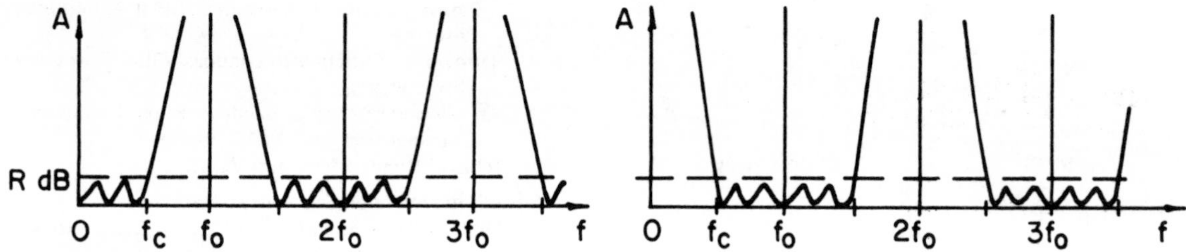

CHEBYSHEV

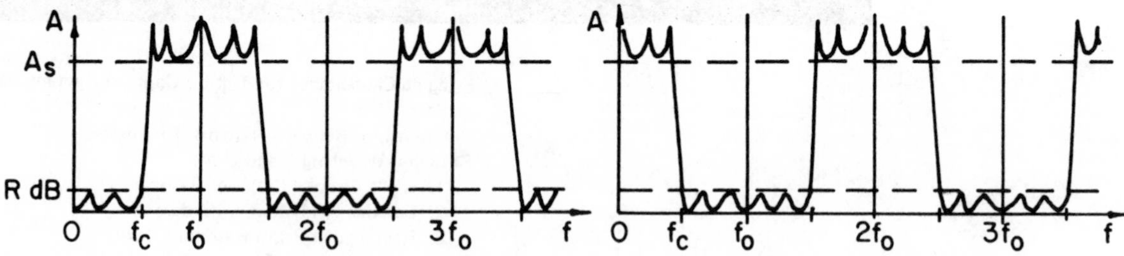

ELLIPTIC FUNCTION

Typical Response Characteristics For Commensurate Linelength Filters

- All Linelengths θ_o Equal 90 Degrees at $f = f_o$.
- Response is Symmetric About f_o in All Cases.

Courtesy of R. Wenzel

INTERDIGITAL

Bandpass filter with a single d-c attenuation pole for SCTL designs and a third-order d-c attenuation pole for OCTL designs (assuming no coupling between non-adjacent lines). A very compact filter suitable for bandwidths of a few percent to octave and greater. Can be fabricated in stripline or without dielectric support.

Approximate Design: Narrowband (1) - (3), Wideband (1), (2).

Exact Design: Arbitrary Bandwidth (4) - (6).

Element Value Tables for Exact Design: OCTL and SCTL designs for maximally flat and Chebyshev response (6). Data applicable to SCTL maximally flat designs (7). Partial tables for OCTL case (8).

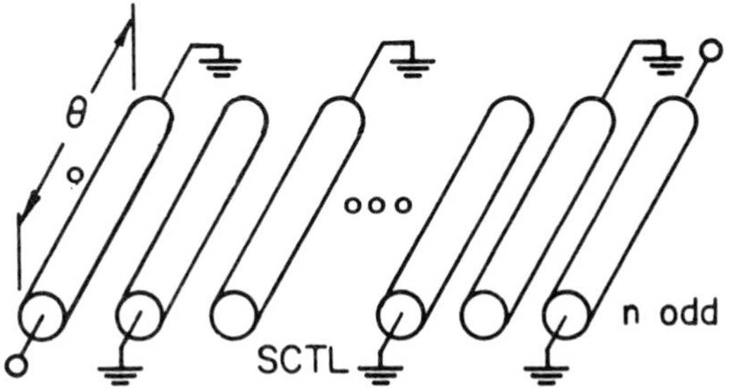

SHORT-CIRCUITED TERMINATING LINES

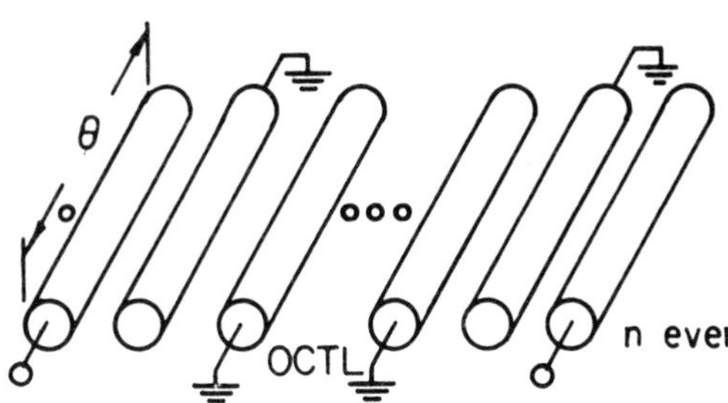

OPEN-CIRCUITED TERMINATING LINES

(Ports on same side of filter for number of sections (N) even, and on opposite side for (N) odd.)

PARALLEL COUPLED

Bandpass filters with the same basic prototype as the SCTL interdigital. The OC and SC filters are duals and have a single pole of attenuation at dc. Can be utilized for both narrow and wide bandwidths, with solid bars or an overlapped stripline configuration being required for wideband applications. The OC structure is normally preferred for narrowband applications and is usually realized using printed circuit stripline techniques.

Approximate Design: Narrowband (2), (9), (10) Wideband (2), (9).

Exact Design: Arbitrary Bandwidth (4) - (6), (11), (12).

Element Value Tables for Exact Design: Chebyshev and maximally flat element values can be obtained from SCTL interdigital tables (6) or from (7) for maximally flat designs.

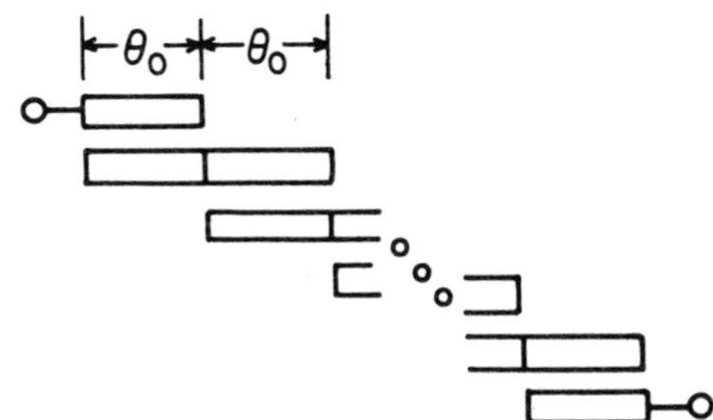

OC - OPEN-CIRCUITED COUPLED LINES

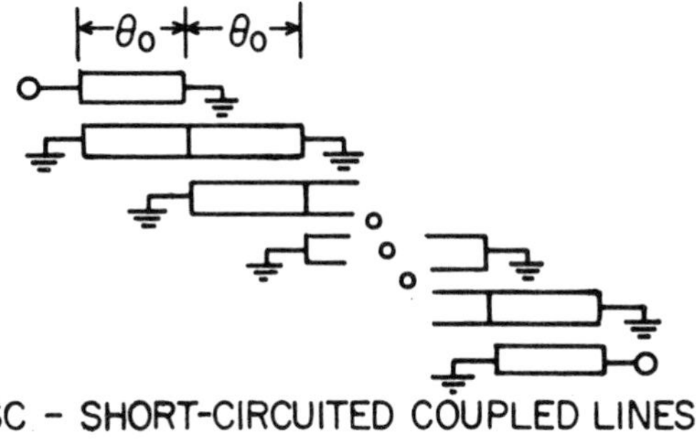

SC - SHORT-CIRCUITED COUPLED LINES

SHUNT SHORTED STUB

Bandpass filter with same prototype and response characteristics as SCTL interdigital and SC parallel-coupled filters. Large in size in comparison to the interdigital configuration, but practical to construct for wide bandwidths of octave and greater and for use at high frequencies where linelengths are short. The attenuation response deteriorates with increasing bandwidth due to the existence of only one d-c attenuation pole. Readily fabricated in stripline or without dielectric support.

Approximate Design: (2), (9).

Exact Design: (11), (12), (13)

Element Value Tables for Exact Design: Chebyshev and maximally flat element values can be obtained from SCTL interdigital tables (6) or from (7) for maximally flat designs.

SHUNT-SHORTED STUB

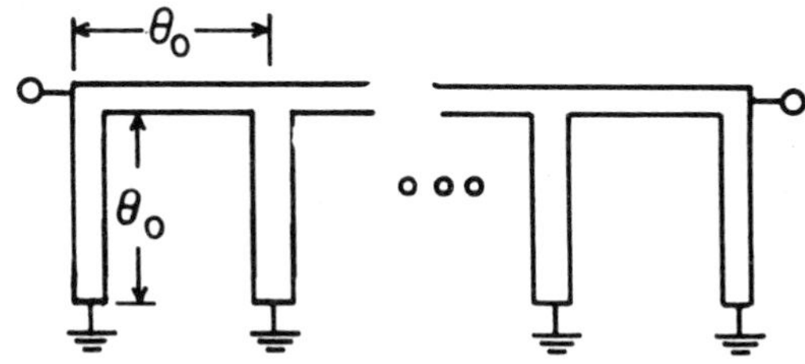

DIGITAL-ELLIPTIC BANDPASS AND BANDSTOP

A very compact structure for achieving high-selectivity wideband designs. Provides equal-ripple response in both passband and stop-band with optimum transition characteristics. Particularly good for bandwidths of octave and greater. Difficult to construct at frequencies above C-band due to mechanical complexity.

Exact Design: (14), (15)

Element Value Tables: (16), (17), (18).

DIGITAL-ELLIPTIC BANDPASS AND BANDSTOP

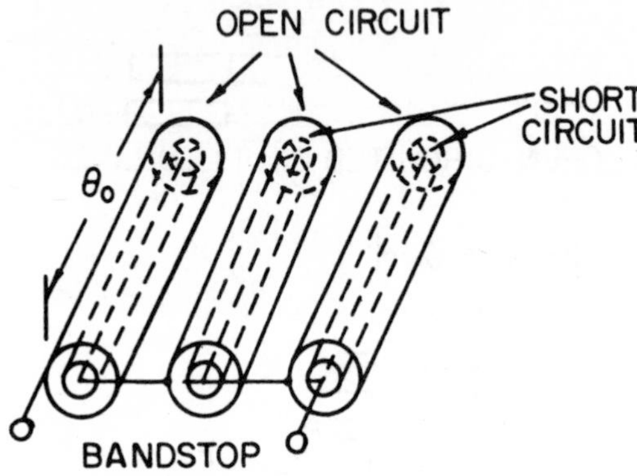

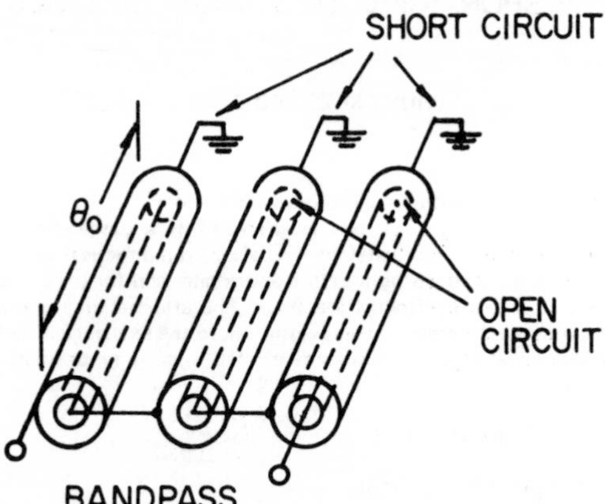

ELLIPTICAL FUNCTION WITH NO SERIES STUBS

Representative network structures for elliptic-function response that do not require series stubs. Many other similar line configurations can be utilized. Physical realizations are substantially larger than the digital-elliptic configuration, however, realizations (A) and (C) can be used to achieve moderate or narrowband designs. Impedance values for the stub-type filter (B) are often difficult to realize in a practical structure when redundant line elements are utilized (19). Recent investigations (20) (21) indicate that optimum designs (i.e., designs where all line elements contribute to the attenuation characteristic) not only improve performance, but also result in improved element values. Optimum designs, however, do not utilize available element value tables.

Exact Design: Type A - (22)
Type B - (19) - (21), (23)
Type C - (23)

Element Value Tables: All types can be designed using lumped-element prototype tables (16) - (18). Tables giving line impedances are available for type B with n = 5 (19). Optimum designs can be obtained from (15), (19), (20).

ELLIPTICAL FUNCTION WITH NO SERIES STUBS

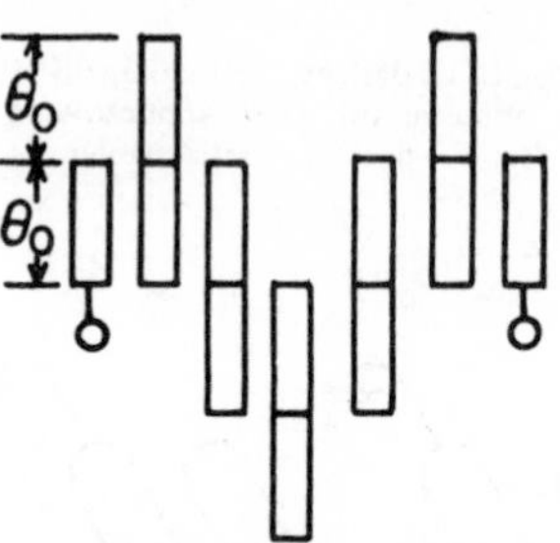

A. INTERDIGITAL TYPE BANDPASS

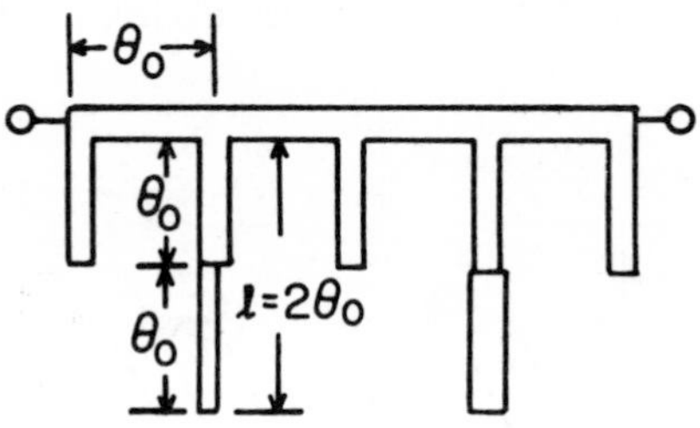

B. STUB-TYPE BANDSTOP

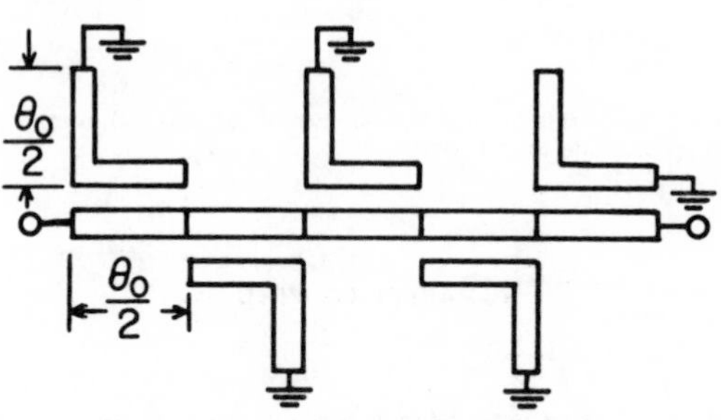

C. NARROWBAND COUPLED LINE CONFIGURATION BANDSTOP

BANDSTOP FILTERS

A class of bandstop filters suitable for both narrowband and wideband applications. All configurations have an nth order pole of attenuation at the quarter wave frequency (where n is the number of stubs or coupled line sections). Type (A) is often used as a lowpass filter and is suitable for wide bandstop designs. Type (B) (spurline) provides a more compact structure for moderate bandwidth applications, while types (C) and (D) are useful for narrow bandstop designs. Can be designed in an exact manner using a lowpass lumped-element prototype and redundant line sections or in an optimum manner by use of special approximating functions. The optimum design provides significant improvement in skirt selectivity for wideband designs, but negligible improvement for narrowband designs.

Exact Design: From lumped-element prototypes using redundant line elements (2), (11), (24), (25), (26), and others.

Optimum Design: (12)

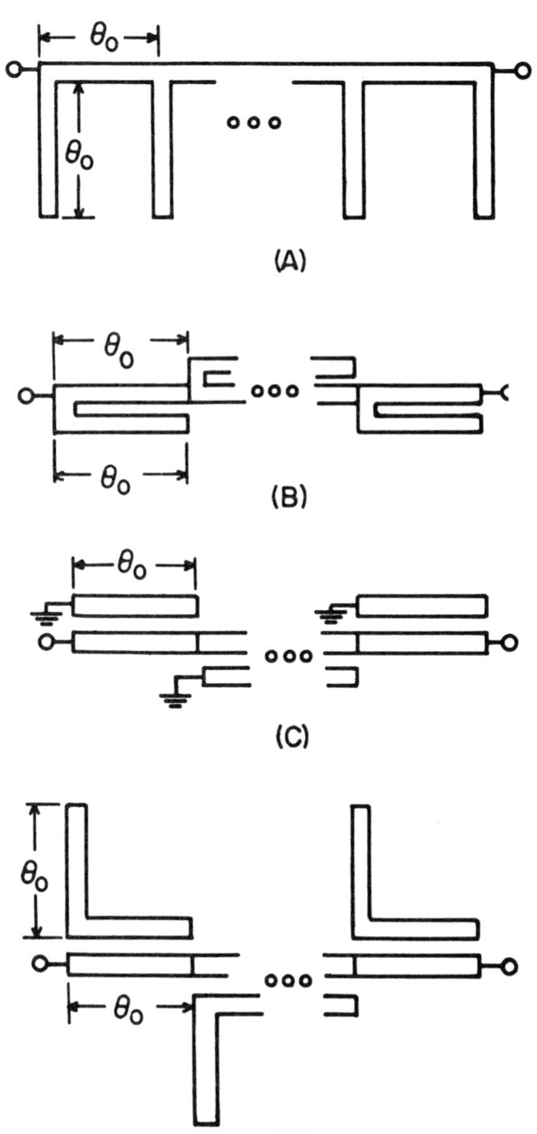

SERIES STUB FILTERS

Bandpass and bandstop structures suitable for moderate band to wideband applications. Bandpass structure (A) has a single pole of attenuation at dc and a prototype identical to the OC parallel-coupled filter (Type 2). Bandstop structure (B) has an nth order pole of attenuation at the quarterwave frequency and a prototype identical with the bandstop structures of type ⑥ . For design references, see filter types ② and ⑥

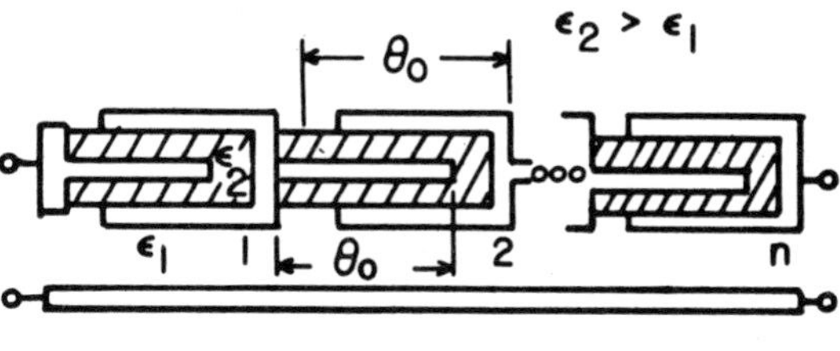

(A) BANDPASS

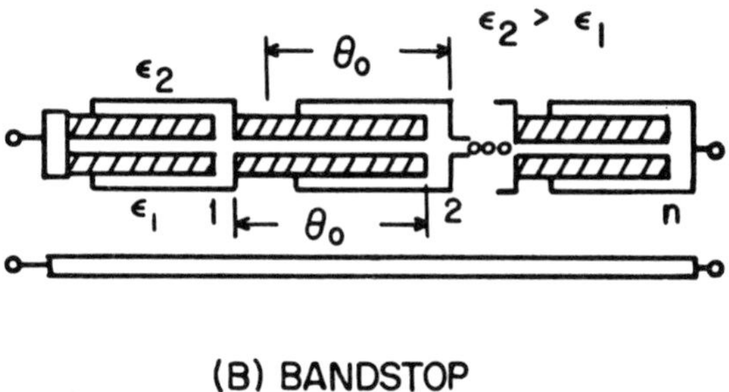

(B) BANDSTOP

FILTERS WITH SERIES AND SHUNT STUBS

Bandstop and bandpass structures with multiple poles of attenuation at the quarterwave frequency and dc, respectively. Practical structures for achieving precise designs with good skirt selectivity for very wide bandwidths of octave to 5:1 and greater. Impractical impedance values occur for narrowband designs. Many physical realizations are possible and multiple stub configurations can be effectively utilized. May be designed from lumped-element prototypes using redundant line sections or in an optimum manner using special synthesis methods.

Exact Design: From lumped-element prototypes using redundant line elements (11), (24), (25).

Optimum Design: (12), (13)

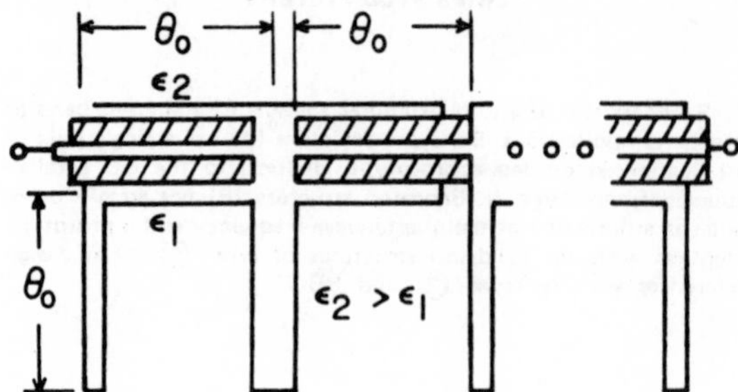

(A) BANDSTOP

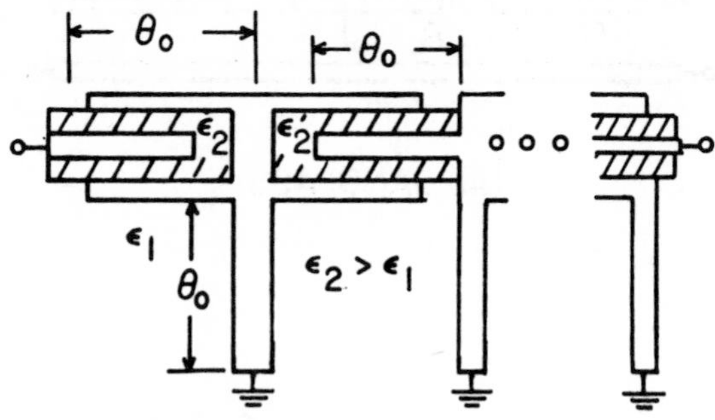

(B) BANDPASS

STEPPED IMPEDANCE FILTERS

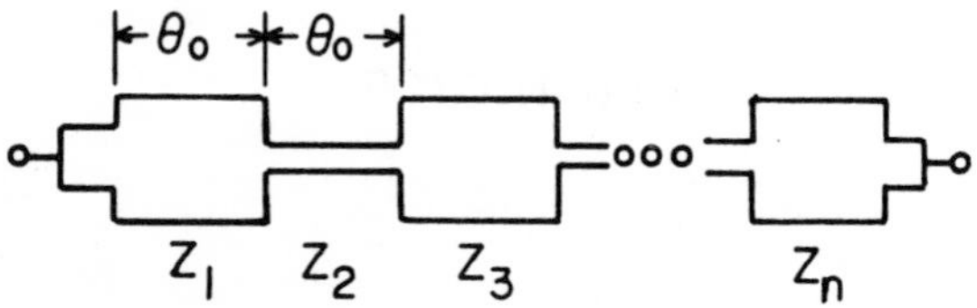

Bandstop filter normally used as a lowpass filter. Maximum stopband attenuation is finite due to no real frequency poles of attenuation. A relatively large and inefficient structure in comparison to other bandstop or lowpass designs.

Exact Design and Element Value Tables: (27)

II. SEMI-LUMPED-ELEMENT FILTERS

Semi-lumped-element filters utilize a combination of distributed elements and lumped elements. At the present time, all design procedures are approximate. These filters are normally used for narrow or moderate bandwidth designs, and are widely used because of relative simplicity of design and construction. Because the elements utilized are non-commensurable, spurious responses do not necessarily occur at integer multiples of the primary response, and filters with relatively wide stopbands can be achieved. Many structural forms are used, and several common types are summarized below.

COMB-LINE FILTER

A compact bandpass filter suitable for narrow bandwidth designs using distributed line elements loaded with lumped-element capacitors. θ_1 can be of arbitrary length for a given passband frequency, but is normally in the vicinity of 45 degrees or less at band center. Normally yields a design with a very broad upper stopband. Attenuation characteristics are non-symmetric.

Approximate Design: (2), (28).

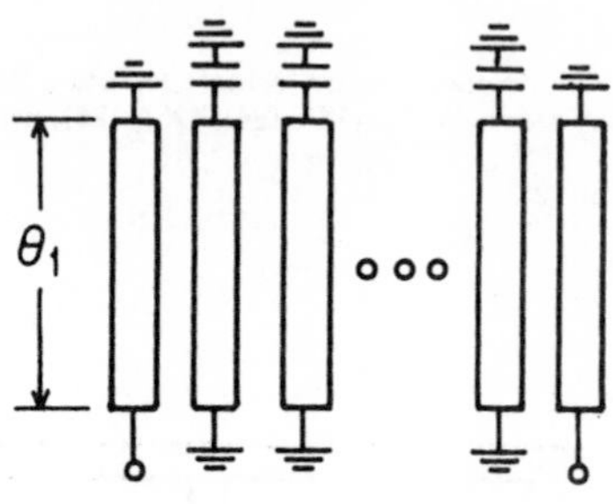

CAPACITATIVE GAP FILTER

Bandpass filter with a single pole of attenuation at dc and finite maximum attenuation above the passband. Dielectric support is required. Suitable for use as a narrowband bandpass filter. Can be used as a pseudo-highpass filter of approximately octave band with large capacitive coupling values being required.

Approximate Design: (2), (29), (30).

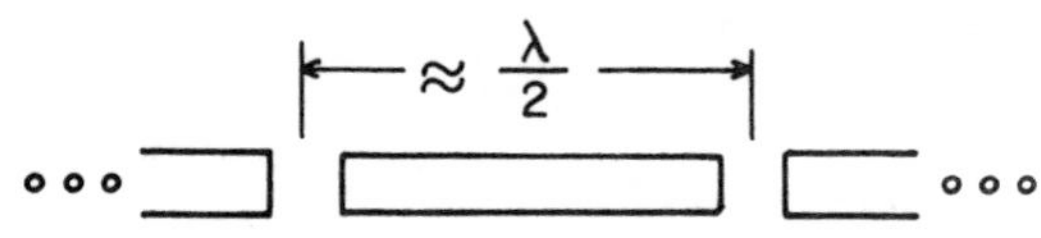

LOW PASS FILTERS USING SEMI-LUMPED ELEMENTS

Common lowpass filter form where short lengths of high and low impedance lines are used to approximate series inductors and shunt capacitors, respectively. Relatively easy to construct and capable of providing good performance with first spurious response not occurring until five times the cutoff frequency or greater.

Approximate Design for many types: (2).

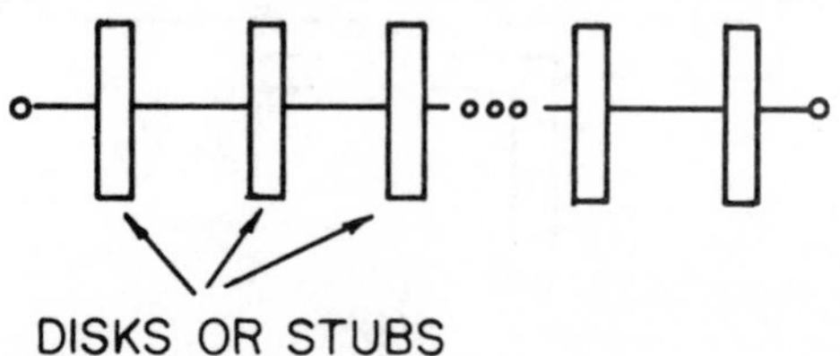

HIGH PASS FILTERS USING SEMI-LUMPED ELEMENTS

Common filter form used to achieve psuedo-highpass designs with good response for somewhat greater than an octave band. Usually constructed using split-block construction. For typical design procedures, see (2).

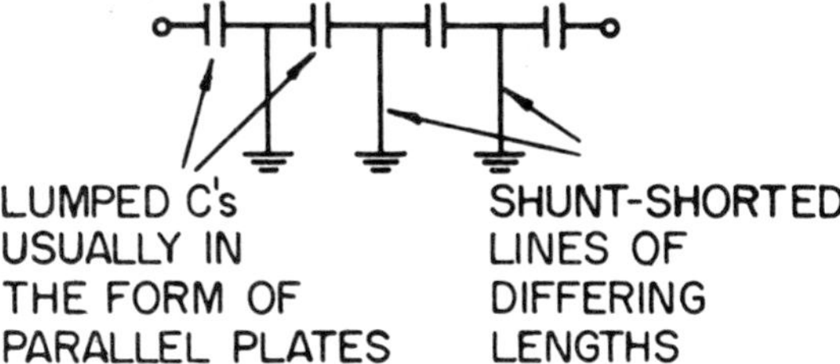

III. WAVEGUIDE AND CAVITY FILTERS

In general, waveguide and cavity filters are of two basic types: direct coupled and quarter-wave coupled. Available design procedures are approximate and are based on either a lumped-element lowpass prototype or a stepped-impedance prototype. The lumped-element prototype approach is usually employed for bandwidths up to 20% with moderate passband ripple values, with the stepped-impedance prototype being preferable for low passband ripple values and/or wide bandwidths.

DIRECT COUPLED FILTERS

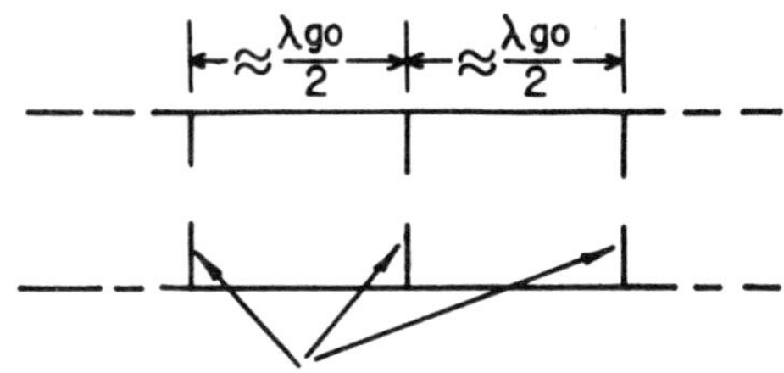

POSTS, VANES, OR IRISES

QUARTER-WAVE COUPLED FILTERS

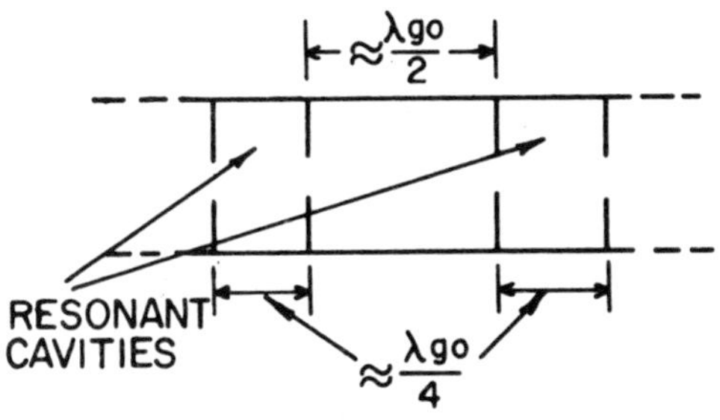

DIELECTRIC RESONATOR FILTERS

Allows the achievement of low-loss narrowband filters in a very compact structure. With present materials, center frequency change as a function of temperature is excessive.

Design References: (36), (37).

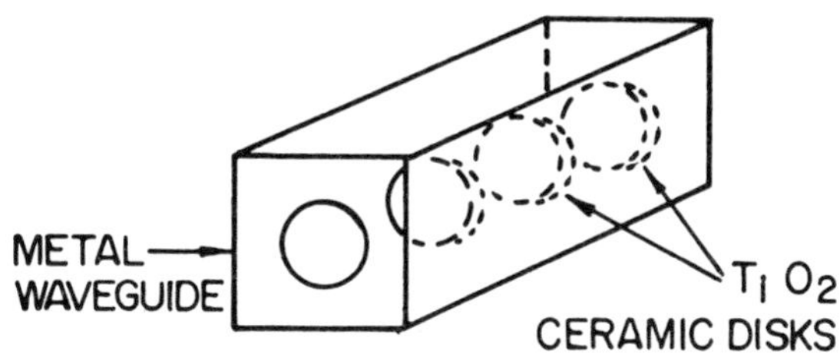

IV. DIPLEXERS AND MULTIPLEXERS

Multiplexing filters provide a means of subdividing a wide frequency band into a number of narrower bands, or of combining frequency bands at a common junction. They are of two general types: non-contiguous and contiguous. In a non-contiguous multiplexer, the frequency bands of interest are separated in frequency, whereas for the contiguous type, the frequency bands are adjacent, with no intervening guard band. Because of practical limitations of interconnecting many filters at a common junction, most microwave multiplexers are constructed using a cascade of suitable diplexers. The achievement of good performance in a multiplexer requires that special design and interconnection techniques be utilized. In the following summary, emphasis is placed on diplexers, with extension to multiplexers following a straightforward manner.

NARROW BAND NON-CONTIGUOUS FILTERS

Narrowband non-contiguous diplexers are readily constructed by interconnecting narrowband doubly-terminated bandpass (DTBP) filters with lengths of transmission line (ℓ_1 and ℓ_2) such that each filter presents essentially an open circuit at the common junction in the passband of the other filter. Detailed interconnection schemes for multi-channel devices can be found in [2], [38].

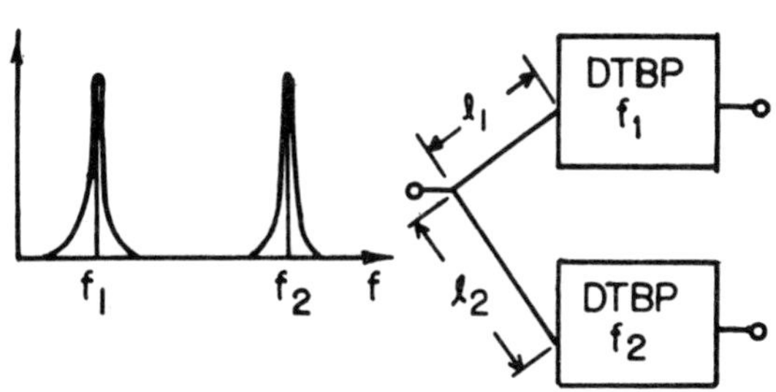

WIDEBAND NON-CONTIGUOUS FILTERS

Interconnections of doubly-terminated bandpass filters with wide passbands usually results in harmful interaction because each filter presents an undesirable reactance in the passband of the other. Special compensating networks can be used to improve the performance, but design is not straightforward, and, in many cases, will never yield satisfactory performance. A cascade connection of a bandpass-bandstop contiguous diplexer and a bandpass filter can be used to provide the desired performance.

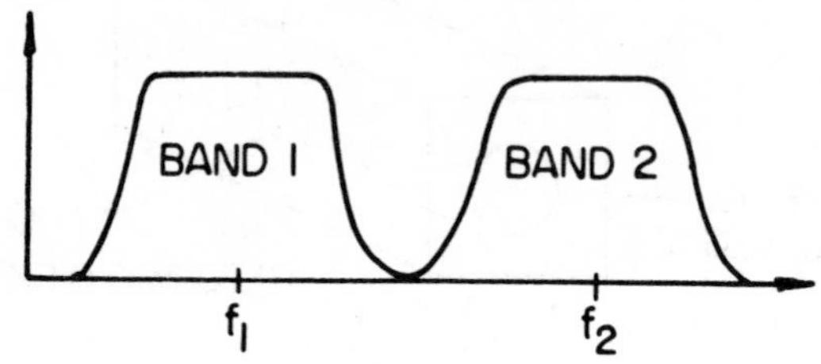

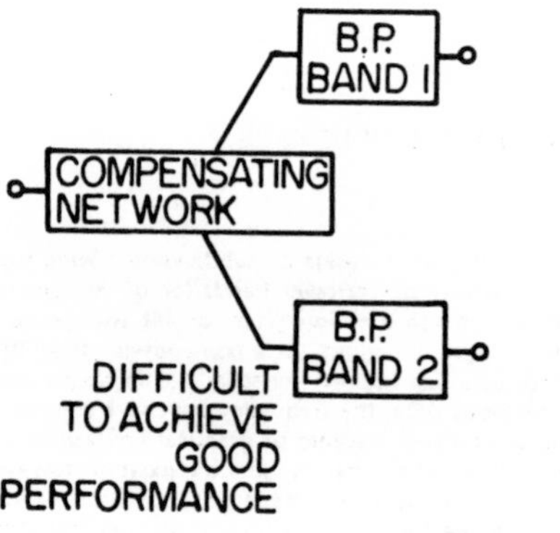

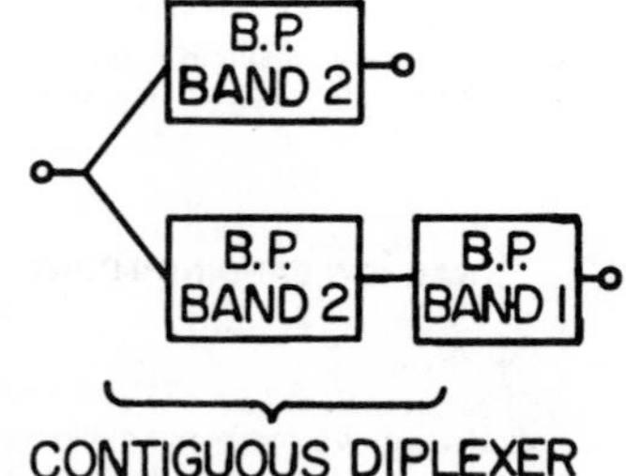

CONTIGUOUS BAND FILTERS

Filters that separate adjacent bands with a perfect match at the common port are defined to be complementary and require that the component filters be designed on a singly-terminated basis. If filters with ripple in the passband and monotonic stopbands are utilized, some mismatch must be introduced at the common port so that the resulting component filters are not perfectly complementary. However, with proper design, filters of this latter type can provide better selectivity for a given number of sections than complementary designs. Such filters, termed pseudo-complementary, can be designed to provide a very good input match, and are normally used in contiguous band designs. All complementary and pseudo-complementary designs provide a 3-dB or near 3-dB power split at the crossover frequencies.

COMPLEMENTARY FILTERS

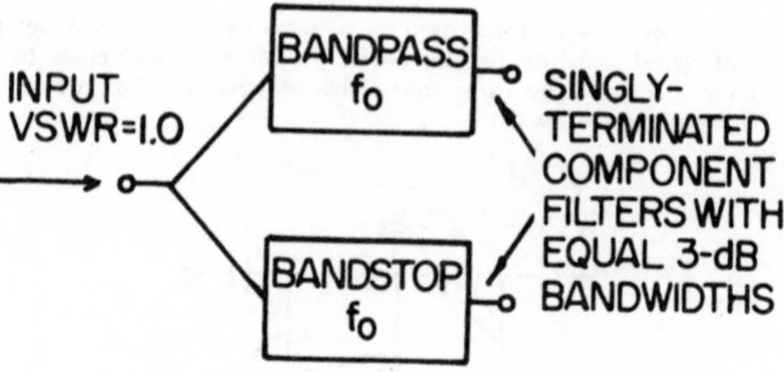

COMPLEMENTARY FILTERS

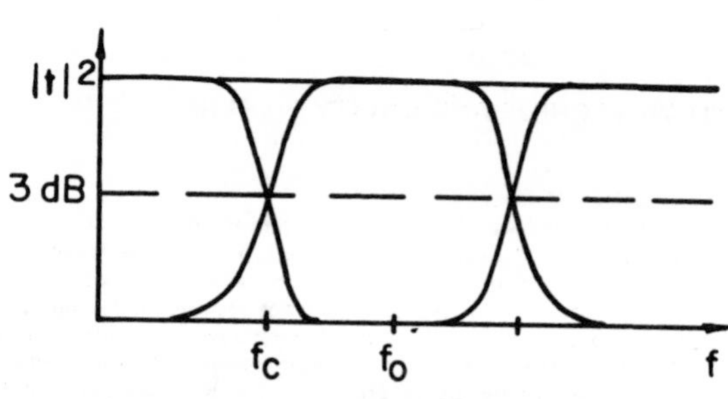

PSEUDO-COMPLEMENTARY FILTERS

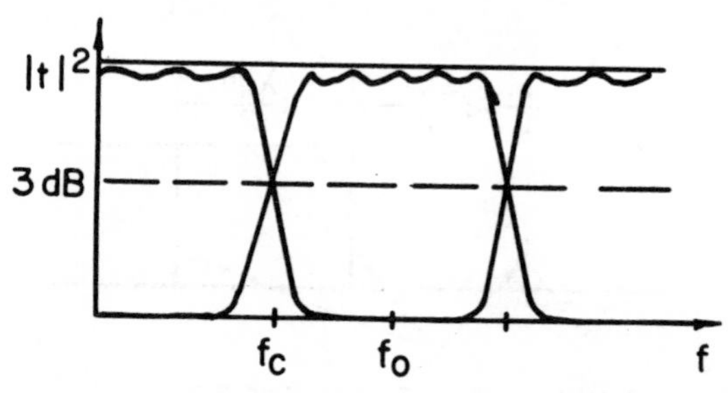

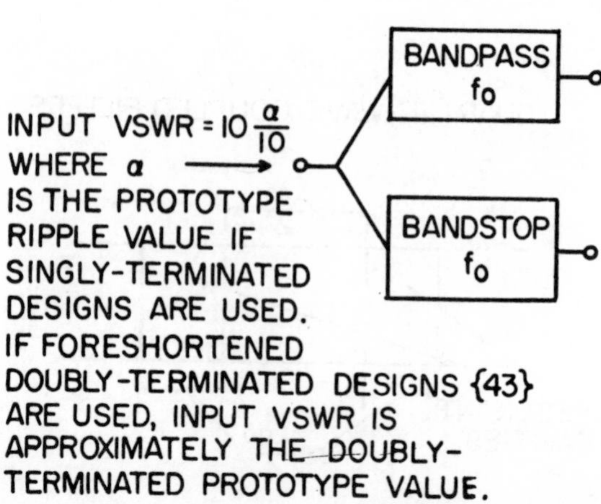

BANDPASS f_o
BANDSTOP f_o
INPUT VSWR = $10^{\frac{a}{10}}$
WHERE a
IS THE PROTOTYPE
RIPPLE VALUE IF
SINGLY-TERMINATED
DESIGNS ARE USED.
IF FORESHORTENED
DOUBLY-TERMINATED DESIGNS {43}
ARE USED, INPUT VSWR IS
APPROXIMATELY THE DOUBLY-
TERMINATED PROTOTYPE VALUE.

Several representative diplexer configurations are shown below with many other configurations being possible. Detailed discussions of complementary and psuedo-complementary filter design and interconnection can be found in [39] - [45].

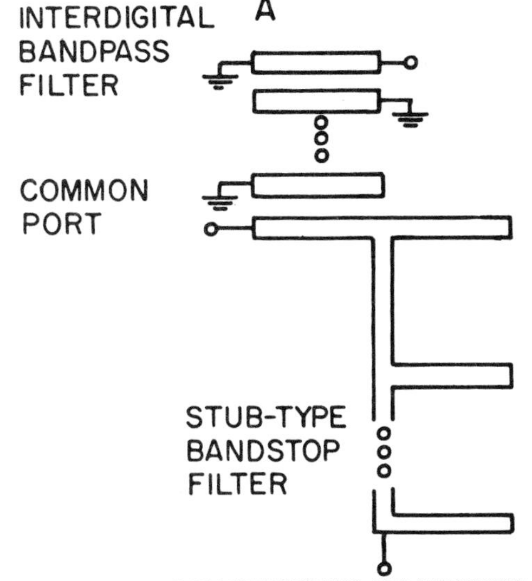

SUITABLE FOR BOTH NARROWBAND AND WIDEBAND DESIGNS. SEE (42), (43).

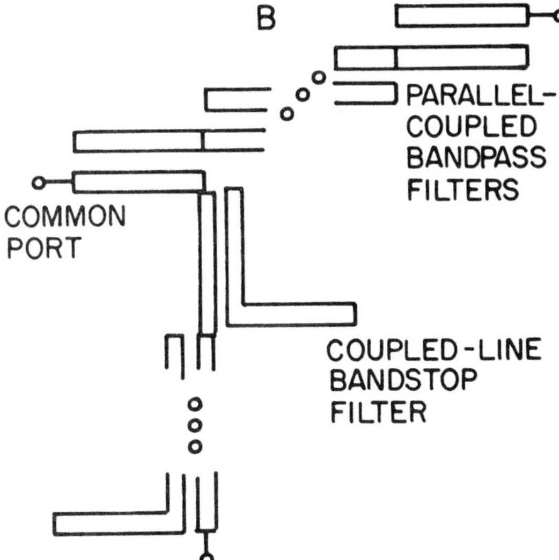

SUITABLE FOR NARROWBAND DESIGNS IN STRIPLINE WITH NO SHORT CIRCUITS. SEE (44).

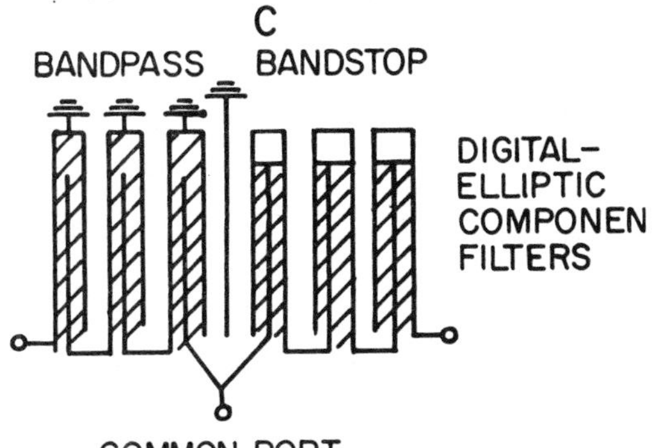

SUITABLE FOR WIDEBAND HIGH-SELECTIVITY DESIGNS. SEE (46).

OTHER MULTIPLEXING NETWORKS

A. DIRECTIONAL FILTERS

Constant resistance networks that provide contiguous-band diplexing. Can be cascaded without harmful interaction. Somewhat difficult to align for multiple section design. Typically do not provide extremely high isolation at the bandstop port due to misalignment, reflection, and dissipation loss. Can also be constructed in various types of waveguide. See [47], [48], [49].

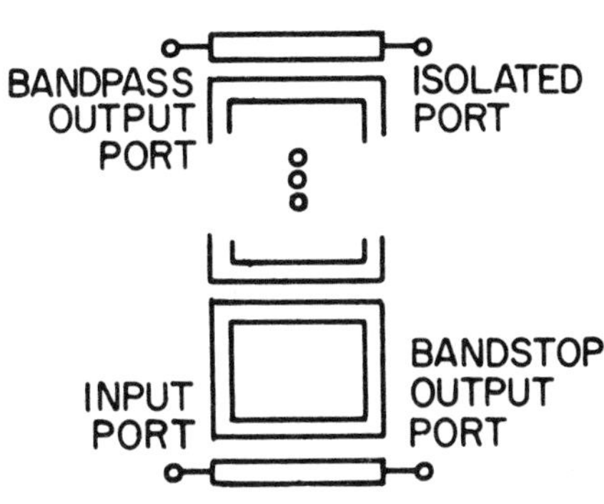

B. HYBRID DIPLEXERS

A convenient method for wideband or narrowband diplexing. Filters are identical and can be of bandpass or bandstop doubly-terminated design. Overlapped stripline couplers shown provide convenient port location, but conventional bar-line couplers can also be used. Major drawbacks are (1) poor isolation at the reflected port output due to finite directivity of couplers and mismatch of filters and (2) large size.

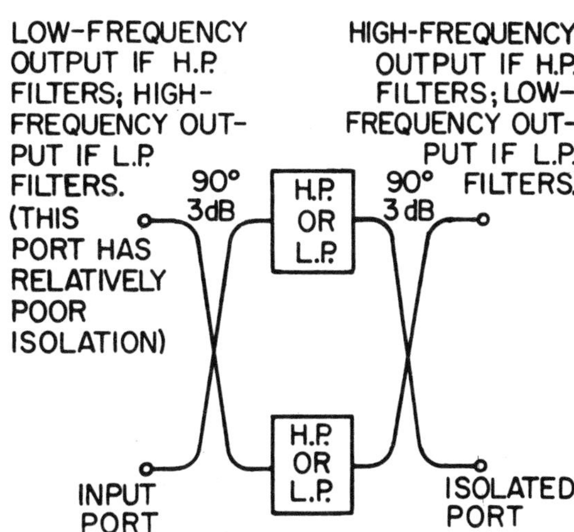

REFERENCES

(Extensive bibliographies and general reviews can be found in [50] - [54])

1. G. L. Matthaei, "Interdigital Band-Pass Filters," IRE TRANS. ON MICROWAVE THEORY AND TECHNIQUES, Vol. MTT-10, November, 1962, pp. 479-91.
2. G. L. Matthaei, L. Young, and E. M. T. Jones, Microwave Filters, Impedance Matching Networks, and Coupling Structures, (New York: McGraw-Hill), 1964.
3. M. Dishal, "A Simple Design Procedure for Small Percentage Bandwidth Round-Rod Interdigital Filters," (Correspondence), IEEE TRANS. ON MICROWAVE THEORY AND TECHNIQUES, Vol. MTT-13, No. 5, September, 1965, pp. 696-8.
4. R. J. Wenzel, "Exact Theory of Interdigital Band-Pass Filters and Related Coupled Structures," IEEE TRANS. ON MICROWAVE THEORY AND TECHNIQUES, Vol. MTT-13, No. 5, September, 1965, pp. 559-75.
5. R. J. Wenzel, "Exact Design Techniques For Microwave TEM Filters," Quarterly Progress Report, Contract DA28-043, AMC-00399(E), Bendix Research Laboratories, Southfield, Michigan, January, 1965. ASTIA No. AD-462-039.
6. R. J. Wenzel and M. C. Horton, "Exact Design Techniques For Microwave TEM Filters," Final Report, Contract DA28-043, AMC-00399(E), Bendix Research Laboratories, Southfield, Michigan, May, 1965. ASTIA No. AD 471-203.
7. W. W. Mumford, "Tables of Stub Admittances for Maximally Flat Filters Using Shorted Quarter-Wave Stubs," IEEE TRANS. ON MICROWAVE THEORY AND TECHNIQUES, Vol. MTT-13, No. 5, September, 1965, pp. 695-6.
8. R. J. Wenzel, "Theoretical and Practical Applications of Capacitance Matrix Transformations to TEM Network Design," IEEE TRANS. ON MICROWAVE THEORY AND TECHNIQUES, Vol. MTT-14, December, 1966, pp. 635-47.
9. G. L. Matthaei, "Design of Wide-Band (and Narrow-Band) Band-Pass Microwave Filters on the Insertion Loss Basis," IRE TRANS. ON MICROWAVE THEORY AND TECHNIQUES, Vol. MTT-8, No. 6, November, 1960, pp. 580-93.
10. S. B. Cohn, "Parallel-Coupled Transmission-Line-Resonator Filters," IRE TRANS. ON MICROWAVE THEORY AND TECHNIQUES, Vol. MTT-6, No. 2, April, 1958, pp. 223-31.
11. R. J. Wenzel, "Exact Design of TEM Microwave Networks Using Quarter-Wave Lines," IEEE TRANS. ON MICROWAVE THEORY AND TECHNIQUES, Vol. MTT-12, January, 1964, pp. 94-111.
12. M. C. Horton and R. J. Wenzel, "General Theory and Design of Optimum Quarter-Wave TEM Filters," IEEE TRANS. ON MICROWAVE THEORY AND TECHNIQUES, Vol. MTT-13, May, 1965, pp. 316-27.
13. H. J. Carlin and W. Kohler, "Direct Synthesis of Band-Pass Transmission Line Structures," IEEE TRANS. ON MICROWAVE THEORY AND TECHNIQUES, Vol. MTT-13, May, 1965, pp. 283-97.
14. M. C. Horton and R. J. Wenzel, "Realization of Microwave Filters with Equal-Ripple Response in Both Pass and Stop Bands," Proceedings of the Symposium on Generalized Networks, Vol. XVI, Polytechnic Institute of Brooklyn Press, Brooklyn, New York, April, 1966, pp. 257-87.
15. M. C. Horton and R. J. Wenzel, "The Digital-Elliptic Filter – A Compact Sharp-Cutoff Design for Wide Bandstop or Bandpass Requirements," IEEE TRANS. ON MICROWAVE THEORY AND TECHNIQUES, Vol. MTT-15, May, 1967, pp. 307-14.
16. R. Saal and E. Ulbrich, "On the Design of Filters by Synthesis," IRE TRANS. ON CIRCUIT THEORY, Vol. CT-5, December, 1958, pp. 284-327.
17. R. Saal, The Design of Filters Using the Catalogue of Normalized Low-Pass Filters, (Backang, West Germany: Telefunken, G.m.b.H.), 1961.
18. J. K. Skwirzynski, Design Theory and Data for Electric Filters, (London: Van Nostrand), 1965.
19. B. M. Schiffman and L. Young, "Design Tables fpr An Elliptic-Function Band-Stop Filter (N = 5)," IEEE TRANS. ON MICROWAVE THEORY AND TECHNIQUES, Vol. MTT-14, October, 1966, pp. 474-82.
20. L. Fraiture and J. Neirynck, "Optimum Elliptic-Function Filters For Distributed Constant Systems," IEEE TRANS. ON MICROWAVE THEORY AND TECHNIQUES, Vol. MTT-15, No. 8, August, 1967, pp. 482-3.
21. M. C. Horton and R. J. Wenzel, "The Effectiveness of Component Elements in Commensurate Linelength Filters," to be published in the IEEE TRANS. ON MICROWAVE THEORY AND TECHNIQUES, August, 1968.
22. R. Levy, "Three-Wire-Line Interdigital Filters of Chebyshev and Elliptic-Function Characteristics For Broad Bandwidths," Electronic Letters, Vol. 2, No. 12, December, 1966, pp. 13-4.
23. R. Levy and I. Whiteley, "Synthesis of Distributed Elliptic-Function Filters From Lumped-Constant Prototypes," IEEE TRANS. ON MICROWAVE THEORY AND TECHNIQUES, Vol. MTT-14, November, 1966, pp. 506-17.
24. N. Ozaki and J. Ishii, "Synthesis of a Class of Strip-Line Filters," IRE TRANS. ON CIRCUIT THEORY, Vol. CT-5, June, 1958, pp. 104-9.
25. A. I. Grayzel, "A Synthesis Procedure for Transmission-Line Networks," IRE TRANS. ON CIRCUIT THEORY, Vol. CT-5, September, 1958, pp. 172-81.
26. B. M. Schiffman and G. L. Matthaei, "Exact Design of Band-Stop Microwave Filters," IEEE TRANS. ON MICROWAVE THEORY AND TECHNIQUES, Vol. MTT-12, January, 1964, pp. 6-15.
27. R. Levy, "Tables of Element Values for the Distributed Low-Pass Prototype Filter," IEEE TRANS. ON MICROWAVE THEORY AND TECHNIQUES, Vol. MTT-13, No. 5, September, 1965, pp. 514-36.
28. G. L. Matthaei, "Comb-Line Band-Pass Filters of Narrow or Moderate Bandwidth," Microwave Journal, Vol. 6, August, 1963, pp. 82-91.
29. S. B. Cohn, "Direct-Coupled-Resonator Filters," PROCEEDINGS OF THE IRE, February, 1957, pp. 187-96.
30. G. L. Ragan, Microwave Transmission, (New York: McGraw-Hill), 1948, p. 641.
31. W. W. Mumford, "Maximally-Flat Filters in Waveguide," Bell System Technical Journal, Vol. 27, October, 1948, pp. 684-713.
32. S. B. Cohn, "Direct-Coupled-Resonator Filters," PROCEEDINGS OF THE IRE, Vol. 45, February, 1957, pp. 187-96.
33. L. Young, "Stepped Impedance Transformers and Filter Prototypes," IRE TRANS. ON MICROWAVE THEORY AND TECHNIQUES, Vol. MTT-10, September, 1962, pp. 339-59.
34. L. Young, "Direct-Coupled Cavity Filters For Wide and Narrow Bandwidths," IRE TRANS. ON MICROWAVE THEORY AND TECHNIQUES, Vol. MTT-11, May, 1963, pp. 162-78.
35. R. Levy, "Theory of Direct-Coupled-Cavity Filters," IEEE TRANS. ON MICROWAVE THEORY AND TECHNIQUES, Vol. MTT-15, No. 6, June, 1967, pp. 340-8.
36. W. H. Harrison, "A Miniature High-Q Bandpass Filter Employing Dielectric Resonators," IEEE TRANS. ON MICROWAVE THEORY AND TECHNIQUES, Vol. 16, No. 4, April, 1968, pp. 210-8.
37. S. B. Cohn, "Microwave Bandpass Filters Containing High-Q Dielectric Resonators," IEEE TRANS. ON MICROWAVE THEORY AND TECHNIQUES, Vol. 16, No. 4, April, 1968, pp. 218-27.
38. G. C. Southworth, Principles and Applications of Waveguide Transmission, (New York: D. Van Nostrand), 1950, pp. 306-17.
39. E. G. Cristal and G. L. Matthaei, "A Technique for the Design of Multiplexers Having Contiguous Channels," IEEE TRANS. ON MICROWAVE THEORY AND TECHNIQUES, Vol. MTT-12, January, 1964, pp. 83-93.
40. R. G. Veltrop and R. B. Wilds, "Modified Tables for the Design of Optimum Diplexers," Microwave Journal, Vol. 7, June, 1964, pp. 76-80.
41. R. J. Wenzel, "Application of Exact Synthesis Methods to Multichannel Filter Design," IEEE TRANS. ON MICROWAVE THEORY AND TECHNIQUES, Vol. MTT-13, January, 1965, pp. 5-15.
42. G. L. Matthaei and E. G. Cristal, "Multiplexer Channel-Separating Units Using Interdigital and Parallel-Coupled Filters," IEEE TRANS. ON MICROWAVE THEORY AND TECHNIQUES, Vol. MTT-13, May, 1965, pp. 328-34.
43. G. L. Matthaei and E. G. Cristal, "Theory and Design of Diplexers and Multiplexers," Advances in Microwaves, Vol. 2, (New York: Academic Press), 1966.
44. R. J. Wenzel, "Wideband, High-Selectivity Diplexers Utilizing Digital-Elliptic Filters," IEEE TRANS. ON MICROWAVE THEORY AND TECHNIQUES, Vol. 15, No. 12, December, 1967, pp. 669-80.
45. R. J. Wenzel, "Printed Circuit Complementary Filters For Narrow Bandwidth Multiplexers," IEEE TRANS. ON MICROWAVE THEORY AND TECHNIQUES, Vol. 16, No. 3, March, 1968, pp. 147-57.
46. R. J. Wenzel, "Some General Properties of Commensurate Linelength Complementary and Psuedo-Complementary Microwave Filters," IEEE TRANS. ON MICROWAVE THEORY AND TECHNIQUES, Vol. MTT-16, No. 3, March, 1968, pp. 191-2.
47. F. S. Coale, "A Traveling-Wave Directional Filter," IRE TRANS. ON MICROWAVE THEORY AND TECHNIQUES, Vol. MTT-4, No. 4, October, 1956, pp. 256-60.
48. R. D. Standley, "Frequency Response of Strip-Line Traveling Wave Directional Filters," IEEE TRANS. ON MICROWAVE THEORY AND TECHNIQUES, Vol. MTT-11, July, 1963, pp. 264-65.
49. R. L. Williams, "A Three-Cavity Circularly Polarized Waveguide Directional Filter Yielding a Maximally Flat Response," IRE TRANS. ON MICROWAVE THEORY AND TECHNIQUES, Vol. MTT-10, September, 1962, pp. 321-8.
50. L. Young, "Microwave Filters – 1965," IEEE TRANS. ON MICROWAVE THEORY AND TECHNIQUES, Vol. MTT-13, September, 1965, pp. 488-508.
51. L. Young, "Reflections on Microwave Filters and Couplers," Microwave Journal, Vol. 11, No. 4, April, 1968, pp. 54-63.
52. L. Young, "Microwave Filters to Combat RF Interference," IEEE TRANS. ON ELECTROMAGNETIC COMPATIBILITY, to be published in June, 1968.
53. R. J. Wenzel, "The Modern Network Theory Approach to Microwave Filter Design," IEEE TRANS. ON ELECTROMAGNETIC COMPATIBILITY, to be published in June, 1968.
54. The Microwave Engineers' Handbook and Buyers' Guide, (Dedham, Massachusetts: Horizon House, Inc.), 1967 and 1968.

1. Normalized Lowpass Prototype

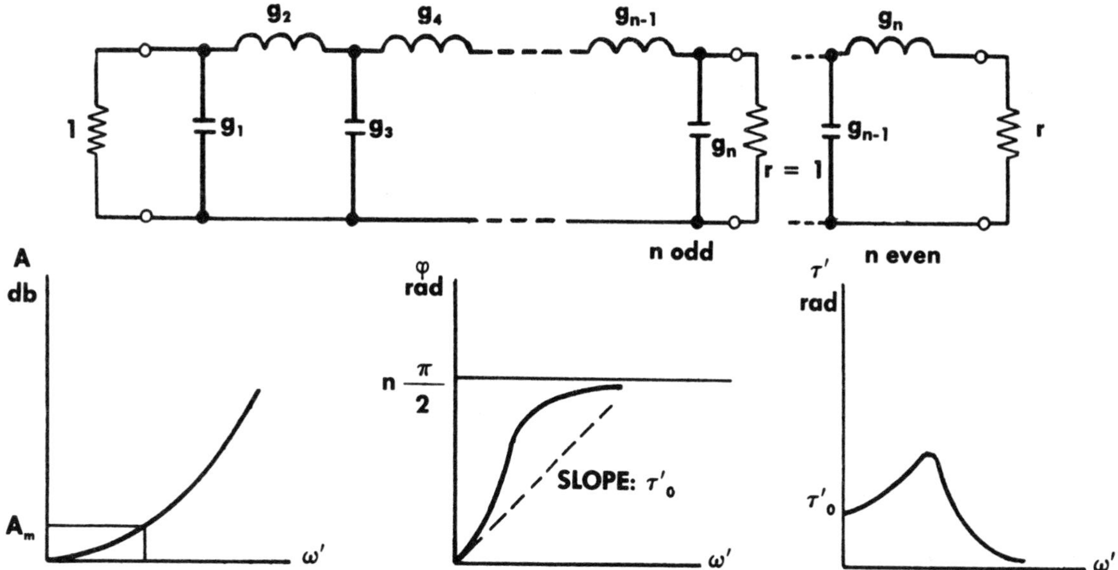

g_k : Element values
ω' : Normalized frequency variable
ω'_c : Normalized cut-off frequency
A : Attenuation in db
A_m : Max. passband attenuation in db
φ : Phase response
τ' : Normalized delay $\frac{d\varphi}{d\omega'}$ in radians
τ'_0 : Normalized zero-frequency delay $= \frac{1}{2} \sum_{k=1}^{n} g_k \; (r = 1)$

a. MAXIMALLY FLAT AMPLITUDE RESPONSE

$$r = 1 \text{ for all } n$$

$$g_k = 2 \sin \left[\frac{(2k-1)\pi}{2n}\right], k = 1,2,\ldots,n$$

$$A = 10 \log_{10}(1 + \omega'^{2n}) \text{ db}$$

$$\varphi(\omega'_c) = n\frac{\pi}{4}$$

$$\tau'_0 = \frac{1}{\sin \frac{\pi}{2n}}$$

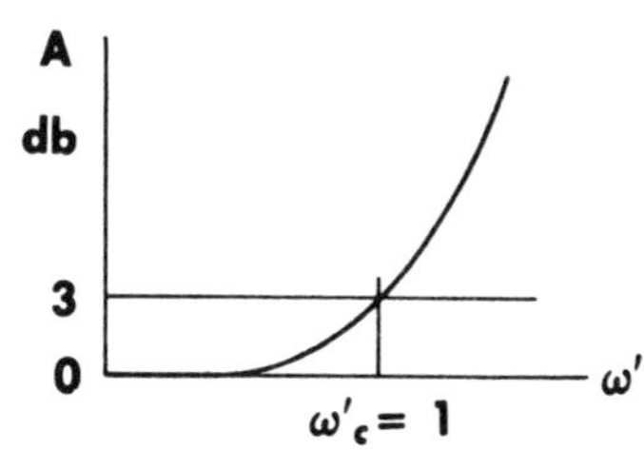

b. CHEBYSHEV RESPONSE

$r = 1$ for n odd, $r = \tanh^2(\beta/4)$ for n even

$$g_1 = 2a_1/\gamma$$

$$g_k = \frac{4a_{k-1}a_k}{b_{k-1}g_{k-1}}, k = 2,3,\ldots,n$$

check: $g_n = g_1 r$

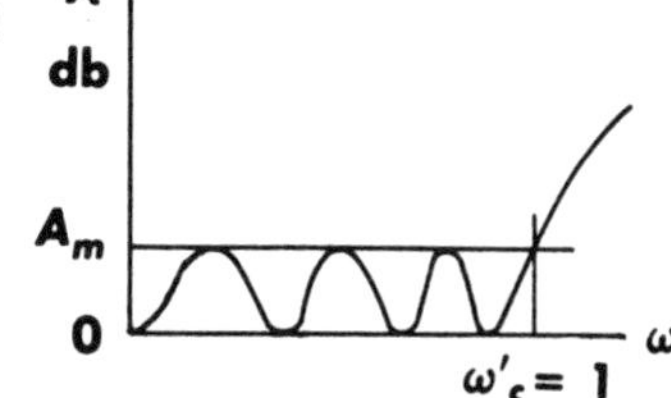

$$\beta = \ln\left(\coth \frac{A_m}{17.37}\right) \qquad a_k = \sin\left[\frac{(2k-1)\pi}{2n}\right], k = 1,2,\ldots,n$$

Adapted from Seymour Cohn, Direct Coupled Resonator Filters, Proc. I.R.E., February 1957, and other publications.

FILTER DESIGN (cont.)

$$\gamma = \sinh\left(\frac{\beta}{2n}\right) \qquad b_k = \gamma^2 + \sin^2\left(\frac{k\pi}{n}\right),\ k = 1,2,\ldots,n$$

$$A = 10 \log_{10}[1 + (10^{A_m/10} - 1)\cos^2(n \cos^{-1}\omega')],\ \omega' \leq 1$$

$$A = 10 \log_{10}[1 + (10^{A_m/10} - 1)\cosh^2(n \cosh^{-1}\omega')],\ \omega' \geq 1$$

2. Lowpass Filter

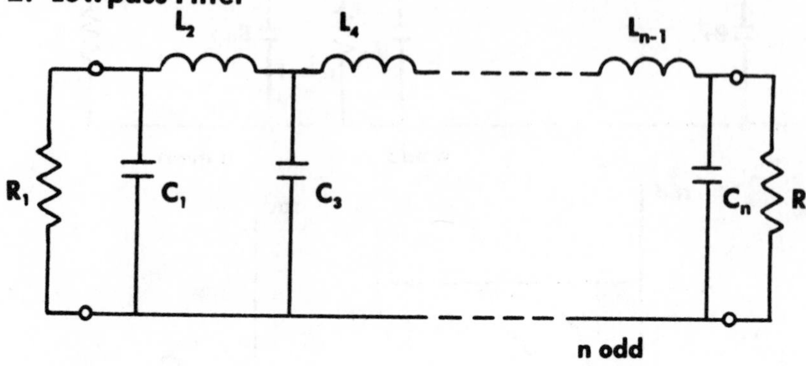

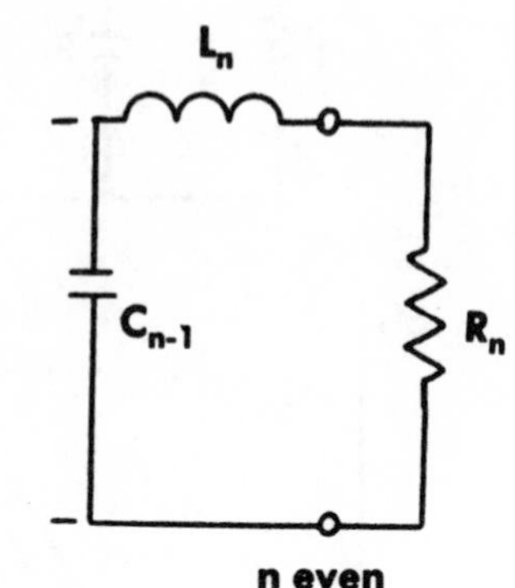

$R_n = r \cdot R_1$, r from Prototype

$\omega_c = 2\pi f_c$ = cutoff frequency in rad/sec

Frequency transformation: $\omega' = \frac{\omega}{\omega_c} = \frac{f}{f_c}$

$L_k = \frac{R_1}{\omega_c} \cdot g_k$ in henrys

$C_k = \frac{1/R_1}{\omega_c} \cdot g_k$ in farads

g_k from Prototype

Amplitude and phase response of lowpass filter at $\omega = 2\pi f$ equal prototype response at

$$\omega' = \frac{\omega}{\omega_c}$$

Delay: $\tau(\omega) = \frac{d\varphi}{d\omega} = \frac{d\varphi}{d\omega'} \cdot \frac{d\omega'}{d\omega} = \frac{\tau'(\omega')}{\omega_c}$ (in seconds)

Zero-frequency delay: $\frac{\tau'_0}{\omega_c}$ seconds

3. Highpass Filter

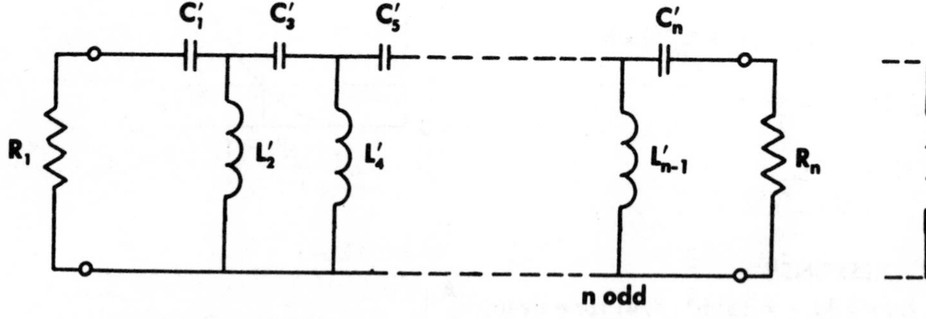

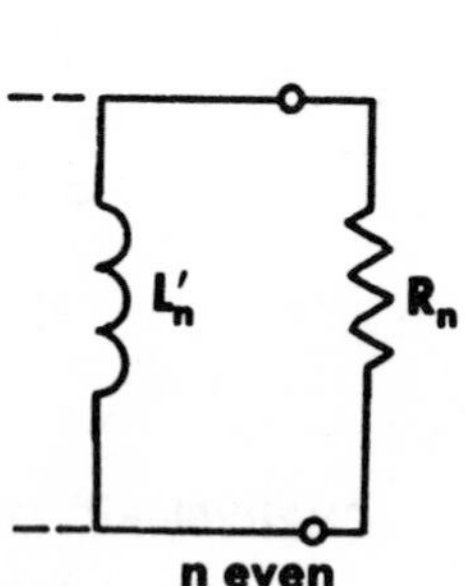

Lowpass-Highpass Frequency Transformation:

$$\omega' = \frac{\omega}{\omega_c}\bigg|_{\text{lowpass}} \longleftrightarrow \frac{\omega_c}{\omega}\bigg|_{\text{highpass}}$$

$R_n = r \cdot R_1$, r from Prototype

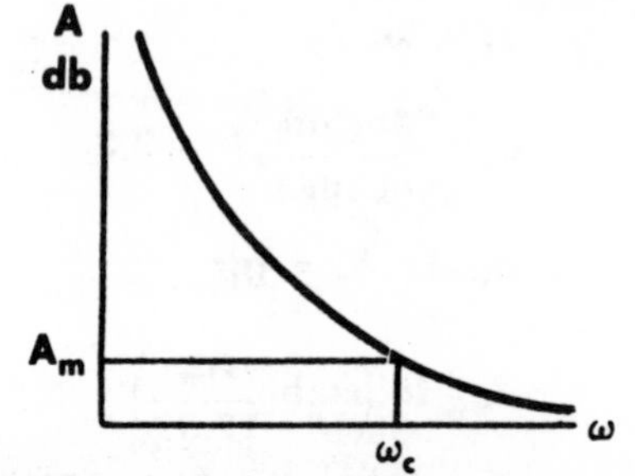

Adapted from Seymour Cohn, Direct Coupled Resonator Filters, Proc. I.R.E., February 1957, and other publications.

FILTER DESIGN (cont.)

$$C'_k = \frac{1}{R_1 \omega_c g_k} \text{ in farads}$$

$$L'_k = \frac{R_1}{\omega_c g_k} \text{ in henrys}$$

g_k from prototype

4. Bandpass Filters

Lowpass-Bandpass Frequency Transformations:

General: $$\omega' = \frac{\omega}{\omega_c} \longleftrightarrow \frac{\omega_0}{\omega_2 - \omega_1} \cdot \left(\frac{\omega}{\omega_0} - \frac{\omega_0}{\omega}\right) = \frac{f_0}{f_2 - f_1} \cdot \left(\frac{f}{f_0} - \frac{f_0}{f}\right)$$

$\omega_0 = 2\pi f_0$ = band center frequency

$\omega_1 = 2\pi f_1$, $\omega_2 = 2\pi f_2$ = passband edges

Delay: $$\frac{d\varphi}{d\omega} = \frac{d\varphi}{d\omega'} \cdot \frac{d\omega'}{d\omega} = \tau'(\omega') \frac{d\omega'}{d\omega} \text{ (in seconds)}$$

Narrow-band approximation: $$\omega' = \frac{\omega}{\omega_c} \longleftrightarrow 2\,\frac{\omega - \omega_0}{\omega_2 - \omega_1} = 2\,\frac{f - f_0}{f_2 - f_1}$$

Delay at band center: $$\tau_0 = \frac{2}{\omega_2 - \omega_1} \cdot \tau'_0 = \frac{1}{\omega_2 - \omega_1} \sum_{k=1}^{n} g_k \text{ (in seconds)}$$

Dissipation Loss at band center: $$A_0 \approx 4.34 \frac{f_0}{f_2 - f_1} \sum_{k=1}^{n} \frac{g_k}{Q_{\mu k}} \text{ (in db)}$$

g_k from Lowpass Prototype

$Q_{\mu k}$: Unloaded Q of kth resonator

a. INDUCTIVE—IRIS COUPLED WAVEGUIDE FILTER

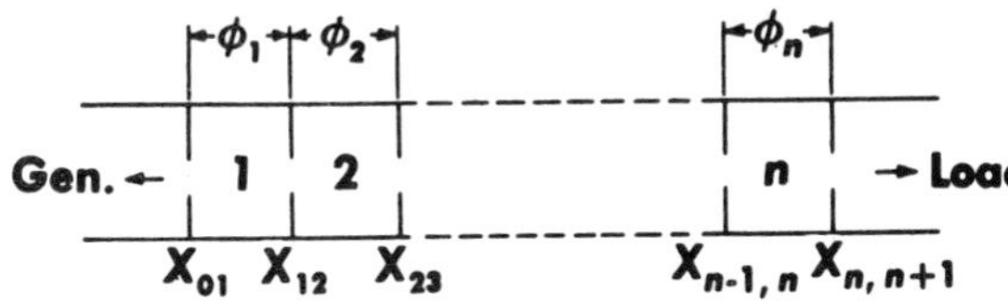

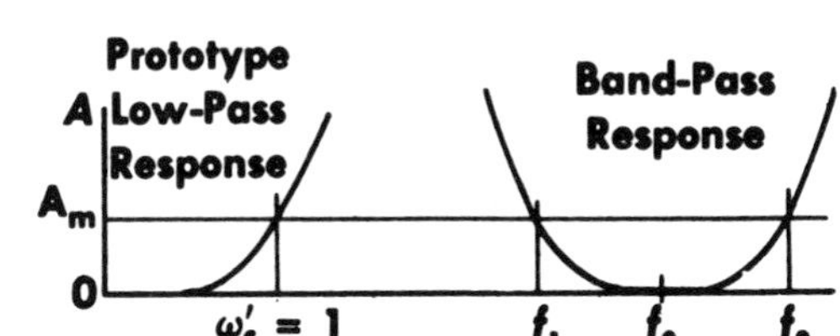

$$X_{k,k+1} = \frac{\dfrac{\Omega}{\sqrt{g_k g_{k+1}}}}{1 - \dfrac{\Omega^2}{g_k g_{k+1}}}$$

Note: $X_{k,k+1} = X_{n-k,n+1-k}$ and $\phi_k = \phi_{n+1-k}$; *i.e.*, the structure is symmetrical.

$$\phi_k = 180^\circ - \tfrac{1}{2}\left[\tan^{-1}(2X_{k-1,k}) + \tan^{-1}(2X_{k,k+1})\right]$$

$X_{k,k+1}$ = normalized iris reactance at λ_{go}, ϕ_k = phase length at λ_{go}

λ_{go}, λ_{g1}, λ_{g2}: Guide wavelength corresponding to f_0, f_1, f_2

$g_1, g_2, \ldots, g_n$ = Prototype elements in farads and henrys from 1.

Adapted from Seymour Cohn, Direct Coupled Resonator Filters, Proc. I.R.E., February 1957, and other publications.

165

FILTER DESIGN (cont.)

$$g_0 = \Omega, g_{n+1} = \frac{\Omega}{r}, \text{ r from Prototype} \qquad \Omega = \pi\left[\frac{\lambda_{g1} - \lambda_{g2}}{\lambda_{g1} + \lambda_{g2}}\right],$$

b. CAPACITIVE-GAP COUPLED TRANSMISSION-LINE FILTER

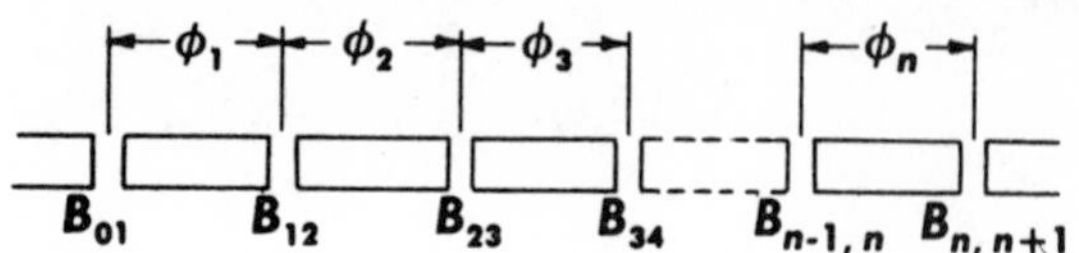

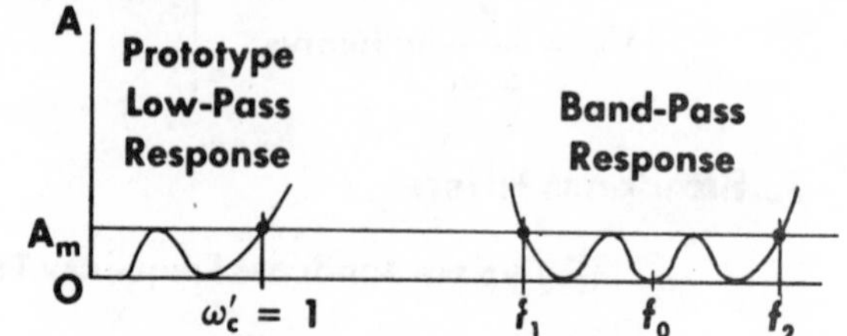

$$B_{k,\,k+1} = \frac{\dfrac{\Omega'}{\sqrt{g_k g_{k+1}}}}{1 - \dfrac{\Omega'^2}{g_k\, g_{k+1}}}$$

Note: $B_{k,\,k+1} = B_{n-k,\,n+1-k}$ **and** $\phi_k = \phi_{n+1-k}$; ***i.e.*, the structure is symmetrical.**

$$\phi_k = 180^\circ - \tfrac{1}{2}\left[\tan^{-1}(2B_{k-1,\,k}) + \tan^{-1}(2B_{k,\,k+1})\right]$$

$B_{k,\,k+1}$ = **normalized gap susceptance at** f_0

ϕ_k = **phase length at** f_0 $\qquad f_0 = \dfrac{2f_1 f_2}{f_1 + f_2}$

$g_1, g_2, \ldots, g_n$ = **Prototype elements in farads and henrys from 1.**

$g_0 = \Omega'$, $g_{n+1} = \dfrac{\Omega'}{r}$, **r from 1.** $\qquad \Omega' = \pi\dfrac{f_2 - f_1}{f_2 + f_1}$

VALUES OF ELEMENTS (g_k) FOR NORMALIZED LOWPASS PROTOTYPE FILTERS ($\omega'_c = 1$)

MAXIMALLY FLAT AMPLITUDE RESPONSE

	n						
k	2	3	4	5	6	7	8
1	1.414	1.0000	0.7654	0.6180	0.5176	0.4450	0.3902
2	1.414	2.0000	1.848	1.618	1.414	1.247	1.111
3		1.0000	1.848	2.000	1.932	1.802	1.663
4			0.7654	1.618	1.932	2.000	1.962
5				0.6180	1.414	1.802	1.962
6					0.5176	1.247	1.663
7						0.4450	1.111
8							0.3902

CHEBYSHEV RESPONSE
(A_m = 0.01 db)

	n						
k	2	3	4	5	6	7	8
1	0.4488	0.6291	0.7128	0.7563	0.7813	0.7969	0.8072
2	0.4077	0.9702	1.2003	1.3049	1.3600	1.3924	1.4130
3		0.6291	1.3212	1.5773	1.6896	1.7481	1.7824
4			0.6476	1.3049	1.5350	1.6331	1.6833
5				0.7563	1.4970	1.7481	1.8529
6					0.7098	1.3924	1.6193
7						0.7969	1.5554
8							0.7333

CHEBYSHEV RESPONSE
(A_m = 0.1 db)

	n						
k	2	3	4	5	6	7	8
1	0.8430	1.0315	1.1088	1.1468	1.1681	1.1811	1.1897
2	0.6220	1.1474	1.3061	1.3712	1.4039	1.4228	1.4346
3		1.0315	1.7703	1.9750	2.0562	2.0966	2.1199
4			0.8180	1.3712	1.5170	1.5733	1.6010
5				1.1468	1.9029	2.0966	2.1699
6					0.8618	1.4228	1.5640
7						1.1811	1.9444
							0.8778

CHEBYSHEV RESPONSE
(A_m = 0.25 db)

	n						
k	2	3	4	5	6	7	8
1	1.113	1.303	1.378	1.382	1.437	1.447	1.454
2	0.688	1.146	1.269	1.326	1.341	1.356	1.365
3		1.303	2.056	2.209	2.316	2.348	2.367
4			0.851	1.326	1.462	1.469	1.489
5				1.382	2.178	2.348	2.411
6					0.885	1.356	1.462
7						1.447	2.210
8							0.898

Adapted from Seymour Cohn, Direct Coupled Resonator Filters, Proc. I.R.E., February 1957, and other publications.

FILTER DESIGN (cont.)

5. Diplexers (Highpass - Lowpass Normalized Prototype)

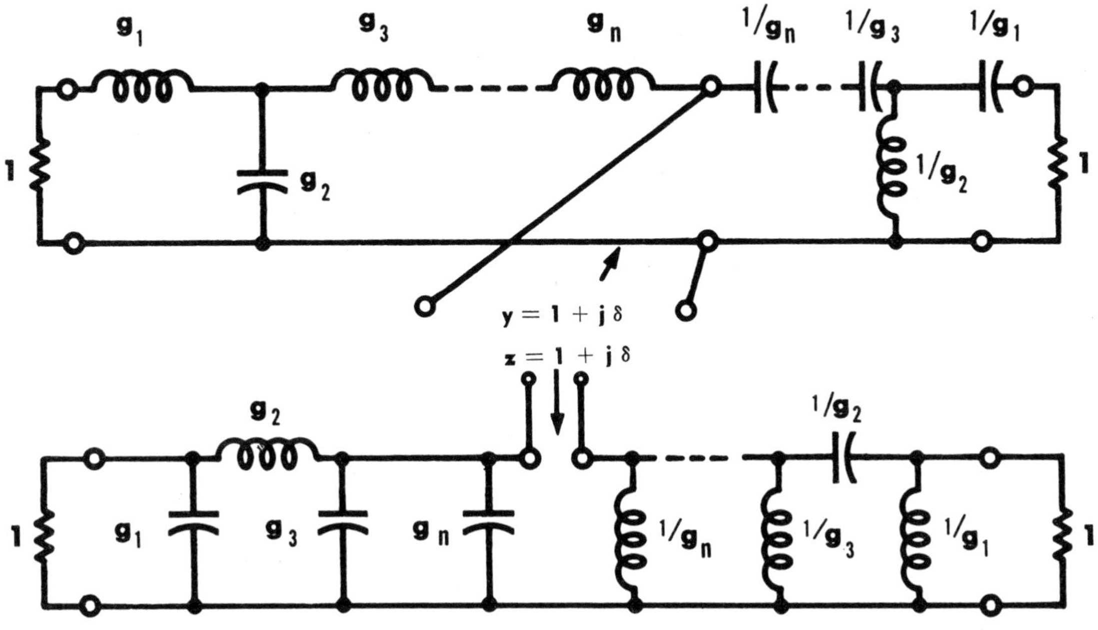

n	g_1	g_2	g_3	g_4	g_5	g_6	g_7	g_8	g_9	g_{10}
Max. Flat Amplitude ($\delta=0$)										
1	1.0000									
2	0.7071	1.4142								
3	0.5000	1.3333	1.5000							
4	0.3827	1.0824	1.5772	1.5307						
5	0.3090	0.8944	1.3820	1.6944	1.5451					
6	0.2588	0.7579	1.2016	1.5529	1.7593	1.5529				
7	0.2225	0.6560	1.0550	1.3972	1.6588	1.7988	1.5576			
8	0.1951	0.5776	0.9370	1.2588	1.5283	1.7287	1.8246	1.5607		
9	0.1736	0.5155	0.8414	1.1408	1.4037	1.6202	1.7772	1.8424	1.5628	
10	0.1564	0.4654	0.7626	1.0406	1.2921	1.5100	1.6869	1.8121	1.8552	1.5643

Adapted from R. G. Veltrop and R. B. Wilds, "Modified Tables for the Design of Optimum Diplexers," the Microwave Journal, June 1964.

FILTER DESIGN (cont.)

Chebyshev — $A_m = 0.1$ dB $(\delta << < 1)$

n	g_1	g_2	g_3	g_4	g_5	g_6	g_7	g_8	g_9	g_{10}
3	.7162	1.5085	1.5128							
4	.6747	1.4597	1.7739	1.5156						
5	.6508	1.4174	1.7661	1.8072	1.5614					
6	.6392	1.3954	1.7508	1.8328	1.8862	1.5358				
7	.6308	1.3786	1.734	1.827	1.9210	1.8578	1.5748			
8	.6264	1.3697	1.7247	1.8218	1.9271	1.9027	1.9125	1.5437		
9	.6223	1.3612	1.7152	1.8137	1.923	1.9095	1.9585	1.8729	1.5804	
10	.6202	1.3566	1.7099	1.8093	1.9205	1.9112	1.9711	1.9227	1.9211	1.5468

Chebyshev — $A_m = 0.25$ dB $(\delta << < 1)$

n	g_1	g_2	g_3	g_4	g_5	g_6	g_7	g_8	g_9	g_{10}
3	.8163	1.5280	1.5342							
4	.7910	1.5169	1.8341	1.4925						
5	.7524	1.4738	1.8225	1.7822	1.5763					
6	.7639	1.4768	1.8392	1.8256	1.9280	1.5114				
7	.7559	1.4629	1.8261	1.8235	1.9663	1.8284	1.6013			
8	.7537	1.4591	1.8235	1.8249	1.9790	1.8780	1.9486	1.5176		
9	.7500	1.4522	1.8156	1.8191	1.9769	1.8862	1.9965	1.8412	1.6071	
10	.7491	1.4508	1.8142	1.8186	1.9785	1.8917	2.0130	1.8932	1.9561	1.5207

Chebyshev — $A_m = 0.5$ dB $(\delta << < 1)$

n	g_1	g_2	g_3	g_4	g_5	g_6	g_7	g_8	g_9	g_{10}
3	.9316	1.5176	1.5718							
4	.9241	1.5398	1.9119	1.4537						
5	.9034	1.5136	1.9216	1.7397	1.6298					
6	.9032	1.5162	1.9361	1.7903	1.9910	1.470				
7	.8946	1.5034	1.9236	1.7893	2.0304	1.7772	1.6462			
8	.8954	1.5052	1.9243	1.7968	2.0505	1.8307	2.0086	1.4757		
9	.8911	1.4982	1.9199	1.7911	2.0482	1.8383	2.0571	1.7891	1.6533	
10	.8919	1.4997	1.9224	1.7943	2.0538	1.8472	2.0777	1.8425	2.0151	1.4784

Chebyshev — $A_m = 1$ dB $(\delta << < 1)$

n	g_1	g_2	g_3	g_4	g_5	g_6	g_7	g_8	g_9	g_{10}
3	1.1078	1.4597	1.6520							
4	1.1274	1.5174	2.0510	1.3768						
5	1.1035	1.4929	2.0612	1.6446	1.7215					
6	1.1126	1.5080	2.0935	1.7048	2.1163	1.3898				
7	1.1018	1.4947	2.0789	1.7024	2.1557	1.6773	1.7412			
8	1.1072	1.5022	2.0915	1.7160	2.1848	1.7334	2.1307	1.3943		
9	1.1012	1.4944	2.0815	1.7094	2.1807	1.7392	2.1798	1.6881	1.7497	
10	1.1047	1.4992	2.0889	1.7161	2.1914	1.7510	2.2060	1.7418	2.1360	1.3964

Adapted from R. G. Veltrop and R. B. Wilds, "Modified Tables for the Design of Optimum Diplexers," the Microwave Journal, June 1964.

LENGTH OF Kth RESONATOR IN DIRECT-COUPLED RESONATOR FILTERS

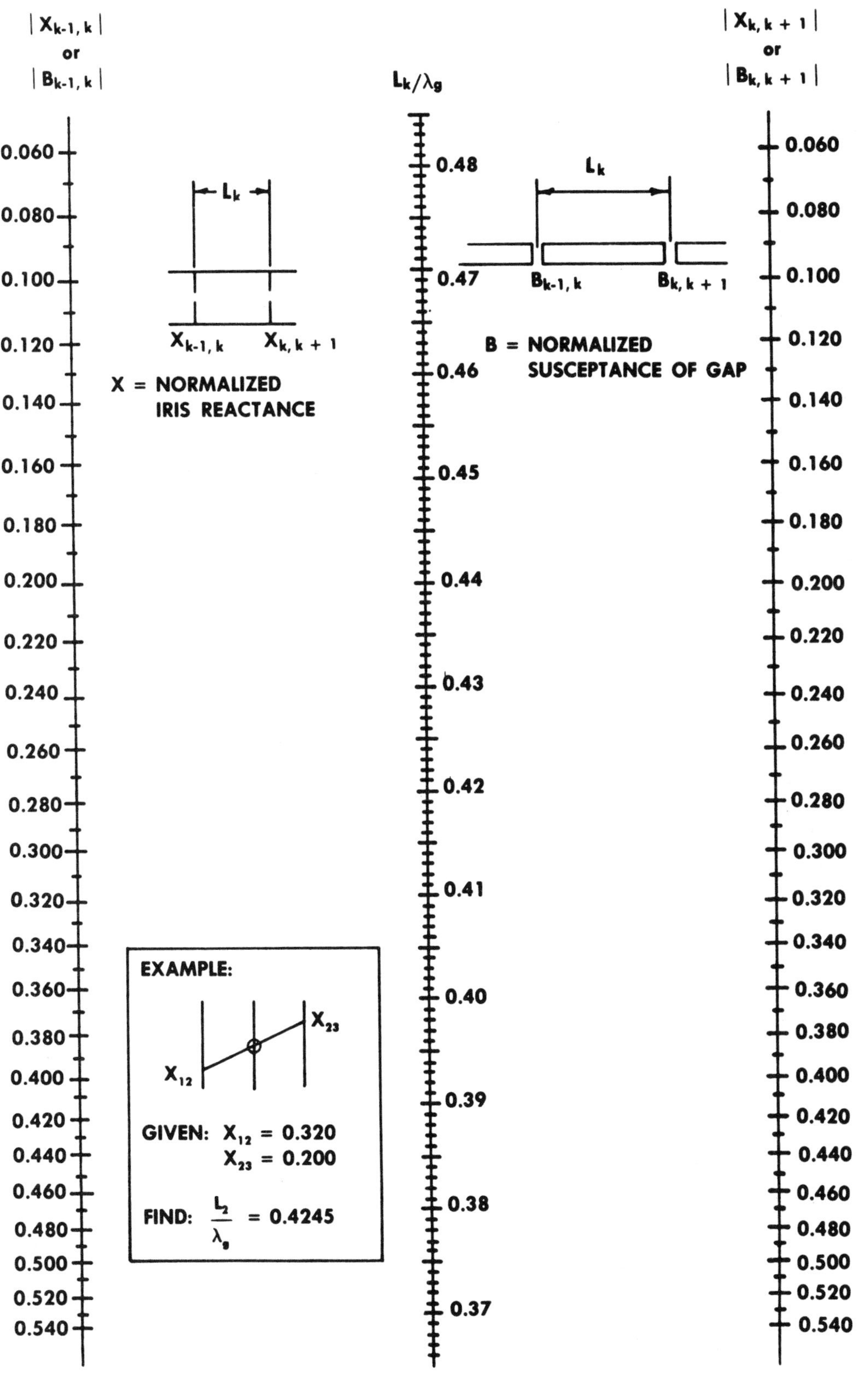

Courtesy of E. A. Cota, Sylvania Electric Products, Inc.

STOPBAND INSERTION LOSS OF NORMALIZED CHEBYSHEV LOWPASS PROTOTYPE FILTERS

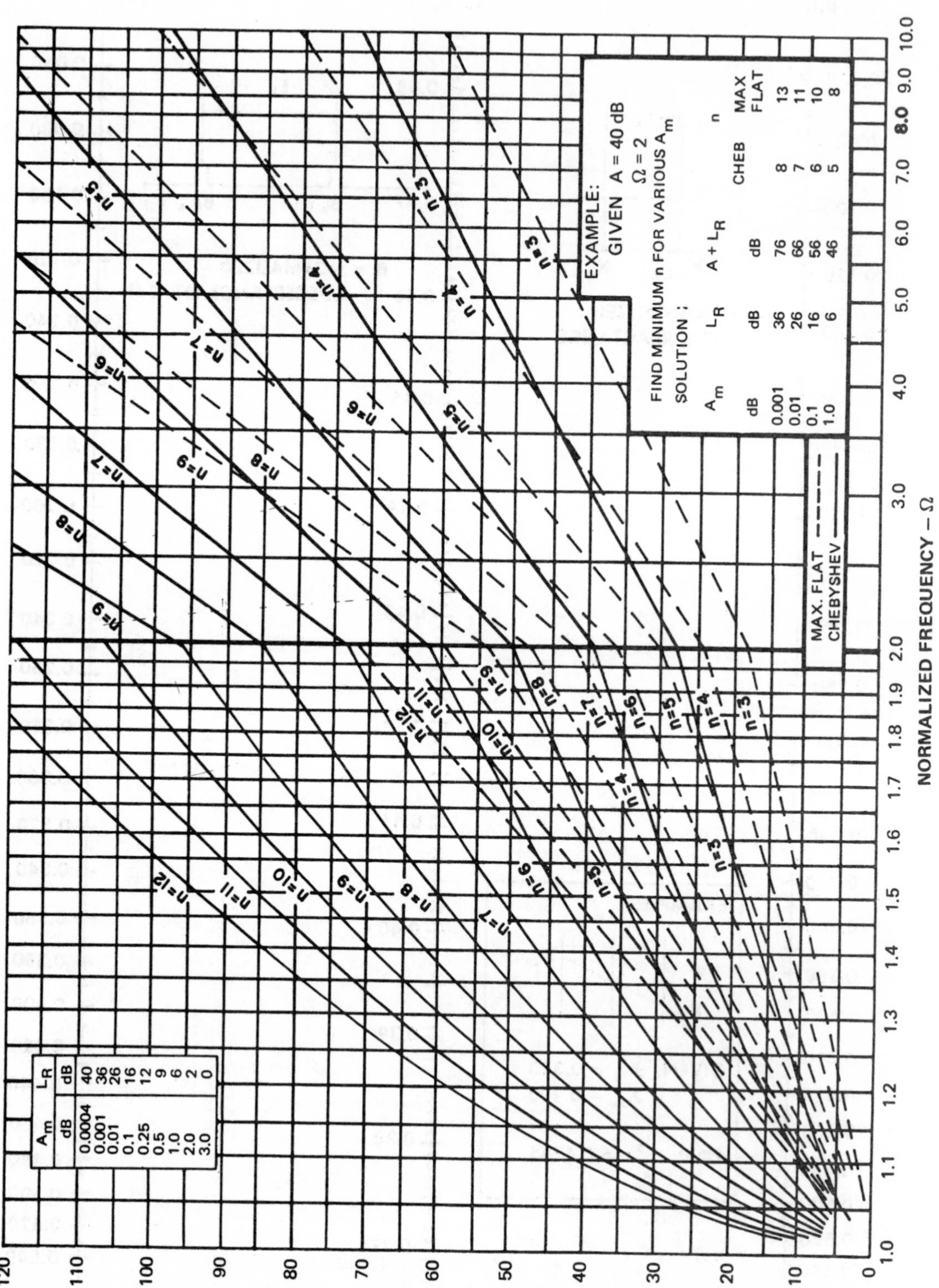

Courtesy of N.K.M. Chitre and M.V.O'Donovan, RCA Victor Co, Ltd., Montreal

Unified Filter Design Chart

Stopband Insertion Loss of Normalized Chebyshev Lowpass Prototype Filters

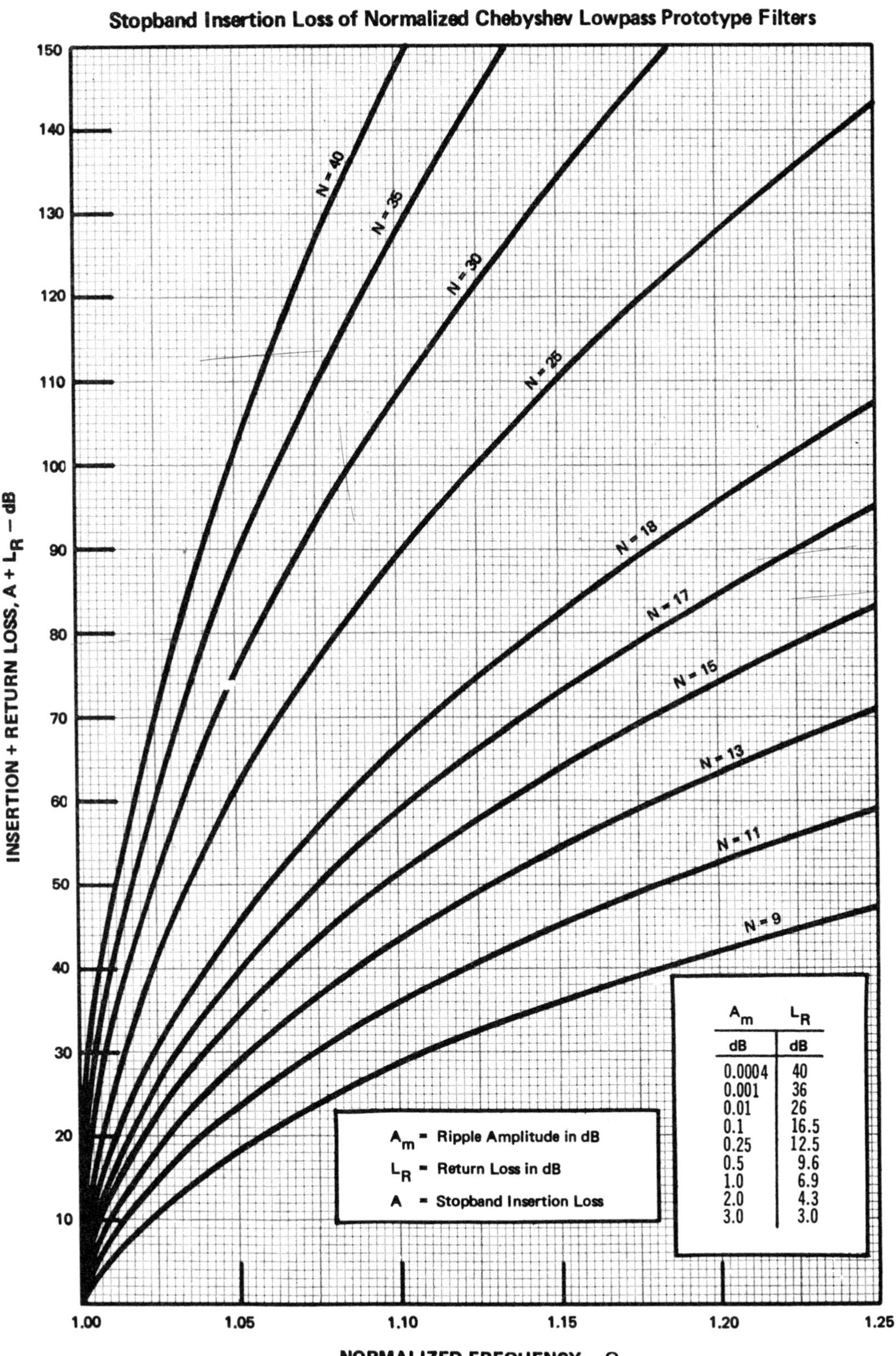

A_m dB	L_R dB
0.0004	40
0.001	36
0.01	26
0.1	16.5
0.25	12.5
0.5	9.6
1.0	6.9
2.0	4.3
3.0	3.0

Courtesy of N.K.M. Chitre and M.V.O'Donovan, RCS Victor Co. Ltd., Montreal

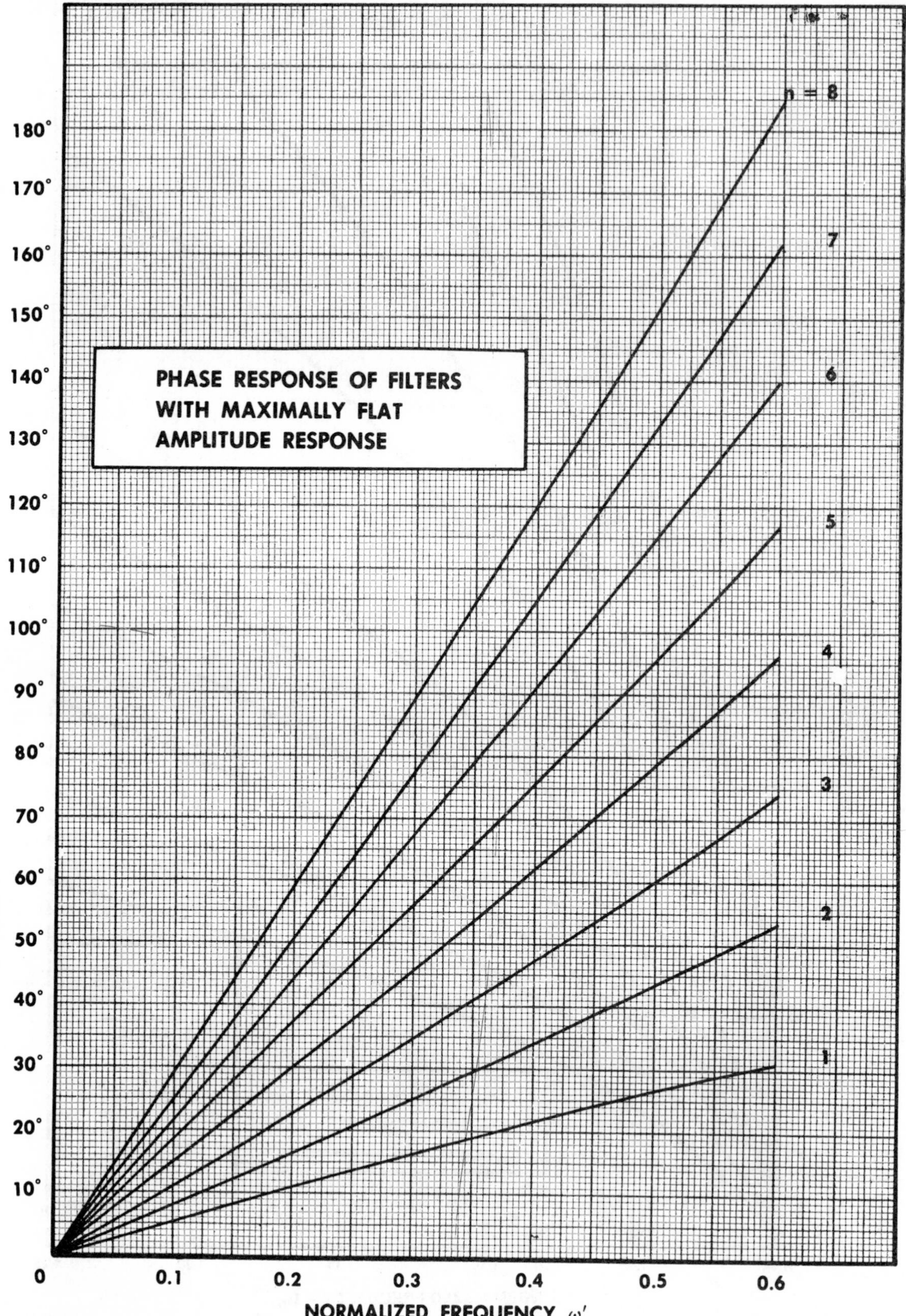

Courtesy of the Radio Corporation of America.

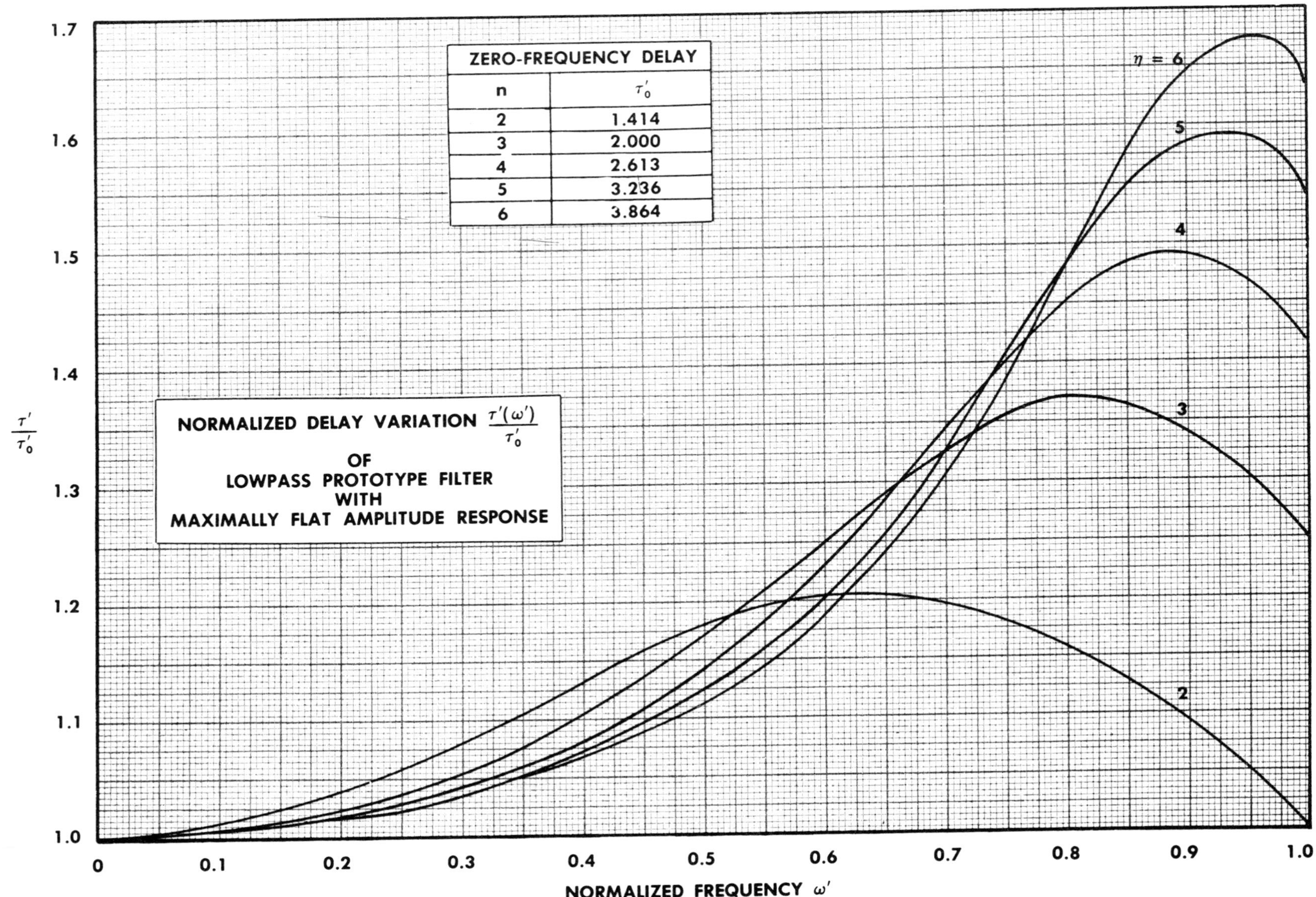

n	τ'_0
2	1.414
3	2.000
4	2.613
5	3.236
6	3.864

Courtesy of the Radio Corporation of America.

Narrowband Butterworth Bandpass Filter Selectivity Characteristics

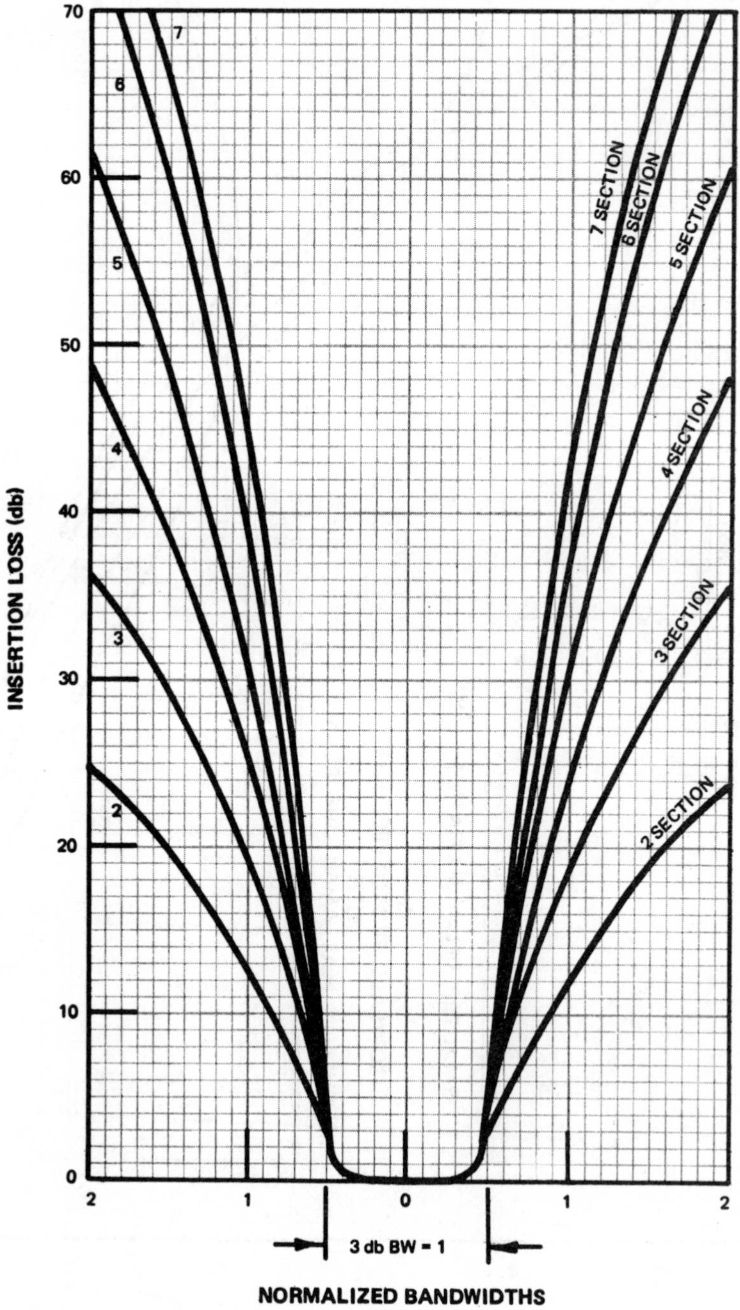

Courtesy of American Electronic Laboratories, Inc., Colmar, Pa.

Narrowband Chebyshev Bandpass Filter Selectivity Characteristics

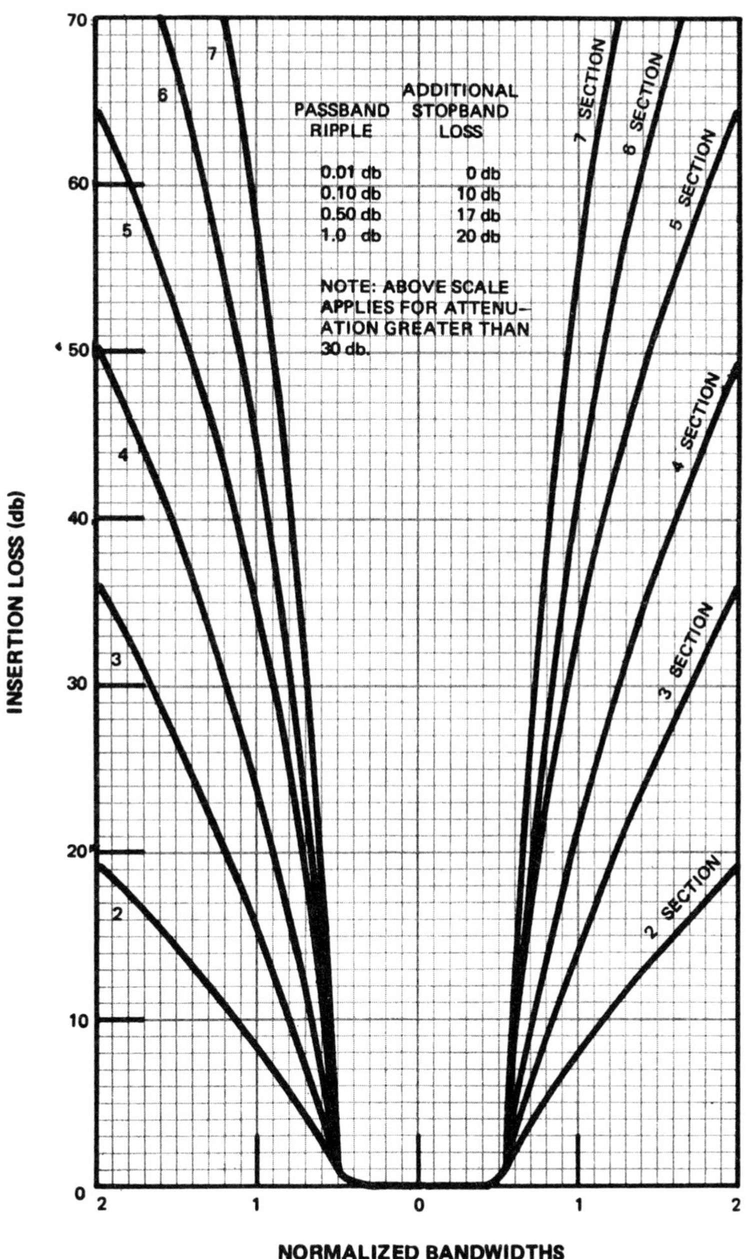

Courtesy of American Electronic Laboratories, Inc., Colmar, Pa.

Table of Ripple Factor and VSWR

Am dB	VSWR	Am dB	VSWR
.000100	1.009643	.080000	1.312406
.000200	1.013665	.090000	1.334303
.000300	1.016762	.100000	1.355361
.000400	1.019380	.200000	1.538553
.000500	1.021692	.300000	1.696697
.000600	1.023787	.400000	1.843452
.000700	1.025717	.500000	1.984956
.000800	1.027517	.600000	2.121178
.000900	1.029210	.700000	2.256408
.001000	1.030814	.800000	2.390785
.002000	1.043855	.900000	2.525042
.003000	1.053974	1.000000	2.659722
.004000	1.062582	2.000000	4.095396
.005000	1.070224	3.000000	5.808900
.006000	1.007181	4.000000	7.921304
.007000	1.083618	5.000000	10.554363
.008000	1.089645	6.000000	13.852095
.009000	1.095362	7.000000	17.991909
.010000	1.100747	8.000000	23.195181
.020000	1.145424	9.000000	29.739504
		10.000000	37.973666
.030000	1.180953		
.040000	1.211778		
.050000	1.239617		
.060000	1.265351		
.070000	1.289591		

Courtesy of Robert J. Wenzel.

Elliptic Function Selectivity Chart

Diagram for the estimation of the required degree (n=3 up to 12) for Elliptic Function low-pass filters.
Relation between n, Ω_S, A_S ($\geqq$ 2 [N] and p.
From R. Saal, "Der Entwurf von Filtern mit Hilfe des kataloges normierter Tiefpässe" Telefunken GMBH (West German, 1963)

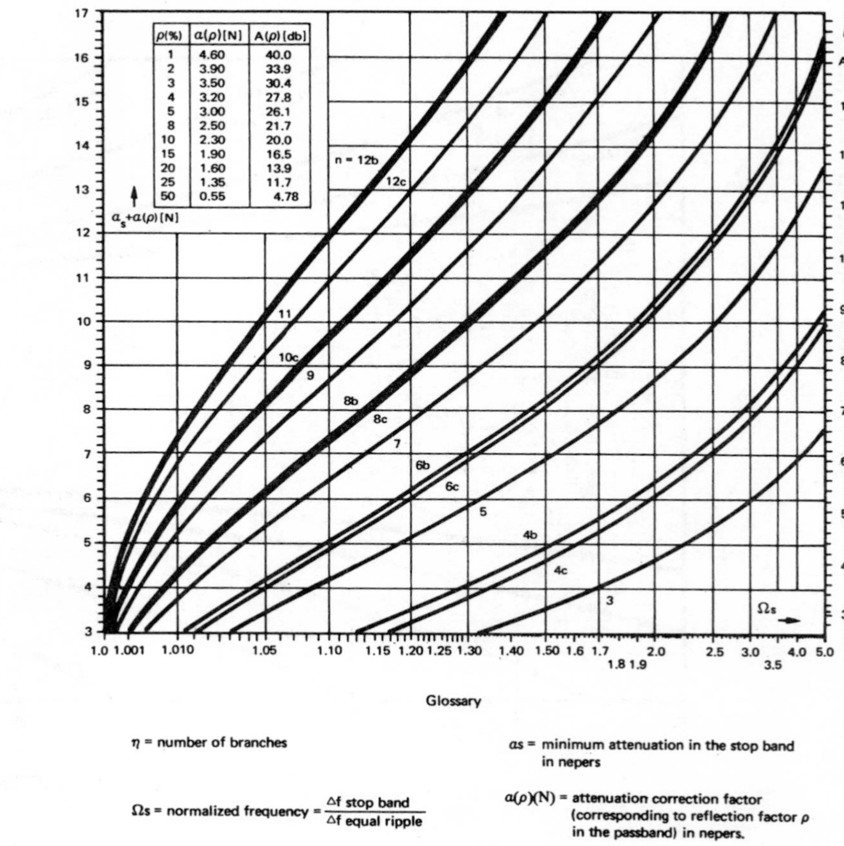

Glossary

η = number of branches

Ωs = normalized frequency = $\frac{\Delta f \text{ stop band}}{\Delta f \text{ equal ripple}}$

ρ = peak voltage reflection in the passband in %

αs = minimum attenuation in the stop band in nepers

$\alpha(\rho)(N)$ = attenuation correction factor (corresponding to reflection factor ρ in the passband) in nepers.

b has reflection factor = ρ at center of passband

c has reflection factor = o at center of passband

Courtesy of R. Saal.

Midband Dissipation Loss For Narrow Band Filters

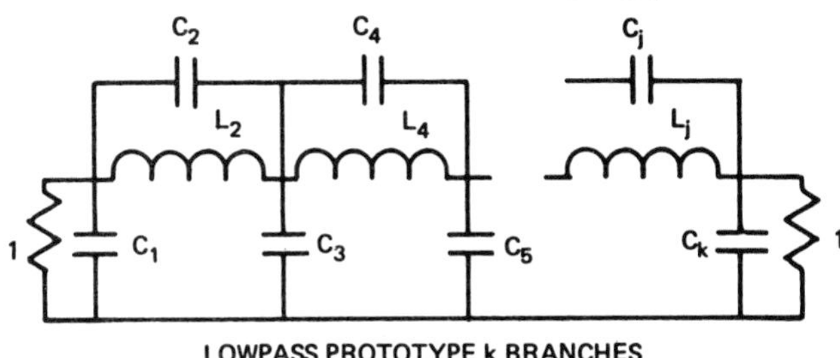

LOWPASS PROTOTYPE k BRANCHES

C_r, C_j, L_j = Normalized LP Prototype Element Values

w = Fractional Passband Bandwidth

Ωs = Passband to Stopband Selectivity Factor

Qu = Unloaded Resonator Q

As = Minimum Stopband Attenuation

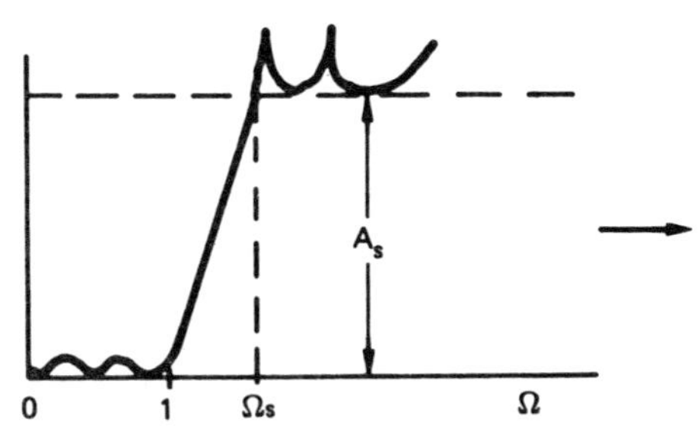

LP PROTOTYPE RESPONSE

$\omega = \frac{\Delta f}{fo}$

$\Omega s = \frac{\Delta fs}{\Delta f}$

Δfs

Δf

As

fo

NARROW BANDWIDTH MAPPED RESPONSE

$$\text{MIDBAND LOSS} \approx \frac{4.34}{\omega}\left[\sum^{\text{ODD R}} \frac{C_R}{Q_{ur}} + \sum^{\text{EVEN J}} \frac{L_j}{Q_{uj}}\right] = \frac{4.34}{\omega Q_u}\left[\sum^{\text{ODD R}} C_r + \sum^{\text{EVEN J}} L_j\right] \text{ FOR } Q_{ur} = Q_{uj} = Q_u$$

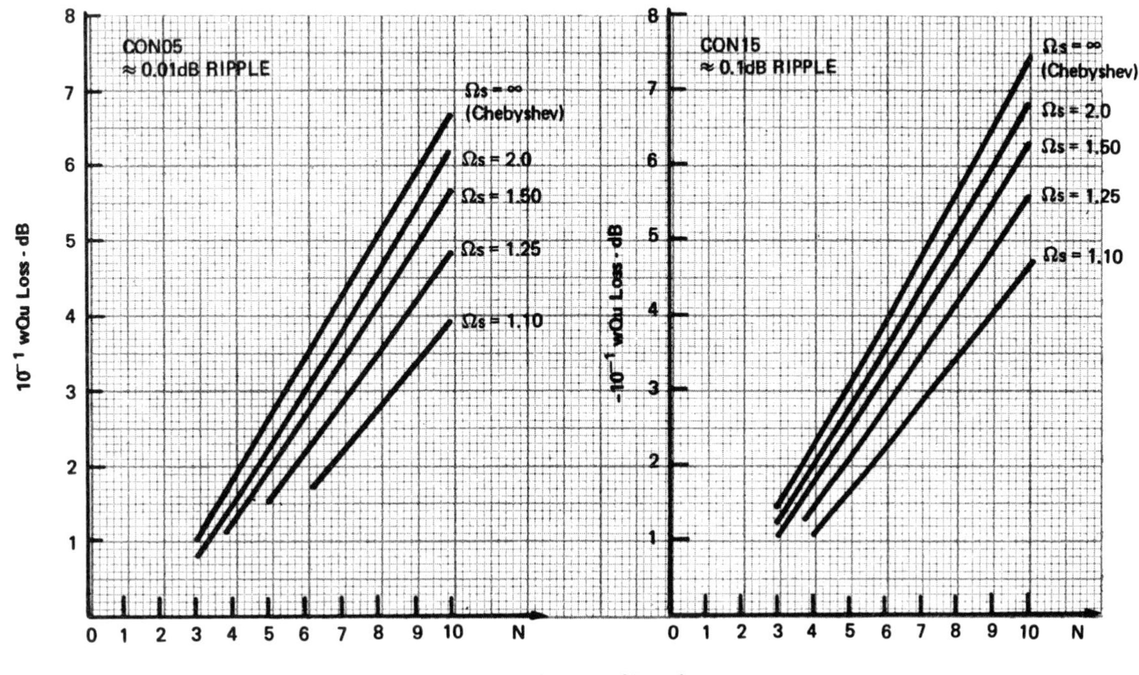

N = Number of Branches

Courtesy of Robert J. Wenzel.

Fringing Capacitance for Tightly Coupled Rectangular Bars

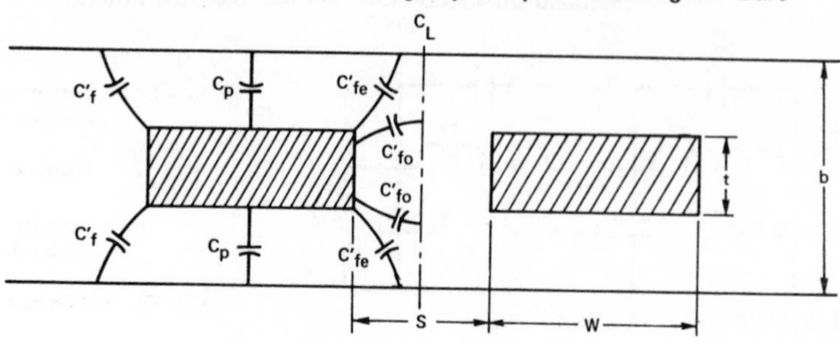

$$Z_{oe}\sqrt{\epsilon_r} = \frac{376.7}{(C_{oe}/\epsilon)} \text{ ohms} \quad Z_{oo}\sqrt{\epsilon_r} = \frac{376.7}{(C_{oo}/\epsilon)} \text{ ohms}$$

$$C_{oe}/\epsilon = 2\,(C_p/\epsilon + C'_{fe}/\epsilon + C'_f/\epsilon)$$

$$C_{oo}/\epsilon = 2(C_p/\epsilon + C'_{fo}/\epsilon + C'_f/\epsilon)$$

$$C_p/\epsilon = 2\,\frac{\omega/b}{1 - t/b}$$

$$\Delta C/\epsilon = \tfrac{1}{2}\,(C_{oo}/\epsilon - C_{oe}/\epsilon) = C'_{fo}/\epsilon - C'_{fe}/\epsilon$$

$$\Delta C = \tfrac{1}{2}\,(C_{oo} - C_{oe})$$

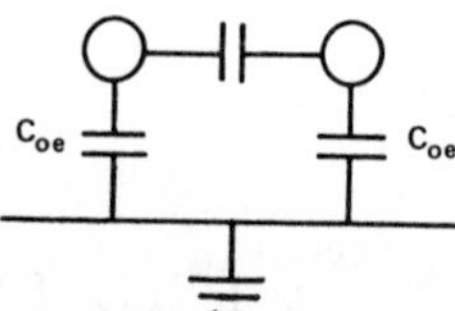

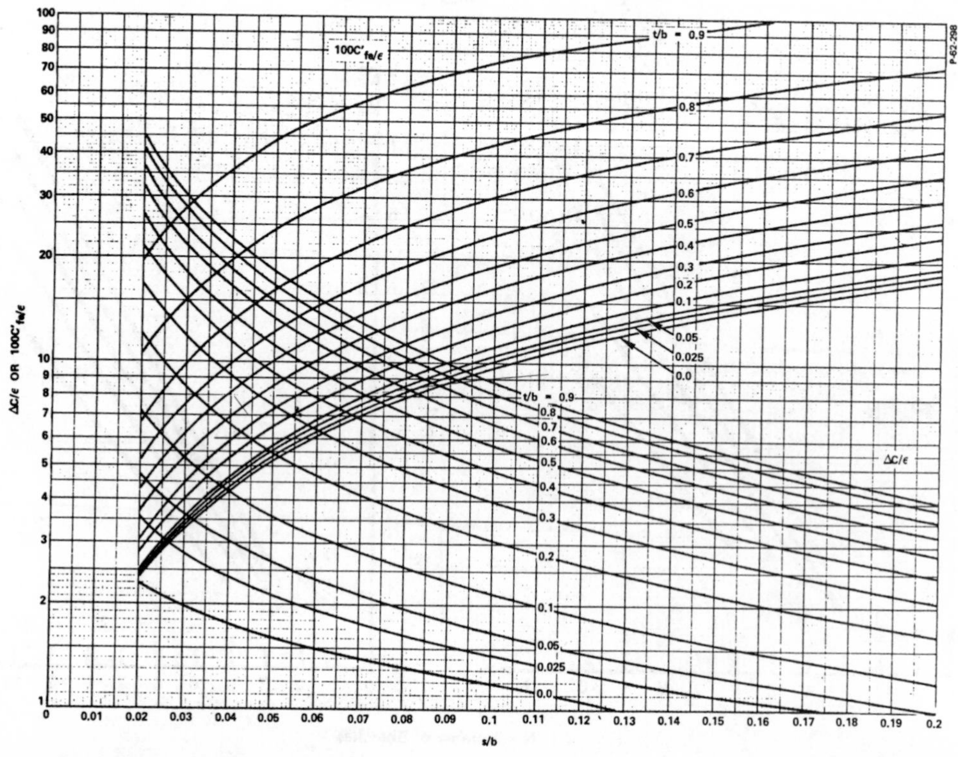

Courtesy of R.R.Gupta. Reference: Special Issue of IEEE MIT TRANSACTIONS on Computer Aided Design, July 1969.

Relationships Between Network Parameters

$$v = Zi, \quad i = Yv$$
$$b = Sa$$

$$\begin{bmatrix} v_1 \\ i_1 \end{bmatrix} = \begin{bmatrix} A & B \\ C & D \end{bmatrix} \begin{bmatrix} v_2 \\ -i_2 \end{bmatrix}$$

$$\begin{bmatrix} b_1 \\ a_1 \end{bmatrix} = \begin{bmatrix} r_{11} & r_{12} \\ r_{21} & r_{22} \end{bmatrix} \begin{bmatrix} a_2 \\ b_2 \end{bmatrix}$$

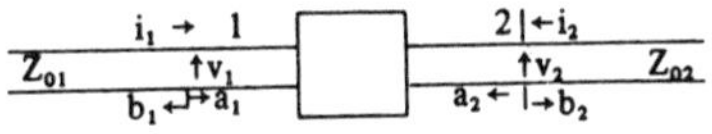

$i_1 \rightarrow$ 1 | 2 $\leftarrow i_2$
Z_{01} $\uparrow v_1$ | $\uparrow v_2$ Z_{02}
$b_1 \leftarrow \rightarrow a_1$ | $a_2 \leftarrow \rightarrow b_2$

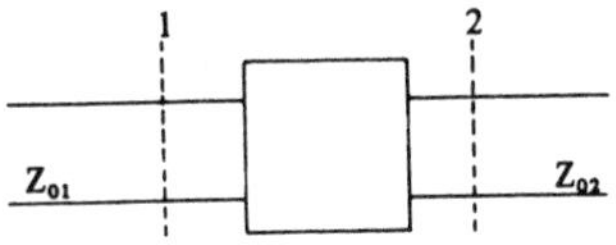

1 | 2
Z_{01} | Z_{02}

$$\begin{bmatrix} Z_{11} & Z_{12} \\ Z_{21} & Z_{22} \end{bmatrix} = \frac{1}{Y_{11}Y_{22} - Y_{12}Y_{21}} \begin{bmatrix} Y_{22} & -Y_{12} \\ -Y_{21} & Y_{11} \end{bmatrix}$$

$$\begin{bmatrix} Y_{11} & Y_{12} \\ Y_{21} & Y_{22} \end{bmatrix} = \frac{1}{Z_{11}Z_{22} - Z_{21}Z_{12}} \begin{bmatrix} Z_{22} & -Z_{12} \\ -Z_{21} & Z_{11} \end{bmatrix}$$

$$\begin{bmatrix} Z_{11} & Z_{12} \\ Z_{21} & Z_{22} \end{bmatrix} = \frac{1}{C} \begin{bmatrix} A & AD - BC \\ 1 & D \end{bmatrix}$$

$$\begin{bmatrix} Y_{11} & Y_{12} \\ Y_{21} & Y_{22} \end{bmatrix} = \frac{1}{B} \begin{bmatrix} D & -(AD - BC) \\ -1 & A \end{bmatrix}$$

$$\begin{bmatrix} A & B \\ C & D \end{bmatrix} = \frac{1}{Z_{21}} \begin{bmatrix} Z_{11} & (Z_{11}Z_{22} - Z_{12}Z_{21}) \\ 1 & Z_{22} \end{bmatrix}$$

$$\begin{bmatrix} A & B \\ C & D \end{bmatrix} = \frac{1}{-Y_{21}} \begin{bmatrix} Y_{22} & 1 \\ (Y_{11}Y_{22} - Y_{12}Y_{21}) & Y_{11} \end{bmatrix}$$

$$\begin{bmatrix} S_{11} & S_{12} \\ S_{21} & S_{22} \end{bmatrix} = \frac{1}{r_{22}} \begin{bmatrix} r_{12} & (r_{11}r_{22} - r_{12}r_{21}) \\ 1 & -r_{21} \end{bmatrix}$$

$$\begin{bmatrix} r_{11} & r_{12} \\ r_{21} & r_{22} \end{bmatrix} = \frac{1}{S_{21}} \begin{bmatrix} -(S_{11}S_{22} - S_{12}S_{21}) & S_{11} \\ -S_{22} & 1 \end{bmatrix}$$

$$\begin{bmatrix} S_{11} & S_{12} \\ S_{21} & S_{22} \end{bmatrix} = \frac{1}{\left(\frac{Z_{11}}{Z_{01}} + 1\right)\left(\frac{Z_{22}}{Z_{02}} + 1\right) - \frac{Z_{12}Z_{21}}{Z_{01}Z_{02}}} \begin{bmatrix} \left(\frac{Z_{11}}{Z_{01}} - 1\right)\left(\frac{Z_{22}}{Z_{02}} + 1\right) - \frac{Z_{12}Z_{21}}{Z_{01}Z_{02}} & 2\frac{Z_{12}}{Z_{02}} \\ 2\frac{Z_{21}}{Z_{01}} & \left(\frac{Z_{11}}{Z_{01}} + 1\right)\left(\frac{Z_{22}}{Z_{02}} - 1\right) - \frac{Z_{12}Z_{21}}{Z_{01}Z_{02}} \end{bmatrix}$$

$$\begin{bmatrix} S_{11} & S_{12} \\ S_{21} & S_{22} \end{bmatrix} = \frac{1}{\left(1 + \frac{Y_{11}}{Y_{01}}\right)\left(1 + \frac{Y_{22}}{Y_{02}}\right) - \frac{Y_{12}Y_{21}}{Y_{01}Y_{02}}} \begin{bmatrix} \left(1 - \frac{Y_{11}}{Y_{01}}\right)\left(1 + \frac{Y_{22}}{Y_{02}}\right) + \frac{Y_{12}Y_{21}}{Y_{01}Y_{02}} & -2\frac{Y_{12}}{Y_{01}} \\ -2\frac{Y_{21}}{Y_{02}} & \left(1 + \frac{Y_{11}}{Y_{01}}\right)\left(1 - \frac{Y_{22}}{Y_{02}}\right) + \frac{Y_{12}Y_{21}}{Y_{01}Y_{02}} \end{bmatrix}$$

$$\begin{bmatrix} S_{11} & S_{12} \\ S_{21} & S_{22} \end{bmatrix} = \frac{1}{(B + CZ_{01}Z_{02}) + (AZ_{02} + DZ_{01})} \begin{bmatrix} (B - CZ_{01}Z_{02}) + (AZ_{02} - DZ_{01}) & 2Z_{01}(AD - BC) \\ 2Z_{02} & (B - CZ_{01}Z_{02}) - (AZ_{02} - DZ_{01}) \end{bmatrix}$$

$$\begin{bmatrix} Z_{11} & Z_{12} \\ Z_{21} & Z_{22} \end{bmatrix} = \frac{1}{(1 - S_{11})(1 - S_{22}) - S_{12}S_{21}} \begin{bmatrix} Z_{01}[(1 + S_{11})(1 - S_{22}) + S_{12}S_{21}] & 2Z_{01}S_{12} \\ 2Z_{02}S_{21} & Z_{02}[(1 - S_{11})(1 + S_{22}) + S_{12}S_{21}] \end{bmatrix}$$

$$\begin{bmatrix} Y_{11} & Y_{12} \\ Y_{21} & Y_{22} \end{bmatrix} = \frac{1}{(1 + S_{11})(1 + S_{22}) - S_{12}S_{21}} \begin{bmatrix} Y_{01}[(1 - S_{11})(1 + S_{22}) + S_{12}S_{21}] & -2Y_{01}S_{12} \\ -2Y_{02}S_{21} & Y_{02}[(1 + S_{11})(1 - S_{22}) + S_{12}S_{21}] \end{bmatrix}$$

$$\begin{bmatrix} A & B \\ C & D \end{bmatrix} = \frac{1}{2S_{21}} \begin{bmatrix} [(1 + S_{11})(1 - S_{22}) + S_{12}S_{21}] & Z_{02}[(1 + S_{11})(1 + S_{22}) - S_{12}S_{21}] \\ \frac{1}{Z_{01}}[(1 - S_{11})(1 - S_{22}) - S_{12}S_{21}] & \frac{Z_{01}}{Z_{02}}[(1 - S_{11})(1 + S_{22}) + S_{12}S_{21}] \end{bmatrix}$$

$$\begin{bmatrix} A & B \\ C & D \end{bmatrix} = \frac{1}{2} \begin{bmatrix} [(r_{22} + r_{11}) + (r_{21} + r_{12})] & Z_{02}[(r_{22} - r_{11}) - (r_{21} - r_{12})] \\ \frac{1}{Z_{01}}[r_{22} - r_{11}) + (r_{21} - r_{12})] & \frac{Z_{02}}{Z_{01}}[r_{22} + r_{11}) - (r_{21} + r_{12})] \end{bmatrix}$$

Courtesy of R.W. Beatty and D.M. Kerns, Reference: Proceedings of the IEEE, January 1964.

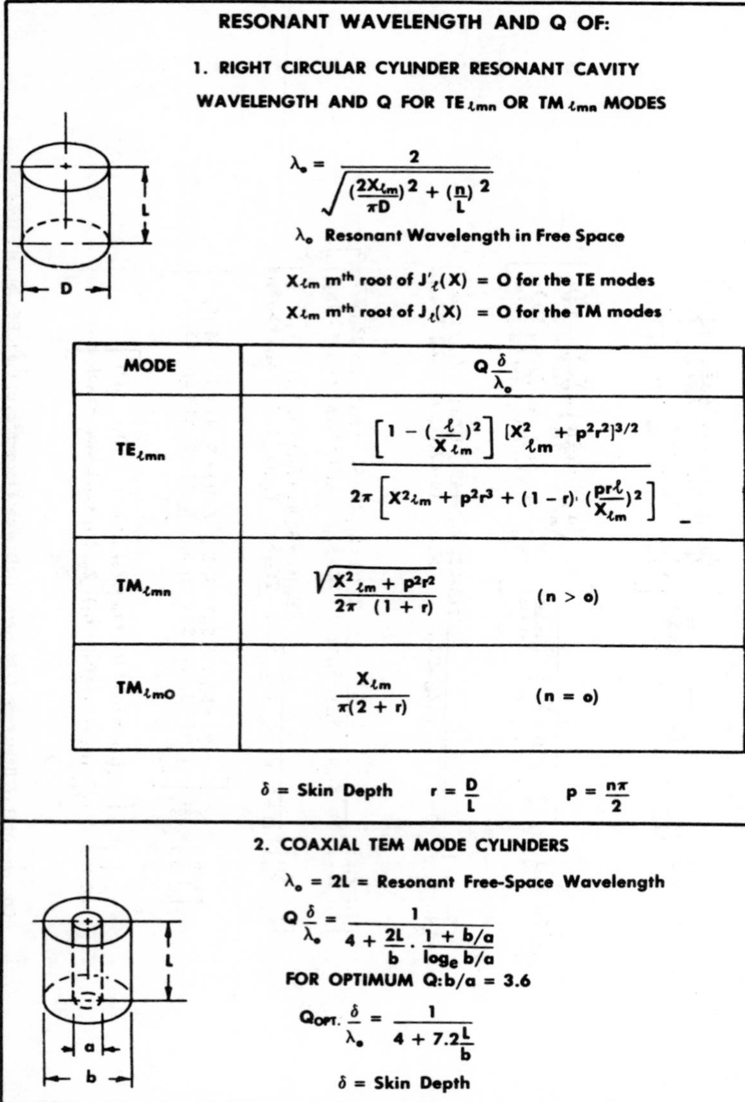

RESONANT WAVELENGTH AND Q OF:

1. RIGHT CIRCULAR CYLINDER RESONANT CAVITY

WAVELENGTH AND Q FOR $TE_{\ell mn}$ OR $TM_{\ell mn}$ MODES

$$\lambda_o = \frac{2}{\sqrt{\left(\frac{2X_{\ell m}}{\pi D}\right)^2 + \left(\frac{n}{L}\right)^2}}$$

λ_o Resonant Wavelength in Free Space

$X_{\ell m}$ m^{th} root of $J'_\ell(X) = O$ for the TE modes

$X_{\ell m}$ m^{th} root of $J_\ell(X) = O$ for the TM modes

MODE	$Q\frac{\delta}{\lambda_o}$
$TE_{\ell mn}$	$\dfrac{\left[1 - \left(\frac{\ell}{X_{\ell m}}\right)^2\right] [X^2_{\ell m} + p^2r^2]^{3/2}}{2\pi\left[X^2_{\ell m} + p^2r^3 + (1-r)\left(\frac{pr\ell}{X_{\ell m}}\right)^2\right]}$
$TM_{\ell mn}$	$\dfrac{\sqrt{X^2_{\ell m} + p^2r^2}}{2\pi\ (1+r)}$ (n > o)
$TM_{\ell mO}$	$\dfrac{X_{\ell m}}{\pi(2+r)}$ (n = o)

δ = Skin Depth $\quad r = \frac{D}{L} \quad p = \frac{n\pi}{2}$

2. COAXIAL TEM MODE CYLINDERS

$\lambda_o = 2L$ = Resonant Free-Space Wavelength

$$Q\frac{\delta}{\lambda_o} = \frac{1}{4 + \frac{2L}{b}\cdot\frac{1 + b/a}{\log_e b/a}}$$

FOR OPTIMUM Q: b/a = 3.6

$$Q_{OPT.}\frac{\delta}{\lambda_o} = \frac{1}{4 + 7.2\frac{L}{b}}$$

δ = Skin Depth

RESONANT WAVELENGTH AND Q OF:

3. RECTANGULAR PRISM RESONANT CAVITY

$$\lambda_o = \frac{2}{\sqrt{\left(\frac{\ell}{a}\right)^2 + \left(\frac{m}{b}\right)^2 + \left(\frac{n}{c}\right)^2}}$$

MODE	$Q\frac{\delta}{\lambda_o}$
$TE_{\ell mn}$	$\frac{abc}{4}\cdot\dfrac{(p^2+q^2)(p^2+q^2+r^2)^{3/2}}{ac[p^2r^2 + (p^2+q^2)^2] + bc[q^2r^2 + (p^2+q^2)^2] + abr^2(p^2+q^2)}$
TE_{Omn}	$\frac{abc}{2}\cdot\dfrac{(q^2+r^2)^{3/2}}{q^2c(b+2a) + r^2b(c+2a)}$
$TE_{\ell On}$	$\frac{abc}{2}\cdot\dfrac{(p^2+r^2)^{3/2}}{p^2c(a+2b) + r^2a(c+2b)}$
$TM_{\ell mn}$	$\frac{abc}{4}\cdot\dfrac{(p^2+q^2)\ (p^2+q^2+r^2)^{1/2}}{p^2b(a+c) + q^2a(b+c)}$
$TM_{\ell mO}$	$\frac{abc}{2}\cdot\dfrac{(p^2+q^2)^{3/2}}{p^2b(a+2c) + q^2a(b+2c)}$

$p = \frac{\ell}{a} \quad q = \frac{m}{b} \quad r = \frac{n}{c}$

λ_o = Resonant Free-Space Wavelength

δ = Skin Depth

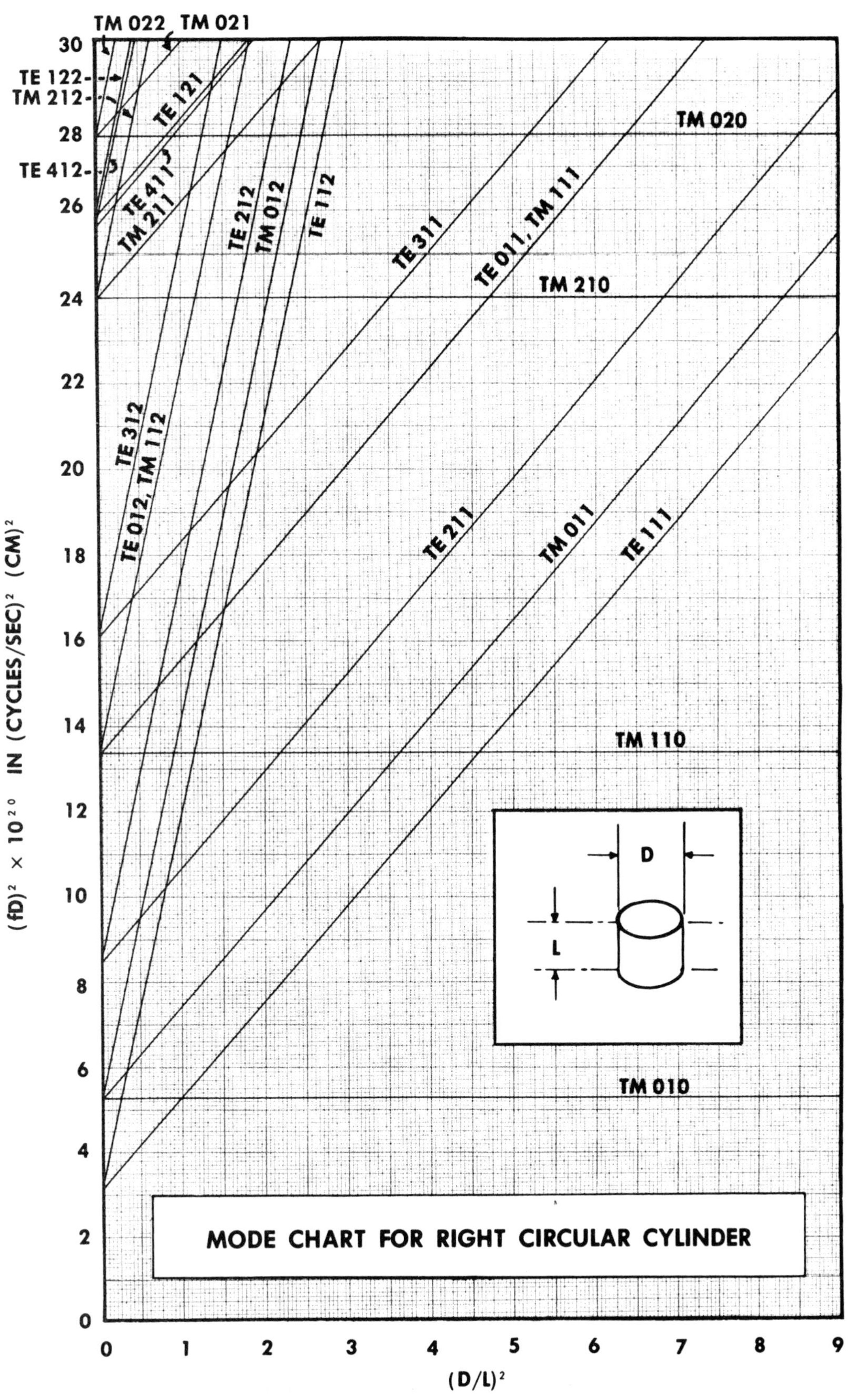

MODE CHART FOR RIGHT CIRCULAR CYLINDER

181

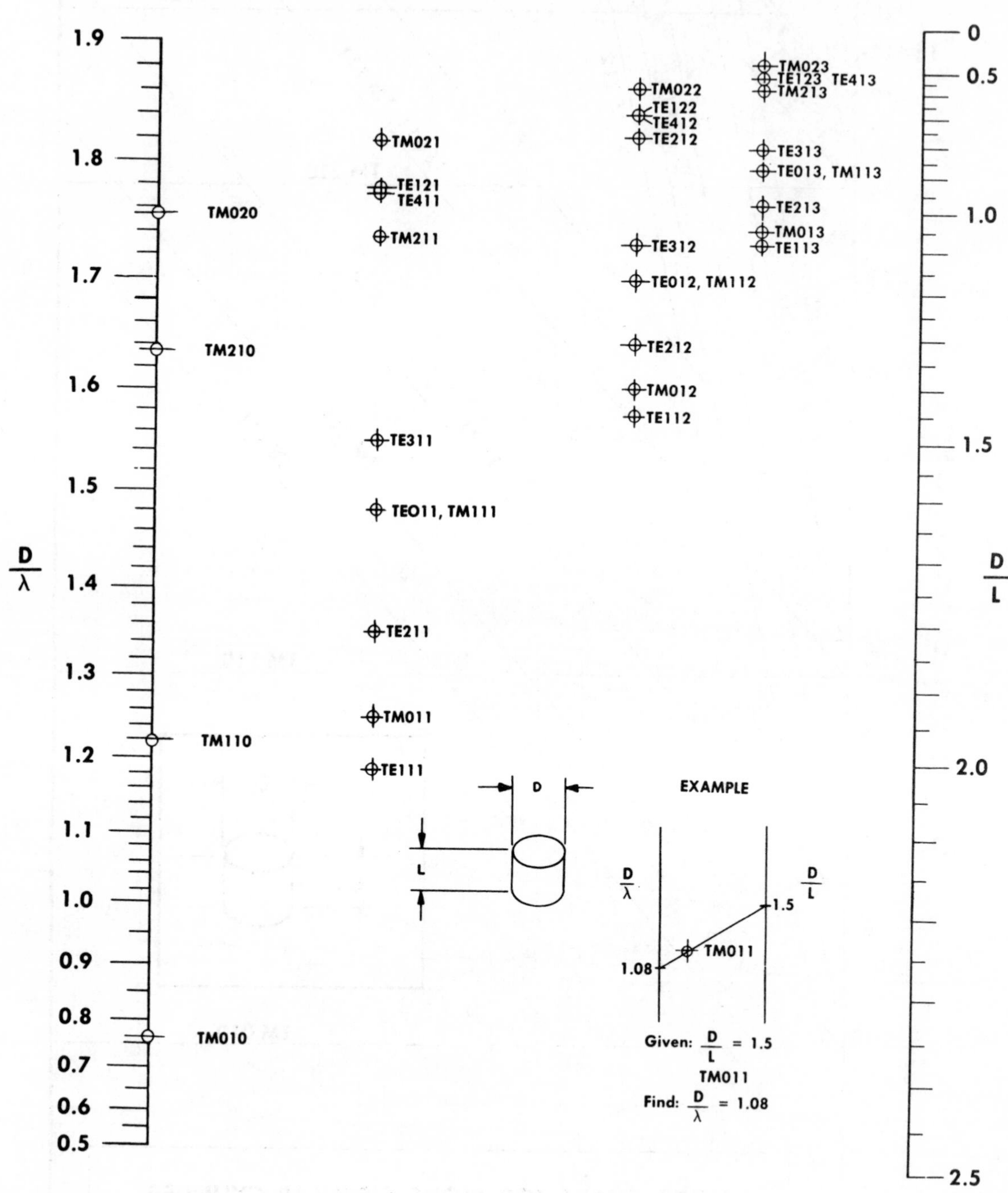

Reprinted from Charts for Resonant Frequencies of Cavities, R. N. Bracewell, Proc. of the IRE, Aug. 1947.

MODE LATTICE FOR SQUARE PRISM RESONATORS

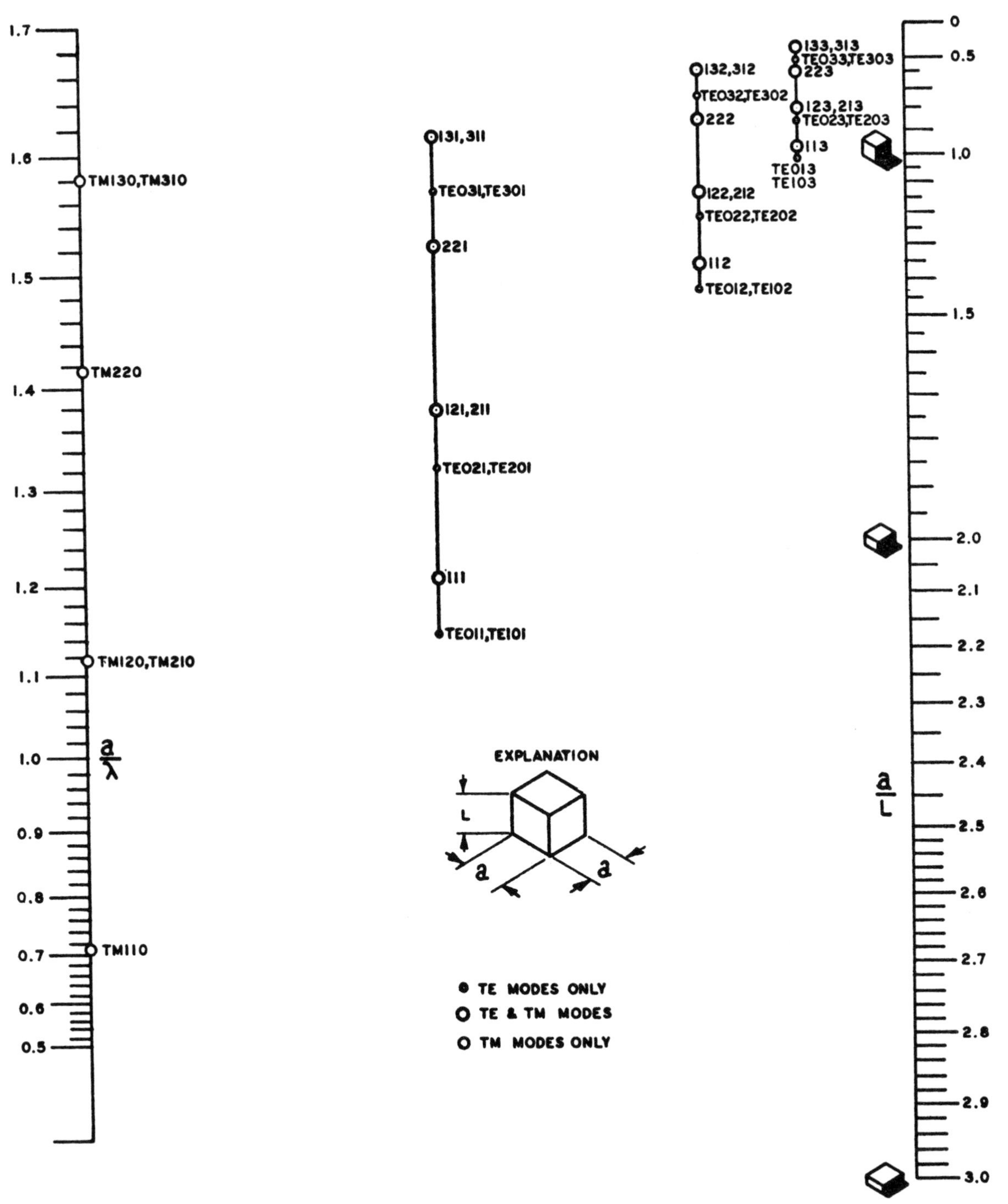

Reprinted from Mode Lattice for Square Prism Resonators, R. N. Bracewell, Proceedings of the IRE, Aug., 1947.

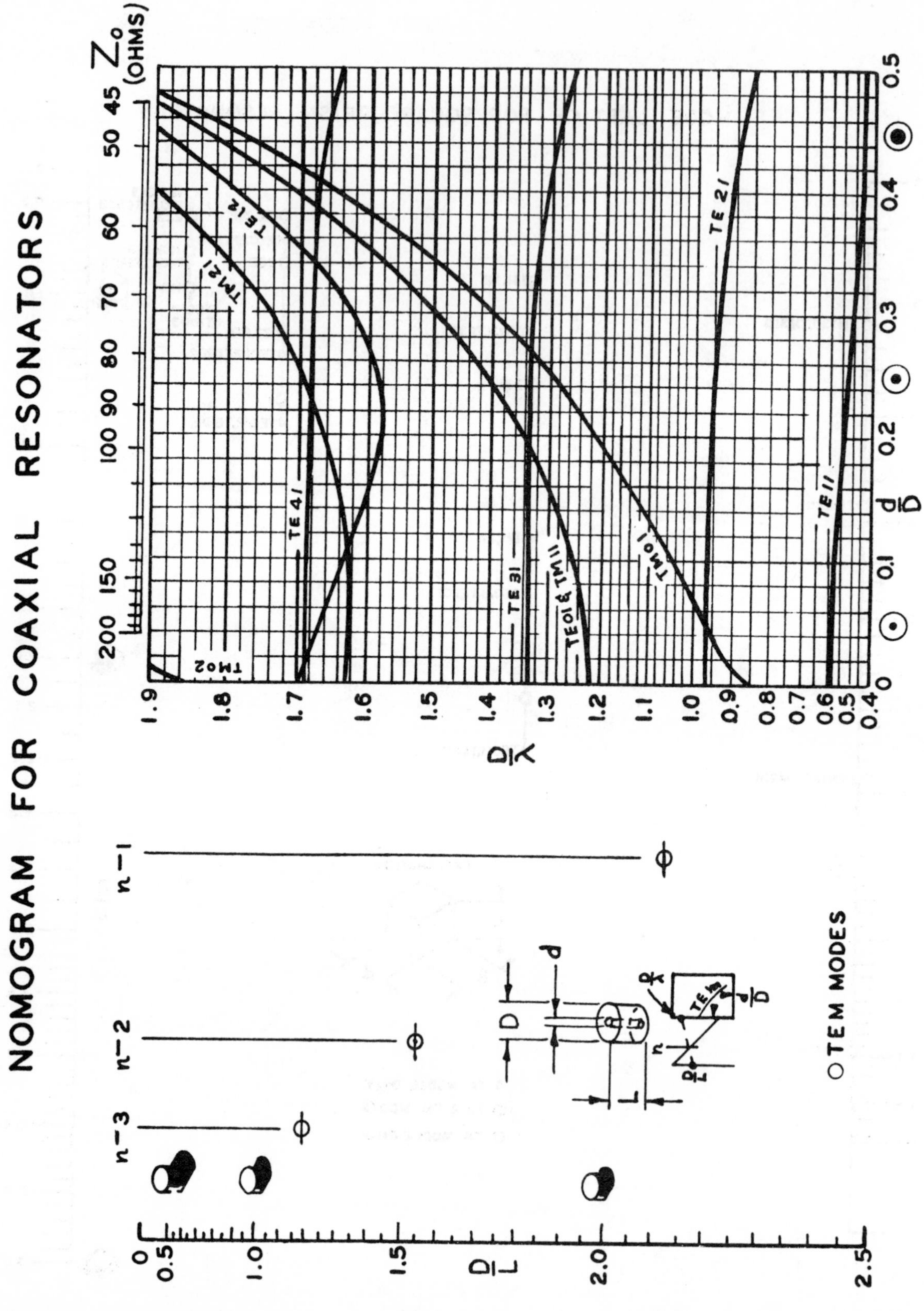

NOMOGRAM FOR COAXIAL RESONATORS

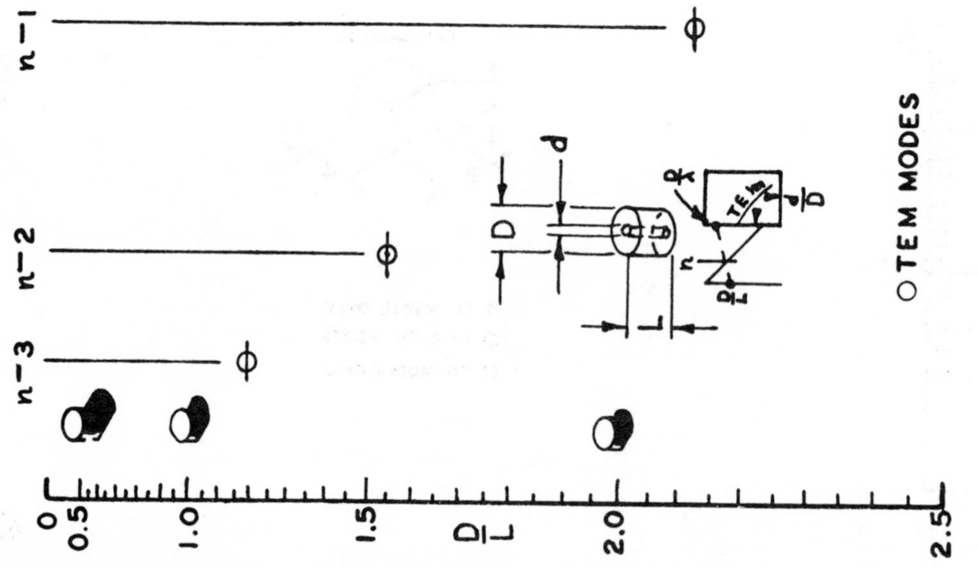

Reprinted from Nomogram for Coaxial Resonators, R. N. Bracewell, Proceedings of the IRE, Aug., 1947.

EFFECT OF HUMIDITY ON THE RESONANT FREQUENCY OF A CAVITY RESONATOR

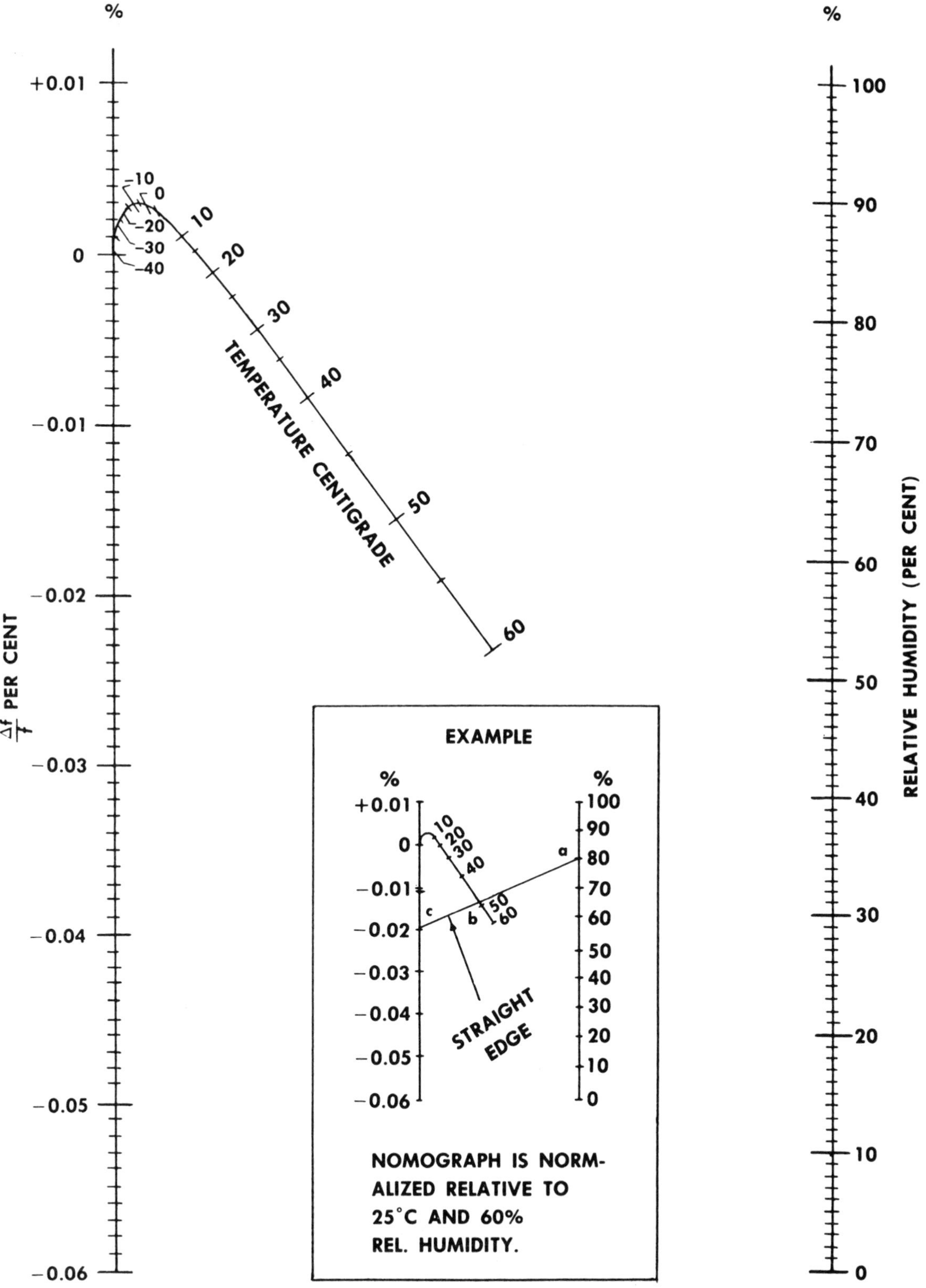

UNLOADED Q(Q_U) vs FREQUENCY FOR VARIOUS RESONATORS

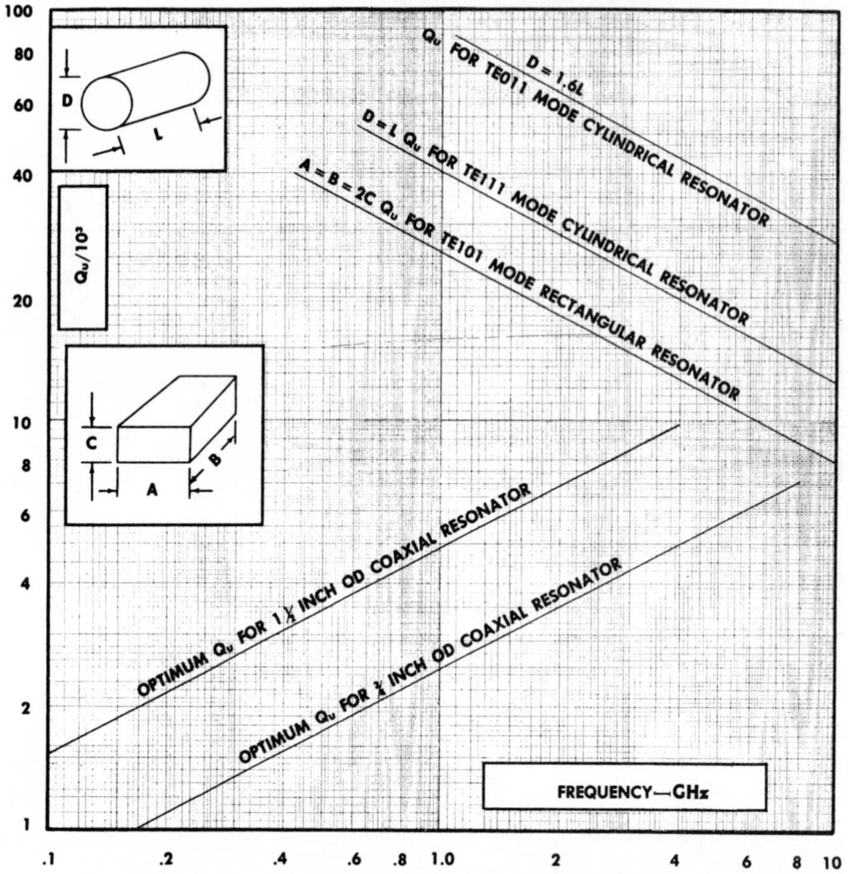

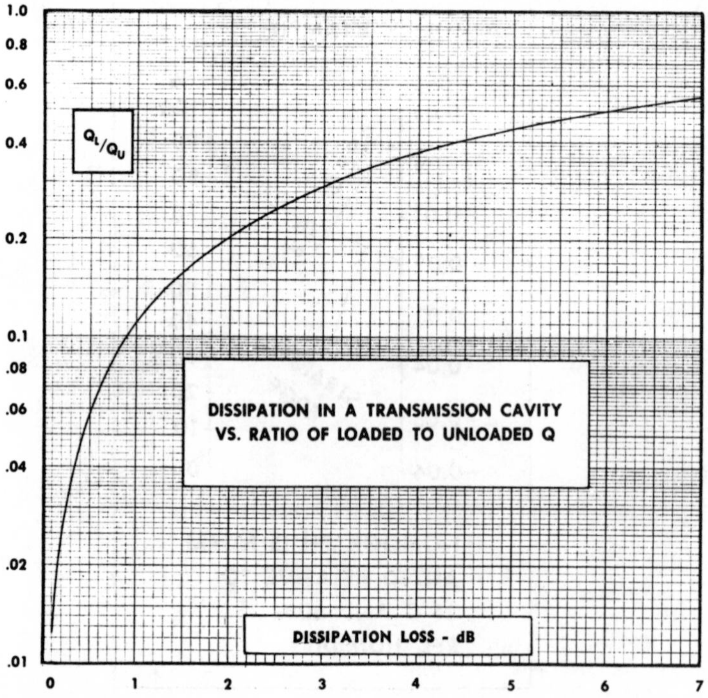

Courtesy of Frequency Engineering Laboratories, Asbury Park, N. J.

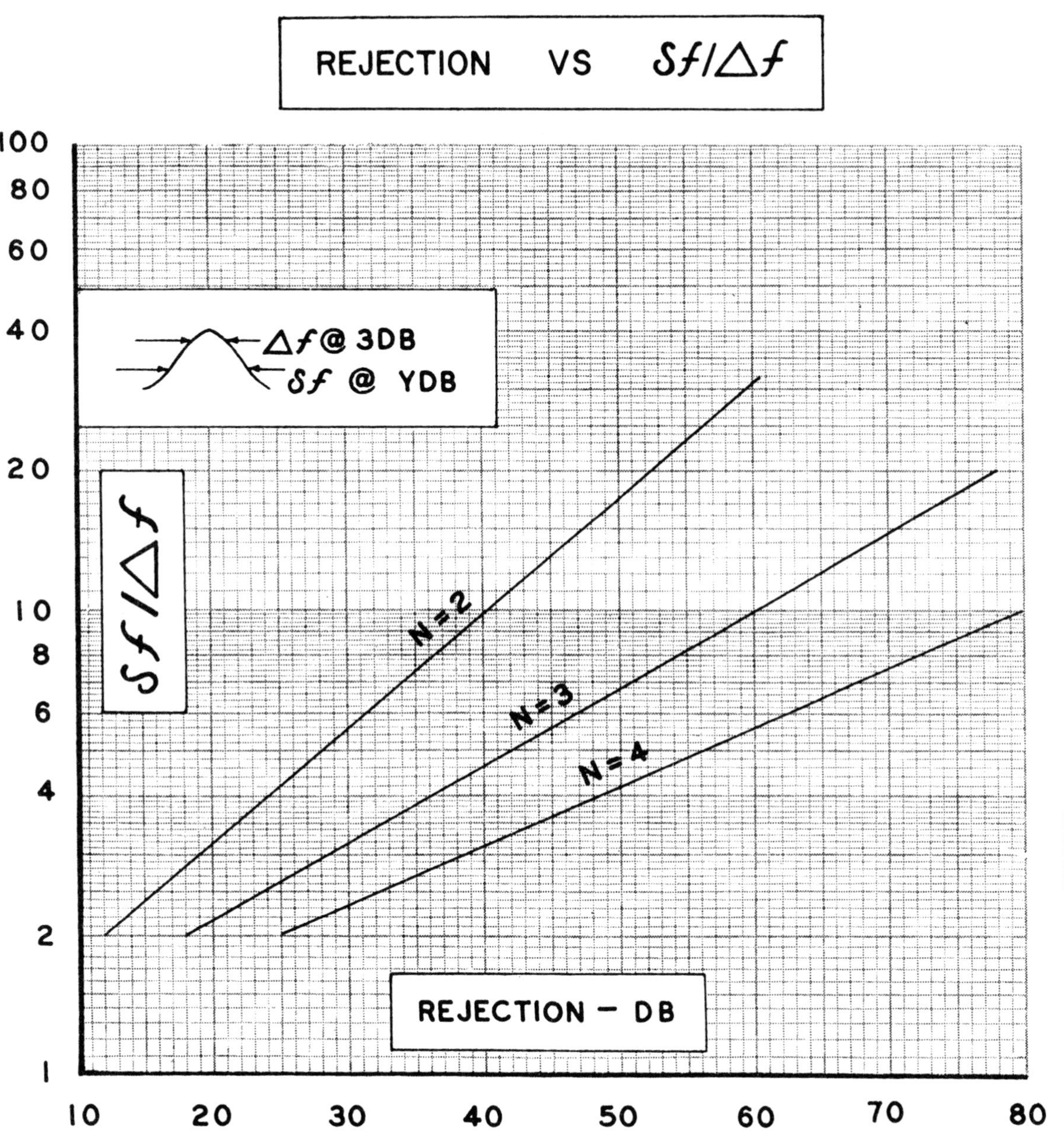

Courtesy of Frequency Engineering Laboratories, Asbury Park, N. J.

RESONANT WAVELENGTH OF RE-ENTRANT COAXIAL CAVITY

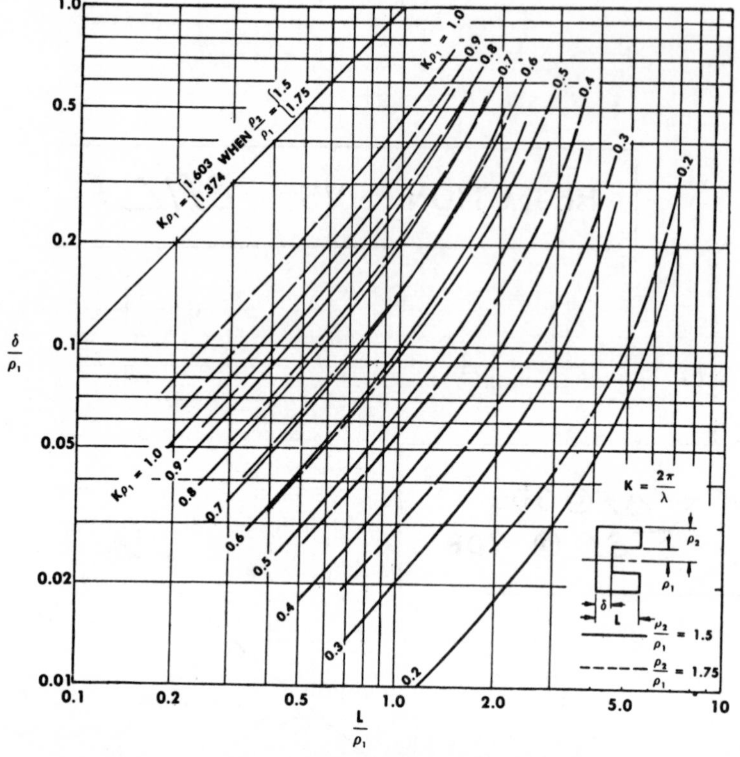

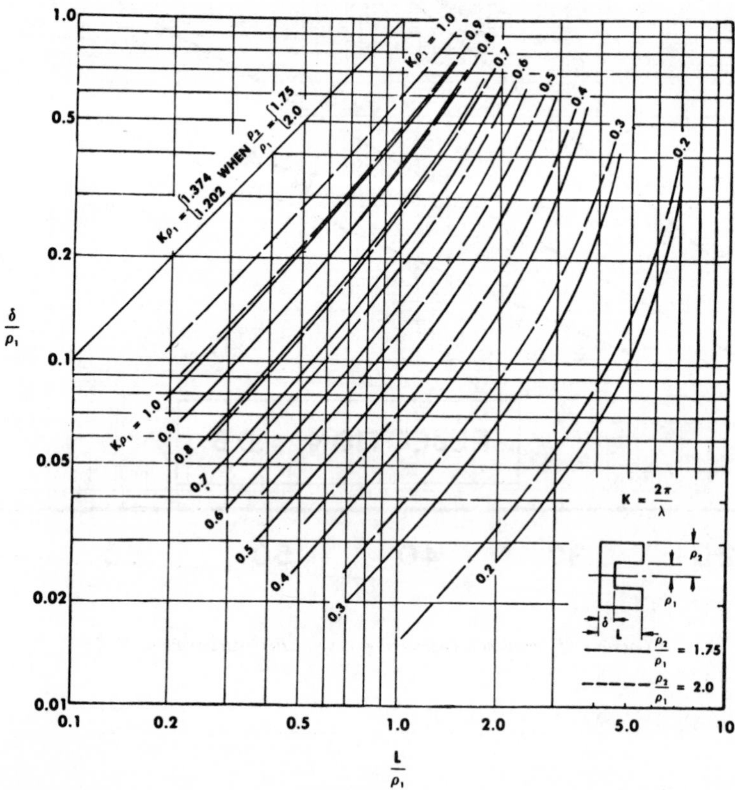

Courtesy of The Sperry Gyroscope Co., Great Neck, L. I., N. Y., from Moreno, Microwave Transmission Design Data, McGraw-Hill Book Co., 1948.

RESONANT WAVELENGTH OF RE-ENTRANT COAXIAL CAVITY

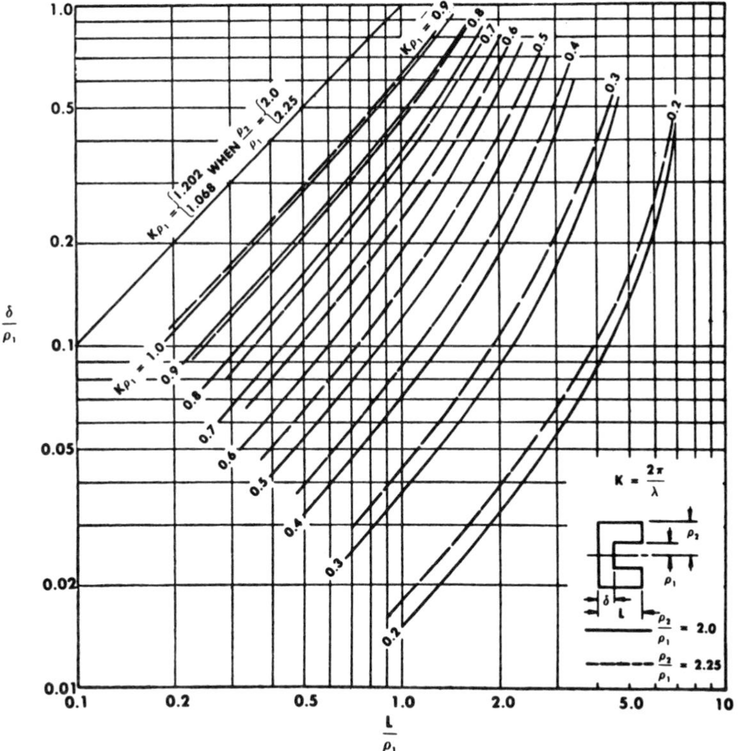

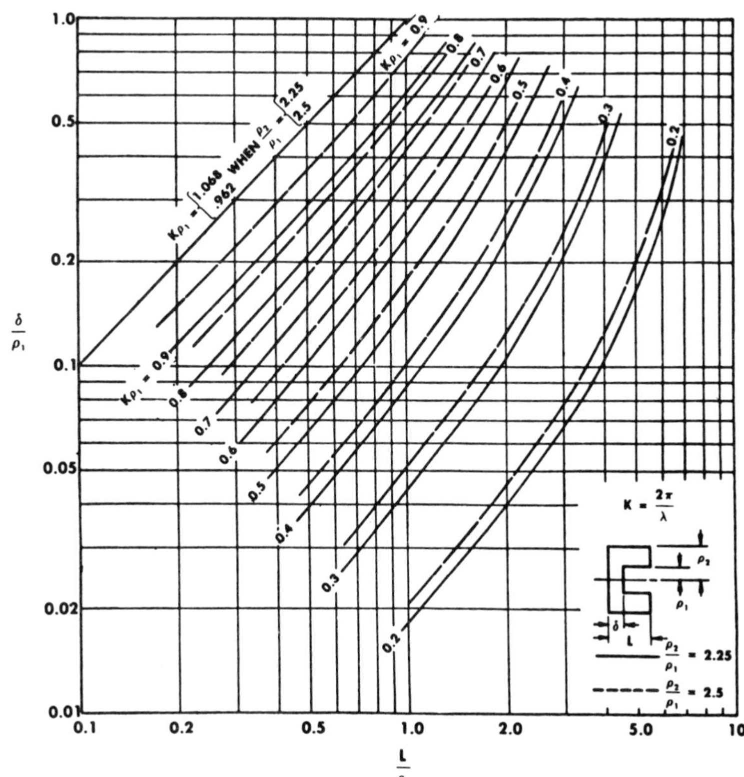

Courtesy of The Sperry Gyroscope Co., Great Neck, L. I., N. Y., from Moreno, Microwave Transmission Design Data, McGraw-Hill Book Co., 1948.

RESONANT WAVELENGTH OF RE-ENTRANT COAXIAL CAVITY

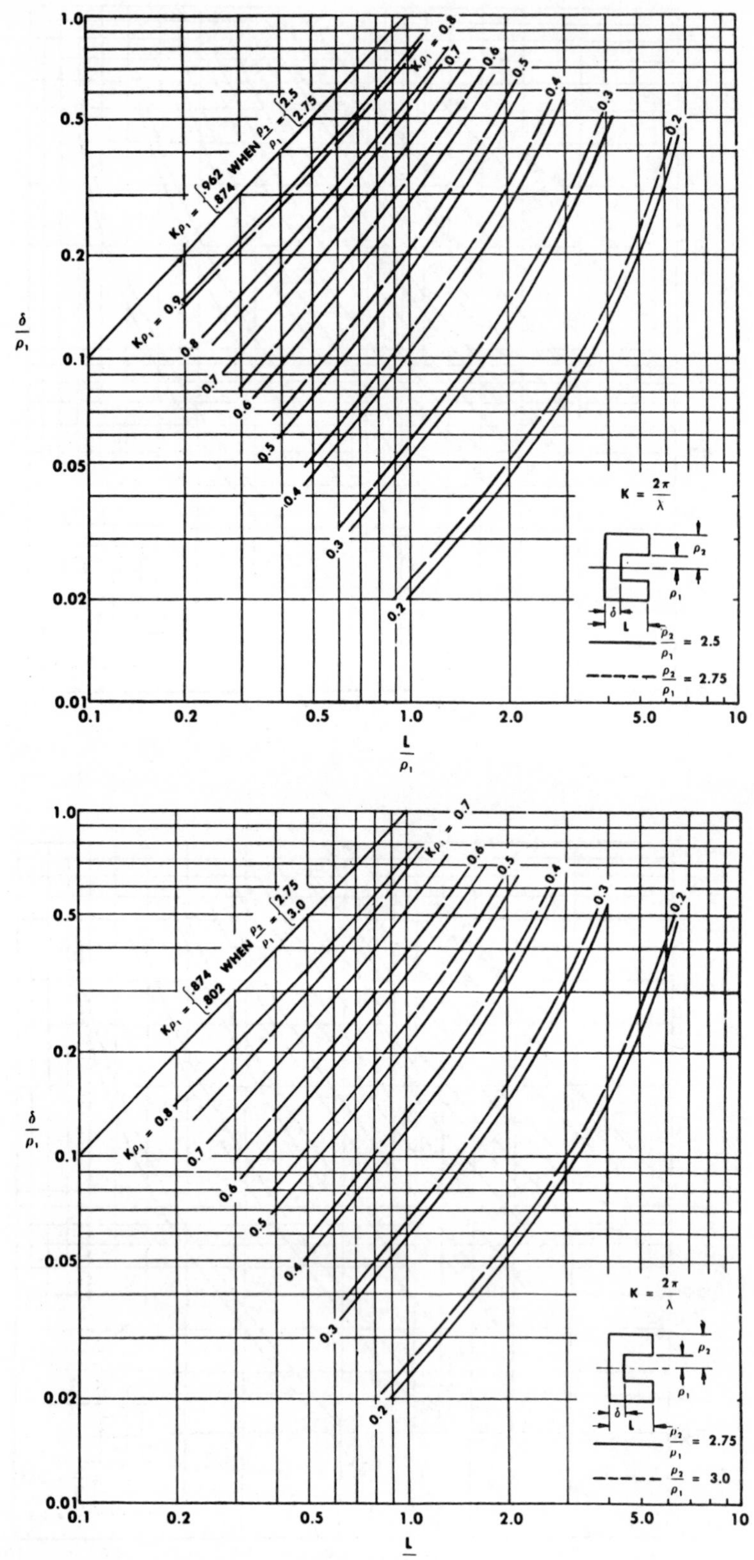

Courtesy of The Sperry Gyroscope Co., Great Neck, L. I., N. Y., from Moreno, Microwave Transmission Design Data, McGraw-Hill Book Co., 1948.

RESONANT WAVELENGTH OF RE-ENTRANT COAXIAL CAVITY

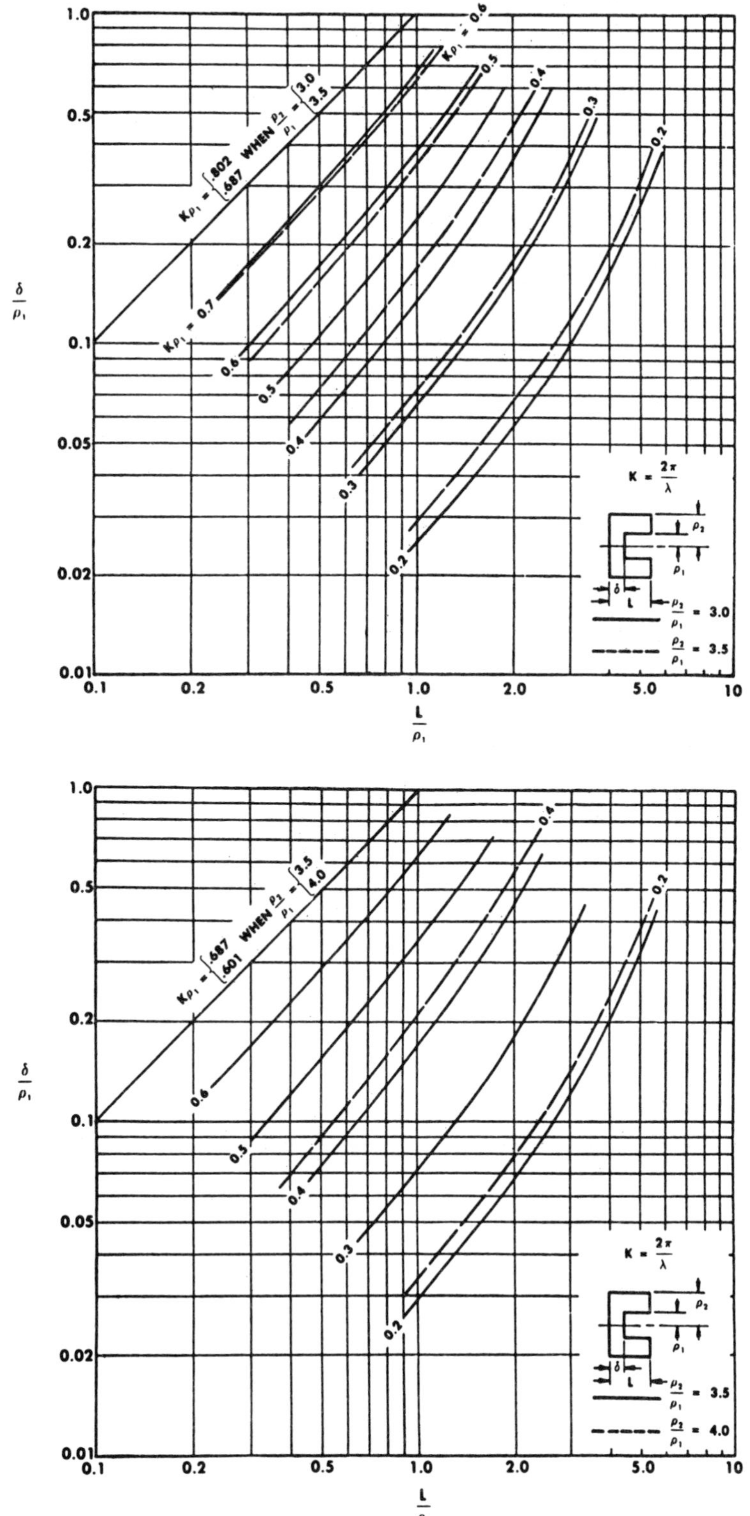

Courtesy of The Sperry Gyroscope Co., Great Neck, L. I., N. Y., from Moreno, Microwave Transmission Design Data, McGraw Hill Book Co., 1948.

RESONANT WAVELENGTH OF RE-ENTRANT COAXIAL CAVITY

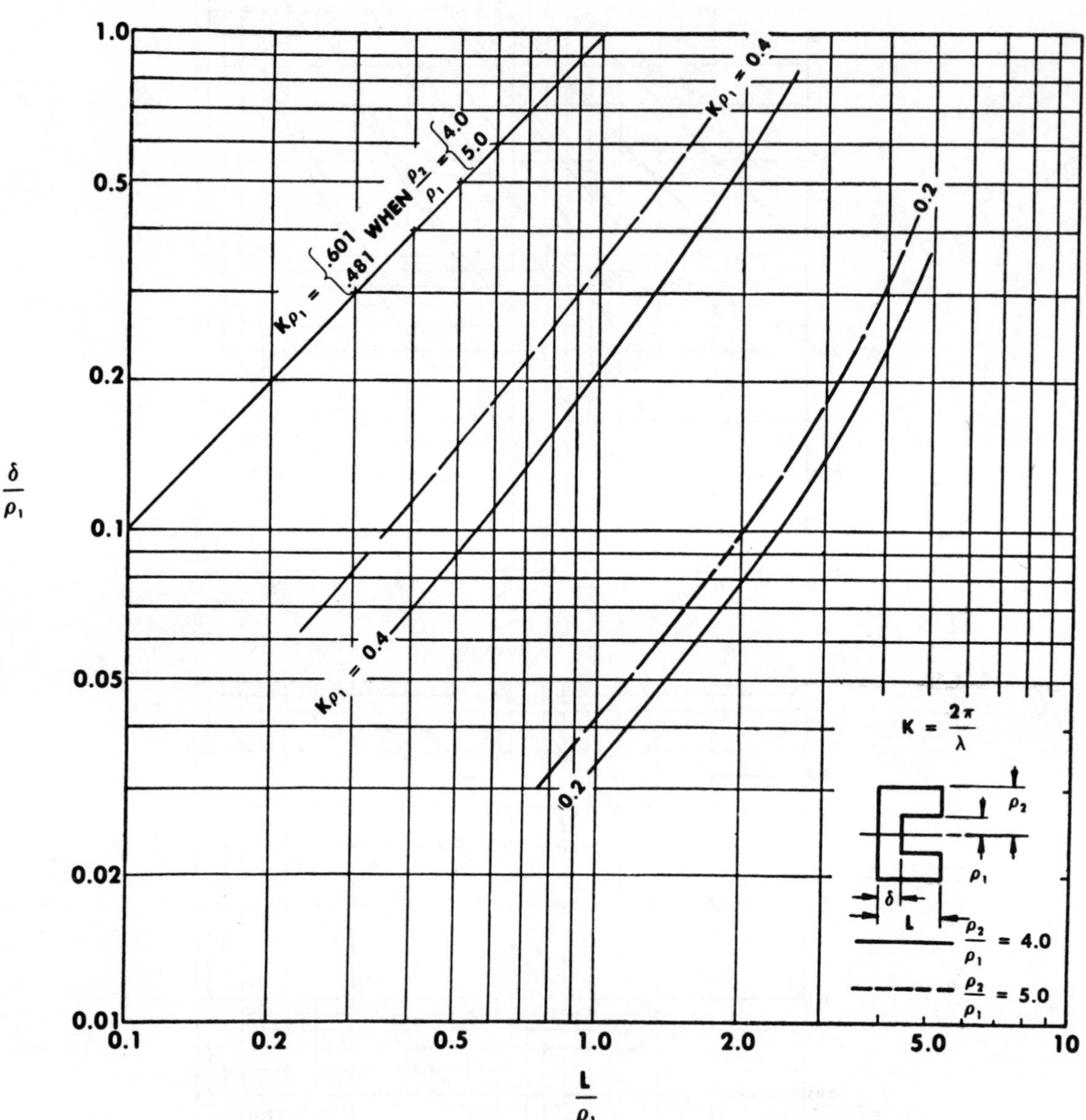

Courtesy of the Sperry Gyroscope Co., Great Neck, L.I., N.Y., from Moreno, Microwave Transmission Design Data, McGraw-Hill Book Co., 1948.

The Artech House Microwave Library

Introduction to Microwaves by Fred E. Gardiol
Microwaves Made Simple by W. Stephen Cheung and Frederic Levien
Microwave Tubes by A. Scott Gilmour, Jr.
Electric Filters by Martin Hasler and Jacques Neirynck
Microwave Technology by Erich Pehl
Receiving Systems Design by Stephen J. Erst
Applications of GaAs MESFETs by R.A. Soares, et al.
GaAs Processing Techniques by R.E. Williams
GaAs FET Principles and Technology by J.V. DiLorenzo and D. Khandelwal
Dielectric Resonators, Darko Kajfez and Pierre Guillon, eds.
Modern Spectrum Analyzer Theory and Applications by Morris Engelson
Microwave Materials and Fabrication Techniques by Thomas S. Laverghetta
Handbook of Microwave Testing by Thomas S. Laverghetta
Microwave Measurements and Techniques by Thomas S. Laverghetta
Principles of Electromagnetic Compatibilty by Bernhard E. Keiser
Design and Analysis of Linear Active Circuits by William Rynone, Jr.
The Design of Impedance-Matching Networks for Radio-Frequency and Microwave Amplifiers by P.L.D. Abrie
Microwave Filters, Impedance Matching Networks and Coupling Structures by G.L. Matthaei, Leo Young, and E.M.T. Jones
Microwave Engineer's Handbook, 2 vol., Theodore Saad, ed.
Handbook of Microwave Integrated Circuits by R.K. Hoffmann
Microwave Integrated Circuits, Jeffrey Frey and Kul Bhasin, eds.
Computer-Aided Design of Microwave Circuits by K.C. Gupta, R. Garg, and R. Chadha
Microstrip Lines and Slotlines by K.C. Gupta, R. Garg, and I.J. Bahl
Microstrip Antennas by I.J. Bahl and P. Bhartia
Antenna Design Using Personal Computers by David M. Pozar
Microwave Circuit Design Using Programmable Calculators by J. Lamar Allen and Max Medley, Jr.
Stripline Circuit Design by Harlan Howe, Jr.
Microwave Transmission Line Filters by J.A.G. Malherbe
Electrical Characteristics of Transmission Lines by W. Hilberg
Multiconductor Transmission Line Analysis by Sidney Frankel
Microwave Diode Control Devices by Robert V. Garver
Tables for Active Filter Design by Mario Biey and Amedeo Premoli
Active Filter Design by A.B. Williams
Laser Applications by W.V. Smith
Ferrite Control Components, 2 vol., Lawrence Whicker, ed.
Microwave Remote Sensing, 3 vol., by F.T. Ulaby, R.K. Moore, and A.K. Fung

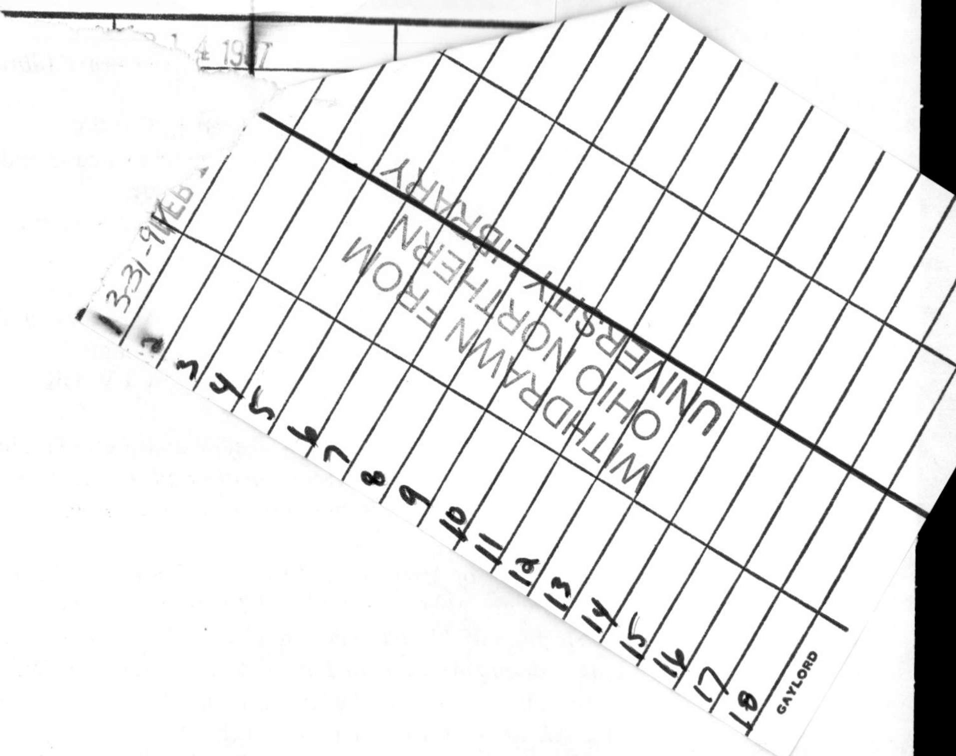
WITHDRAWN FROM
OHIO NORTHERN
UNIVERSITY LIBRARY
GAYLORD
PRINTED IN U.S.A